Motion and time study

FIFTH EDITION

Motion and time study

BENJAMIN W. NIEBEL

Head of Department and Professor of
Industrial Engineering
The Pennsylvania State University

1972

Richard D. Irwin, Inc.
Homewood, Illinois   60430
IRWIN-DORSEY INTERNATIONAL
London, England   WC2H 9NJ
IRWIN-DORSEY LIMITED
Georgetown, Ontario   L7G 4B3

Fifth Edition

First Printing, January, 1972
Second Printing, June, 1973
Third Printing, June, 1974

Library of Congress Catalog Card No. 71–176051
Printed in the United States of America

Preface

The pressures of international competition are more prevalent than ever before. The impact of West German, Japanese, Korean, French, and British "know-how" is apparent in the production of both soft and hard goods, basic equipment, and end-use products. More than ever before, there is need for the application of the most modern techniques of methods development, worker motivation, sound time standards, and wage payment plans fair both to the worker and the company. The need for the application of these techniques is not only in the production areas of industry and business but also in the indirect areas such as maintenance, quality control, and office management. There is an increasing interest on the part of business and industry in cost improvement through methods study and work measurement.

This fifth edition has been written primarily for the purpose of introducing new material that has proven successful during the past five years and updating some of the older material that still has application to modern business and industry. Specifically, new material relative to fundamental motion data systems has been introduced. Perhaps the most important new material that has been added in this area is related to M.T.M.–2.

The chapter on formula development has been enlarged to cover multiple-correlation techniques. Also, the use of regression methods has been broadened. These modern analytical tools allow the development of algebraic expressions for estimating time standards both accurately and rapidly.

More emphasis has been given to job enlargement and job enrichment

v

in the development of the ideal work center. Also, a more thorough introduction to work sampling has been made.

The suggestions of the many colleges and universities, industries, labor unions, and technical institutes that have adopted the text have helped materially in writing the new edition. This edition has the same objectives as the first four—that is, to provide a practical up-to-date college text in the area of methods, time study, and wage payment; and to give practicing analysts from both labor and management an authentic source of reference material.

The author wishes to acknowledge in particular Professor Joseph Siphron, who has taught regularly from this text for the past five years; Mr. Nicholas Kralles of Eastman Kodak Company; Mr. Kenneth Knott of Kenneth Knott Limited, England; and Dr. Richard Zindler, all of whom have offered many helpful suggestions.

December, 1971   BENJAMIN W. NIEBEL

Contents

1. Methods, time study, and wage payment today   **1**

The production function. Scope of methods engineering and time study. Methods engineering. Time study. Wage payment.

2. Development of motion and time study   **9**

The work of Taylor. Motion study. Early contemporaries. Organizations. Present trends.

3. The operation and flow chart   **19**

Operation process chart. Constructing the operation process chart. Using the operation process chart. Flow process chart. Constructing the flow process chart. Using the flow process chart. The flow diagram. Summary.

4. Operation analysis   **40**

Approach to operation analysis. Operation analysis procedure. The 10 primary approaches to operation analysis. PURPOSE OF OPERATION: Summary: purpose of operation. DESIGN OF PART: Summary: design of part. TOLERANCES AND SPECIFICATIONS: Summary: tolerances and specifications. MATERIAL: Finding a less expensive material. Finding a material easier to process. Using material more economically. Salvage materials. Full use of supplies and tools. Summary: material.

5. Operation analysis (Continued)   82

PROCESS OF MANUFACTURE: Effects on subsequent operations by changing present operation. Mechanize manual operation. Utilize more efficient machine. Operate mechanical facilities more efficiently. Summary: process of manufacture. SETUP AND TOOLS: Reduce setup time by better planning and production control. Design tooling to utilize the full capacity of the machine. Introduce more efficient tooling. Summary: setup and tools. WORKING CONDITIONS: Improve lighting. Control temperature. Provide for adequate ventilation. Control sound. Promote orderliness, cleanliness, and good housekeeping. Arrange for disposal of irritating and harmful dusts, fumes, gases, and fogs. Provide guards at nip points and points of power transmission. Provide at cost necessary personal protective equipment. Sponsor and enforce a well-formulated first-aid program. Utilizing work physiology. Summary: working conditions. MATERIAL HANDLING: Reduce time spent in picking up material. Reduce material handling by using mechanical equipment. Make better use of existing handling facilities. Handle parts with greater care. Summary: material handling. PLANT LAYOUT: Layout types. Making the layout. Making the floor plan. Summary: plant layout. PRINCIPLES OF MOTION ECONOMY: Both hands should work at the same time. Each hand should go through as few motions as possible. The workplace should be arranged to avoid long reaches. Avoid using hand as a holding device. Summary: principles of motion economy. Summary: 10 primary approaches to operation analysis.

6. Man and machine relationships   141

Man and machine process charts. Construction of the man and machine process chart. Using the man and machine process chart. Gang process charts. Construction of the gang process chart. Using the gang process chart. Quantative techniques for man and machine relationships. Line balancing. Operator process chart. Constructing the operator process chart. Using the operator process chart. Summary: man-machine, gang, and operator process charts.

7. Motion study   171

The fundamental motions. Definitions of basic divisions of accomplishment. Therblig summary. Principles of motion economy. EXPLANATION OF LAWS OF MOTION ECONOMY.

PRACTICAL USE OF MOTION STUDY IN THE PLANNING STAGE: Motion analysis as applied in planning.

8. **Micromotion study**   211

Preparing for micromotion study. Micromotion study as a training aid. Micromotion equipment. The motion-picture camera. The lens. The shutter. Black-and-white versus color film. Light meter. Tripod. Floodlights. Projection equipment. Michrochronometer. Splicer and viewer. Optical screen. Storage of films. Summary.

9. **Taking motion pictures for micromotion study and film analysis**   230

Taking the moving pictures. Analyzing the film. Create an improved method. Teach and standardize the new method. Other motion study techniques involving photographic methods.

10. **Presentation and installation of proposed method**   250

The proposed method report. Reporting recovery of capital investment. Oral presentation. Installation.

11. **Making the job analysis and the job evaluation**   257

Job analysis. Job evaluation. Selection of factors. Conclusion.

12. **Time study requirements**   268

A fair day's work. Time study requirements. Responsibilities of the time study man. Foreman's responsibility. The union's responsibility. Operator's responsibility. Conclusion.

13. **Time study equipment**   278

The stopwatch. Time-recording machines. Motion-picture camera. Time study board. Time study forms. Auxilliary equipment. Training equipment.

14. **Elements of time study**   292

Choosing the operator. Approach to the operator. Analysis of materials and methods. Recording the significant information. Observer's position. Dividing the operation into elements. Taking the study. Snapback method. The continuous method. Recording the time consumed by each element. Difficulties encountered. Number of cycles to study.

Rating the operator performance. Apply allowances. Calculate the study. Summary of computing the study.

15. Performance rating   325

Definition. Concept of normal. Uses and effects. The learning curve. Characteristics of a sound rating system. Rating at the work station. Rating elements versus overall study. METHODS OF RATING: Westinghouse system. Synthetic rating. Speed rating. Objective rating. OPERATOR SELECTION: Analysis of rating. Training for rating.

16. Allowances   356

Personal delays. Fatigue. Unavoidable delays. Machine interference. Avoidable delays. Extra allowances. Clean work station and oil machine. Power feed machine time allowance. Application of allowance. Typical allowance values. Summary.

17. The standard time   377

Expressing the standard time. Temporary standards. Setup standards. Partial setups. Maintenance of standard times. Conclusion.

18. Standard data   387

Development of standard time data. Calculation of cutting times. Drill press work. Lathe work. Milling machine work. Determining horsepower requirements. Plotting curves. The least squares method. Solving by regression line equations. Using standard data. Conclusion.

19. Synthetic basic motion times   417

Definition of synthetic basic motion times. Necessity of synthetic basic motion times. Work-factor. Detailed Work-Factor system. Simplified Work-Factor system. Abbreviated Work-Factor system. Ready Work-Factor. Methods-Time Measurement (M.T.M.-1). M.T.M.—General Purpose Data. M.T.M.-2. Basic Motion Timestudy. Basic motions. Variable factors. Turns. Simultaneous arm motion. Application technique. Motion-Time Analysis. Dimensional Motion Times. Master Standard Data. Applying synthetic basic motion times. Development of standard data. Summary.

20. Formula construction   463

Application of formulas. Advantages and disadvantages of formulas. Characteristics of the usable formula. Steps to follow in formula construction. Analyzing the elements. Compute expressions for variables. Graphic solutions for more than one variable. Least squares and regression techniques. Multiple regression. Some precautions. Develop synthesis. Compute expression. Check for accuracy. Write formula report. Formula number. Part. Operation and work station. Normal time. Application. Analysis. Procedure. Time studies. Table of detail elements. Synthesis. Inspection, payment, and signatures. Representative formula. Use of the digital computer. Description of a modern digital computer. Computers as logic processors. Operations with computers. Types of problems economic to solve on digital computer. Numerical analysis and flow charting. Programming. Conclusion.

21. Work sampling studies   511

Illustrative example. Selling work sampling. Planning the work sampling study. Determining observations needed. Determining the frequency of the observations. Designing the work sampling form. Use of control charts. Observing and recording the data. Using random activity analysis camera. Work sampling for the establishment of allowances. Work sampling for determination of machine utilization. Work sampling in establishing indirect and direct labor standards. Conclusion.

22. Establishing standards on indirect and expense work   542

Automation. Methods improvement on indirect and expense work. Indirect labor standards. Factors affecting indirect and expense standards. Basic queueing theory equations. Monte Carlo simulation. Expense standards. Supervisory standards. Standard data on indirect and expense labor. Universal indirect standards. Advantages of work standards on indirect work. Conclusion.

23. Follow-up method and uses of time study   572

Making the follow-up. Methods of establishing standards. Basis for wage incentive plans. Common denominator in comparing various methods. Securing an efficient layout of available space. Means for determining plant capacity. Basis for purchasing new equipment. Basis for balancing working force with available work. Improving production control. Accurate control and determination of labor costs. Requisite for standard cost methods. As a basis for budgetary control. As a basis for supervisory bonus. Quality standards are enforced. Personnel standards are raised. Problems of management are simplified. Service to customers is bettered. Conclusion.

24. Methods and standards automation   **586**

Data processing and the establishment of standards. Advantages of methods and standards automation. Approach to automation through data processing. The work measurement system. A computer program for indirect labor standards.

25. Significant wage payment plans   **605**

Direct financial plans. Indirect financial plans. Plans other than financial. Classification of direct wage financial plans. Piecework. Standard hour plan. Taylor differential piece rate. Merrick multiple piece rate. Measured daywork. Halsey plan. Bedaux point system. Rowan plan. Emerson plan. Profit sharing. Methods of distribution under profit sharing. Criteria for successful profit sharing plan. Attitude toward profit sharing. Conclusion.

26. Characteristics of a sound wage incentive system   **627**

Prerequisites for a sound wage incentive plan. Design for a sound wage incentive plan. Motivation for incentive effort. Reasons for incentive plan failures. Administration of the wage incentive system. Conclusion.

27. Training and research for methods, time study, and wage payment   **640**

Individual plant method training programs. Training in motion and time study. Developing creativity. Decision-making methods and processes. Labor relations and work measurement. Union objectives. Employee reactions. The human approach. Research in methods, time study, and wage payment. Methods. Time study. Job evaluation. Summary.

Appendix 1   Glossary of terms used in methods, time study, and wage payment   **665**

Appendix 2   Collection of helpful formulas   **674**

Appendix 3   Special tables   **676**

Index   **697**

CHAPTER 1

Methods, time study, and wage payment today

The production function

The continued success of most industries and businesses is due to a large extent to the effectiveness of their methods, time study, and wage payment programs. Today not only the production phase, but all aspects of a business or industry—sales, finance, engineering, cost, and maintenance—provide fertile areas for the application of methods, time study, and sound wage payment. For example, in the field of sales, modern information retrieval methods usually will introduce significant savings, product quotas for specific territories provide a base or standard that individual salesmen will endeavor to exceed, and payment for results will always result in above-standard performance.

Since the field of production within industry utilizes the greatest number of young men and women in methods, time study, and wage payment work, this field will be treated in more detail than any other in this text. The areas of opportunity existing in the field of production for students enrolled in engineering, industrial management, business administration, industrial psychology, and labor-management relations are: (1) work measurement, (2) work methods, (3) production engineering, (4) manufacturing analysis and control, (5) facilities planning, (6) wage administration, (7) safety, (8) production and inventory control, and (9) quality control. Other position areas, such as personnel or industrial relations, cost, and budgeting, are closely related to, and dependent on, the production group.

1

These opportunities are not confined to manufacturing industries. They exist and are equally important in such enterprises and businesses as department stores, hotels, hospitals, educational institutions, and any other area where the combined effects of men, materials, and facilities are used to fulfill an objective. However, it is in the production of goods and services that the greatest demand has been made for personnel who have received training in the area of methods, time study, and wage payment.

The production section of an industry may well be called the heart of that industry, and once the activity of this section is interrupted, the whole industry ceases to be productive. The production department includes the methods engineering, time study, and wage payment activity, which offers the young technical graduate one of the most satisfying fields of endeavor.

It is in the production department that material to produce is requisitioned and controlled; sequence of operations and methods determined; tools ordered; time values assigned; work scheduled, dispatched, and followed up; and customers kept satisfied. Training in this field demonstrates how production is accomplished, where it is done, when it is performed, and how long it takes to do it. A background including such training will prove invaluable, whether one's ultimate objective is in sales, production, or cost.

If the production department is considered the heart of an industrial enterprise, the *methods, time study, and wage payment* activity is the center of the production group. Here, more than any other place, is determined whether a product is going to be produced on a competitive basis. Here is where initiative and ingenuity are used to develop efficient tooling, man and machine relationships, and work stations on new jobs in advance of production, thus assuring that the product will stand the test of facing stiff competition. Here is where creativity is continually used to improve existing methods and help assure the company of leadership in its product line. In this department good labor relations are maintained through establishing fair labor standards, or may be impeded by setting one inequitable rate.

Methods, time study, and wage payment offer real challenges. Industries with competent engineers, business administrators, industrial relations personnel, specially trained supervisors, and psychologists carrying out methods, time study, and wage payment techniques are inevitably better able to meet competition and better equipped to operate profitably.

The objective of the manufacturing manager is to produce a quality product, on schedule, at the lowest possible cost, with a minimum of capital investment and with the maximum of employee satisfaction. The quality control manager centers his objectives in the control of quality so that engineering specifications are maintained and customers are kept satisfied by the quality level. The production control manager is principally interested in establishing and maintaining production schedules with due regard both for customer needs and for the favorable economics obtainable with careful scheduling. The manager of methods, time study, and wage payment is mostly concerned with combining the lowest possible production cost and maximum employee satisfaction. The maintenance manager is primarily concerned with minimizing facility downtime because of unscheduled breakdowns and repairs. Figure 1–1 illustrates the relationship of the manager of the methods, time study, and wage payment department to the staff and line departments under the General Manager.

Scope of methods engineering and time study

The field of methods engineering and time study includes designing, creating, and selecting the best manufacturing methods, processes, tools, equipment, and skills to manufacture a product after working drawings have been released by the product engineering section. The best method must then be interfaced with the best skills available so that an efficient man-machine relationship exists. Once the complete method is established, the responsibility of determining the time required to produce the product falls within the scope of this work. Also included is the responsibility of following through to see that predetermined standards are met and that workmen are adequately compensated for their output.

This procedure includes defining the problem related to expected cost, breaking the job down into operations, analyzing each operation to determine the most economical manufacturing procedures for the quantity involved, applying proper time values, and then following through to assure that the prescribed method is put into operation. Figure 1–2 illustrates the opportunities for reducing manufacturing time through the application of methods engineering and time study.

Methods engineering

The terms "operation analysis," "work simplification," and "methods engineering" are frequently used synonymously. In most cases the person is referring to a technique for increasing the production per unit of time and, consequently, reducing the unit cost. However, "methods engineering," as defined in this text, entails analysis work at two different times during the history of a product. Initially, the methods engineer is responsible for designing and developing the various work centers where the product will be produced. Secondly, he continually restudies the work center to find a better way to produce the product. The more thorough the methods study made during the planning stages, the less necessity for additional methods studies during the life of the product.

FIGURE 1-1. Typical organization chart showing the influence of methods, time study, and wage payment on the operation of the enterprise

A—Cost is largely determined by manufacturing methods.
B—Time standards are the bases of standard costs.
C—Standards (direct and indirect) provide the bases for measuring performance of production departments.
D—Time is a common denominator for comparing competitive equipment and supplies.
E—Good labor relations maintained with equitable standards and fair base rates.

F—Methods and processes strongly influence product designs.
G—Standards provide the bases for preventive maintenance.
H—Standards enforce quality.
I—Scheduling is based on time standards.
J—Methods and standards provide how the work is to be done and how long it will take.

In developing the work center to produce the product, the methods engineer should follow a systematic procedure. This will include:

1. Gathering all the facts related to the design, such as drawings, quantity requirements, delivery requirements, and so on.
2. Listing all facts in orderly form. The development of process charts is recommended.

FIGURE 1–2

Opportunities for savings through the application of methods engineering and time study

3. Making an analysis. Consider the primary approaches to operation analysis and the principles of motion study.
4. Developing a method.
5. Presenting the method.
6. Installing the work center.
7. Developing a job analysis of the work center.
8. Establishing time standards at the work center.
9. Following up the method.

When methods studies are made to improve the existing method of operation, experience has shown that to achieve the maximum returns, a systematic procedure similar to that advocated for designing the initial work center should be followed. The Westinghouse Electric Corporation, in its Operation Analysis program, advocates the following steps for assuring most favorable results:

1. Make a preliminary survey.
2. Determine extent of analysis justified.
3. Develop process charts.
4. Investigate the approaches to operation analysis.
5. Make motion study when justified.
6. Compare the old and the new method.
7. Present the new method.
8. Check installation of the new method.
9. Correct time values.
10. Follow up the new method.

Actually, methods engineering includes the procedures of all these 10 steps.

Methods engineering can be defined as the systematic procedure for subjecting all direct and indirect operations to close scrutiny to introduce improvements resulting in making work easier to perform and allowing work to be done in less time and with less investment per unit. Thus, the real objective of methods engineering is profit improvement.

Time study

Time study involves the technique of establishing an allowed time standard to perform a given task, based upon measurement of work content of the prescribed method, with due allowance for fatigue, personal and unavoidable delays. The time study analyst has several techniques available that can be used to establish a standard: stopwatch time study, standard data, fundamental motion data, work sampling, and estimates based on historical data. Each of these techniques has application under certain conditions. The time study analyst must know when it is best to use a certain technique and then use that technique judiciously and correctly.

A close association exists between the functions of the time study analyst and the methods engineer. Although their objectives differ, a good work measurement man is a good methods engineer, since he will include methods engineering as a basic component of his position.

To be assured that the prescribed method is the best, the time study engineer frequently finds himself in the role of a methods engineer. In small industries these two activities are often handled by the same individual. Note that establishing time values is a step in the systematic procedure of developing new work centers and improving methods related to existing work centers.

Wage payment

The wage payment function, similarly, is closely associated with the time study and methods sections of the production activity. In general, the wage payment section is responsible for releasing standards of production to the factory and maintaining the incentive plans or plan so they function smoothly and efficiently. Because of the nature of an enterprise, it may be necessary to have two entirely different wage payment plans in effect, or even three (daywork, piecework, group incentives), and the administration of these falls on the wage payment group.

The function of job evaluation, a technique for equitably determining the relative worth of the different work assignments within an organization, is usually a responsibility of the wage payment section.

Production control, plant layout, purchasing, cost accounting and control, and process and product design are additional areas closely related both to the methods and the standards functions. All of these provinces depend on time and cost data, facts, and procedures of operation from the methods and standards department to operate effectively. These relationships are briefly discussed in Chapter 23.

TEXT QUESTIONS

1. What job opportunities exist in the general field of production?
2. What is the scope of methods engineering?
3. What activities are considered the key links to the production group within a manufacturing enterprise?
4. What is meant by the terms "operation analysis," "work simplification," and "methods engineering"?
5. What steps has the Westinghouse Electric Corporation advocated to assure real savings during a method improvement program?
6. What is the function of the time study department?
7. Is it possible for one enterprise to have more than one type of wage payment plan? Explain.
8. What is the principal objective of methods engineering?
9. What four broad opportunities are there for savings through methods and time study?
10. Explain in detail what a "work center" encompasses.
11. What is the function of job evaluation?

GENERAL QUESTIONS

1. How do well-organized methods, time study, and wage payment procedures benefit the company?
2. Show the relationship between time study and methods engineering. Explain each fully.
3. Discuss the reasoning behind the statement, "A good time study man is a good methods engineer."
4. Comment on the general responsibility of the wage payment group.
5. Why does the purchasing department need data and information from the methods, time study, and wage payment department? Give several examples.
6. Why is job evaluation a part of the wage payment function?
7. What is meant by fundamental motion data?
8. Based on your reading of Chapter 1, what percentage savings do you estimate is possible in the direct labor payroll of a plant that has never practiced methods engineering and time study? Do you feel this is a realistic estimate?

CHAPTER 2

Development of motion and time study

The work of Taylor

Frederick W. Taylor is generally conceded to be the father of modern time study in this country. However, time studies were conducted in Europe many years before the time of Taylor. In 1760, a Frenchman, Perronet, made extensive time studies on the manufacture of No. 6 common pins, and arrived at a standard of 494 per hour. Sixty years later an English economist, Charles Babbage, made time studies on No. 11 common pins, and as a result of these studies determined that one pound (5,546 pins) should be produced in 7.6892 hours.[1]

Taylor began his time study work in 1881 while associated with the Midvale Steel Company in Philadelphia. After 12 years' work, he evolved a system which is based upon the "task" idea. Here Taylor proposed that the work of each employee be planned out by the management at least one day in advance, and that each man receive complete written instructions describing his task in detail and noting the means to be used in accomplishing it. Each job was to have a standard time which was to be fixed after time studies had been made by experts. This time was to be based upon the work possibilities of a first-rate man, who, after being instructed, was able to do the work regularly. In the timing process Mr. Taylor advocated the breaking of the work assignment into small divisions

---

[1] Charles Babbage, *On the Economy of Manufactures,* 1832.

of effort known as "elements." These were timed individually, and their collective values were used to determine the allowed time of the task.

In June, 1895, Taylor presented his findings and recommendations at a Detroit meeting of the American Society of Mechanical Engineers. His paper was received without enthusiasm because many of the engineers present interpreted his findings to be a new piece rate system rather than a technique for analyzing work and improving methods.

The distaste that prevailed in the minds of many of the engineers of the time relative to piecework can well be appreciated. Standards were established by estimates made by supervisors, and, at best, these were far from being accurate or consistent. Both management and employees were rightfully skeptical of piece rates based on the foreman's guess. Management looked upon the rates with doubt, in view of the possibility of the foreman making a conservative estimate so as to protect the performance of his department. The worker, because of unfortunate past experiences, was concerned over any rate established merely by judgment and guess, since the rate vitally affected his earnings.

Then in June, 1903, Taylor presented his famous paper, "Shop Management," at the Saratoga meeting of the A.S.M.E. in which he gave the elements of the mechanism of scientific management as follows:

- Time-study, with the implements and methods for properly making it.
- Functional, or divided, foremanship, with its superiority to the old-fashioned single foreman.
- The standardization of all tools and implements used in the plants, and also of the acts or movements of workmen for each class of work.
- The desirability of a planning room or department.
- The "exception principle" in management.
- The use of slide rules and similar timesaving implements.
- Instruction cards for the workman.
- The task idea in management, accompanied by a large bonus for the successful performance of the task.
- The "differential rate."
- Mnemonic systems for classifying manufactured products as well as implements used in manufacturing.
- A routing system.
- Modern cost system.

Tayor's "Shop Management" technique was well received by many factory managers, and with modifications had many satisfactory installations.[2]

---

[2] C. Bertrand Thompson in 1917 reported on the record of 113 plants which had installed "scientific management." Of these, 59 were considered to have completely successful installations, 20 had partly successful installations, and 34 plants considered their installation failures. C. Bertrand Thompson, *The Taylor System of Scientific Management* (Chicago: A. W. Shaw Co., 1917).

It was at this time that the country was going through an unprecedented inflationary period. The word "efficiency" became passé and most businesses and industry were looking for new ideas that would improve their performance. The railroad industry too felt at that time the necessity to substantially increase shipping rates to cover general cost increases. Louis Brandeis, who at that time represented the eastern business associations, contended that the railroads did not deserve or in fact, need the increase because they had been remiss in not introducing the new "science of management" into their industry. Mr. Brandeis claimed that the railroad companies could save $1 million a day by introducing the techniques advocated by Taylor. Thus, it was Brandeis and the Eastern Rate Case (as the hearing came to be known) that first introduced Taylor's concepts as "scientific management."

At this time many men without the qualifications of Taylor, Barth, Merrick, and other early pioneers, but eager to make a name for themselves in this new field, established themselves as "Efficiency Experts" and endeavored to install scientific management programs in industry. Here they encountered a natural resistance to change from employees, and since they were not equipped to handle problems of human relations, they met with great difficulty. Anxious to make a good showing and equipped with only a pseudoscientific knowledge, they generally established rates that were too difficult to meet. The situation would become so acute that management would be obliged to discontinue the whole program in order to continue operation.

In other instances, factory managers would allow the establishment of time standards by the foreman, and, as has been pointed out, this seldom was satisfactory.

Then, too, once standards were established, many factory managers of that time, interested primarily in the reduction of labor costs, would unscrupulously cut rates once some employee made what the employer felt was too much money. The result was harder work at the same take-home pay and sometimes less take-home pay; naturally, violent worker reaction resulted.

These developments spread in spite of the many favorable installations started by Taylor. At the Watertown Arsenal, labor objected to the new time study system to such an extent that in 1910 the Interstate Commerce Commission started an investigation of time study. Several derogatory reports on the subject influenced Congress in 1913 to add a rider to the government appropriation bill, stipulating that no part of the appropriation should be made available for the pay of any person engaged in time study work. This restriction applied to the government-operated plants where government funds were used to pay the employees.

The Military Establishment Appropriation Act, 1947 (Public Law 515, 79th Congress) and the Navy Department Appropriation Act, 1947 (Public Law 492, 79th Congress) provide as follows:

Sec. 2. No part of the appropriation made in this Act shall be available for the salary or pay of any officer, manager, superintendent, foreman or other person having charge of the work of any employee of the United States Government while making or causing to be made with a stopwatch, or other time-measuring device, a time study of any job of any such employee between the starting and completion thereof, or of the movements of any such employee while engaged upon such work; nor shall any part of the appropriation made in this Act be available to pay any premiums or bonus or cash reward to any employee in addition to his regular wages, except as may be otherwise authorized in this Act.

Finally, in July, 1947, the House of Representatives passed a bill which allows the War Department to use time study, and in 1949, the prohibition against using stopwatches was dropped from appropriation language, and now no restriction of time study practice prevails.

Motion study

Frank B. Gilbreth was the founder of the modern motion study technique that may be defined as the study of body motions used in performing an operation, with thought toward improving the operation by eliminating and simplifying necessary motions, and then establishing the most favorable motion sequence for maximum efficiency.

Gilbreth originally introduced his ideas and philosophies in the bricklayer's trade where he was employed. After introducing methods improvements through motion study and operator training, he was able to increase the average production of laying bricks to 350 bricks per man per hour. Prior to Gilbreth's studies, 120 bricks per man per hour was considered a satisfactory rate of performance.

The Gilbreths more than anyone else were responsible for industry's recognition of the importance of a minute study of body motions to its ability to increase production, reduce fatigue, and instruct operators in the best method of performing the operation.

Frank Gilbreth, with assistance from his wife, Lillian Gilbreth, also developed the moving-picture technique for studying motions, which has carried through many walks of life today. In industry, this technique is known as micromotion study, but the study of movements through the aid of the slow motion moving picture is by no means confined to industrial application. The world of sports finds it invaluable as a training tool to show development of form and skill.

The Gilbreths also developed the cyclegraphic and chronocyclegraphic analysis techniques for studying motion paths made by an operator. The cyclegraphic method involves attaching a small electric light bulb to the finger or hand or part of body being studied and then photographing the motion while the operator is performing the operation. The resulting picture gives a permanent record of the motion pattern employed and can be analyzed for possible improvement.

The chronocyclegraph is similar to the cyclegraph, but in this case the electric circuit is interrupted regularly, causing the light to flash. Thus the resulting photograph instead of showing solid lines of the motion patterns as in the cyclegraph, will show short dashes of light spaced in proportion to the speed of the body motion being photographed. Consequently, with the chronocyclegraph it is possible to compute velocity, acceleration, and deceleration as well as study the body motions.

Early contemporaries

Carl G. Barth, an associate of F. W. Taylor, developed a production slide rule for determining the most efficient combination of speeds and feeds for cutting metals of various hardness, considering depth of cut, size of tool, and life of tool.

Barth is also noted for the work he did in determining allowances. He invesigated the number of foot-pounds of work a man could do in a day. He then developed a rule that for a certain push or pull on a man's arms it is possible for him to be under load for a certain percentage of the day.

Harrington Emerson applied scientific methods to work on the Santa Fe Railroad and wrote a book, *Twelve Principles of Efficiency,* in which he made an effort to inform management of procedures for efficient operation. He reorganized the company, integrated its shop procedures, installed standard costs and a bonus plan, and transferred its accounting work to Hollerith tabulating machines. This effort resulted in annual savings in excess of $1.5 million.

It was Emerson who coined the term "efficiency engineering." His ideal was efficiency everywhere and in everything. His philosophy of efficiency as a basis for operation in all fields of endeavor first appeared in 1908 in the *Engineering Magazine.* When, in 1911, Emerson enlarged his ideas in *Twelve Principles of Efficiency,* this volume was perhaps the earliest and most comprehensive guide to good management.

Henry Laurence Gantt in 1917 developed simple graphs that would measure performance while visually showing projected schedules. This production control tool was enthusiastically adopted by the shipbuilding industry during the World War I period. For the first time, this tool made it possible to compare actual performance against the original plan, and to adjust daily schedules in accordance with capacity, backlog, and customer requirements.

Gantt is also known for his invention of the task and bonus wage system. This was developed in 1901, after he spent six years as Taylor's rig'1t-hand man at Midvale and Bethlehem Steel Company. His wage payment system rewarded the worker for above-standard performance and eliminated any penalty for failure. Perhaps more important than the deviation from Taylor's advocation of penalizing the below-standard operator, was offering the foreman a bonus for every one of his workers who performed above standard. Gantt made it obvious that scientific management could and should be much more than an inhuman "speedup" of labor. Gantt proclaimed, "We do not approve of foremen 'cussing' their men, but we do approve of their showing the men how the work is to be done."

Morris L. Cooke, former director of the Department of Public Works in Philadelphia, made an effort to bring the principles of scientific management into city governments. In 1940, Cooke and Philip Murray, past president of the CIO, published a manuscript, "Organized Labor and Production," in which they brought out that both labor and management have as their goal "Optimum Productivity." This they defined as "the highest possible balanced output of goods and services that management and labor skills can produce, equitably shared and consistent with a rational conservation of human and physical resources."

After Taylor retired, Dwight V. Merrick started a study of unit times, and these were published in the *American Machinist* edited by L. P. Alford. Merrick, with the assistance of Carl Barth, developed a technique for determining allowances on a rational basis. Merrick is also known for his multiple piece rate wage payment plan in which he recommends three graded piece rates.

Motion and time study received added stimulus during World War II when Franklin D. Roosevelt, through the Department of Labor, advocated establishing standards, from which increases in production resulted. On November 11, 1945, Regional War Labor Board III (for Pennsylvania, southern New Jersey, Maryland, Delaware, and the District of Columbia) issued a memorandum stating the policy of the War Labor Board on incentive proposals. Sections I, II, and IV are reproduced since they contain matter pertinent to standards and wage incentives.

I—General Considerations Applicable to All Incentive Proposals

1. The expected effect of an incentive plan should be an increase in the present production per man-hour without increasing the unit labor cost in the plant, department, or job affected.

2. The proposal should not be in effect merely a means of giving a general increase in wages, nor should it result in wage decreases.

3. The plan should offer more pay only for more output.

4. If a union has bargaining rights for workers affected, the plan in all of its details should be collectively bargained.

5. No incentive wage plan should be proposed as a substitute for carrying out the responsibilities of both the management and employees.

6. No incentive plan should be put into operation, even if the money is held rather than advanced to the workers, until the approval of the War Labor Board has been secured.

II—*Establishing Incentive Rates for a Specific Production Operation*

When incentive rates are proposed for a specific production job or job classification the following principles apply:

1. Where feasible the operation should be *time studied* carefully to set the production standard. Results of this time study in as much detail as possible should appear in the application. If a time study is impracticable, the application should show why.

2. If a time study is impracticable, the production standard may be based upon *records of past production* provided: (*a*) The records for an appropriate production period are submitted with the application; (*b*) The applicant establishes that the period is representative and that the present product, methods, prospective volume of work, and work force are comparable to those existing during the particular period of past production; (*c*) Exceptionally high or low production figures for short periods are satisfactorily explained in the application.

3. The production standard should be a quantity of output *higher than has been attained previously* by the average worker, or at least, higher than has been attained customarily. If the production standard is below an amount previously attained at some one or more times, the application should explain fully the reasons therefor.

IV—*Plant-wide Incentive Plans*

Because plant-wide incentive plans are comparatively new to American industry and because the effects of such plans on worker efficiency and production are difficult to predict, the Regional Board is not adopting a position on them at this time, but will consider each case on its individual merits. The general considerations set forth in I above are applicable here.

Organizations

Since 1911 there has been an organized effort to keep industry abreast of the latest developments started by Taylor and Gilbreth. Technical organizations have contributed much toward bringing the science of time study, motion study, work simplification, and methods engineering up to present-day standards.

In 1911 the Conference of Scientific Management, under the leadership of Morris L. Cooke and Harlow S. Persons, was started at Amos Tuck School of Dartmouth College.

In 1912 the Society to Promote the Science of Management was organized and operated until 1915, when it was renamed the Taylor Society.

The Society of Industrial Engineers was organized in 1917 by men interested in production methods.

The American Management Association was formed in 1922 by groups interested in training personnel through so-called "Corporation Training

Schools." Today its main purpose is "to advance the understanding of the principles, policies, practices, and purposes of modern management and of the method of creating and maintaining satisfactory relations in commerce and industry; to work toward the practical solution of current business problems and the development of the science of management." Annually the A.M.A. presents the Gantt Memorial Medal for the most distinguished contribution to industrial management as a service to the community.

The Society for the Advancement of Management (S.A.M.) was organized in 1936 by the merging of the Society of Industrial Engineers and the Taylor Society. This organization has continuted the emphasis on the importance of time study and methods and wage payment up to the present time. Annually, it offers the "Taylor" key for the outstanding contribution to the advancement of the art and science of management as conceived by Frederick W. Taylor. Also, the "Gilbreth" medal is awarded annually for noteworthy achievement in the field of motion, skill, and fatigue study.

The American Institute of Industrial Engineers has had a rapid growth since its founding at Columbus, Ohio, on September 9, 1948. It is a national technical society of Industrial Engineers. The purpose of the A.I.I.E. is to maintain the practice of industrial engineering on a professional level; to foster a high degree of integrity among the members of the industrial engineering profession; to encourage and assist education and research in areas of interest to the industrial engineer; to promote the interchange of ideas and information among members of the industrial engineering profession; to serve in the public interest by identifying men qualified to practice as industrial engineers; to promote professional registration of industrial engineers.

Present trends

Time and motion study has steadily improved since the 1920's until today it is recognized as a necessary tool for the effective operation of business or industry. The practitioner of the art and science of time and motion study has come to realize the necessity of considering the "human element" in his work. No longer is the "cut and dried" procedure so characteristic of the "efficiency expert" acceptable. Today, consideration, through employee testing and training, is given to the fact that individuals differ in performance potential. Such factors as sex, age, health and well-being, physical size and strength, aptitude, training, attitudes, and response to motivation have a direct bearing on output. Furthermore, the analyst of today recognizes that workers object, and rightfully so, to being treated as machines. Workers tend to dislike and fear a purely scientific approach to methods, work measurement, and wage incentives. They inherently dislike any change from their present way of operation. This psychological reaction is not characteristic of factory workers only but is the normal reaction of all people. Management frequently will reject worthwhile methods' innovations because of their reluctance to change. In fact, in the experience of the writer, management has been harder to sell on new ideas than any other group within the plant. After all, they are responsible for the existing method or procedure, and they frequently will defend it regardless of the potential savings through change.

Workers tend to fear methods and time study, for they see that this will result in an increase in productivity. To them, this means but one thing: less work and consequently less pay. They must be sold on the fact that they, as consumers, benefit from lower costs, and that with lower costs, broader markets result, meaning more work for more men for more weeks of the year.

Some fear of time study today is without a doubt due to the unpleasant experiences in the days of the efficiency expert. To many workers, motion and time study is synonymous with the "speed up" or the "stretch out." These terms denote using incentives to spur employees to higher levels of output, followed by establishing new levels as normal production, thus forcing the workers to still greater exertions to maintain even their previous earning power. In years past, undoubtedly some shortsighted and unscrupulous managements did resort to this practice.

The practitioner of motion and time study today must use the "humane" approach. He must be well versed in the study of human behavior and be accomplished in the art of communication. He must be a good listener at all times, indicating he respects the ideas and thinking of others, particularly the man on the bench. He must give credit where credit is due. In fact, he should get in the habit of always giving the "other fellow" credit, even if there is some question of the other fellow's deserving it.

Regardless of one's technical knowledge and ability, he will have little success in motion and time study work unless he is competent in dealing with the human element.

A great number of colleges and universities in their industrial engineering curricula are teaching the principles, techniques, and philosophies of this field. Most labor unions are training their representatives in the results and uses of the technique. Managements of both small and large industries are embarking on mass training programs, realizing the potentialities of a well-formulated program utilizing this tool.

The Industrial Management Society annually presents a Time and Motion Study and Management Clinic. Here leaders of government, labor, and industry, along with engineers, gather to discuss common problems and to increase their knowledge of what is being done in the area of methods, standards, and wage payment.

TEXT QUESTIONS

1. Where were time studies originally made and who conducted them?
2. Explain Frederick W. Taylor's principle of functional foremanship.
3. What effect has Congress had on time study?
4. What is meant by motion study, and who is generally conceded to be the founder of the motion study technique?
5. What is Carl G. Barth primarily noted for in the production end of industry?
6. Which organizations are concerned with advancing the ideas of Taylor and the Gilbreths?
7. Was the skepticism of management and labor toward rates established by "efficiency experts" understandable? Why?
8. What psychological reaction is characteristic of workers when method changes are suggested?
9. Explain the importance of the humanistic approach in methods and time study work.
10. What contributions in the area of motion study have been made by the Gilbreths?
11. What was Emerson's philosophy of efficiency?
12. What was Gantt's contribution to motion and time study?
13. Who was Louis Brandeis and what part did he play in the introduction of scientific management?
14. How did the Military Establishment Appropriation Act, 1947 submerge the development of work measurement methodology?

GENERAL QUESTIONS

1. How is time and motion study used in industry today?
2. Why are labor unions training their representatives in the time and motion study technique?
3. Explain the function of the A.M.A. as compared to the A.I.I.E.
4. Why was the government restriction on the use of stopwatches carried through the World War II years?
5. Interview a group of five industrial workers and obtain their opinions on the necessity of motion and time study.
6. In the 1971 collective bargaining agreements within the basic steel industry, what resolutions occurred that have an impact on work measurement?

CHAPTER 3

The operation and flow process chart

No matter if methods work is being used to design a new work center or improve one already in operation, it is helpful to present in clear, logical form the factual information related to the process. In Chapter 1, it was brought out that the first step in methods work, after a preliminary survey indicates the desirability of going ahead with a study, is to gather all the necessary facts related to the operation or process. Pertinent information—such as quantity to be produced, delivery schedules, operational times, facilities, machine capacities, special materials, special tools, and so on—may have an important bearing on the solution of the problem. This chapter will discuss the techniques that best present the factual data.

Every craftsman has his tools to facilitate his performance. Just as the machinist has his micrometers and calipers and the patternmaker his chisels and plane, so does the methods analyst have at his disposal tools to help him do a better job in a shorter time. One of the most important tools of the methods engineer is the process chart. A process chart is defined as a graphic presentation of any manufacturing process. In methods work, one usually uses five different types of process charts, each of which has its specific application. These are:

1. Operation process chart
2. Flow process chart
3. Man and machine process chart

4.   Gang process chart
5.   Operator process chart

The operation and flow process charts are used principally to present the problem. A problem cannot be solved unless it is properly presented. Consequently, these charts will be discussed at this time. Man and machine, gang, and operator process charts are presented in Chapter 6.

Frank Gilbreth is generally credited with being the original designer of process charts, although superintendents, methods engineers, and general foremen have always used this tool in one form or another, but not under the name "process chart." Process charts have wide application in improving a method; however, they must be used with caution because considerable time can be consumed in their construction.

The methods analyst must exercise judgment on the amount of detail he attempts to include on any job. He, more than any one else in the factory, must be governéd by the law that we never introduce any change, adjustment, or modification unless it is going to pay for itself within a reasonable time. Thus, the methods analyst must know when it is economically wise to construct a process chart or charts, and be fully cognizant of the type he should use. The methods analyst must avoid getting the reputation of being "chart happy." If he spends all his time constructing charts, he will have no time for creative thinking that leads to actual methods improvement.

Operation process chart

The operation process chart shows all operations, inspections, time allowances, and materials used in a manufacturing process. It clearly shows the sequence of events in chronological order from the raw material to the packaging of the finished product. It points out the entrance of all components and subassemblies to the main assembly. Just as a blueprint gives design details such as fits, tolerances, and specifications at a glance, so does an operation process chart give manufacturing details at a glance.

The A.S.M.E. standard definition of an operation process chart is as follows:

An operation process chart is a graphic representation of the points at which materials are introduced into the process, and of the sequence of inspections and all operations except those involved in material handling. It includes information considered desirable for analysis such as time required and location.[1]

---

[1] Extracted from *ASME Operation and Flow Process Chart Standard,* with permission of the publisher, The American Society of Mechanical Engineers, 29 West 39th Street, New York, N.Y.

3–1

ntional practice to show that no juncture
s when necessary to cross vertical flow
and horizontal material line

tions will be performed. If no disassembly operations occur in the process, then the analyst should begin his chart in the upper right-hand corner of the paper. In the event disassembly operations compose part of the process, it is well to start plotting the major item more to the left and closer to the center of the paper. This will allow room for portraying disassembly operations shown as other operations, but material is represented as flowing from the process by a horizontal material line drawn to the right from the vertical flow line. Material introduced to the main component of assembly is portrayed by horizontal lines entering the vertical flow lines from the left.

Once the component to be charted first has been selected, it should be identified, as well as the material from which it is produced. This is done by drawing a horizontal material line. Above this line should be a brief description of the material, with an indication of the quantity required. If a drawing number or specification number applies, it should be included. To identify the part itself, the name of the part and its drawing number are shown in capital letters directly above the material description (see Figure 3–2).

Next, a vertical flow line is drawn in a downward direction from the right-hand end of the horizontal material line. The vertical flow line is extended a short distance (about ¼ inch), and then the symbol for the first operation or inspection, as the case may be, is drawn. To the right of the symbol is placed a brief but specific description of the event, such as

J–1108–1 DRIVE SHAFT
12" 1 1/2" DIAM. S.A.E. 1112

FIGURE 3–2

Identification of part in constructing
the operation process chart

Before we can improve a design, w~
product as it is presently designed. L.
manufacturing process, it is well to cons
so we understand the problem fully and v
areas afford most possibilities of attack with
ment. The operation process chart effectively s
problem cannot be stated, it usually cannot be s.

Constructing the operation process chart

In constructing the operation process chart, two syr.
small circle usually ⅜ inch in diameter, denotes an operat.
square, ⅜ inch on a side, denotes an inspection.

An operation takes place when the part being studied is i.
transformed or when it is being studied or planned prior to p
productive work on it.

 OPERATION INSPECTION

An inspection takes place when the part is being examined to determine
its conformance to standard.

Before beginning the actual construction of the operation process chart,
the analyst should identify it with the title placed at the top of the paper.
Usually, the identifying information—which would include part number,
drawing number, process description, present or proposed method, date,
and name of person doing the charting—would be headed with the words
"Operation Process Chart." Sometimes additional information may be
added to identify completely the subject being charted. This may include
items such as chart number, plant, building, and department.

Vertical lines are used to indicate the general flow of the process as
work is being accomplished, while horizontal lines feeding into the vertical flow lines are used to introduce material, either purchased or upon
which work has been performed during the process. In general, the operation process chart should be constructed so vertical flow lines and horizontal material lines do not cross. If for some reason it has become
necessary to cross a vertical and a horizontal line, conventional practice
to show that no juncture occurs, is to draw a small semicircle in the horizontal line at the point where the vertical flow line crosses (see Figure 3–1).

When starting the actual construction of the operation process chart,
the analyst first selects the major item of the assembly for charting. This
usually would be the component on which the greatest number of opera-

"Drill, Ream, and Chamfer" or "Check O.D. and I.D." Immediately under the operation or inspection is recorded the facility on which the event is performed, as "#3 W. & S." or "Single End Plug Gage." To the left of the symbol is shown the time required to perform the work on one piece. After this information has been recorded, the vertical flow line is extended from the bottom of the symbol, and the next event is recorded. This charting procedure is continued until a second component joins the first. A horizontal material line is drawn to indicate the point at which the second component enters the process (see Figure 3–3).

FIGURE 3–3

Entrance of second and third component and disassembly of second component in a manufacturing process

Purchased items that subsequently enter the process are introduced by a horizontal line, the same as manufactured items. The purchased material or component is identified by part name, drawing number, and the source of supply (see Figure 3–4).

As each component of the assembly enters the process shown on the vertical line to the right, the charting of the events occurring to the combined components is continued along the vertical flow line. Thus, the final operation or inspection occurring to the complete assembly will appear in the lower right-hand corner of the charting paper.

All operations and inspections are numbered chronologically for identification and reference purposes. The first operation is identified with an "O–1" in the center of its symbol, the second "O–2" and so on. Inspections are numbered in a similar manner in their own independent series. Thus, the first inspection is identified with an "INS–1" in the center of its symbol, the second "INS–2" and so on.

All operations taking place on the various components are numbered in the same series. Likewise, all inspections appearing on the operation process chart are numbered in one series. For example, if the first component on the chart had six operations performed upon it, they would be numbered O–1, O–2, O–3, O–4, O–5, and O–6. If, at this point, a second component joins the first, and three operations were performed on the second component prior to its assembly to the first component, then these three operations would be identified as O–7, O–8, and O–9. The first operation performed after the first and second components are brought together would be O–10.

A typical completed operation process chart appears in Figure 3–5.

FIGURE 3–4

Entrance of purchased component
into a manufacturing process

J–1108–3 DRIVE PULLEY
A.B. JONES MFG. CO.

Using the operation process chart

After the analyst has completed the operation process chart, he is ready to use it. He should review each operation and inspection from the standpoint of the primary approaches to operation analysis (see Chapters 4 and 5). In particular, the following approaches apply when studying the operation process chart:

1. Purpose of operation
2. Design of part
3. Tolerances and specifications
4. Materials
5. Process of manufacture
6. Setup and tools
7. Working conditions
8. Plant layout

The procedure is for the analyst to adopt the questioning attitude on each of the above criteria that influence the cost and output of the product under study.

The most important question that the analyst should ask when study-

FIGURE 3–5

Operation process chart illustrating manufacture of telephone stands

```
                    OPERATION PROCESS CHART

        Manufacturing Type 2834421 Telephone Stands--Present Method
                  Part 2834421  Dwg. No. SK2834421
                     Charted By B.W.N. 4-12-
```

SUMMARY:

Event	Number	Time
Operations	20	17.58 minutes
Inspections	5	Day work

ing the events on the operation and flow process chart is: "Why?" Typical questions that should be asked are:

"Why is this operation necessary?"
"Why is this operation performed in this manner?"

"Why are these tolerances this close?"
"Why has this material been specified?"
"Why has this class of operator been assigned to do the work?"

The analyst should take nothing for granted; he should ask these and other pertinent questions about all phases of the process and then proceed to gather the information to answer the questions, so a better way of doing the work may be introduced.

The question "Why" immediately suggests other questions including What, How, Who, Where, and When. For example, the analyst should ask:

1. "*What* is the purpose of the operation?"
2. "*How* can the operation be better performed?"
3. "*Who* can best perform the operation?"
4. "*Where* could the operation be performed at a lower cost?"
5. "*When* should the operation be performed to give the least amount of material handling?"

For example, in the operation process chart shown in Figure 3–5, the analyst might ask the questions listed in Table 3–1 to determine the practicability of the method improvements indicated.

By answering these questions, the analyst will be aware of other questions that may lead to improvement. Ideas seem to generate ideas, and the experienced analyst will always arrive at several possibilities for improvement. He must keep an open mind and not let previous disappointments discourage the trial of new ideas.

The completed operation process chart helps visualize the present method with all its details, so new and better procedures may be devised. It shows the analyst what effect a change on a given operation will have on preceding and subsequent operations. The mere construction of the operation chart will inevitably suggest possibilities for improvement to the alert analyst.

This process chart indicates the general flow of all components entering into a product, and since each step is shown in its proper chronological sequence, the operation process chart is in itself an ideal plant layout. Consequently, methods analysts, plant layout engineers, and those in related fields will find this tool extremely helpful in making new layouts and in improving existing ones.

TABLE 3–1

	Question	Method Improvement
1.	Can fixed lengths of 1½″ x 14″ white maple be purchased at no extra square footage cost?	Eliminate waste ends from lengths that are not multiples of 14″.
2.	Can purchased maple boards be secured with edges smooth and parallel?	Eliminate jointing of ends (operation 2).
3.	Can boards be purchased to thickness size and have at least one side planed smooth? If so how much extra will this cost?	Eliminate planing to size.
4.	Why cannot two boards be stacked and sawed into 14″ sections simultaneously?	
5.	What percentage of rejects do we have at the first inspection station?	Reduce time of 0.18 (operation 4). If the percentage is low, perhaps this inspection can be eliminated.
6.	Why should the top of the table be sanded all over?	Eliminate sanding one side of top and reduce time (operation 5).
7.	Can fixed lengths of 1½″ x 3″ yellow pine be purchased at no extra square footage cost?	Eliminate waste ends from lengths that are not multiples of 12″.
8.	Can purchased yellow pine boards be secured with edges smooth and parallel?	Eliminate jointing of one edge.
9.	Can sill boards be purchased to thickness size and have one side planed smooth? If so, how much extra will this cost?	Eliminate planing to size.
10.	Why cannot two or more boards be stacked and sawed into 14″ sections simultaneously?	Reduce time of 0.10 (operation 9).
11.	What percentage of rejects do we have at the first inspection of the sills?	If the percentage is low, perhaps this inspection can be eliminated.
12.	Why is it necessary to sand the sills all over?	Eliminate some sanding and reduce time (operation 10).
13.	Can fixed lengths of 2½″ x 2½″ white maple be purchased at no extra square footage cost?	Eliminate waste ends from lengths that are not multiples of 16″.
14.	Can a smaller size than 2½″ x 2½″ be used?	Reduce material cost.
15.	Can purchased white maple boards be secured with edges smooth and parallel?	Eliminate jointing of edges.
16.	Can leg boards be purchased to thickness size and have sides planed smooth? If so, how much extra will this cost?	Eliminate planing to size.
17.	Why cannot two or more boards be stacked and sawed into 14″ sections simultaneously?	Reduce time (operation 15).
18.	What percentage of rejects do we have at the first inspection of the legs?	If the percentage is low, perhaps this inspection can be eliminated.
19.	Why is it necessary to sand the legs all over?	Eliminate some sanding and reduce time (operation 16).
20.	Could a fixture facilitate assembly of sills to top?	Reduce assembly time (operation 11).
21.	Can sampling inspection be used on first inspection of assembly?	Reduce inspection time (operation 4).
22.	Is it necessary to sand after one coat of shellac?	Eliminate operation 19.

The operation process chart is an aid in promoting and explaining a proposed method. Since it gives so much information so clearly, it provides an ideal comparison between two competing solutions.

Flow process chart

By A.S.M.E. standard definition, a flow process chart is a "graphic representation of all operations, transportations, inspections, delays, and storages occurring during a process or procedure, and includes information considered desirable for analysis such as time required and distance moved."[2]

In general, the flow process chart contains considerably more detail than the operation process chart. Consequently, it is not adapted to com-

FIGURE 3–6

Standard flow process chart symbols

○ OPERATION   ▽ STORAGE

□ INSPECTION   D DELAY

⇨ TRANSPORTATION   ⊙ COMBINED ACTIVITY

plicated assemblies as a whole. It is used primarily on one component of an assembly at a time to effect maximum savings in manufacturing that particular component. The flow chart is especially valuable in recording hidden costs, such as distances traveled, delays, and temporary storages. Once these nonproductive periods are highlighted, the analyst can take steps for improvement.

The flow process chart, in addition to recording operations and inspections, shows all the moves and delays in storage encountered by an item as it goes through the plant. In addition to the operation and inspection symbols used in the construction of operation process charts, several other symbols are used. A small arrow signifies a transportation, which can be defined as the moving of an object from one place to another, except when the movement takes place during the normal course of an operation or an inspection. A large capital "D" indicates a delay. A delay occurs when a part is not permitted to be immediately processed at the

---

[2] *Ibid.*

next work station. An equilateral triangle standing on its vertex signifies a storage, which occurs when a part is held and protected against unauthorized removal. When it becomes necessary to show a combined activity, such as one operator performing an operation and an inspection at a work station, then a square, ⅜ inch on a side with a small circle ⅜ inch in diameter inscribed within the square, is used as the identifying symbol.

FIGURE 3–7

Examples of process chart symbols

Figure 3–7 illustrates how one company uses process chart symbols to identify industrial activity.

Constructing the flow process chart

As in the operation process chart, the flow process chart should be properly identified with a title appearing at the top. It is customary practice to head the identifying information with the words "Flow Process Chart." The identifying information usually shown includes part number, drawing number, process description, present or proposed method, date, and the name of the person doing the charting.

Sometimes additional data is valuable to identify completely the job being charted. This may include the plant, building or department, chart number, quantity, and cost information.

Since the flow chart represents only one item rather than an assembly, a neat-appearing chart can be constructed by starting on the top central section of the paper. First, a horizontal material line is drawn, over which is shown the part number and description as well as the material from which the part is processed. A short vertical flow line (about ¼ inch) is then drawn to the first event symbol, which may be an arrow indicating a transportation from the storeroom. Just to the right of the transportation symbol is recorded a brief description of the move, such as "moved to cutoff saw by material handler." Immediately under this is shown the type of material handling equipment (if any) used. For example, "hand two-wheeled truck" or "gasoline-powered fork truck" would identify the equipment employed. To the left of the symbol is shown the time required to perform the event, and about 1 inch still further to the left, the distance in feet moved is recorded (see Figure 3–8).

This charting procedure is continued by recording all operations, inspections, moves, delays, permanent storages, and temporary storages that occur during the processing of the part. All events are numbered chronologically for reference purpose, using a separate series for each event class.

The transportation symbol is used to indicate the direction of the flow. Thus, when straight-line flow is taking place, the symbol is plotted with the arrow pointing to the right side of the paper. When the process reverses or backtracks, the change of direction is illustrated by plotting the arrow so it points to the left. If a multifloor building is housing the process, the arrow pointing upward indicates that the process is moving upward, and a downward direction of the arrow shows the flow of work to be descending.

To determine the distance moved, it is not necessary to measure accurately each move with a tape or 6-foot rule. Usually, a sufficiently correct figure will result by counting the number of columns that the material is moved past and then multiplying this number, less 1, by the span. Moves of 5 feet or less are usually not recorded; however, they may be if the analyst feels that it will affect materially the overall cost of the method being plotted.

It is important that all delay and storage times be included on the chart. It is not sufficient just to indicate that a delay or storage takes place. Since the longer a part stays in storage or is delayed, the more cost it accumulates, it is therefore important to know the length of time it spends at each delay and at each storage.

The most economical method of determining the duration of delays and storages is to mark several parts with chalk indicating the exact time they went into a storage or were delayed. Then periodically check the

FIGURE 3-8

Distance, unit time, and element description as shown on flow process chart

section to see when the parts marked are brought back into production. By taking a number of cases and recording the elapsed time and then averaging the results, the analyst will obtain sufficiently accurate time values.

Using the flow process chart

The flow process chart, like the operation process chart, is not an end in itself, but merely a means to an end. It is used as a tool of analysis for eliminating the hidden costs of a component. Since the flow chart clearly shows all transportations, delays, and storages, it is helpful in reducing either the quantity or duration of these elements.

Once the analyst has constructed the flow process chart, he uses the questioning approach based on the considerations primary to operation analysis. With the flow process chart, special consideration will be given to:

1. Material handling
2. Plant layout
3. Delay time
4. Storage time

In all probability, the analyst has already constructed and analyzed an operation process chart of the assembly of which the part under study in the flow chart is a component. The flow chart was constructed of the components of the particular assembly where it was thought further study of the hidden costs would be practical. If the operations and inspections performed on the component have already been studied, then the analyst would not spend a great deal of time restudying them when analyzing the flow chart. He would be more concerned in studying the distance parts must be moved from operation to operation, and what delays occur. Of course, if the flow chart was constructed initially, then all of the primary approaches to operation analysis should be used for studying the events shown on the flow process chart. The analyst is principally interested in improving the following: first, the time for each operation, inspection, move, delay, and storage; and second, the distance in feet each time the item being plotted is transported.

To eliminate or minimize delay and storage time to improve deliveries to customers, as well as reduce cost, the analyst should consider these check questions in studying the job:

1. How often is the full amount of material not delivered to the operation?
2. What can be done to schedule materials to come in more even quantities?
3. What is the most efficient batch or lot size, or manufacturing quantity?
4. How can schedules be rearranged to provide longer runs?
5. What is the best sequence for scheduling orders to allow for type of operation, tools required, colors, and so on?
6. What can be done to group similar operations to be performed at the same time?
7. How much can downtime and overtime be reduced by improved scheduling?
8. What is the cause of emergency maintenance and rush orders?
9. How much delay and storage time can be saved by making schedules more regular by running certain products on certain days?
10. What alternate schedules can be developed to use materials most efficiently?
11. Would it be worthwhile to accumulate pickups, deliveries, and shipments?

12. What is the proper department to do the job so it will be done with the same class of work and save a move, delay, or storage?
13. How much would be saved by doing the job on another shift? At another plant?
14. What is the best and most economical time to run tests and experiments?
15. What information is lacking on orders issued to the factory that may cause a delay or storage?
16. How much time is lost by shifts changing at different hours in related departments?
17. What are the frequent interruptions to the job, and how should they be eliminated?
18. How much time does the employee lose waiting for or by not receiving the proper instructions, blueprints, and specifications?
19. How many holdups are caused by congested aisles?
20. What improvements can be made in locating doorways and aisles and making aisles that will reduce delays?

Specific check questions, to shorten distance traveled and reduce material handling time, that should be used by the analyst include:

1. Can a facility be economically relocated to reduce distances traveled?
2. What can be done to reduce handling of materials?
3. What is the correct equipment for handling materials?
4. How much time is lost in getting materials to and from the work station?
5. Should product grouping be considered rather than process grouping?
6. What can be done to increase the size of the unit of material handled to reduce handling, scrap, and downtime?
7. How can elevator service be improved?
8. What can be done about runways and roadways to speed up transportation?
9. What is the proper position in which to place material to reduce the amount of handling required by the operator?
10. What use can be made of gravity delivery?

A study of the completed flow chart (Figure 3–9) will familiarize the analyst with all pertinent details related to the direct and indirect costs of a manufacturing process so they can be analyzed for improvement. Unless all the facts relating to a method are known, it is difficult to improve that method. Casual inspection of an operation will not provide the information needed to do a thorough job of method improvement. Since distances are recorded on the flow process chart, it is exceptionally valu-

FIGURE 3–9

Flow process chart

FLOW PROCESS CHART

SUBJECT CHARTED___Shower head face_____CHART NO.__1128_____

DRAWING NO._BA-14782_____PART NO._B-14782-2____CHART OF METHOD_Present____

CHART BEGINS_Bar stock storage_____CHARTED BY___E. Dunnick____

CHART ENDS__Assembly Department Storeroom_____DATE_9-7_SHEET_1_OF_2__

DIST. IN FEET	UNIT TIME IN MIN.	CHART SYMBOLS	PROCESS DESCRIPTION	DIST. IN FEET	UNIT TIME IN MIN.	CHART SYMBOLS	PROCESS DESCRIPTION
		1	In bar stock storage until requisitioned.	60		6	Waiting press operator
20	.02	1	Bars loaded on truck upon receipt of requisition.	100		5	To Bliss 74 1/2 press #16 by operator.
600	.05	1	Extruded rod to air saw #72		.075	6	Pierce 6 holes
15	.02	2	Bars removed from truck and stored on rack near machine.		120	7	Waiting drill press operator.
	120	1	Waiting for operation to begin.	50		6	To drill press by operator.
	.077	3	Saw slug on air saw		.334	7	Rough ream and chamfer L. & G. drill press #19.
	30	2	Waiting for move--man.	30		8	Waiting drill press operator.
70	.03	2	Slugs to Nat. Maxi-press #8.	20		7	To Avey drill press #21 by operator.
	15	3	Awaiting forging operation.		.152	8	Drill three 13/64" holes Avery press #21.
	.234	1	Forge (3-man operation) and inspect.		20	9	Awaiting turret lathe operator.
	10	4	Waiting for press operator.	60		8	To turret lathe section by operator.
30		3	To press by operator.		.522	9	Turn stem and face #3 W. & S.
	.061	4	Trim Flash Bliss 74 1/2 press #16.		60	10	Awaiting turret lathe operator.
	30	5	Waiting for pickling operator.	30		9	To adjacent turret lathe operator.
100		4	To pickling tanks by operator.		.648	10	From outside diameter and face back.
	.007	5	Pickle (HCL tank)		15	11	Waiting press operator.

FIGURE 3–9 (Continued*)*

FLOW PROCESS CHART

SUBJECT CHARTED Shower head face   CHART NO. 1128

DRAWING NO. BA-14782 ___ PART NO. B-14782-2 ___ CHART OF METHOD Present

CHART BEGINS Bar stock storage   CHARTED BY E. Dunnick

CHART ENDS Assembly Department Storeroom   DATE 9-7 SHEET 2 OF 2

DIST. IN FEET	UNIT TIME IN MIN.	CHART SYMBOLS	PROCESS DESCRIPTION	DIST. IN FEET	UNIT TIME IN MIN.	CHART SYMBOLS	PROCESS DESCRIPTION
60		10	To Bliss 20B press by operator.				
	.097	11	Stamp identification Bliss 20B press #21.				
	15	12	Waiting next press operator.				
	.167	12	Broach six holes to size Bliss 20B press #22.				
	60	13	Waiting for move--man.				
350	.012	11	To inspection by move--man.				
	20	14	Waiting for inspector.				
	.05	1	Inspect complete (10% spot check).				
75		12	To storeroom by in-spector.				
		2	Stored until requi-sitioned.				

SUMMARY			
EVENT	NUMBER	TIME	DISTANCE
OPERATIONS	13	2.414 min.	
INSPECTIONS	1	.050 min.	
COMBINED ACTIVITY	1	.234 min.	
TRANSPORTATIONS	12		1580 ft.
STORAGES	2	undetermined	
DELAYS	14	605 min.	

able in showing how the layout of a plant can be improved. Intelligent use of the flow process chart will result in improvements.

The flow diagram

Although the flow process chart gives most of the pertinent information relative to a manufacturing process, it does not show a pictorial plan of the flow of work. Sometimes this added information is helpful in developing a new method. For example, before a transportation can be shortened, it is necessary to see or visualize where room can be pro-

FIGURE 3–10

Flow diagram of old layout of group of operations on the Garand rifle (shaded section of plant represents total floor space needed for revised layout [Figure 3–11]. This represented a 40 percent savings in floor space.)

R. A. Olsen

vided to add a facility so the transportation distance can be diminished. Likewise, it is helpful to visualize potential temporary and permanent storage areas, inspection stations, and work points. The best way to provide this information is to take an existing drawing of the plant layout of the areas involved, and sketch in the flow lines indicating the movement

FIGURE 3–11

Flow diagram of revised layout of group of operations on the Garand rifle

R. A. Olsen

of the material from one activity to the next. Such a pictorial presentation of the layout of floors and of buildings which shows the location of all activities on the flow process chart is known as a flow diagram.

When constructing a flow diagram, the analyst should identify each activity by symbol and number corresponding to those appearing on the flow process chart. The direction of movement is indicated by placing small arrows periodically along the flow lines. These arrows will point the direction of flow.

If it is desirable to show the flow of more than one item, a different color can be used to show the flow of each part.

Figure 3–10 illustrates a flow diagram made in conjunction with a flow process chart to improve the production of the Garand (M1) rifle at Springfield Armory. This pictorial presentation together with the flow process chart resulted in savings that increased production from 500 rifle barrels per shift to 3,600—with no more employees. Figure 3–11 illustrates the flow diagram of the revised layout.

It can be seen that the flow diagram is a helpful supplement to the flow process chart because it shows up backtracking and areas of possible traffic congestion, and facilitates making an ideal plant layout.

Summary

The methods analyst should become familiar with the operation and flow process charts and the flow diagram so he will be able to use these valuable tools in solving problems. Just as there are several types of tools available for a particular job, so several designs of charts can be utilized in assisting in solving an engineering problem. However, in determining a specific solution, one chart usually has advantages over another. The analyst should know the specific functions of each of the process charts and only resort to those he needs to help solve his specific problems. In summary, their functions are as follows.

1. Operation process chart. Used to analyze relations between operations. Good for studying operations and inspections on assemblies involving several components. Helpful for plant layout work.

2. Flow process chart. Used to analyze hidden or indirect costs, such as delay time, storage cost, and material handling costs. Best chart for complete analysis of the manufacture of one component part.

3. Flow diagram. Used as a supplement to the flow chart, especially where considerable floor space is involved in the process. Shows up backtracking and traffic congestion. Necessary tool in making revised plant layouts.

Both the operation and flow process chart and the flow diagram have their place in developing improvements. Their correct use will aid in presenting the problem, solving the problem, selling the solution, and installing the solution.

TEXT QUESTIONS

1. Who uses process charts?
2. Who is credited as being the original designer of process charts? *Frank Gilbreth*
3. What does the operation process chart show? *ops. + insps. present the problem*
4. What symbols are used in constructing the operation process chart? *O- operation ☐- inspection*
5. How are materials introduced into the general flow when constructing the operation? *Horiz. lines*
6. How does the flow process chart differ from the operation process chart? *more detailed*
7. What is the principal purpose of the flow process chart?
8. What symbols are used in constructing the flow process chart? *O ▽ ☐ ⇨ D*
9. When would you advocate using the flow diagram? *on one component*
10. How can the flow of several different products be shown on the flow diagram? *Use different colors*
11. Why are the operation and flow process charts merely a means to an end? *only defining problem*
12. In the construction of the flow process chart, what method can be used to estimate distances moved? *count no. of columns passed. Multi by span.*
13. How can delay times be determined in the construction of the flow process chart? Storage times? *Mark several parts with chalk indicating time they went into storage. Then find when came out*

GENERAL QUESTIONS

1. What are the limitations of the operation and flow process charts, and the flow diagram?

2. What relation is there between the flow chart and material handling? Between the flow diagram and plant bottlenecks? Between the operation process chart and material specifications?
3. What is the connection between effective plant layout and the operation process chart?
4. Distinguish between process and product grouping.

CHAPTER 4

Operation analysis

Operation analysis is a procedure used by the methods analyst to analyze all productive and nonproductive elements of an operation with the thought of improvement. Methods engineering in itself is concerned with devising methods to increase production per unit of time and reduce unit costs. Operation analysis is in reality a technique for accomplishing the goal of methods engineering.

The operation analysis procedure is just as effective in planning new work centers as it is in improving ones already in operation. By using the questioning approach on all facets of the work station and dependent work stations and design of the product, an efficient work center will be developed.

Since the improvement of existing operations is a continuing process in industry, this chapter will deal principally with this process, recognizing however, that the principles are equally valid and important in planning new work centers. Investigating the approaches to operation analysis is the step immediately following presentation of facts in the form of the operation or the flow process charts. This is the step where analysis takes place and where the various components of the method to be proposed are crystallized.

With foreign competition becoming increasingly keen at the same time that labor and material costs are spiraling, the subject of operation analysis has become increasingly important. It is a procedure that can never be regarded as complete. Competition usually necessitates continuing study of a given product so the manufacturing processes can be improved and a part of the gains can be passed on to the consumer in the form of a better product at a reduced selling price. Once this is done by a given producer, competitors invariably introduce similar improvement programs, and it is only a matter of time until they have produced a more salable product at a reduced price. This starts a new cycle in which the given producer again reviews his operations, improves his manufacturing processes, and again necessitates improvements in competitive plants. Conditions in industry cannot be static; otherwise bankruptcy would result. Progress is the only key to continued profitable operation.

Another basic economic law, that of supply and demand, must be considered when savings are effected. The volume of goods consumed is inversely proportional to the selling price. As we develop improvements that inaugurate real savings, we broaden the market through lower selling price. This procedure has been proven time and time again. This was done with electric lighting, refrigerators, radios, automobiles, television, home air conditioning, and many other products. As progress allowed reduction in cost, more people could afford to purchase. The increased volume permitted further economies, which again resulted in lower prices, and lower prices further increased the volume. Each time the selling price of any commodity is reduced as little as 5 percent, the product is immediately brought within reach of more people's pocketbooks.

Experience has proved that practically all operations can be improved if sufficient study is given to them. Since the procedure of systematic analysis is equally effective in large and small industries, job shop and mass production, we can safely conclude that the subject of operation analysis is applicable in all areas of manufacturing, business, and government establishments. When properly utilized, it can be expected to develop a better method of doing the work by simplifying the operational procedure and the material handling, and utilizing the equipment more effectively to increase output and reduce unit cost; to ensure quality and reduce defective workmanship; and to facilitate operator enthusiasm by improving the working conditions and minimizing operator fatigue.

Approach to operation analysis

Probably one of the most common attitudes of industrialists is that their problems are unique. Consequently, they feel that any new method will be impractical for them. Actually all work, whether it be clerical, machine, assembly, or general labor, is much the same. The Gilbreths concluded that any work, whether productive or nonproductive, was done by using combinations of 17 basic movements they call "therbligs." Regardless of what the operation is, when considered in the light of its basic divisions, it will be found to be quite similar to others. For example, the elements of work in driving a car are much like those required to operate a turret lathe; the basic motions employed in dealing a bridge hand are almost identical with certain manual inspection and machine loading elements. The fact that all work is similar in many respects verifies the principle that if methods can be improved in one plant, opportunities exist for methods improvement in all plants.

History repeats itself over and over in accounts of the unwillingness of people to accept something new. Iron ships, steamboats, automobiles, airplanes, radios, telephones, and television are just a few examples of products that are commonplace today; yet at one time all these were considered impractical by most people. Today, the average person will scoff at the idea of interplanetary travel and atomic power plants for private vehicles.

Anyone engaged in methods work is well aware of the natural, inherent resistance to change prevailing in all men's minds, regardless of their level in the organization. Overcoming this resistance to change is one of the major obstacles in the path of an improvement program. Managers will continually make statements to the effect that, "It might have worked at the —— plant, but our operation is quite different." Supervisors will say, "It can't work here," and even the operator will bluntly declare, "It won't work." Selling the whole organization on "It will work here" is a never-ending job for the methods analyst. One who is successful in this type of work never accepts anything as being right just because it exists today or has been done this way for years. Instead, he questions, probes, investigates, and finally, after all angles are considered, he makes his decision for the moment. Always he is conscious that this method may be satisfactory today, but it will not be tomorrow, for there is always a better way.

In order to reduce the resistance-to-change which the methods analyst knows is characteristic of all people, he will endeavor to establish an atmosphere of participation, understanding, and friendliness. He will recognize the knowledge other people have of their job and will solicit their assistance in making improvements. He sees to it that all communication channels are kept open and are utilized, so that all personnel who are affected by the contemplated change are kept informed. He provides information freely, and openly discusses facts related to the investigation; thus, he obtains confidence rather than mistrust and suspicion.

Operation analysis procedure

The use of a systematic procedure as outlined in Chapter 1 is invaluable if real savings are to be realized. The first step is to get all information related to the anticipated volume of the work. It is necessary to determine the expected volume, the chance of repeat business, the life of the job, the chance for design changes, and the labor content of the job, so it can be determined how much time and effort should be devoted toward improving the present method or planning the new job. If the job promises to be quite active, a more detailed study will be justified than if the volume appears to be low.

Once an estimate is made of quantity, job life, and labor content, then all factual manufacturing information should be collected. This information would include all operations, facilities used to perform the operations, and operational times; all moves or transportations, facilities used for transportation, and transportation distances; all inspections, inspection facilities, and inspection times; all storages, storage facilities, and time spent in storage; all vendor operations together with their prices; and all drawings and design specifications. After all this information affecting cost is gathered, it must be presented in a form suitable for study. One of the most effective ways of doing this is through the Flow Process Chart (see Chapter 3). This chart graphically presents all manufacturing information, much as a blueprint shows all design information.

Upon completing the flow process chart, the analyst reviews the problem with thought toward improvement. Up to this point he has merely stated the problem, which is a necessary preliminary to solving it. One of the most common techniques used by methods men is to prepare a check sheet for asking questions on every activity shown on the flow chart. Typical questions are: "Is this operation necessary? Can the operation be better performed another way? Can it be combined with some other operation? Are tolerances closer than necessary? Can a more economical material be used? Can better material handling be incorporated?"

A typical checklist of pertinent questions developed by the Methods Engineering Council of Pittsburgh, Pennsylvania, is shown in Figure 4–1. This figure also illustrates how this form was used to make a cost reduction study on an electric blanket control knob shaft. By redesigning the shaft so it could be economically produced as a die casting rather than a screw machine part, the cost was reduced from $68.75 per thousand pieces to $17.19 per thousand pieces.

The analyst asks and answers all related questions on the check sheet for all steps appearing on the flow chart. This procedure invariably evolves efficient ways of performing the work. As these ideas develop, it is well to record them immediately so they will not be forgotten. It is also wise to include sketches at this time. Usually, the analyst is surprised at the numerous inefficiencies that prevail and will have little trouble in compiling many improvement possibilities. One improvement usually leads to another. The analyst must have an open mind and creative ability if he is to be a real success in this type of work. The check sheet is also useful in giving methods training to factory foremen and superintendents. Thought-provoking questions, when intelligently used, help factory supervisors to develop constructive ideas. The check sheet serves as an outline which can be referred to by the discussion leader handling the methods training.

FIGURE 4-1

Date	9/15	Dwg.	18-4612	Sub.	2

Date ____9/15____ Dept. ____11____ Dwg. ____18-4612____ Sub. ____2____

Mould _____ Die _____ Style _____ Item ____2____

Pattern _____ Ins. Spec. ____C____ L. Spec. _____ Sub. _____

Part Description ____Blanket control knob shaft____

Operation ____Turn, groove, drill, tap, knurl, thread, cut-off____ Operator ____Blazer____

DETERMINE AND DESCRIBE

DETAILS OF ANALYSIS

1. PURPOSE OF OPERATION

To form contours of 3/8" S.A.E. 1112 rod on automatic screw machine to achieve drawing specifications.

Can purpose be accomplished better otherwise?
Yes - by die casting

2. COMPLETE LIST OF ALL OPERATIONS PERFORMED ON PART

No.	Description	Work Sta.	Dept.
1.	Turn, groove, drill, tap, knurl, thread, cut-off	B. & S.	11
2.	Burr	Bench	12
3.	Inspect 1%	Bench	18
4.			
5.			
6.			
7.			
8.			
9.			
10.			

Can oprn. being analyzed be eliminated? *No*

be combined with another? *No*

be performed during idle period of another? *Yes by machine coupling*

Is sequence of oprns. best possible? *Yes*

Should oprn. be done in another dept. to save cost or handling? *Perhaps can be purchased outside at a savings.*

3. INSPECTION REQUIREMENTS

a—Of previous oprn.

b—Of this oprn. Yes. Perhaps S.Q.C. will reduce amount of inspection.

Are tolerance, allowance, finish and other requirements necessary?

4. MATERIAL   Zinc base die cast metal would be less expensive.

Cutting compounds and other supply materials

5. MATERIAL HANDLING

a—Brought by 4 wheel truck to automatics

b—Removed by hand 2 wheel trucks

c—Handled at work station by

6. SET-UP (Accompany description with sketches if necessary)

    This is satisfactory as being done.

a—Tool Equipment

    Present

Suggestions   Redesign part to be made as zinc base die casting rather than S.A.E. 1112 screw machine part.

ANALYSIS SHEET

Methods Engineering Council
Form No. 101

*Checklist (right margin):*

...itable to purpose?

Consider size, suitability, straightness, and condition.

Can cheaper material be substituted?

Should crane, gravity conveyors, totepans, or special trucks be used?

Consider layout with respect to distance moved. *Perhaps gravity to burring station.*

How are dwgs. and tools secured?

Can set-up be improved?

Trial pieces.

Machine Adjustments.

Tools
Suitable?
Provided?
Ratchet Tools
Power Tools
Spl. Purpose Tools
Jigs, Vises
Special Clamps
Fixtures
Multiple
Duplicate

FIGURE 4-1 (Continued)

7. **CONSIDER THE FOLLOWING POSSIBILITIES.**

    1. Install gravity delivery chutes.
    2. Use drop delivery
    3. Compare methods if more than one operator is working on same job.
    4. Provide correct chair for operator.
    5. Improve jigs or fixtures by providing ejectors, quick-acting clamps, etc.
    6. Use foot operated mechanisms.
    7. Arrange for two handed operation.
    8. Arrange tools and parts within normal working area.
    9. Change layout to eliminate back tracking and to permit coupling of machines.
    10. Utilize all improvements developed for other jobs.

8. **WORKING CONDITIONS.**

    Generally satisfactory.

    a—Other Conditions

9. **METHOD** (Accompany with sketches or Process Charts if necessary.)

    a—Before Analysis and Motion Study.

RECOMMENDED ACTION

Yes, to accumulate for tumbling.

Light *O.K.*

Heat *O.K.*

Ventilation, Fumes *O.K.*

Drinking Fountains *O.K.*

Wash Rooms *O.K.*

Safety Aspects *O.K.*

Design of Part *O.K.*

Clerical Work Required (to fill out time cards, etc.) *O.K.*

Probability of Delays *O.K.*

Probable Mfg. Quantities *O.K.*

Arrangement of Work Area

Placement of

Tools.

Materials.

Control knob shaft designed as screw machine part.

b—After Analysis and Motion Study

Parting line

Control knob redesigned as die cast part. Threads on left-hand extension cover only 50 percent of periphery; likewise knurl on right end and extension on half of periphery thus allowing piece to be easily removed from die.

See Supplementary Report Entitled *Die Cast.*
Control shaft.

Date

OBSERVER ____ R. Guild ____   APPROVED BY ____ R. Hussey ____

The 10 primary approaches to operation analysis

The Westinghouse Electric Corporation has developed an operation analysis program in which it gives emphasis to using the "10 Primary Approaches to Operation Analysis" when studying the flow chart of the prevailing method.

These approaches include:

1. Purpose of Operation
2. Design of Part
3. Tolerances and Specifications
4. Material
5. Process of Manufacture
6. Setup and Tools
7. Working Conditions
8. Material Handling
9. Plant Layout
10. Principles of Motion Economy

When all these points are considered in studying each individual operation, attention is focused on the items most likely to produce improvement. All these points will not be applicable to each activity appearing on the flow chart, but usually more than one should be considered. The method of analysis recommended is to take each step in the present method individually and analyze it with a specific approach toward improvement clearly in mind, considering all key points of analysis. Then follow with the same procedure on succeeding operations, inspections, moves, storages, and so on, shown on the chart. After each element has been thus analyzed, it is well to consider the product being studied as a whole rather than in the light of its elemental components and to reconsider all points of analysis with thought toward overall improvement possibilities. There are usually unlimited opportunities for methods improvement in every plant. The best technique for developing the maximum savings is in the careful study of individual and collective operations as outlined. Wherever this procedure has been followed by competent engineers, beneficial results have always been realized.

PURPOSE OF OPERATION

Probably the most important of the 10 points of operation analysis used for improving an existing method or planning a new job is the purpose of the operation. A cardinal rule that the analyst should observe is to try to eliminate or combine an operation before improving it. In my experience, as much as 25 percent of the operations being performed by diversified American industry can be eliminated if sufficient study is given the design and process.

Far too much unnecessary work is done today. In many instances, the job or the process should not be a subject for simplification or improvement, but rather it should be eliminated entirely. If a job can be eliminated, there is no need to spend money on installing an improved method. No interruption or delay is caused while an improved method is being developed, tested, and installed. It is not necessary to train new operators for the new method. The problem of resistance to change is minimized when a job or activity that is found to be unnecessary is eliminated. The best way to simplify an operation is to devise some way to get the same or better results at no cost at all.

The Procter & Gamble Company has found this matter of work elimination and cost elimination so profitable that it has established a formal procedure which it calls "The Elimination Approach."

Although much time is spent in constantly improving methods and simplifying work, it is believed that the ideal solution is to eliminate the cost. The approach to cost elimination is as follows.

1. Select the cost for question. It is suggested that a major cost should be selected first in order to get the greatest money returns. If the major cost is eliminated, this will often lead to the elimination of many smaller operations as well. Labor costs, material costs, clerical costs, and overhead costs of all kinds are possible subjects for elimination. Efficient operations can be eliminated just as easily as those not as well done. The questioning procedure is easy to use. No paper work or calculations are necessary, and in fact, complete knowledge of the job or activity is usually not required.

2. Identify the basic cause. A search should be made to determine the basic cause which makes the cost necessary. A basic cause is the reason, purpose, or intent on which the elimination of the cost depends. The basic cause is that factor which controls the elimination of the cost. The key question is, "This cost could be eliminated if it were not for what basic cause?" At this stage we do not ask such an obvious question as "Why is this operation necessary?", or, "How could this operation be done better?" These questions are avoided because the answer tends to justify and defend the job's continued existence. Instead, the objective is to find the basic cause. Operations for which there is no basic cause, or for which a basic cause no longer exists, can be eliminated at once. When a basic cause has been identified, it is necessary to proceed to the next step, step 3.

3. Question the basic cause for elimination. If the basic cause has been identified, then it can be questioned in two ways.

a) Disregard the basic cause—consider what would happen if the operation were not done. If the same results or better results can be obtained without the operation, then consideration should be given to eliminating it at once. However, disregarding the basic cause can be dangerous. In this connection it is necessary to consider two points: (1) determine the area of influence of the basic cause, i.e., what else might happen if this basic cause were eliminated; and (2) determine the associated "price tag" of the basic cause: is there a proper return on the money spent to obtain the desired results? If the basic cause cannot be disregarded, the second opportunity for elimination is———

b) Apply "why?" questioning. If the job under consideration seems to be necessary, can the job immediately preceding it be eliminated, thus perhaps making all succeeding jobs unnecessary? If complete elimination is not possible, try for partial elimination. Perhaps there are alternate possibilities, such as adopting the lowest cost alternative. Identify the basic cause of each supporting factor and question for elimination or change.

It is often desirable to undertake cost elimination on a department-wide or plantwide basis. Thus several qualified members of supervision working as a group can help identify basic causes of specific costs selected for study.

Unnecessary operations are frequently a result of improper planning when the job was first set up. Once a standard routine is established, it is difficult to make a change, even if such a change would allow eliminating a portion of the work and make the job easier. When new jobs are planned, the planner usually will include an extra operation if there is any question of the possibility of rejecting the product without extra work. For example, if there is some question of whether to take two or three cuts in turning a steel shaft to maintain a 40-microinch finish, invariably the planner will specify three cuts, even though proper maintenance of cutting tools, supplemented with ideal feeds and speeds, would allow the job to be done with two cuts. Likewise, if there is some question of the ability of a drill press to hold a 0.005-inch tolerance on a $\frac{1}{4}$-inch drilled hole, the planner, when setting up the job, will call for a reaming operation. Actually, the drilling operation would be adequate if all variable factors (speed, feed, cutting lubricant, drill size) are controlled.

Many times an unnecessary operation may develop because of the improper performance of a previous operation. A second operation must be done to touch up or make acceptable the work done by the first operation. For example, in one plant, armatures were previously spray painted in a fixture, making it impossible to cover the bottom of the armature with paint because the fixture shielded the bottom from the spray blast. It was necessary to touch up the armature bottoms after spray painting. A study of the job resulted in a redesigned fixture that held the armature and still allowed complete coverage. The new fixture permitted spray painting of seven armatures simultaneously, while the old method called for spray painting one at a time. Thus, it was possible to eliminate the touch-up operation by considering that an unnecessary operation may develop because of the improper performance of a previous operation.

In manufacturing large gears it was necessary to introduce a hand-

FIGURE 4–2A

Painted armature as removed from old fixture and as removed from improved fixture

FIGURE 4–2B

Armature in spray-painting fixture allowing complete coverage of armature bottom

scraping and lapping operation to remove waves in the teeth after they had been hobbed. An investigation disclosed that contraction and expansion brought about by temperature changes in the course of the day were responsible for the waviness in the teeth surface. By inclosing the whole unit and installing an air-conditioning system within the enclosure, proper temperature was maintained during the whole day. Immediately the waviness disappeared, and it was no longer necessary to continue the hand-scraping and lapping operations.

Sometimes unnecessary operations develop because an operation was introduced to facilitate an operation that followed. For example, it was thought necessary to twist each pair of wires when wiring commutators to keep the correct pair of wires together and also to increase the strength. It was found however, after analysis, that the correct pair of wires could be placed in the proper slot without twisting. Also, observation revealed that twisting caused the wires to be unequal in length, and the uneven tension in the twisted wire weakened rather than strengthened the wires.

It was discovered that winding the wire was unnecessary when someone asked: "Can a change in assembly eliminate the need for a previous operation?"

In endeavoring to eliminate operations, the analyst should consider the question: Is an additional operation justified by savings it will effect in a subsequent operation? For example, a brush holder was originally planned so two holes were drilled and tapped in each holder. One hole

FIGURE 4–3

Large gear completely housed to maintain constant temperature during hobbing operation

was drilled and tapped in the bottom, another was drilled and tapped in the top. The brush holder was assembled so alternately a holder with the drilled and tapped hole in the bottom and with the hole tapped in the top were used. Since all parts had tapped holes in both bottom and top, it was merely a matter of positioning the part for assembly. By questioning the need for both tapped holes in each piece, it was discovered to be more economical to have two parts—one with the hole tapped in the top, the other with the hole tapped in the bottom. The two parts were then assembled alternately. Drilling and tapping a hole in each brush holder was eliminated because someone questioned the necessity of performing this operation.

Again, an unnecessary operation may develop because it was thought it would give the product greater sales appeal. One company originally used cast brass nameplates for various lines of its products. Although the cast nameplate was attractive, it was found that by using instead an etched steel nameplate the appearance was still kept attractive, and cost was notably reduced.

To have a smooth joint in producing electric fan guards, it was thought necessary to perform a coining operation where the ends of the wire

FIGURE 4–4

Twisting wires during commutator winding operation was found unnecessary because correct pair of wires could be placed in proper slot without twisting

cage were joined by butt welding. By slightly modifying the design, it was possible to place the joined wire ends directly behind the crossbars of the fan guard, making it impossible to see the joined ends. Since the butt-welded ends could not be seen, it was no longer necessary to perform the coining operation. This design made it difficult to reach the butt-welded portion so there was no chance of scratching hands on the rough welded area.

Frequently an unnecessary operation will exist because of inadequate or outmoded tools and equipment. In one shop an eight-hole jig was used for drilling the holes on a fan-cooled motor frame. This jig was also used for locating and drilling 8 of the 16 holes necessary on an explosion-proof motor. The remaining eight holes had to be laid out prior to drilling. By adopting a new 16-bushing drill jig, the hand-laying-out operation was eliminated. By asking and answering the question, "Can better tooling eliminate an operation?" it was possible to inaugurate improvement.

To eliminate, combine, or shorten each operation, the analyst should ask and answer the following question: Does an outside supplier's tooling enable him to perform the operation more economically? Ball bearings purchased from an outside vendor had to be packed in grease prior to assembly. A study of bearing vendors revealed that "sealed-for-life" bearings could be purchased from another supplier, and at lower cost.

The above examples highlight the desirability of establishing the purpose of each operation before endeavoring to improve the operation. Once the necessity of the operation is determined, then determine how it can be improved by considering the remaining nine approaches to operation analysis.

Summary: purpose of operation

Many operations being performed by every manufacturing establishment and business are unnecessary and can be eliminated if sufficient study is given the procedure or process. Before accepting any operation as absolutely necessary, the analyst should determine the purpose of the operation. While determining the purpose of the operation, "checklist" questions should be asked and answered to stimulate ideas that may result in eliminating the operation being studied or some component of it.

Almost everyone is familiar with the tubeless automobile tire. The inner tube in the automobile tire has been eliminated because consideration was given the alternative possibility of designing the automobile wheel and casing so that the casing would contain the air, and the inner tube would not be necessary. This was done and the inner tube was eliminated.

At one time, lettuce was packed and shipped in large wooden crates holding a total of approximately 125 pounds. Ice was interspersed between the layers to be sure the lettuce arrived at the distributors' plants in a fresh condition. By questioning the purpose of the operation, a better method of packing has been developed, using a carton which holds approximately 50 pounds. Now the lettuce is cut, selected, and packed directly into the carton in the field. Subsequently, the packaged lettuce is quickly cooled to 36°–38°F., and it is not necessary to place ice in the carton. Today more than 75 percent of all lettuce grown in California is packed in cartons instead of boxes. The result is a savings of approximately $3 per box—and some 60,000 carloads of lettuce are shipped out of California each year. The use of ice in packing lettuce was eliminated, and the substitution of a fiberboard carton for a wooden crate further reduced the packing cost.

DESIGN OF PART

The methods engineer often is inclined to feel that once a design has been accepted his only recourse is to plan its manufacture in the most economical way. Granted, it is usually difficult to introduce even a slight change in design; still, a good methods analyst should review every design for possible improvements. Designs are not permanent; they can be changed; and if improvement is the result, and the activity of the job is significant, then the change should be made.

To improve the design, the analyst should keep in mind the following pointers for lower cost designs:

1. Reduce the number of parts, simplifying the design.
2. Reduce the number of operations and length of travel in manufacturing by joining parts better and making the machining and assembly easier.
3. Utilize a better material.
4. Rely for accuracy upon "key" operations rather than upon series of closely held limits.

These general observances should be kept in mind as consideration is given to design analysis on each component and each subassembly.

The General Electric Company has summarized the ideas shown in Table 4–1 to be kept in mind for developing minimum cost designs.

When one observes almost any article and thinks back only a few years, the changes of design that have taken place begin to become apparent. The automobile, refrigerator, typewriter, telephone, washing machine, home, watch, toothbrush, lead pencil, all have gone through significant design changes in the past 10 years—even the last 5 years. It is a poor policy to think of any design as permanent. It is much better to consider that all designs are wrong, and that the only reason they are in effect is because a better design or process has not been discovered.

Figures 4–5 and 4–6 give some examples of good and poor casting and forging design.

One manufacturer always used cast-iron brackets on its motors. A methods analyst questioned this design, and this led to the redesign of the bracket, making it from welded sheet steel. Not only was the new design stronger, lighter, and more eye-appealing, but it was less expensive to produce.

A similar design improvement was in the construction of conduit boxes. Originally, they were built of cast iron, while the improved design, making a stronger, neater, lighter, and less expensive conduit box, was fabricated from sheet steel.

In another instance a brass cam switch used in control equipment was made as a brass die casting. By slightly altering the design, the less

TABLE 4-1

Castings

1. Eliminate dry sand (baked-sand) cores.
2. Minimize depth to obtain flatter castings.
3. Use minimum weight consistent with sufficient thickness to cast without chilling.
4. Choose simple forms.
5. Symmetrical forms produce uniform shrinkage.
6. Liberal radii—no sharp corners.
7. If surfaces are to be accurate with relation to each other, they should be in the same part of the pattern, if possible.
8. Locate parting lines so that they will not affect looks and utility, and need not be ground smooth.
9. Specify multiple patterns instead of single ones.
10. Metal patterns are preferable to wood.
11. Permanent molds instead of metal patterns.

Moldings

1. Eliminate inserts from parts.
2. Design molds with smallest number of parts.
3. Use simple shapes.
4. Locate flash lines so that the flash does not need to be filed and polished.
5. Minimum weight.

Punchings

1. Punched parts instead of molded, cast, machined, or fabricated parts.
2. "Nestable" punchings to economize on material.
3. Holes requiring accurate relation to each other to be made by the same die.
4. Design to use coil stock.
5. Punchings designed to have minimum sheared length and maximum die strength with fewest die moves.

Formed Parts

1. Drawn parts instead of spun, welded, or forged parts.
2. Shallow draws if possible.
3. Liberal radii on corners.
4. Bent parts instead of drawn.
5. Parts formed of strip or wire instead of punched from sheet.

Fabricated Parts

1. Self-tapping screws instead of standard screws.
2. Drive pins instead of standard screws.
3. Rivets instead of screws.
4. Hollow rivets instead of solid rivets.
5. Spot or projection welding instead of riveting.
6. Welding instead of brazing or soldering.
7. Use die castings or molded parts instead of fabricated construction requiring several parts.

Machined Parts

1. Use rotary machining processes instead of shaping methods.
2. Use automatic or semiautomatic machining instead of hand-operated.
3. Reduce the number of shoulders.
4. Omit finishes where possible.
5. Use rough finish when satisfactory.
6. Dimension drawings from same point as used by factory in measuring and inspecting.
7. Use centerless grinding instead of between-center grinding.
8. Avoid tapers and formed contours.
9. Allow a radius or undercut at shoulders.

Screw Machine Parts

1. Eliminate second operation.
2. Use cold-rolled stock.
3. Design for header instead of screw machine.
4. Use rolled threads instead of cut threads.

Welded Parts

1. Fabricated construction instead of castings or forgings.
2. Minimum sizes of welds.
3. Welds made in flat position rather than vertical or overhead.
4. Eliminate chamfering edges before welding.
5. Use "burnouts" (torch cut contours) instead of machined contours.
6. Lay out parts to cut to best advantage from standard rectangular plates and avoid scrap.
7. Use intermittent instead of continuous weld.
8. Design for circular or straight-line welding to use automatic machines.

Treatments and Finishes

1. Reduce baking time to minimum.
2. Use air drying instead of baking.
3. Use fewer or thinner coats.
4. Eliminate treatments and finishes entirely.

Assemblies

1. Make assemblies simple.
2. Make assemblies progressive.
3. Make only one assembly and eliminate trial assemblies.
4. Make component parts RIGHT in the first place so that fitting and adjusting will not be required in assembly. This means that drawings must be correct, with proper tolerances, and that parts be made according to drawing.

General

1. Reduce number of parts.
2. Reduce number of operations.
3. Reduce length of travel in manufacturing.

FIGURE 4–5

The rights and wrongs of details of castings and forgings

From *Product Engineering*, Sixth Series Design Work Sheets
(McGraw-Hill Publishing Co.)

FIGURE 4–6

The rights and wrongs of details of castings and forgings

From *Product Engineering*, Sixth Series Design Work Sheets
(McGraw-Hill Publishing Co.)

FIGURE 4–7

Improved design of conduit box (new design fabricated from sheet steel)

FIGURE 4–8A

Redesigned brass cam switch allowing part to be made from extrusion

FIGURE 4–8B

New design shown cut to length from section of brass extrusion

FIGURE 4–9

Projection welding of nuts to surface provides neat-appearing and inexpensive method of joining

FIGURE 4–10A

Mounting bracket changed so spot welding may be used rather than arc welding

FIGURE 4–10B

Illustration of bracket arc welded to resistor tube indicates unsightly appearance necessitated through the old method

FIGURE 4–11A

Old design required tinned and soldered connection

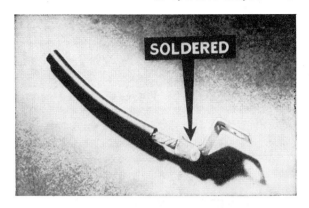

FIGURE 4–11B

Improved design illustrating resistance welded clip to wire conductor

FIGURE 4–12A

Old thumb screw was in 3 parts

FIGURE 4–12B

Improved one-piece design of motor cover thumbscrew

expensive process of extruding was utilized. The extruded sections were cut to desired length to produce the cam switch.

These method improvements were brought about by considering a better material in an effort to improve the design.

Attaching nuts were originally arc welded to transformer cases. This proved to be a slow, costly operation. Furthermore, the resulting design had an unsightly appearance due to the overflow and spatter from the arc-welding process. By projection welding nuts to the transformer case, not only were time and money saved but the resulting design had considerably more sales appeal.

A similar improvement was brought about by changing from arc welding to spot welding to join mounting brackets to resistor tubes.

Another example of design simplification through better joining of parts was in assembling terminal clips to their mating conductors. It had been the policy to turn the end of the clip up to form a socket. This socket was filled with solder, and the wire conductor was then tinned and inserted in the solder-filled socket and held until the solder solidified. By altering the design to call for resistance welding the clip to the wire conductor, both the forming and dipping operations were eliminated.

A motor cover thumbscrew was originally made of three parts: head, pin, and screw. These components were assembled by joining the head to the screw with the pin. A much less costly thumbscrew was developed by redesigning the part for an automatic screw machine that was able to turn out the part complete with no secondary operations. A simplified design resulted in a less expensive part that still met all service and operating requirements.

Design simplification can be applied to the process as well as to the product. For example, Figure 4–13 illustrates a simple improvement in machine design which eliminated a division of work between operating and maintenance people.

The old design, bolted, required the services of a maintenance mechanic every time it was necessary to change the yarn guide because tools were required. The improved design, snap-in, permits the operator to pull out the guide and replace it with a new one. This new design permits more timely changing of guides; the operator can change this as soon as it is found to be defective without tools or coordination with another group. In addition, it takes less time to make the yarn guide change.

The foregoing examples are characteristic of the possibilities for improvement when the design of the part is investigated. It is always wise to check the design for improvement because design changes can be valuable. To be able to recognize good design, the methods engineer should have had some training and practical experience in this area. Good designs do not just happen; they are the result of broad experience and creative thinking, tempered with an appreciation of cost.

FIGURE 4–13

Old and improved snap-in design of rotating yarn guide

E. I. du Pont de Nemours & Co., Inc.

Summary: design of part

Designs should never be regarded as permanent. Experience has shown that practically every design can be improved. The method analyst should question the present design to determine if it is possible to improve it. He should learn to recognize good design and if he encounters poor design, he should assume the responsibility of reporting his findings to the product design department. He should then follow through to assure that the proposed design improvements are carried out.

TOLERANCES AND SPECIFICATIONS

The third of the 10 points of operation analysis to be considered in an improvement program is tolerances and specifications. Many times this point is considered in part when reviewing the design. This, however, usually is not adequate, and it is well to consider tolerances and specifications independent of the other approaches to operation analysis.

Designers have a natural tendency to incorporate more rigid specifications than necessary when developing a product. This is brought about by one or both of two reasons: (1) lack of appreciation for the elements of cost, and (2) the feeling that it is necessary to specify closer tolerances and specifications than actually needed to have the manufacturing departments produce to the required tolerance range.

The methods analyst should be versed in the aspects of cost and be fully aware of what unnecessarily close specifications can do to the selling price. Figure 4–14 illustrates the relationship between cost and machining time. If it appears that designers are being needlessly "tight" in establishing tolerances and specifications, it may be wise for management to embark on a training program in which the economies of specifications are clearly presented.

The analyst must be alert for too liberal, as well as too restricted specifications. By closing up a tolerance, it is often possible to facilitate an assembly operation or some other subsequent step. This may be economically sound, even though the time required to perform the present operation has been increased by reducing a manufacturing tolerance. In this connection, the analyst should recognize that overall tolerance is equal to the square root of the sum of the squares of the individual tolerances comprised in the overall tolerance.

Beyond the principle of operating economies through correct tolerances and specifications is the consideration of establishing the ideal inspection procedure. Invariably, inspection is a verification of the quantity, the quality, the dimensions, and the performance. Inspection in all these areas usually can be performed by numerous methods and techniques. One way is usually better, not only from the standpoint of quality control, but also from the time and cost consideration. The methods analyst should question the present way with thought toward improvement.

The possibilities for installing spot inspection, lot-by-lot inspection, or statistical quality control should be considered.

FIGURE 4–14

Approximate relationship between cost and machining tolerance

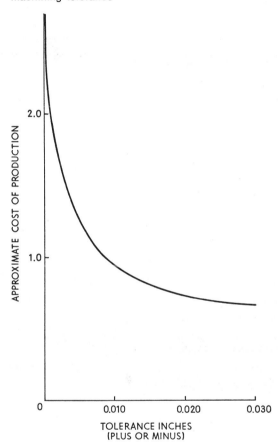

Spot inspection is a periodic check to assure that established standards are being realized. For example, a nonprecision blanking and piercing operation set up on a punch press should have a spot inspection to assure maintenance of size and the absence of burrs. As the die begins to wear or deficiencies in the material being worked begin to show up, the spot inspection would catch the trouble in time to make the necessary changes without generating any scrap.

Lot-by-lot inspection is a sampling procedure in which a sample is examined to determine the quality of the production run or lot. The size of the sample selected depends on the allowable percentage defective and the size of the production lot under check.

Statistical quality control is an analytical tool employed to control the desired quality level of the process.

If a 100 percent inspection is being encountered, it is well to consider the possibility of spot inspection or lot-by-lot inspection. One hundred percent inspection refers to the process of inspecting every unit of product and rejecting the defective ones. Experience has shown that this type of inspection does not assure a perfect product. The monotony of screening tends to create fatigue, thus lowering operation attention. There is always a good chance that the inspector will pass some defective parts as well as reject good parts. Because a perfect product is not assured under 100 percent inspection, acceptable quality may be realized from the considerably more economical methods of either lot-by-lot or spot inspection.

Usually, any elaborate quality control procedure is not justified if the product does not require close tolerances, if its quality is easily checked, and if the generation of defective work is unlikely.

Just as there are several mechanical methods for checking a 0.500″/0.502″ reamed hole, so there are several overall policy procedures that can be adopted as a means of a control. The methods analyst must be alert and well grounded in the various techniques, so he can make sound recommendations for improvement.

In one shop a certain automatic polishing operation was found to have a normal rejection quantity of 1 percent. It would have been quite expensive to subject each lot of polished goods to 100 percent inspection. It was decided, at an appreciable saving, to consider 1 percent the allowable percentage defective, even though this quantity of defective material would go through to plating and finishing only to be thrown out in the final inspection before shipment.

The analyst must always be aware that the reputation and demand for his company's product depend upon the care taken in establishing correct specifications and in maintaining them. Once quality standards are established, no deviations will be permitted. In general, tolerances and specifications can be investigated in these three ways by asking: "Are they absolutely correct?" "Are ideal inspection methods and inspection procedures being used?," and "Are modern quality control techniques being exercised?"

One manufacturer's drawings called for a 0.0005-inch tolerance on a shoulder ring for a DC motor shaft. Original specifications called for a 1.8105 to 1.8110 inches tolerance on the inside diameter. It was thought necessary to hold this close tolerance, for the shoulder ring was shrunk on the motor shaft.

An investigation revealed that a 0.003-inch tolerance was adequate for the shrink fit. The drawing was immediately changed to specify a 1.809 to 1.812 inches inside diameter. A reaming operation was saved because someone questioned the absolute necessity of a close tolerance.

In another instance, it was possible to introduce an automatic control on an external cylindrical grinder. Formerly, it was necessary to manually feed the grinding wheel to the required stop. Each piece had to be carefully inspected to assure maintenance of tolerance on the outside

FIGURE 4–15

Automatic control attached to external cylindrical grinder

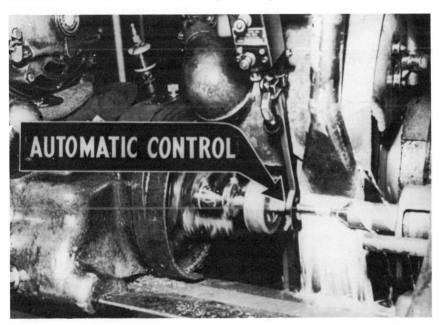

diameter. With the automatic machine control, the feed is tripped and the piece released upon completion of the infeed. The automatic machine control made the operator free to do other work because some methods analyst endeavored to develop an ideal inspection procedure.

In an automatic screw machine shop, it was thought necessary to inspect 100 percent parts coming off the machine because of the critical tolerance requirements. However, it developed that adequate quality control would be maintained by inspecting every sixth piece. This sampling procedure allowed one inspector to service three machines rather than one machine.

By investigating tolerances and specifications and taking action when desirable, costs of inspection will be reduced, scrap will be minimized, repair costs diminished, and quality will be kept high.

Summary: tolerances and specifications

The methods analyst, because of his familiarity with shop operations, is in an ideal position to question the tolerances and specifications assigned to a product. He should understand well the additional cost incurred through establishing close tolerances. Frequently, tolerances and specifications can be liberalized to decrease unit cost with no detrimental effects on quality.

FIGURE 4–16

New method involves both inspection and packing at the machine work station

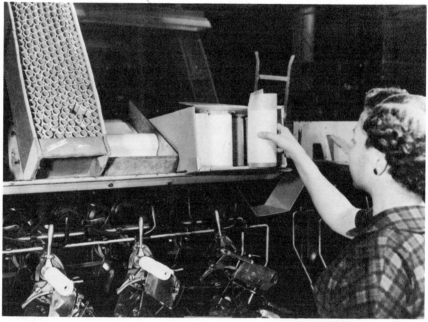

E. I. du Pont de Nemours & Co., Inc.

In other instances, tolerances and specifications should be made more rigid to facilitate certain manufacturing operations.

Occasionally, the method of inspection as well as the inspection procedure can be changed to effect savings.

For example, one large producer of acetate yarn found inspection and packing at the machine to be equivalent or superior to that in the inspection area and packing area and was able to introduce significant savings in view of the reduced handling. The new method of giving the responsibility of final quality inspection to the machine operators using statistical sampling as well as packing eliminated 10 yarn handlings with an estimated annual savings of about $200,000. (See Figure 4–16.)

Tolerances and specifications must be investigated carefully by the analyst to be assured of a successful operation analysis program.

MATERIAL

One of the first questions an engineer considers when he is designing a new product is, "What material shall I use?" Since the ability to choose the right material is based upon the engineer's knowledge of materials and since it is difficult to choose the correct material because of the great variety of materials available, many times it is possible and practical to incorporate a better and more economical material in an existing design.

There are five considerations the methods analyst should keep in mind relative to direct and indirect materials utilized in a process. These are (1) finding a less expensive material; (2) finding materials easier to process; (3) using materials more economically; (4) possible use of salvage materials; and (5) economical use of supplies and tools.

Finding a less expensive material

Prices of materials can be compared by their basic costs. Monthly publications available to all engineers summarize the approximate cost per pound of steel sheets, bars, and plates, and the cost of cast iron, cast steel, cast aluminum, cast bronze, and other basic materials (see Table 4–2). These costs can be used as anchor points from which one can judge the application of new materials. Developments of new processes for producing and refining materials are continuously taking place. Thus, a material that was not competitive in price yesterday may be so today.

In one company, micarta spacer bars were used between windings of transformer coils. They were placed to separate the windings and permit circulation of air between the windings. An investigation revealed that glass tubing could be substituted for the micarta bars at a saving. Not only was the glass tubing less expensive, but it met service requirements better because the glass could withstand higher temperatures. Furthermore the hollow tubing permitted more air circulation than the solid micarta bars.

Another example of starting with a less expensive material that still meets service requirements was in the production of distribution transformers. Originally, a porcelain plate was used to separate and hold the wire leads coming out of the transformers. A fullerboard plate was substituted which stood up just as well in service, yet was considerably less expensive.

The methods analyst should keep in mind that such items as valves, relays, air cylinders, transformers, pipe fittings, bearings, couplings,

TABLE 4-2

Fabricated form	Raw material costs	Tool and die costs	Optimum lot sizes
Sand castings.......	5¢ per lb. for iron to 25¢ per lb. for magnesium (At the spout.)	Pattern costs are low as compared to making dies and molds.	Wide range—from 100 to 10,000.
Permanent mold castings........	Medium cost—aluminum, copper, magnesium alloys most used—iron and steel sometimes used.	Moderate—less than die casting, but more than for other casting methods.	Large quantities—in the thousands.
Plaster mold castings........	Medium—28¢ aluminum; 55¢ bronze, etc.	Medium—between permanent mold and sand castings.	Short runs—100 to 2,000.
Die castings.........	Medium—about 15¢ per lb. for zinc, other materials somewhat higher.	High—more than other casting methods. Typical dies cost $500 to $7,000.	Large quantities—1,000 to hundreds of thousands.
Precision castings....	High generally—the process is best suited to special alloys which are usually costly.	Low—if model is available; moderate if model must be made.	Wide range, although best for quantities of from 10 to 1,000.
Drop forgings........	Low to moderate—most used steels 20–25¢ per lb., but alloys up to 55¢ per lb. or more are used.	High—dies must be carefully made to withstand heat and impact—$300 to $1,500 or more.	Large quantities—10,000 to 100,000 or more, but used on small quantities when properties are required.
Press forgings........	Low to moderate—compares with drop forgings.	High—but usually somewhat lower than dies for drop forgings.	Medium to high production lots.
Upset forgings.......	Low to moderate—as with press and drop forgings.	High—often because of large number of impressions or difficult design.	Medium to high lot production best.
Cold headed parts....	Low to moderate 9 or 10¢ per lb. for steel wire, up to 60¢ for other materials.	Medium—sometimes to a few hundred dollars.	Large lots are best.
Stampings, formed parts.............	Low to moderate, ranging from ordinary steel to stainless.	High—$700 to $2,000 is common for dies for small parts—more for large parts.	Large lots—over 10,000 best.
Spinnings...........	Low to moderate. Steel 8 to 12¢ per lb., up to stainless steel sheet 50 to 70¢ per lb.	Low—form can cost from $50 up to $500.	Quantities under 1,000.

Screw machine parts..	Low to medium—steel (8 to 10¢ per lb.) most common up to brasses (55 to 70¢), with a few more expensive materials.	Medium—$100 to $600 common tooling cost range.	Large lots best—more than 1,000 essential—the higher the quantity the better.
Powder metal parts...	Medium to high—powders run 25¢ to $1.15 per lb. for iron; 40 to 50¢ for copper, 40 to 60¢ for brass, $1.25 per lb. for nickel & stainless steel.	Medium—usually more than $200, range $300 to $3,000.	Large lots best to amortize die costs—10,000 pieces. However, small runs may be necessary.
Electro-formed parts............	Low to high, depending upon the material used: iron lowest, chromium highest.	Medium—master mold doesn't wear out. However, due to small lots die costs may be relatively high.	Best where small lots are involved.
Sectional tubing......	High—invariably 30¢ per lb. or over; some tubing much higher.	Low—cutting is done with simple tools.	Wide range—good for small lots as well as large quantities.
Cut extrusions........	High—usually over 35¢ per lb.	Low—cutting is done with simple tools.	Wide range—useful for large and small quantities.
Impact extrusions.....	Moderate—mostly used for aluminum, zinc, lead.	Medium—dies often cost less than $200.	Wide range—quantities can vary from thousands to millions.
Welded or Brazed Assemblies..........	Low cost materials can be used (carbon, steel, etc.).	Low to moderate—assembly jigs sometimes required.	Small quantities best, although small assemblies can be mass produced at low cost.
Molded plastics.......	Medium to high—material varies from 25¢ per lb. to over $2 per lb.	Medium to high—depending upon type of mold or die required; from $200 up, generally.	Large lots—over 5,000 pieces best.
Molded nonmetallic...	Moderate to high.	Medium—molds are often rather simple.	Wide—because of need for parts of some materials, quantities must be low.

FIGURE 4–17A

Rectangular micarta bars were formerly used to separate windings of transformer coils

FIGURE 4–17B

Use of glass tubing instead of bars provide substantial savings

FIGURE 4–18A

Porcelain plate was formerly used to hold wire leads from distribution transformers

FIGURE 4–18B

Fullerboard plate makes economical and effective substitute

chains, hinges, hardware, and motors can usually be purchased at less cost than they can be manufactured.

Finding a material easier to process

One material is usually more readily processed than another. By referring to handbook data of the physical properties, it is usually easy to discern which material will react most favorably to the process it must be subjected to in its transposition from raw material to finished product. For example, machinability varies inversely with hardness and hardness usually varies directly with strength.

The partial list of properties of materials shown in Table 4–3 form the basis on which a material is chosen. The tabulation shows the relation

TABLE 4–3

Using steel as 100 for comparison

Basis of comparison	Material	Thickness	Stiffness	Strength	Weight
Equal Thickness.........	Structural Steel	100	100	100	100
Equal Thickness.........	Alum–52S ½ H	100	34	81	36
Equal Thickness.........	Mag. FS–1a	100	22	53	23
Equal Thickness.........	Titanium	100	52	200	57
Equal Stiffness..........	Structural Steel	100	100	100	100
Equal Stiffness..........	Alum–52S ½ H	143	100	164	51
Equal Stiffness..........	Mag. FS–1a	165	100	143	37
Equal Stiffness..........	Titanium	125	100	312	72
Equal Strength..........	Structural Steel	100	100	100	100
Equal Strength..........	Alum–52S ½ H	111	47	100	40
Equal Strength..........	Mag. FS–1a	137	59	100	31
Equal Strength..........	Titanium	71	19	100	41
Equal Weight..........	Structural Steel	100	100	100	100
Equal Weight..........	Alum–52S ½ H	281	765	647	100
Equal Weight..........	Mag. FS–1a	444	1,954	1,040	100
Equal Weight..........	Titanium	173	270	600	100

SOURCE: Data taken from B. W. Niebel and E. N. Baldwin, *Designing for Production.*

between various materials and properties when one of the variables, such as thickness, stiffness, strength or weight, is held constant.

By keeping in mind the thought of selecting a material that is easy to process, one methods analyst was able to show real savings when he changed the procedure of producing stainless steel bearing shells. Originally, they were made by drilling and boring to size cut lengths of stainless steel bar stock. By specifying stainless steel tubing as a material source, material was conserved, rate of production was increased, and cost of manufacture was reduced.

Using material more economically

A fertile field for analysis is the possibility of using material more economically. If the ratio of scrap material to that actually going into the

FIGURE 4–19

Packing Ivory bars before methods change

product is high, then consideration should be given to greater utilization.

For example, if a part required 18 inches of 2-inch × 14-gage seamless steel tubing (including the width of the cutoff tool) and random lengths had been supplied, it would be well to specify to the source that this tubing should be delivered in exact multiple lengths of 18 inches. This procedure would prevent short ends being left over.

FIGURE 4–20

Packing Ivory bars after methods change (small end of box requires 15 percent less boxboard because of smaller overlapping flaps)

In the production of stampings from sheet, if the skeleton seems to contain an undue amount of scrap material, it may be possible to go to the next higher standard width of material and utilize a multiple die. If a multiple die is used, care should be exercised in the arrangement of the cuts to assure greatest utilization of material. Figure 4–21 illustrates how careful nesting of parts permits maximum utilization of flat stock.

FIGURE 4–21

Method of torch cutting heavy gear case side plates (note nesting of the point and the heel for most effective use of plate)

General Electric Co.

At one time the Procter & Gamble Company packed bars of Ivory soap into boxes with the opening on the largest face of the cardboard box. This operation is shown in Figure 4–19. Flaps on the four edges of the open case fold over to form a double cover over that part of the box during packing. As the result of a method study, consideration was given to using material more economically. It was found that the bars could be packed satisfactorily, with no increase in time, by passing them through an open end. This permitted redesign of the case so the overlapping of the flaps was at the smallest face of the case, using approximately 15 percent less boxboard. The end packing is shown in Figure 4–20. This change resulted in a substantial reduction in the cost of the container.

Another example of economical use of material is in compression molding of plastic parts. By preweighing the amount of material put into the mold, only the exact amount of material required to fill out the cavity will be used and excessive flash will be eliminated.

Salvage materials

The possibility of salvaging materials that would otherwise be sold as scrap should not be overlooked. Sometimes by-products resulting from the unworked portion or scrap section offer real possibilities for savings. One manufacturer of stainless steel cooling cabinets had sections of stainless steel 4 to 8 inches wide left as cuttings on the shear. An analysis brought out a by-product of electric light switch plate covers.

Another manufacturer, after salvaging the steel insert from defective bonded rubber ringer rolls, was able to utilize the cylindrical hollow rubber rolls as bumpers for protecting motor- and sailboats while moored. Figure 4–22 illustrates how one manufacturer used pieces of circular plate scrap to produce needed components.

If it is not possible to develop a by-product, then scrap materials should be segregated for top scrap prices. Separate bins should be provided in the shop for tool steel, steel, brass, copper, aluminum; and chip haulers and floor sweepers should be instructed to keep the scrap segregated.

It is usually wise to salvage items such as electric light bulbs if large quantities are used. The brass socket should be stored in one area, and after breaking and disposing of the glass bulb, the tungsten filament should be removed and stored separately for greatest residual value.

Wooden boxes from incoming shipments should be saved and the boards sawed to standard lengths for use in making smaller boxes for outgoing shipments. This practice is always economical and is being followed by many large industries today as well as service maintenance centers.

Full use of supplies and tools

Full use of all shop supplies should be encouraged. One manufacturer of dairy equipment introduced the policy that no new welding rod was to be distributed to workers without return of old tips under 2 inches long. The cost of welding rods was reduced immediately by more than 15 percent.

It is usually economical to repair by brazing or welding expensive cutting tools such as broaches, special form tools, and milling cutters. If it has been company practice to discard tools of this nature, once broken, it would be well to investigate the potential savings brought about by a tool salvage program.

The unworn portion of grinding wheels, emery disks, and so forth, should be checked for possible use in the plant. Such items as gloves and rags should not be discarded once they are soiled. It is less expensive to store the dirty items in containers to await laundering than to replace them.

FIGURE 4–22A

Circular piece is scrap from motor frame head fabrication part (this scrap part is used to produce gusset support pieces for locomotive platform)

FIGURE 4–22B

Airco No. 50 Travo-graph 8 torch burner cutting gusset support pieces from scrap blank

General Electric Co.

Waste of material benefits no one. The methods analyst can make a real contribution to his company by preventing material wastes which today claim about one fifth of our material.

Summary: material

In every manufacturer's shop, materials constitute a large percentage of the total costs of the products of production. Consequently, the proper selection and use of materials is important not only from the standpoint of giving the customer a more satisfactory product, but also because by selecting a material more economical to process, production will be performed at a lower cost.

Whether the product being produced is chemical, vegetable, or mineral, the chances are that material costs can be reduced and product quality can be improved by asking and answering these questions:

1. Have you reexamined materials specifications for chances to use:
   a) Less expensive materials?
   Eliminate "special" grades whenever possible.
   b) Lighter gage or less strong materials? Less pure materials?
   Such techniques as corrugating metal sheet to increase rigidity, or changing processing methods to hold dilution of chemicals to a minimum, may achieve real savings.
   c) Stronger materials and more concentrated chemicals?
   This is the reverse of question (*b*) but both possibilities rate consideration.
   d) Lighter weight materials that can save on handling and shipping?
   Even if they've been considered before, it's worth taking another look at such materials as aluminum, magnesium, resin-impregnated glass fibers, and paper.
   e) Other forms of materials that can cut handling costs?
   For instance, sugar in liquid form can be piped around the plant. It is much easier to handle than bulk sugar in bags, so should be considered even when initial cost is higher.
   f) Standard grades, gauges, and formulations in place of special materials that are harder to get—and often harder to process?
   Often a very slight change in part size or shape will make it possible to cut scrap to a minimum while using standard sheet or strip.
   g) Fewer varieties of each material?
   For example, standardizing on half a dozen colors instead of specifying a rainbow can reduce paint and pigment inventory, minimize chances for error, and make matching of colors easier.
   h) Disposable or expendable materials that not only reduce original cost, but save on maintenance and repair?

2. Have you reexamined sources of supply for chances to:
    a) Obtain materials in more convenient quantities?
    b) Obtain better prices, better delivery?
    c) Get help in design and processing?
    d) Work with vendors to help them slice their costs and improve quality?
    e) Buy parts now made in the plant; or make parts now bought?
    Changing labor and equipment situation may have reversed price and production picture which existed when decision on a given part was originally made.
3. Have you reexamined scrap and waste for chances to:
    a) Use waste material in making another part or product?
    b) Replace materials whose scrap cannot be reused with those which have usable scrap?
    For example, replace thermosetting plastics with thermoplastics that can be remelted.
    c) Use dark-colored and other less easily contaminated materials in place of the light-colored, easily contaminated ones?
    d) Turn waste material into usable by-products?
    For instance, waste sulfur dioxide from refineries is being recovered as usable sulfur; waste pickle liquor is being made into wallboard.
4. Are you paying special attention to materials which are easily contaminated, or which evaporate or deteriorate on storage?
    a) Is it possible to eliminate use of such materials?
    b) Could better containers and better storage methods be devised?
    For instance, materials which evaporate should be stored in containers with tight-fitting covers that close automatically.
    c) Would a slight change in product specifications and processing methods make it possible to convert such materials into a more stable form as soon as they arrive in the plant?
    d) Is corrosion resistance of processing equipment now being used taken into account when new materials are considered?

TEXT QUESTIONS

1. Explain how design simplification can be applied to the manufacturing process.
2. How is operation analysis related to methods engineering?
3. Does increased competition submerge the necessity for operation analysis? Explain. *No*
4. Explain the relationship between market price and volume as related to production. *price inversely related to volume.*
5. What is the major obstacle in the path of the methods analyst?
    Selling the new method

6. How do unnecessary operations develop in an industry?

7. What four thoughts should the analyst keep in mind to improve design?

8. Explain why it may be desirable to "tighten up" in tolerances and specifications? *make some assembly process possible*

9. What is meant by lot-by-lot inspection? *sample examined to determine quality of lot*

10. When is an elaborate quality control procedure not justified? *If does not require close tolerances, easily checked, defective work unlikely*

11. What five points should be considered when endeavoring to reduce material cost?

12. Explain why corrugated metal sheet is more rigid than flat sheet of the same material.

13. How does a changing labor and equipment situation affect the cost of purchased components?

14. Explain "the elimination approach" as practiced by the Procter & Gamble Company.

15. The finish tolerance on a shaft was changed from 0.004 to 0.008. How much cost improvement resulted from this change?

16. What overall tolerance would be applied to three components making up the overall dimension if component one had a tolerance of 0.002, component two, 0.004 and component three, 0.005?

$$\sqrt{(.002)^2 + (.004)^2 + (.005)^2}$$

GENERAL QUESTIONS

1. Formulate a checklist that would be helpful in improving operations.

2. Show the calculations that indicate that Titanium is .19 as stiff as a section of steel having equal strength when loaded as a beam. Both bars have equal width.

3. Explain how conservation of welding rod can result in 20 percent material savings.

4. Investigate the operations required to convert waste sulfur dioxide to usable sulfur.

5. Explain why this country has lost a large share of its steel business to Japan since 1970.

CHAPTER 5

Operation analysis
(continued)

PROCESS OF MANUFACTURE

Just as there are a great number of materials to select from when designing a part, so there are several manufacturing processes to choose from when planning for its production. New and improved methods are constantly being developed. A new process may be developed in one plant to satisfy a particular design or project. Investigation will often reveal several other places in the plant where it could be used to advantage over the existing process. For example, to finish the outside diameter of a product, a setup on an infeed centerless grinder may have been developed. A survey may disclose that the centerless grinding can produce other products faster that were formerly turned down on a lathe, and still have a better machine finish.

No methods analyst can ever expect to learn every process and be informed on the various operations of the equipment and its limitations as to tolerance, capacities, and various applications. However, by keeping the basic fundamentals in mind, he will be in a position to foresee opportunities for improved processes throughout his organization. For example, the requirements of clean surface, proper fusion temperature at joint, and pressure to force the metal together and hold it while cooling, are applicable to forge welding, butt welding, flash welding, spot welding, projection welding, seam welding, and percussion welding.

If the methods analyst understands these fundamental requirements, he will be in a position not only to see possibilities for developing better joining techniques, but will be able to clear up troubles encountered in welding processes. Thus, the methods analyst will find that by grouping the processes under fundamental principles and requirements, the vast varieties of processes can be understood without knowing the detailed construction or characteristics of the process equipment.

It is wise for the methods analyst to review current technical periodicals, as ideas for method improvement are often crystallized when he sees "what the other fellow is doing." Possible application for improve-

FIGURE 5–1

Methods of resistance welding

ments should be clipped and filed for future reference, and in time an invaluable manufacturing methods library can be developed.

By systematically questioning and investigating manufacturing processes, new and better methods will be evolved. It is well for the methods analyst to adopt the philosophy, "There is no best way to do a job— there is always a better way."

From the standpoint of improving the processes of manufacture, investigation should be made in four ways: (1) when changing an operation, consider possible effects on other operations; (2) mechanize manual operations; (3) utilize more efficient facilities on mechanical operations; and (4) operate mechanical facilities more efficiently.

Effects on subsequent operations by changing present operation

Before changing any operation, it is wise to consider detrimental effects that may result on subsequent operations down the line. Reducing

TABLE 5-1

Similar and dissimilar metal combinations that may be spot welded

	Aluminum	Ascoloy	Brass	Copper	Gal Iron	Iron	Lead	Monel	Nickel	Ni-chrome	Tin-plate	Zinc	Phos. Bronze	Nickel Silver
Aluminum	o										o	o		
Ascoloy		o	o	o	o	o		o	o	o	o		o	o
Brass		o	o	o	o	o	o	o	o	o	o	o	o	o
Copper		o	o	o	o	o		o	o	o	o	o	o	o
Galv. iron		o	o	o	o	o	o	o	o	o	o		o	o
Iron		o	o	o	o	o		o	o	o	o		o	o
Lead			o		o		o				o	o		o
Monel		o	o	o	o	o		o	o	o	o		o	o
Nickel		o	o	o	o	o		o	o	o	o		o	o
Nichrome		o	o	o	o	o		o	o	o	o		o	o
Tinplate	o	o	o	o	o	o	o	o	o	o	o	o	o	o
Zinc	o		o	o			o				o	o		
Phos. bronze		o	o	o	o	o		o	o	o	o		o	o
Nickel silver		o	o	o	o	o	o	o	o	o	o		o	o

Note: The "o" means the metals can be spot welded.

FIGURE 5–2

Machine-wrapped
copper bands prove
unsatisfactory in
manufacture of AC
field coils

Method of forming
heavy copper bands

Hand-wrapped field
coils

CRACKED INSULATION

Cracked insulation in
coils machine wrapped
prior to forming

costs of one operation can result in higher costs on others. For example, the following change in manufacturing of AC field coils resulted in higher costs and was, therefore, not practical. The field coils were made of heavy copper bands which were formed and then insulated with mica tape. The mica tape was hand wrapped on the already coiled parts. It was thought advantageous to machine wrap the copper bands prior to coiling. This did not prove practical as the forming of the coils cracked

FIGURE 5–3

Grinding after drilling automatically removes burrs thrown up in the drilling operation

the mica tape, and time-consuming repairs were necessitated prior to acceptance.

Rearranging operations often results in savings. The flange of a motor conduit box required four holes to be drilled—one in each corner. Also, the base had to be smooth and flat. Originally, the job was planned by first grinding the base, then drilling the four holes in a drill jig. The drilling operation threw up burrs which had to be removed in the next step. By rearranging operations so that the holes were drilled first, and the base then ground, it was possible to eliminate the deburring operation. The base grinding operation automatically removed the burrs.

By combining operations, costs can usually be reduced. Formerly, the fan motor supports and outlet box of electric fans were completely fabricated, painted separately, and then riveted together. By riveting the outlet box and fan motor support together prior to painting, and then painting the assembly, appreciable savings in time was effected on the painting operation.

Mechanize manual operation

Any time heavy manual work is encountered, consideration should be given to possible mechanization. To clean insulation and dried varnish from armature slots, one company resorted to tedious hand filing. By

FIGURE 5–4

This tedious hand-filing operating was improved by performing the operation with an end mill placed in a power air drill

questioning this process of manufacture, an end mill placed in a power air drill was developed. This not only took most of the physical effort out of this job, but allowed a considerable higher rate of production.

The utilization of power assembly tools, such as power nut and screwdrivers, electric or air hammers, and mechanical feeders, often are more economical than hand tool methods.

Utilize more efficient machine

Can a more efficient method of machining be used? is a question that should be foremost in the analyst's mind. If the operation is done mechanically, there is always the possibility of a more efficient means of mechanization. Let us look at some examples. Turbine blade roots were machined by performing three separate milling operations. Cycle time was high, as well as costs. By means of external broaching, all three surfaces were finished at once. A pronounced saving was the result.

The possibility of utilizing press operation should never be overlooked. This process is one of the fastest for forming and sizing operations. A stamped bracket had four holes that were drilled after the bracket was formed. By designing a die to pierce the holes, the work was performed in a fraction of the drilling time.

Operate mechanical facilities more efficiently

A good slogan for the methods analyst to keep in mind is, "Design for two at a time." Usually, multiple die operation in presswork is more economical than single-stage operation. Again, multiple cavities in die casting, molding, and similar processes, should always be considered when there is sufficient volume.

On machine operations the analyst should be sure that proper feeds and speeds are being used. He should investigate the grinding of cutting tools so maximum performance will result. He should check to see if the cutting tools are properly mounted, if the right lubricant is being used, and if the machine tool is in good condition and is being adequately maintained. Many machine tools are being operated at a fraction of their possible output. Always endeavoring to operate mechanical facilities more efficiently will pay dividends.

Summary: process of manufacture

There are usually a number of ways to produce a part. Better production methods are continually being developed. By systematically questioning and investigating manufacturing processes, the analyst is bound to find a more efficient method. Always question the process of manufacture with an idea toward improvement. There is no best way to do a job—there is always a better way.

SETUP AND TOOLS

One of the most important elements applying to all forms of work holders, tools, and setup is the economic one. The amount of "tooling up" that proves most advantageous depends on (1) the quantity to be produced; (2) the chance for repeat business; (3) the amount of labor involved; (4) delivery requirements; and (5) amount of capital required. One of the most prevalent mistakes made by planners and toolmakers is to tie up money in fixtures that may show a large saving when in use, but that are seldom used. For example, a saving of 10 percent in direct labor cost on a job in constant use would probably justify greater expense in tools than an 80 or 90 percent saving on a small job appearing only a few times per year on the production schedule. The economic advantage of lower labor costs is the controlling factor in the determination of the tooling; consequently, jigs and fixtures may be desirable even where only small quantities are involved. Other considerations, such as improved interchangeability, increased accuracy, or reduction of labor trouble, may provide the dominant reason for elaborate tooling, although this usually is not the case.

For example, the production engineer in a machining department has under study a job being machined in the shop now. He has devised two alternate methods involving different tooling for this same job. Data on the present and proposed methods follow. Which method would be the most economical in view of the activity? The base pay rate is $2.40 per hour. The estimated activity is 10,000 pieces per year. Fixtures are capitalized and depreciated in five years.

Method	Time value	Fixture cost	Tool cost	Average tool life
Present Method.............	3.50 min. each	None	$ 6	10,000 pieces
Alternate 1................	2.80 min. each	$300	$20	20,000 pieces
Alternate 2................	1.85 min. each	$600	$35	5,000 pieces

A cost analysis of the above would reveal that a unit total cost of $0.0930 represented by alternate method No. 2 is the most economical for the quantity anticipated. The elements of cost entering into this total are as follows:

Method	Unit direct labor cost	Unit fixture cost	Unit tool cost	Unit total cost	Annual cost
Present Method..........	$0.140	None	$0.0006	$0.1406	$1,406
Alternate 1..............	$0.112	$0.006	$0.0010	$0.1190	$1,190
Alternate 2..............	$0.074	$0.012	$0.0070	$0.0930	$ 930

A crossover (break-even) chart as illustrated in Figure 5–5 is a helpful tool for deciding which method to use for given quantity requirements.

Once the amount of tooling is determined, or if tooling already exists, the ideal amount needed is determined, then specific points should be kept in mind to produce the most favorable designs. The following points should be considered.

FIGURE 5–5

Crossover (break-even) chart illustrating total costs for
various methods and quantities (note at 10,000 total pieces
the total cost of all three methods is about the same)

Will the fixture be similar to some other that has been used to advantage? If
so, how can you improve upon it?

Has the part undergone any previous operations? If so, can you use any of
these points or surfaces to locate or master from?

Can any stock hardware be used for making the fixture?

Can the part be quickly placed in the fixture?

Can the part be quickly removed from the fixture?

Is the part held firmly so that it cannot work loose, spring, or chatter while
the cut is being made?

Always bear in mind that the cut should be against the solid part of the fixture and not against the clamp.

Can more than one part be placed in the fixture and so increase the output?

Can the chips be readily removed from the fixture?

Are the clamps on the fixture strong enough to prevent them from buckling
when they are tightened down on the work?

In using cams or wedges for binding or clamping the work, always bear in
mind that through the vibration or chatter they are apt to come loose and cause
damage.

Are there any special wrenches to be designed to go with the fixture?

Can a gage be designed, or hardened pins added, to help the operator set the milling cutters or check up on the work?

Must special milling cutters, arbors, or collars be designed to go with the fixture?

Is there plenty of clearance for the arbor collars to pass over the work without striking?

If the fixture is of the rotary type, have you designed an accurate indexing arrangement?

Can the fixture be used on a standard rotary indexing head?

Can the fixture be made to handle more than one operation?

Have you, in the designing of the fixture, brought the work as close to the table of the miller as possible?

Can the part be milled in a standard miller vise by making up a set of special jaws and thus doing away with an expensive fixture?

If the part is to be milled at an angle, could the fixture be simplified by using a standard adjustable milling angle?

Can lugs be cast on part to be machined to enable you to hold it?

How many different-sized wrenches must the operator have in order to tighten all clamps? Why will one not do?

Can the work be gaged in the fixture? Can a snap gage be used?

Can you use jack pins to help support the work while it is being milled?

Have you placed springs under all clamps?

Are all steel contact points, clamps, etc., hardened?

What kind or class of jigs are you going to design? Will any of the standard jig designs shown help you?

What takes the thrust of the drill? Can you use any jack pins or screws to support the work while it is being drilled?

Can you use a double or triple thread on the screw that holds the work in the jig, so that it will take fewer turns to get the screw out of the way in order to remove the part more quickly?

Have you made a note on the drawing, or have you stamped all loose parts with a symbol indicating the jig that they were made for so that in case they are lost or misplaced they can be returned to the jig when found?

Are all necessary corners rounded?

Can the toolmaker make the jig?

Are your drill bushings so long that it will be necessary to make up extension drills?

Are the legs on the jig long enough to allow the drill, reamer, or pilot of the reamer to pass through the part a reasonable distance without striking the table of the drill press?

Are all clamps located in such a way as to resist or help resist the pressure of the drill?

Has the drill press the necessary speeds for drilling and reaming all holes?

Must it have a tapping attachment also?

Always remember that it is not practical to have several small holes and only one large one to be drilled and reamed in the jig, for the reason that quicker results can be obtained by drilling the small holes on a small drill press, while, if there is only one large one, it would require the jig to be used on a large machine. The question then arises, is it cheaper to drill the large hole in another jig, and will the result, after so drilling, be accurate enough? Is the jig too heavy to handle?[1]

Setup ties in very closely with the tooling consideration in that the tooling of a job invariably determines the setup and teardown time. When we speak of setup time, we usually include such items as punching in on the job; procuring instructions, drawings, tools, and material; preparing work stations so production can begin in the prescribed manner (setting up tools, adjusting stops, setting feeds, speeds, depth of cut, and so on); tearing down the setup; and returning tools to the crib.

It can readily be seen that setup operations are of extreme importance in the job shop when production runs tend to be small. Even if this type of shop had modern facilities and high effort were put forth, it would still be difficult to meet competition if setups were long because of poor planning and inefficient tooling. When the ratio of setup time to production-run time is high, then the methods analyst will usually be able to develop possibilities for setup and tool improvement.

To develop better methods, the analyst should investigate the setup and tools in these three ways: (1) reduce setup time by better planning and production control; (2) design tooling to utilize the full capacity of the machine; and (3) introduce more efficient tooling.

Reduce setup time by better planning and production control

The time spent in requisitioning tools and materials and in making ready the work station in preparation for actual production, and the time spent in cleaning up the work station and returning the tools to the tool crib is usually known as setup time. Since this time is often difficult to control, it is the portion of the workday usually performed least efficiently. This time often can be reduced through effective production control. By making the dispatch section responsible for seeing that the tools, gages, instructions, and materials are provided at the correct time, and that the tools are returned to their respective cribs after job completion, the need for the operator to leave his work area will be eliminated. Thus, the operator will have to perform only the actual setting up and tearing down of the machine. The clerical and routine function of providing drawings, instructions, and tools can be performed by those more familiar with this type of work. Thus, large numbers of requisitions for these requirements can be performed simultaneously and setup time will be minimized.

Another function of production control that should be carefully re-

---

[1] Abridged from F. H. Colvin and L. L. Haas, *Jigs and Fixtures* (5th ed.; New York: McGraw-Hill Book Co., 1948), pp. 14–17.

viewed for possible improvement is scheduling. Considerable setup time can be saved by scheduling like jobs in sequence. For example, if a 1-inch bar stock job is scheduled to a No. 3 Warner and Swasey turret lathe, from the standpoint of setup time, it would be economical to have other 1-inch round bar stock work scheduled to immediately follow the first 1-inch job. This would eliminate collet changing time, and probably minimize the number of tool changes in the square and hex turrets.

Usually, it is advisable to provide duplicate cutting tools for the operator rather than to make him responsible for sharpening his own tools. When it becomes necessary for the operator to get a new tool, the dull one should be turned in to the tool crib attendant and replaced with a sharp one. The benefits of standardization cannot be realized when tool sharpening is the responsibility of the operator.

To minimize downtime, there should be a constant backlog of work ahead of each operator. There should never be a question on what each operator's next work assignment will be. A technique frequently used to keep the work load apparent to the operator, supervisor, and superintendent is to provide a board over each production facility with three wire clips or pockets to receive work orders. The first clip contains all work orders scheduled ahead, the second clip holds the work orders currently being worked on, while the last clip holds the completed orders. As the dispatcher issues work orders, they are placed in the "work ahead" station. At the same time, he picks up all completed job tickets from the "work completed" station and delivers them to the scheduling department for record. It is obvious that this system assures the operator of a perpetual load in front of him and does not require him to go to his supervisor for his next work assignment.

By making a record of difficult recurring setups, considerable setup time can be saved when repeat business is received. Perhaps the simplest and yet most effective way to compile a record of a setup is to take a photograph of the setup once it is complete. The photograph should be either stapled and filed with the production operation card, or else be placed in a plastic envelope and attached to the tooling prior to storage in the tool crib.

Design tooling to utilize the full capacity of the machine

In considering the second point of setup and tools, the analyst should ask: Can the work be held to permit all machining operations in one setup? A careful review of many jobs will bring out possibilities for multiple cuts, thus utilizing a greater share of the machine's capacity. For example, it was possible to change a milling setup of a toggle lever so the six faces were simultaneously milled by five cutters. The old setup required the job to be done in three steps. The part had to be placed in a separate fixture three different times. The new setup reduced the total machining time and increased the accuracy of the relationship between the six machined faces.

Another thought to be kept in mind is the possibility of positioning one part while another is being machined. This opportunity exists on many milling machine jobs where it is possible to conventional mill on one stroke of the table and climb mill on the return stroke. While the operator is loading a fixture at one end of the machine table, a similar fixture is holding a piece being machined by power feed. As the table of the machine returns, the first piece is removed from the machine and the fixture is reloaded. While this internal work is taking place, the machine is cutting the piece in the second fixture.

Introduce more efficient tooling

Everyone is aware of the vast number of designs of screwdrivers. Each design provides an efficient driver under a particular set of conditions. A screwdriver efficient under one set of conditions may be very inefficient under another group of conditions.

The analyst should investigate to see if the proper hand tools are being provided and used.

FIGURE 5-6

This milling machine equipped with three carbide-tipped fly cutters resulted in a 60 percent saving over the old milling method

More important than proper hand tools are the proper cutting tools. Grinding wheels should be carefully checked to be sure that the right wheel is being used on the job. Excessive grinding wheel wear, poor finish, and slow rate of cutting are characteristics of having selected the wrong wheel.

Carbide tooling offers large savings over high-speed steel tools on many jobs. For example, a 60 percent saving was realized by changing the milling operation of a magnesium casting. Formerly, the base was

FIGURE 5–7

Carbide-tipped V-shaped gun drill with hole through center for coolant answers deep-hole drilling problem

milled complete in two operations, using high-speed steel milling cutters. An analysis resulted in employing three carbide-tipped fly cutters mounted in a special holder to mill parts complete. Faster feeds and speeds were possible and surface finish was not impaired.

Selection of the correct drill is important. Just as there are a variety of hand tools—each designed for a specific task, so there are broad varieties of cutting tools—each having its own limited range of application.

The old method for drilling a hole ½ inch in diameter and 7 inches deep in a hard steel shaft with a high-speed twist drill resulted in considerable difficulty. It was necessary to back out the drill about 20 times to remove the chips and cool the drill. It was not possible to get the coolant to the cutting edge because of the depth of the hole. By utilizing a carbide-tipped V-shaped gun drill with a hole in the center through which the coolant was pumped, it was possible to drill the hole in about one third the time.

Again, it was possible to greatly reduce the costs of die maintenance by considering the use of carbide as a die-cutting edge material. To produce a certain stamping, it was necessary to resharpen a die with tool steel cutting edges after every 50,000 pieces. A study of die-cutting edges resulted in an improved die with edges of tungsten carbide. Now,

FIGURE 5–8

More than 600,000 pieces are produced on this die before resharpening is necessary

more than 600,000 pieces are produced before resharpening is necessary.

In the introduction of more efficient tooling, develop better methods for holding the work. Be sure that the work is held so it can be positioned and removed quickly. A quick-acting bench vise has been developed, utilizing the feet to open and close the vise while the hands are engaged in doing useful work. The vise is opened by pressing one foot pedal and is closed by pressing a second foot pedal.

Summary: setup and tools

The extent of tooling justified for any job is determined largely by the number of parts to be produced. On low-activity jobs, only elementary tooling is justified; on high-activity, special tooling is required because cost of tooling is prorated over the large number of units. On high-activity work, it is important to bring unit production time down to an absolute minimum. Good setup and tool practice produces worthwhile benefits; it makes the job easier, simpler, and less fatiguing. Time used in analysis of setup and tools will result in better production and improved products at minimum costs.

WORKING CONDITIONS

The methods analyst should accept as part of his responsibility the provision of good, safe, comfortable working conditions. Experience has proved conclusively that plants providing good working conditions will outproduce those that maintain poor conditions. The economic return provided through investment in improved working environment is usually significant. Ideal working conditions will improve the safety record, reduce absenteeism and tardiness, raise employee morale, and improve public relations, in addition to increasing production.

Some common considerations for improving working conditions are as follows:

1. Improve lighting.
2. Control temperature.
3. Provide for adequate ventilation.
4. Control sound.
5. Promote orderliness, cleaniness, and good housekeeping.
6. Arrange for immediate disposal of irritating and harmful dusts, fumes, gases, and fogs.
7. Provide guards at nip points and points of power transmission.
8. Provide, at cost when necessary, personal protective equipment.
9. Sponsor and enforce a well-formulated first-aid program.
10. Utilize work physiology principles.

Improve lighting

The intensity of light required depends primarily on what operations are being performed in the area. It is obvious that a toolmaker or an inspector requires greater intensity of light than would be needed in a storeroom. Glare, quality of light, location of light source, contrasts in color and brightness, flickering and shadows, all must be considered in addition to intensity. Some characteristics of good lighting are as follows:

1. Reduce glare by installing a large number of sources of light to give the total required light output.
2. Enclose filament-type bulbs in opalescent bowls to reduce glare by spreading the light output over a greater surface.
3. White light, or the composition of average sunlight, is generally con-

sidered ideal. A satisfactory approximately white light for most uses can be produced by a filament-type bulb or by a single white fluorescent unit.

4. The correct level of illumination should be provided at all points of the work station which will prohibit all shadow.

The Bausch & Lomb Company reports through its Industrial Vision Service Division that it has been proven to be possible, with a sound vision program, to increase quantity and quality of production by amounts varying between 15 and 20 percent. If this additional amount of production can be achieved through correct placement of visually skilled individuals, then it follows that at least this amount of production may be sacrificed by an outdated lighting program.

Light recommendations in footlamberts are shown in Table 5–2. Foot-

TABLE 5–2

Guide brightness for various categories of seeing at specified footcandles and reflectance*

Category of seeing task	Guide brightness footlamberts	Footcandles for specified reflectance conditions		
		90%	*50%*	*10%*
A. Easy..............	Below 18	Below 20	Below 36	Below 180
B. Ordinary...........	18–42	20–95	36–84	180–420
C. Difficult...........	42–100	45–153	84–240	420–1,200
D. Very difficult.......	120–420	133–455	240–840	1,200–4,200
E. Most difficult.......	420 up	455	840	4,200

* From *Human Factors Engineering* by Ernest J. McCormick (New York: McGraw-Hill Book Co., 1964).

lamberts refer to the brightness determined by multiplying the required illumination in footcandles by the reflectance in percent. Thus, we have the relation:

$$\text{Required illumination } (FC) = \frac{\text{Required brightness } (FL)}{\text{Reflectance}}$$

The footcandle requirement for different seeing tasks where the reflectance is relatively high is shown in Table 5–3.

Control temperature

The human body endeavors to maintain a constant temperature of about 98° F. When the body is exposed to unusually high temperatures, large amounts of perspiration evaporate from the skin. During the perspiration process, sodium chloride is carried through the pores of the skin and is left on the skin surface as a residue when evaporation takes place.

TABLE 5–3

Current light recommendations for different seeing tasks

Tasks	Footcandles in service, i.e., on task or 30" above floor
Most difficult seeing tasks.................................. Finest precision work involving: Finest detail; poor contrasts; long periods of time. Extra-fine assembly; precision grading; extra-fine finishing.	200–1,000
Very difficult seeing tasks................................... Precision work involving: Fine detail; fair contrasts; long periods of time. Fine assembly; high-speed work; fine-finishing.	100
Difficult and critical seeing tasks............................ Prolonged work involving: Fine detail; moderate contrasts; long periods of time. Ordinary benchwork and assembly; machine shop work; finishing of medium-to-fine parts; office work.	50
Ordinary seeing tasks....................................... Involving: Moderately fine detail; normal contrasts; intermittent periods of time. Automatic machine operation; rough grinding; garage work areas; switchboards; continuous processes; conference and file rooms; packing and shipping.	30
Casual seeing tasks... Such as: Stairways; reception rooms; washrooms and other service areas; active storage.	10
Rough seeing tasks... Such as: Hallways; corridors; passageways; inactive storage.	5

SOURCE: International Labour Office, International Labour Office, Geneva, Switzerland.

TABLE 5–4

Provides reflectance factors of typical paint and natural wood finishes

Color or finish	Percent of reflected light	Color or finish	Percent of reflected light
White......................	85	Medium blue................	35
Light cream.................	75	Dark gray...................	30
Light gray..................	75	Dark red....................	13
Light yellow................	75	Dark brown.................	10
Light buff..................	70	Dark blue...................	8
Light green.................	65	Dark green..................	7
Light blue..................	55	Maple......................	42
Medium yellow..............	65	Satinwood..................	34
Medium buff................	63	Walnut.....................	16
Medium gray...............	55	Mahogany.................	12
Medium green..............	52		

This represents a direct loss to the system and may create a disturbance to the normal balance of fluids in the body. The result is heat fatigue and heat cramps, with accompanying slowdown in production. The performance of a very good operator deteriorates as rapidly as the performance of the average and less-than-average operator. In clerical operations such as typing, output not only suffers, but also the number of errors increases.

Conversely, detailed time studies have repeatedly brought to attention the loss in production when working conditions are unduly cold. Temperature should be controlled so it will be between 65 and 75° F. the year round. If this level can be maintained, losses and slowdowns from heat fatigue, heat cramps, and lack of manipulative dexterity will be kept to a minimum.

Provide for adequate ventilation

Ventilation also plays an important role in the control of accidents and operator fatigue. It has been found that disagreeable fumes, gases, dusts, and odors cause fatigue that definitely taxes the physical efficiency of the worker and often creates a mental tension. Laboratory findings indicate that the depressing influence of poor ventilation is associated with air movement as well as temperature and humidity.

When humidity increases, evaporative cooling decreases rapidly, thus reducing the ability of the body to dissipate heat. Under these conditions high heart rates, high body temperatures, and slow recovery after work result in pronounced fatigue.

The New York State Commission of Ventilation disclosed that in heavy manual labor 15 percent less work was done at 75° F. with 50 percent relative humidity than was done at 68° F. with the same humidity; and 28 percent less work was done at 86° F. with 80 percent relative humidity. It was also brought out that 9 percent less work was accomplished in stagnant air than in fresh air when the temperature and humidity remained constant. Further experiment showed a reduced work capacity of 17 percent at 75° F. and 37 percent at 86° F. when compared with work done at 68° F.

Similar experiments made by the American Society of Heating and Ventilating Engineers show that similar gains in production, safety, and employee morale follow when ideal ventilation is introduced to the production floor.

Control sound

Both loud and monotonous noises are conducive to worker fatigue. Constant and intermittent noise also tends to excite the worker emotionally, resulting in loss of temper and difficulty in doing precision work. Quarrels and poor conduct on the part of workmen often can be attributed to disturbing noises. Tests have proven that irritating noise levels heighten the pulse rate and blood pressure and result in irregularities in heart rhythm. The nervous system of the body, in order to overcome the effect of noise, is strained, resulting in neurasthenic states.

Federal Register, Vol. 34, No. 96 dated May 20, 1969 in reference to the Walsh-Healy Act on occupational noise exposure provides the following under Table 5–5.

TABLE 5–5

Permissible noise exposures

Duration per day, hours	Sound level dBA
8	90
6	92
4	95
3	97
2	100
1.5	102
1	105
0.5	110
0.25 or less	115

The law (50–204.10 occupational noise exposure) states:

Protection against the effects of noise exposure shall be provided when the sound levels exceed those shown in Table I [Table 5–5] of this section when measured on the A scale of a standard sound level meter at slow response. When noise levels are determined by octave band analysis, the equivalent A-weighted sound level may be determined as follows:

Noise levels should be controlled to maintain good worker efficiency and morale. It is difficult to control the noise on many operations such as pneumatic hammers, steam forging presses, and woodworking machinery such as planers and jointers. In some instances more quietly operating facilities may be substituted for those operating at a higher noise level. For example, a hydraulic-operated riveter may be substituted for pneumatic equipment, or electrically operated apparatus may be quieter than steam. In any case, noise levels can be controlled to some extent by insulating the surrounding walls and ceiling and the equipment itself to prevent the telegraphing of noise and to control vibration. Insulated noisy work areas free the surrounding work areas from distracting sounds.

Promote orderliness, cleanliness, and good housekeeping

A good industrial housekeeping program will (1) diminish fire hazards; (2) reduce accidents; (3) conserve floor space; and (4) improve employee morale.

Industrial accident statistics indicate that a large percentage of accidents are the result of poor housekeeping practice. Many times the phrase, "A place for everything, and everything in its place," has been cited as the basis for orderliness. This is true, and the methods analyst should be sure that a place is provided for everything and, if necessary, follow through with supervision to see that everything is in its place.

When the general layout of a plant shows management's and supervision's desire to have orderliness, cleanliness, and good housekeeping, then the employees will tend to follow the example set for them, and they will practice good housekeeping themselves.

Arrange for disposal of irritating and harmful dusts, fumes, gases, and fogs

Dusts, fumes, gases, vapors, and fogs generated by various industrial processes constitute one of the major dangers encountered by the workmen. The following classification of dusts alone, prepared by the National Safety Council, gives an indication of the problem:

1. Irritating dusts, such as metal and rock dusts.
2. Corrosive dusts, such as from soda and lime.
3. Poisonous dusts, such as from lead, arsenic, or mercury.
4. Dusts from fur, feathers, and hair may carry disease germs which may infect the worker.

All of these maladies can be either removed or rendered harmless by employing suitable methods, such as exhaust systems, complete enclosing of process, wet or absorbing techniques, and complete protection of operator through personal respiratory protective equipment. Probably the most effective measure for controlling dust and fumes is through local exhaust systems in which a hood is installed for collecting the substance to be removed right at the point of generation. A fan draws the contaminated air through metal pipes or ducts to the outside or to some properly provided place for disposal. The diameter of the exhaust pipe is an important detail that must be determined to insure a satisfactory installation. Generally, the larger the exhaust pipe, the more costly the initial installation. However, larger pipes allow increased efficiency of the motive system since they require less power for the exhaust of air (see Table 5–6).

The analyst can consider the utilization of the dust or fumes collected. Perhaps wood dust can be used as a source of heat as can blast furnace gases and others containing carbon monoxide. One manufacturer in the lead industry claims he salvages enough lead annually to more than pay for the operation of his exhaust system.

TABLE 5–6

Diameter of buffing wheels	Maximum grinding surface Sq. in.	Minimum diameter of pipe In.
6 in. or less, not over 1 in. thick......................	19	3
7 to 9 in., inclusive, not over 1½ in. thick............	43	3½
10 to 16 in., inclusive, not over 2 in. thick............	101	4
17 to 19 in., inclusive, not over 3 in. thick............	180	4½
20 to 24 in., inclusive, not over 4 in. thick............	302	5
25 to 30 in., inclusive, not over 5 in. thick............	472	6

SOURCE: National Safety Council Safe Practices Pamphlet No. 32.

Provide guards at nip points and points of power transmission

In the majority of the states, the employer is legally responsible for properly guarding his facilities, so his employees may be protected. Guards must be designed correctly if they are to provide protection and still not hinder production. The general requisites of good guarding are:

1. Effectively protects employee.
2. Permits normal operation of the facility at a pace equal to, or greater than, that used prior to the guard installation.
3. Permits normal maintenance to the facility.

Since the machine tool builder is in an ideal position to provide satisfactory guards, it is usually advantageous to purchase necessary guards at the same time the machines are procured. Although many homemade guards are doing an excellent job, they are not usually as efficient, attractive, or as inexpensive as a purchased unit.

Production workers are fully aware that unguarded machinery is hazardous. If they are exposed to such working conditions, there will be a natural tendency to execute at low effort as a precautionary measure. Also, an employer who fails to spend any reasonable amount to remove a visible hazard cannot expect full cooperation from his employees.

Provide at cost necessary personal protective equipment

It is not always possible to eliminate certain hazards by revision of methods, equipment, and tools because of economic considerations. When this condition occurs, the operator can often be fully protected by personal protective equipment. Representative personal protective equipment would include goggles, face shields, welding helmets, aprons, jackets, trousers, leggings, gloves, shoes, and respiratory equipment.

To be assured that operating personnel will conscientiously use protective equipment, it should either be furnished to the employee at cost or be provided for him at no expense. The policy of the company to absorb completely the cost of personal protective equipment is becoming more and more common. Innumerable cases can be cited where personal protective equipment has saved an eye, hand, foot, or a life. For example, one steel company reported that 20 fatalities were prevented in one year by enforced wearing of company-provided helmets. A northwest lumber company reported, too, that six serious head injuries were prevented within a 20-day period through the use of protective hats.

Sponsor and enforce a well-formulated first-aid program

The most advanced program in industrial safety will never be able to eliminate completely all accidents and injuries. To care adequately for the injuries that do occur, a well-formulated first-aid program is essential. This will include training and publicity, so the employees will be fully aware of the danger of infection and ease of avoidance of infection through first aid. Also, a complete procedure to be followed in case of injury must be arranged, with proper instruction to all supervisory levels. A well-equipped first-aid room must be provided to care for injured and ill employees until medical aid is available.

Utilizing work physiology

Work physiology can be used to specify the physiological and psychological factors characteristic of a given work environment, so that work stations can be more effectively designed for the available personnel associated with the enterprise. Also, work physiology can assist in the selection and placement of personnel, so that only those endowed with the characteristics essential to a given work station are utilized.

A recent case history will illustrate the potential of work physiology in conjunction with operation analysis. The study involved 16 days of capsule sorting employing three different sorting machines. Four operators were employed who were randomly assigned to the different machines, so that each operator spent a total of four days on each of the three machines. Information recorded for each sorted can of capsules

FIGURE 5–9

Work center showing press operations (note each person has two hand buttons spread well apart so the operator must have both hands in safe position when the press starts)

included: time used to sort, amount of scag removed, number of capsules per can, time of day, number of good capsules sorted out as scag, capsule size, inspection sample size, and transparency. Efficiency scores were computed for cans of work as well as for each total day. These efficiency scores were based on the ratio of the actual performance and the expected performance based on work measurement techniques. The overall average daily efficiency was 95.9 percent. The overall average of the daily efficiencies adjusted for good capsules inadvertently sorted out as scag was 86.3 percent. The overall average number of good capsules sorted out as scag per dag was 5,377 per machine. The overall average number of good capsules sorted and passed through inspection per day was 479,498 per machine.

Figure 5–10 illustrates the effect of monotony and boredom on the average performance of all the operators. Figure 5–11 compares the effects of monotony and boredom on the three different machines. The study revealed that there were significant differences between the machines with flourescent lighting and those with filament lighting.

FIGURE 5–10

A typical relationship between worker efficiency and time of day under daywork operation

FIGURE 5–11

The effect of monotony and boredom in the operation of three different designs of machines

This study revealed that boredom or vigilance factors associated with time of day are apparently a human fatigue characteristic. The decline in performance, regardless of machine type used, suggests this conclusion.

Although all four operators were similar in physical capabilities and all had adequate experience with the work, there were significant differences, as shown in Figure 5–12.

FIGURE 5–12

Operator differences of four typical female employees (connecting lines indicate significant differences)

	Helen	Joy	Judy	Mary
Overall Efficiency for 16 Days	95.2	90.5	87.1	108.1
Average of Daily Efficiencies	94.6	90.7	87.8	108.9
Average of Daily Efficiencies–Adjusted	92.0	82.9	81.1	93.0
Average Daily Number of Good in Scag	1,900	4,700	4,700	10,900
Average Daily Number of Capsules Passed	554,700	501,200	445,000	418,100
Years of Sorting Experience	19	14	1	2
Age	48	37	20	21
Eye Glasses	Yes	No	No	Sometimes
Preferred Hand	RH	RH	RH	RH

The results of this study indicated that the greatest improvements in work of this type can be made by providing work stations and procedures that give the operator maximum opportunity to see imperfections throughout the day and to provide test procedures that help to select those people who are more endowed with the visual ability and mental qualifications that minimize the effect of boredom. It was recommended that rotating operators to different types of sorting stations might help to reduce the effects of monotony or vigilance, or perhaps regularly switching these operators with operators having entirely different work requirements.

Work environments that require heavy demands on human capacities need to be identified so that realistic job specifications are established. No task should have demands that exceed specified human capacity limits. These limits should differentiate between those tasks where the worker is well conditioned to the given task (capable of expending five calories per minute) and those where the worker is not so well conditioned to the given task (capable of expending four calories per minute). Figure 5–13 illustrates the well-conditioned and not-so-well-conditioned

FIGURE 5–13

The relationship between two well-conditioned operators and two not so well-conditioned operators as to capacity to perform work

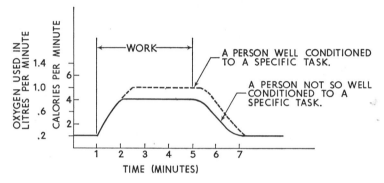

worker from the standpoint of their ability to use up calories, or capacity to perform work. Conditioning reflects the following differences between individuals:

1. Muscle tone—degree of conditioning of the muscle reflexes to a specific task.
2. Endurance—degree to which fuel is made available, fuel is stored, and oxygen is made abundant, owing to a more adequate circulation of blood through active muscle.
3. Transmission—facility of transmission of nerve impulses across the motor end plate in the muscle fiber.
4. Anerobic efficiency—is the efficiency (ratio of work done in calories to net energy used in calories) of the body during very heavy work.
5. Aerobic efficiency—is the efficiency of the body during moderate work where oxygen intake is adequate.
6. Body health—the degree to which the physiological processes function normally.
7. Physical fitness—degree of ability to execute a specific physical task under specific ambient conditions.

These factors are interrelated and affect each other. They cannot be thought of as completely separate entities.

Human capacity to perform a specific task is not determined by efficiency alone, but is determined by the combination of all the physiological processes and their interaction with each other. The degree of training and practice influences the conditioning of a worker for a given assignment, and the importance of this should be recognized in defining the production requirements from the job. Thus, an operator who continually works on an assignment involving heavy muscular demands will condition himself in preparation for this class of work. His output will be considerably more than an operator who performs the same operation at infrequent intervals and who consequently has not been conditioned for this type of work.

Summary: working conditions

Working conditions are continually being improved to make plants clean, healthy, and safe. Good working conditions are reflected in health, output, quality of work, and workers' morale. A better place to work results in better products at lower prices.

MATERIAL HANDLING

The eighth primary approach to operation analysis is material handling. Material handling is not new. Through the years, industry has recognized the application of the old principles of mechanics: the lever, the wheel, and the inclined plane to make the job of moving, shifting, lifting, and carrying easier and faster. Today, material handling has grown into a full study of methods and equipment, which ties together productive and nonproductive operations and makes them a large production unit. The American Material Handling Society defines material handling as being the "art and science involving the movement, packaging, and storing of substances in any form." It will be noted that this definition takes into consideration the smallest particle to the largest unit that can be moved. The methods analyst must realize that the handling of material is an essential part of an operation, and usually consumes the major share of the time of that operation. Also, material handling adds nothing but cost to the product, and the more of it that can be diminished, the more competitive will be the product.

The tangible and intangible benefits of material handling can be reduced to four major objectives, as outlined by the American Material Handling Society. These are:

1. Reduction of handling costs
    a) Reduction of labor costs

    b)   Reduction of material costs
    c)   Reduction of overhead costs
2. Increase of capacity
    a)   Increase of production
    b)   Increase of storage capacity
    c)   Improved layout
3. Improvement in working conditions
    a)   Increase in safety
    b)   Reduction of fatigue
    c)   Improved personnel comforts
4. Better distribution
    a)   Improvement in handling system
    b)   Improvement in routing facilities
    c)   Strategic location of storage facilities
    d)   Improvement in user service
    e)   Increase in availability of product

An axiom that the methods analyst should always keep in mind is that the best handled part is the least manually handled part. Whether distances of moves are large or small, the methods analyst should study them with thought toward improvement. By considering these four points, it is possible to reduce the time and energy spent in handling material:

1. Reduce the time spent in picking up material.
2. Reduce material handling by using mechanical equipment.
3. Make better use of existing handling facilities.
4. Handle material with greater care.

Reduce time spent in picking up material

Many people think of material handling only as transportation and neglect to consider positioning at the work station. It is equally important, and since it is often overlooked, it may offer even greater opportunities for savings than transportation. The job of reducing time spent in picking up material is to minimize tiring, costly manual handling at machine or workplace. It gives the operator a chance to do his job faster and with less fatigue and also with greater safety.

Consider the possibility of avoiding loose piling on the floor. Perhaps the material can be stacked directly on pallets or skids after being processed at the work station. This can result in substantial reduction of terminal transportation time (time material handling equipment stands idle while loading and unloading take place). In fact, a good axiom to remember is, if terminal time is long in the transportation of any material, then an improved material handling installation is needed. A good ex-

FIGURE 5–14

Typical handling equipment used in industry today

FLAT STEEL STRAPPING TOOL	PALLETS – Four-Way Entry	PALLETS – Box Type	SKIDS – Box Types
SKID PLATFORM	PLATFORM TRUCK	HAND TRUCK – Two Wheel	SCREW CONVEYORS
WHEEL CONVEYOR	BRIDGE PLATE	GRAVITY CHUTE	CONVEYOR – Portable, Belt Type
PLATFORM LIFT	HYDRAULIC TABLE ELEVATING	LOW LIFT PLATFORM TRUCK	LOW LIFT PALLET TRUCK

The Material Handling Institute

ample of reducing terminal time to a minimum is utilization of an electromagnet on a crane to lift ferrous loads. The crane is tied up a negligible amount of time at the terminal points. Usually, some type of conveyor or mechanical fingers can be used to bring material to the work station and thus avoid or reduce the time spent in picking up the material. Often gravity conveyors, used in conjunction with automatic removal of finished parts, can be installed, thus minimizing material handling at the work station.

Several types of positioning equipment are available to reduce the time spent in handling material to and from the work station. Hydraulic tables that can place sheets of material at proper feeding height for shears, presses, brakes, and other machines, as well as transport, and bring to position dies and other heavy tools, often have application. The portable elevator or positioning truck is an elevating mechanism supported on a truck mast and base. The hoisting unit is either motorized or has a winch mechanism. Another well-known positioning aid is the welding positioner. Latest models provide for powered rotation and elevation of materials to permit downhand welding motions.

The Bethlehem Steel Company installed a strip-feeding table in their Lebanon, Pennsylvania, plant to position metal strip at the shear punch in their cold-rolled department,[2] with the expectation that the 24-foot table would pay for itself within four years. Again, the Erie Malleable Iron Company of Erie, Pennsylvania, by installation of a positioning table was able to reduce the man-minutes required to load a stack of annealing pots from 30 to 10.[3]

With regard to the time spent in picking up material the analyst should ask the following questions: "Can loose piling on the floor be avoided?" "Can material be weighed without picking it up?" and "Can a conveyor be used to avoid picking it up?"

Reduce material handling by using mechanical equipment

By mechanizing the handling of material, labor costs will usually be reduced, safety improved, fatigue alleviated, and production increased. However, care must be exercised on proper selection of equipment and methods. Standardization of equipment is important because operator training is simplified, interchangeability of equipment is provided, and less stocking of repair parts is needed.

The savings possible through mechanization of material handling equipment are typified by the following examples. One plant installed a monorail hoist over two workplaces and a paint basin. Formerly, 25 tons of tools in process were transported weekly by hand. The return of the monorail installation investment was estimated at 200 percent the first year. In another instance, a 100 percent investment return was realized by moving one heavy cutoff saw close to another cutoff saw, and then furnishing a jib crane to service the two saws.

At the onset of the IBM 360 program, several methods were considered to populate the panels with Solid Logic Technology circuit cards used in the computers manufactured at the Endicott Plant.

---

[2] "Handling Shorts," *Factory Management and Maintenance*, Plant Operation Library No. 134, *Better Material Handling, a $2-Billion Target.*

[3] Donald W. Pennock, "Positioners: for Better Handling at the Workplace," *Factory Management and Maintenance*, Plant Operation Library No. 134, *Better Material Handling, a $2-Billion Target.*

FIGURE 5–15

Typical handling equipment used in industry today

POWERIZED HAND LIFT TRUCK	TRACTOR — 4 Wheel	PORTABLE ELEVATOR	HIGH LIFT PLATFORM TRUCK
CHAIN TROLLEY	PORTABLE GOOSENECK CRANE	BRACKET JIB CRANE	MONORAIL ELECTRIC HOIST
CASTERS — Swivel Plate	ROLLER CONVEYOR	FORK TRUCK — Telescopic Type	AUTOMATIC GRABS
INDUSTRIAL CRANE TRUCK	TRAVELING CRANE	STRADDLE TRUCK	MOTOR TRUCK MOUNTED CRANE

The Material Handling Institute

The previous method (see Figure 5–16) had the circuit cards stored in containers on shelving units in a storage crib area. The operator would go to the storage crib, select the correct cards required for a specific panel based upon its "plug" list, return to his workbench, and then proceed to insert the circuit cards into the panel in accordance with the plug list.

The improved method resulted in the installation of two automated vertical storage machines (see Figures 5–17 and 5–18). Both of these storage machines were located in an area under one of the "sawtooth" sections of the building roof, which literally uses storage space above the

FIGURE 5–16

Previous method to populate computer panels with Solid Logic Technology Cards

1

2

3

4

normal ceiling height. Each automated vertical storage unit has 10 carriers with four pullout drawers per carrier; 20 stop positions were created so that two drawers are available at each stop position. The carriers move up and around in a system which is a compressed version of a Ferris wheel. With 20 possible stop positions on call, the unit always selects the closest route—either forward or backward—to bring the proper drawers to the opening in the shortest possible time.

FIGURE 5–17

Automated vertical storage machine used in conjunction with assembly of computer panels

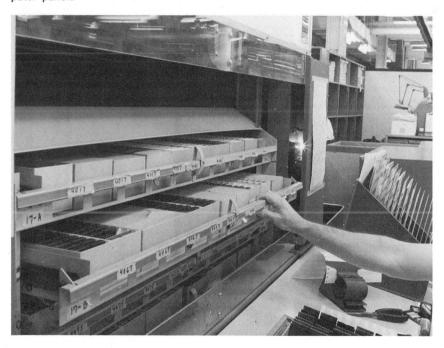

The assembly station is arranged at the opening level where an operator can select cards and place them in the proper position in the panel. From his seated position, the operator dials the correct stop; the drawer is pulled forward into a position exposing the needed cards and the proper card is withdrawn and placed in the panel as designated on the "plug" list.

The improved method has resulted in an approximately 50 percent reduction in storage area required in valuable manufacturing floor space, improved work station layout, and substantial reductions in populating errors attributable to minimizing operator handling, decision making, and fatigue.

FIGURE 5–18

Work area of vertical storage machine used in assembly of computer panels

In consideration of the possible advantages of using mechanical equipment, the following questions apply: "Can heavy material be handled easier with mechanical equipment?" "Can parts be handled quicker with mechanical equipment?" and "Can material be stacked higher mechanically?"

Make better use of existing handling facilities

To assume greatest return from material handling equipment, it must be used effectively. By palletizing material in temporary and permanent storage, greater quantities can be transported and can be transported faster than when stored without the use of pallets. The United Wallpaper, Inc., was able to realize the following gross direct labor savings through palletizing and mechanical material handling:

1. Reduced labor cost of warehousing finished stock 66 percent.
2. Reduced labor cost of assembling and shipping finished goods orders 30 to 65 percent.
3. Reduced labor cost of unloading and warehousing raw stock 80 percent.
4. Reduced labor cost of unloading and warehousing other raw materials 40 percent.[4]

Sometimes, it may be possible to design special racks so the material can be handled in larger or more convenient units. When this is done, the compartments, hooks, pins, or supports for holding the work should be in multiples of 10 for ease of count during processing and final inspection.

If any material handling equipment is used only a portion of the time, consider possibilities for putting it to use a greater share of the time. By relocating production facilities or adapting material handling equipment for diversified areas of work, greater utilization may be achieved.

Here the analyst should ask and answer the following questions: "Can the material be handled in larger or more convenient units?" "Can auxiliary handling equipment facilitate service at the work station?" and "Can piece counting be combined with material handling?"

Handle parts with greater care

Industrial surveys indicate that approximately 40 percent of plant accidents are a result of material handling operations. Of this, 25 percent are caused by lifting and shifting material. When care is exercised in handling material and when the physical effort of material handling is transferred to mechanical mechanisms, fatigue and accidents are reduced. Records prove that the safe factory is also an efficient factory. Although it is factual knowledge that the greater the amount of mechanized material handling, the safer the factory is, the analyst must consider the possibility of making the handling equipment safer, too. Safety guards at points of power transmission, safe operating practices, good lighting, and good housekeeping are essential to make material handling equipment safer.

It is often wise to consider the reduction of product damage by better handling. If the number of reject parts is at all significant in handling parts between work stations, then this area should be investigated. Usually, damage to parts in handling can be kept to a minimum if specially designed racks or trays are fabricated to hold the parts immediately after being processed. For example, one manufacturer of aircraft engine parts

---

[4] Philip F. Cannon, "Palletizing Makes New Warehousing System Really Work," *Factory Management and Maintenance,* Plant Operation Library No. 134.

incurred a sizable number of damaged external threads on one component that was stored in metal tote pans after completion of each operation. When the tote pans filled with parts were moved to the next work station by two-wheeled hand trucks, the machined forgings bumped against each other and the sides of the metal pan to such an extent that they became badly damaged. Someone investigated the cause of the rejects and suggested making wooden racks with individual compartments to support the machined forgings. This prevented the parts from bumping against one another and against the sides of the metal tote pan. Production runs were also more easily controlled in view of faster counting of parts and rejects.

Two typical questions that apply are: "Can the material be handled with greater safety?" and "Can product damage be reduced by better handling?"

Summary: material handling

The analyst should always be on the alert to eliminate inefficient handling of material. Harry E. Stocker covers the following principles that should be considered in doing a better job in materials handling:

1. Maximum economy is obtained in handling materials by reducing the terminal time of materials handling equipment to the minimum.
2. Economy in handling is obtained as the size of the handling unit is increased, whether this be the package prepared by the shipper or a handling unit made up at the terminal by the shipping company.
3. Economy in materials handling is determined by performance, which is measured by comparative expense per unit of material handled.
4. The determination of the best practice under particular conditions is necessary to maximum economy.
5. Economy is obtained when equipment and methods are replaced by new equipment and methods, if the expense of the replacement is exceeded by economies effected within a reasonable time.
6. Economy in materials handling is obtained by the use of equipment and methods that are capable of a variety of uses or applications.
7. Economy is obtained as the speed of the materials handling equipment is increased, provided the cost of the increased speed is exceeded by the savings effected.
8. Economy is obtained as the ratio of dead weight of equipment to load carried is reduced.
9. Productivity of equipment is increased by the provision of automatic couplers, nonfriction bearings, rubber tires, and other equipment details best suited to conditions.
10. The productivity of equipment is increased if repairs and replacements are anticipated.
11. Productivity is increased as safe working conditions are provided.

12. Economy in handling materials is obtained if they are moved in a straight line.
13. The productivity of men is increased as fatigue is reduced by provision of mechanical equipment and other aids to the reduction of fatigue.
14. The unit expense of handling materials decreases as the quantity to be handled increases.
15. The unit expense of material handling increases as the quantity to be transported exceeds the capacity of the plant.
16. Economy is obtained when materials are moved by gravity.[5]

It may be well to reiterate that the predominant principle to be kept in mind is that the less a material is manually handled, the better it is handled.

The following example applies several of the above-enumerated principles. In the Poughkeepsie, New York, Systems Manufacturing Division of IBM Corporation, data processing machines were moved from one assembly operation to the next on individual dollies. Subsequently, an operator-controlled conveyorized assembly system was introduced. Under the new installation, when an operator is ready to work on a unit, he actuates controls which transfer the unit from the main line to the spur. He then operates controls which transfer the unit from the spur to his work station. When the work is complete, the same controls operate in reverse to enable the operator to return the unit to the main line. (See Figures 5–19 and 5–20.)

This flexible, work station-controlled, conveyorized final assembly system has improved space use, reduced in-process inventory, and increased management control in the manufacture of punched card data processing machines.

PLANT LAYOUT

Good plant layout involves designing a plan to place the right equipment in a manner and location that will introduce maximum economy during manufacturing processing.

Although it is difficult and costly to make changes in arrangements that already exist, the methods analyst should be trained to review with a critical eye every portion of every layout that he comes in contact with. Poor plant layouts result in major costs. Unfortunately, most of these costs are hidden and, consequently, cannot be readily exposed. Indirect labor expense of long moves, backtracking, delays, and work stoppage due to bottlenecks are characteristic of a plant that has an antiquated plant layout.

[5] Harry E. Stocker, *Materials Handling* (2nd ed.; Englewood Cliffs, N.J.: Prentice-Hall, Inc., 1951).

FIGURE 5–19

Conveyorized final assembly of data processing machines

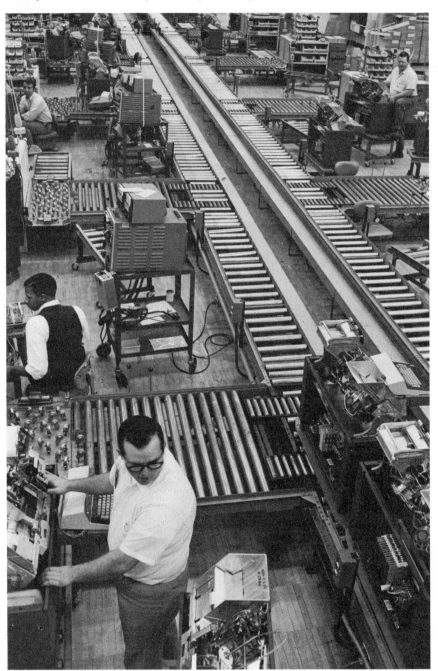

IBM

FIGURE 5–20

Individual work center typical of final assembly area

IBM

Layout types

In general, all plant layouts represent one or a combination of two basic types of layout. These are product or straight-line layouts and process or functional arrangements. In the straight-line layout, the machinery is located so the flow from one operation to the next is minimized for any product class. Thus, in an organization that utilizes this technique, it would not be unusual to see a surface grinder located between a milling machine and a turret lathe with an assembly bench and plating tanks in the immediate area. This type of layout for certain mass-production manufacture is quite popular because material handling costs are lower than when process grouping of facilities is practiced.

There are some distinct disadvantages of product grouping that should be kept in mind before making any major change in plant layout. Since a broad variety of occupations are represented in a small area, employee discontent can readily be fostered. This is especially true when the different opportunities carry a significant money rate differential. Because unlike facilities are grouped together, operator training becomes more cumbersome since no experienced employee on a given facility may be located in the immediate area to train the new man. The problem of finding competent supervisors is also enhanced, due to the variety of facilities and jobs that must be supervised. Then, too, this type of layout invariably necessitates greater initial investment in view of duplicate service lines required, such as air, water, gas, oil, and power. Another disadvantage of product grouping that can result in indirect costs is the fact that this arrangement of facilities tends to give the casual observer the thought that disorder and chaos prevail. With these conditions, it is often difficult to promote good housekeeping.

In general, the disadvantages of product grouping are more than offset by the advantages if production requirements are substantial.

Process or functional layout is the grouping of similar facilities. Thus, all turret lathes will be grouped in one section, department, or building. Milling machines, drill presses, and punch presses would also be grouped in their respective sections.

This type of arangement gives a general appearance of neatness and orderliness, and tends to promote good housekeeping. Another advantage of functional layout is the ease with which a new man can be trained. Since he is surrounded by experienced men operating similar machines, he has the opportunity to learn from them. The problem of finding competent supervisors is lessened because the job demands are not as great with this type of grouping. Since a man need be familiar with but one general type or class of facilities, his background does not have to be as extensive as that of supervisors in shops using product grouping.

Of course, the obvious disadvantage of process grouping is the chance for long moves and backtracking on jobs that require a series of operations on diversified machines. For example, if the operation card of a job specified a sequence of drill, turn, mill, ream, and grind, the movement of the material from one section to the next could prove extremely costly. Another major disadvantage of process grouping is the great volume of paper work required to issue orders and control production between sections.

Usually, if production quantities of similar products are limited and the plant is "job" or special order in form, then a process type of layout will be more satisfactory.

No two plants have completely identical layouts, even though the nature of their operations is similar. Many times, a combination of process grouping and product grouping is in order. Regardless of what type of grouping is contemplated, the analyst should consider the following principal points for layout improvement:

1. For straight-line mass production—material laid aside should be in position for the next operation.
2. For diversified production—the layout should permit short moves and deliveries, and the material should be convenient to the operator.
3. For multiple-machine operations—equipment should be grouped around the operator.
4. For efficient stacking—storage areas should be arranged to minimize searching and rehandling.
5. For better worker efficiency—service centers should be located close to production areas.

Making the layout

Before a new layout can be designed or an old one corrected, the methods analyst will have to accumulate all facts that directly and indirectly influence the layout. These will include many, if not all, of the following:

1. Present and anticipated sales volume of each product, line or class.
2. Labor content of each operation on each product.
3. Complete inventory of existing machines and material handling equipment.
4. Status of existing facilities from the standpoint of condition and book value.
5. Possible changes in product design.
6. Drawings of existing plant indicating location of all service facilities, windows, doors, columns, and reinforced areas.

Once all of these facts are gathered, the analyst should then construct a flow process chart (see Chapter 3), which in itself gives the general form the layout will take. In the construction of the flow chart, suggestions should be encouraged from operators, inspectors, material handlers, and line supervisors. These men are closer to the production work than anyone else, and they will often provide valuable suggestions. Then, too, if they are brought into the picture at an early stage, they will be a lot more enthusiastic when the revised layout is actually introduced.

In making the proposed layout, templates must be prepared of all facilities. There are several possibilities in constructing templates usually constructed to a scale of $\frac{1}{4}$ inch equals 1 foot, unless the size of the project is quite large, when a scale of $\frac{1}{8}$ inch equals 1 foot may be used. If an existing layout is available, a blueprint can be made of it and all facilities can be cut out of the print for use as templates. If no layout exists, two-dimensional templates can be purchased in printed form, as

FIGURE 5–21

Standard templates of representative machine tools

illustrated in Figure 5–21. Of course, the analyst can draw his own templates on a good grade of stiff cardboard and cut them out. The advantages of using stiff cardboard are apparent if the same templates are to be used several times.

The American Society of Mechanical Engineers has recommended the adoption of national standards on plant layout templates and models. These recommendations are stated here:

PART I. TEMPLATES

1) *Scale.* All template shall be drawn to a scale of ¼″ equal to 12″ of full scale or ¼″ equal to 1 ft., U.S. measure. All dimensions shall be shown in feet and inches.

2) *General Outline.* Outline of the equipment in heavy line indicating the contour as it would be described on the floor if a plumb line held at a height of 7 ft. above the floor were to be followed around the periphery of the equipment and touching every extremity point when making a complete circle of the

equipment, except for wheels or handles, etc., which should be indicated as a detail. (See recommended lines below.)

———————— *Thick* ————————	Fixed outline of machine tool or equipment from floor level to 7'–0" elevation above floor level
———————— *Thin* ————————	Detail parts and substructures
— — — — *Thick Dash* — — — —	Clearances for moving parts of machine tools or equipment
———·———·———·———·———·— *Medium Dot and Dash*	Overhead or underground elements—foundations, pits, service clearances and other elements important to the template
———————— *Thin Center Line* ————————	Center lines

3) *Detail.* Particularly on machine tools and mechanical equipment, center lines, loading points, control points, and operating points should be indicated using a lighter line than used for the machine outline. Enough detail of plan view features should be included within the outline of the template to make it clearly distinguishable and important points easily located.

4) *Clearance.* All clearance lines including movable parts, service access points and clearances required for feeding or operating should be shown in broken dash lines. Space allowed for material storage and other purposes, not required specifically for the equipment installation, service or operation *should not be* included in the template.

5) *Interferences.* Parts or structures above the 7 ft. height, or foundations or substructures below floor level, should also be indicated. These are usually of importance to the installation or operation of the machine or might serve as obstructions. It is usually required that they be shown on final drawings. These features should be drawn in light broken lines of a different character than clearance lines.

6) *Data.* On templates of equipment with top surface of varying height, the point of maximum height should be indicated on the templates with a suitable symbol. The over-all length, width, and height, including machine travel clearances, but not including operating or feeding clearances, also weight and horsepower, should be specified on or adjacent to the template.

7) *Identification.* Space should be provided on the template to specify the name, style or model, size, and user's identifying number.

8) *Miscellaneous.* Indication of controls, service facilities, connection points, or conduit or pipe risers, operator's position, and any other special feature should also be included on the template or included in the data. The operator's position should be indicated by a heavy arrow (——→).

9) *Printing.* Templates should be printed on both white and colored stock of at least 110 lb. weight, index bristol or equivalent. Various classes of equipment should be printed with black ink on stock of distinctive colors to permit ease of perception. Colors for colored stock templates are:

Class	*Color*
Machine tools, mechanical equipment, and similar devices..............	Salmon
Office equipment; stationary equipment, such as benches, bins, racks, lockers; service facilities, such as lavatories, toilets, etc..............	Green
Material handling equipment......................................	Yellow
Space occupying portable auxiliaries used for material handling or temporary storage (such as skids, tote pans, pallets, trays, etc.)...........	Red

Part II. Models

10) *Scale.* All models shall be made to a scale of ¼ in. equal to 12 in. of full scale or ¼ in. equal to 1 ft., U.S. measure.

11) *Detail.* The amount of detail to be designed into the model shall be governed by its utilitarian value. Sufficient detail as to form, shape, contours, special design features, etc., should appear to make the model readily distinguishable as representative of the actual equipment. Unless no other means of detailing are possible, no moving parts should be designed into the model. All points of control should be clearly indicated. Hazard areas should be clearly indicated. All normally moving parts should be shown in mid-point or neutral positions. Models should in no way be distorted from actual appearance of the equipment represented.

12) *Finishes.* All models prepared for distribution commercially shall be finished with materials and in colors, duplicating as nearly as practical the finishes most frequently used in the object represented. Where there is a multiplicity of finishes normally used, models can be finished correspondingly. (Example, office furniture.) In the case of machine tools, the manufacturer's standard should be followed insofar as practical or the recommendations of the Machine Tool Builders Association.

In the case of equipment having machined surfaces, these can be indicated with aluminum paint.

Control points can be indicated by application of light-buff paint as recommended for two-tone painting of equipment for better visibility and safety.

Where models are made and/or used exclusively by one company or client, their particular practice should be followed.

13) *Allowances and Clearances.* No dimensions should be exaggerated in the model to allow for clearances. With each three-dimensional model shall be provided a two-dimensional template showing all clearances required under extreme operating and service conditions of the machine proper. The template shall not show requirements of operator, materials, auxiliaries not fixed to the machine, or other conditions not required in the basic machine or equipment. The template shall be imprinted with all pertinent information required by the planning engineer and shall include or provide for at least the following information: Name or description, model number, type, size, owner's identification number, maximum clearance dimensions (length, width, height), center lines and weight. Where the template is too small practically to contain all the foregoing information, the name and model number only shall be provided. Where possible, data on overhead or underground requirements should be shown.

Note: See Part I (of the Standard) covering plant layout templates.

14) *Materials and Construction.* Models shall be made of any suitable material that will permit normal handling without distortion or damage to finish. It should resist fracture or spalling when coming in contact with other models or materials in general. It should resist breakage or distortion when dropped from a height of 2 ft. onto a solid hard surface. Models should have sufficient weight and balance to remain in position when normally arranged and subject to slight jarring or vibrations. The base of the model should be so designed as to permit it to remain in a position once placed or to be fitted with pins to permit fastening in position. These are to be optional with the user.

Where pins are used, the template should be pierced with holes to allow the model to become accurately located in relation to the template, and the entire assembly held in position on board by the pins fitted to the model base.

15) *Identification.* Models shall bear the name and/or trade-mark of the equipment represented. The model number or size description should also be included, if possible. Abbreviations or initials should be used where practical. The markings should be made in the most suitable place, rather than attempting to place them in the same position as on the actual equipment.

16) *General.* Models shall be so designed and constructed to permit them to be used in conjunction with standard templates designed to represent the same identical items of equipment.[6]

Establishing the above standards should prove quite helpful to plant layout and methods engineers by eliminating misunderstandings and consequent errors that have developed in the past through misinterpretation of varying techniques of plant layout templates and models.

Scale models give the third dimension to plant layouts, and are especially helpful to the analyst when he is endeavoring to sell his contemplated layout to a top executive who has neither the time nor the familiarity to grasp all details of the layout when it has been constructed on a two-dimensional basis. (See Figure 5–22.)

Once all necessary templates have been made, a trial layout can be prepared. By giving consideration to the principal points for efficient layout and by providing adequate output capacity at each work station without introducing bottlenecks and interrupting the flow of production, good layouts will be evolved.

After an ideal layout has been designed, it is well to construct a flow chart of the proposed plan so reduction of distances traveled, storages, delays, and overall savings will be highlighted. This will greatly facilitate final approval of the design. A good technique for testing the layout is to wind colored thread around the map tacks holding down the templates, and with the thread follow the flow of the product from its raw material components to its transformation into a finished product. By using a different colored thread for every line of product produced, the

---

[6] Extracted from *ASME Plant Layout Templates and Models, 1949, Standard,* with permission of the publisher, the American Society of Mechanical Engineers, 29 West 38th St., New York, N.Y.

FIGURE 5-22

Three-dimensional layout of a portion of a large industrial plant

Aluminum Co. of America

flow of all work can be visualized quite rapidly. This pictorial presentation, supplemented with the flow chart, will bring to light most flaws of the proposed method.

Making the floor plan

After the layout has been approved, it is converted in final detail on plant layout drawings prior to going ahead with the physical move. No standards have been accepted on either a national or an industrial basis as to just what information should be included on the layout drawing. Too much detail will obviously confuse the interpreters; too little detail is ever worse because many questions that come up will be unanswered. Randolph W. Mallick and Armand T. Gaudreau have summarized 14 items that every layout drawing should include; they are as follows:

1. Title and scale of the drawing.
2. Sketch number.
3. Approval space.
4. Detail notations for use of plant engineer.
5. Construction notations for architects and detail engineers.
6. Notations on heating, lighting, ventilation, and communication facilities.

7. Directional locations and orientation on plant site.
8. Transportation and handling facilities.
9. Overhead obstructions, and obstructions below floor levels where foundations or superstructures are necessary.
10. Machine-tool and equipment identification number.
11. Column numbers.
12. Service outlets for gas, electricity, water, air, and other utilities.
13. Fire protection and other safety apparatus notes.
14. Signature and date.[7]

If all these items are included on the plant layout drawing, it can be used with assurance for installing machinery and equipment.

Photographic copies are frequently substituted for drawings in reproducing template layouts. This method saves the laborious scaling and detailed drawing of machinery and other facilities. One company[8] uses flexible, plastic templates, which are colored, translucent, and matte-finished and their layout sheets are flexible, matte-finished, clear plastic. Templates are made with a photosensitive matte film, thus allowing one drawing of a facility to serve as a master to reproduce templates for all identical equipment. Once the layout is completed, a transparency is made directly from the layout by running it through a standard printing machine.

Frequently, the analyst is called upon to consider the desirability of new plant location, in addition to the layout of an existing plant. At times, the opening of a plant in a new environment will prove advantageous to the expansion of the existing facility or even to the keeping of it in operation. When the problem of plant location is considered, the analyst must make the same thorough gathering of facts and analyses that is required in plant layout. Of course, different tangible and intangible factors will apply.

A technique frequently used is to tabularize all the factors of importance in evaluating possible geographic locations. Such factors as labor cost, transportation costs (inbound materials and outbound products), utility costs, state taxes, insurance, workmen's compensation, real estate taxes, fuel for heating costs, and personal property taxes, are some of the more obvious considerations. Each factor is given a rating (for example: A, B, C, D, E, F) for each geographic location. Thus, a profile is established for each proposed site. These profiles are carefully compared and the site having the most favorable profile is given careful consideration in choosing the location of the new facility. Figure 5–23 illustrates a profile for an industrial complex in an eastern city.

---

[7] Randolph W. Mallick and Armand T. Gaudreau, *Plant Layout Planning and Practice* (New York: John Wiley & Sons, Inc., 1951), p. 110.

[8] G. L. Thuering, "How to Get Faster, Better, Less Expensive Plant Layout Drawings Without Drafting," *Factory Management and Maintenance*, Vol. 110, No. 10.

FIGURE 5–23

Profile of a light manufacturing company in a Pennsylvania city

PLANT LOCATION

Application of a systematic method of determining a geographic location for an industrial complex.

The procedure is to provide a basis for comparing alternate locations, and ranking them in order of preference based on predetermined criteria.

TANGIBLE AND INTANGIBLE FACTORS OF IMPORTANCE IN EVALUATING GEOGRAPHICAL LOCATIONS

No.	Factor	A Excellent	B Very Good	C Good	D Fair	E Poor	F Intolerable
1.	Nearness of raw materials						
2.	Nearness to markets						
3.	Availability of capital						
4.	Availability of land, or rentable space						
5.	Topography--effect on buildings, access						
6.	Climatic conditions						
7.	Cost of land or rentable space						
8.	Local construction costs						
9.	Nearness to related industries						
10.	Type of supporting industry within area						
11.	Population density of area						
12.	Availability of labor						
13.	Cost of labor						
14.	Stability and influence of labor union						
15.	Concept of productivity as evidenced by other industries in the area						
16.	Nearness of trade schools and technical institutes						
17.	Percentage of population in area having high school education						
18.	Availability of a university to furnish research facilities and consulting						
19.	Availability of a university so that personnel can do graduate work						
20.	Nearness of communication services, including airports, railroads, highways, buses						
21.	Availability of water supply--in and out						
22.	Cost of water supply						
23.	Availability of sewer facilities						
24.	Cost of sewer and services						
25.	Availability of electric power						
26.	Cost of electric power						
27.	Availability of freight-handling facilities-- railroads, highways, rivers, airports						
28.	Cost of freight-handling facilities-- railroads, highways, rivers, airports						
29.	Availability of banking facilities						
30.	Community inducements-free taxes, free land						
31.	Government restrictions-air pollution, water						
32.	Attitudes of community relative to new industry entering the area						
33.	Living conditions-cost of living, housing						
34.	Community conditions-schools, churches, play areas						
35.	Rating of high schools						
36.	Recreational opportunities-theaters, parks, golf						
37.	Historic characteristics of area						
38.	Local, county, and state taxes						

Summary: plant layout

Possibilities for plant layout improvement are most likely to be uncovered if they are looked for systematically. Work stations and machines should be arranged to permit the most efficient processing of a product with a minimum of handling. Do not make a change in layout until a careful study of all factors involved has been made. The methods analyst should learn to recognize poor layout and present the facts to the plant engineer for his consideration.

PRINCIPLES OF MOTION ECONOMY

The last of the 10 primary approaches to operation analysis has to do with improving the arrangement of parts at the workplace and of the motions required to perform the task. In Chapter 7, considerable detail is given to the laws of motion economy. At this point, consideration will be given only to investigation of motion economy as practiced by the methods analyst. When studying work performed at a work station, the analyst should ask: "Are both hands working at the same time and in opposite symmetrical directions?" "Is each hand going through as few motions as possible?" "Is the workplace arranged so long reaches are avoided?" and "Are both hands being used effectively and not being used as a holding device?"

If the answer to any of the above questions is no, then there are opportunities for improvment of the work station.

Both hands should work at the same time

The left hand, in right-handed people, can be used just as effectively as the right hand and should be given just as much consideration for use. It is common knowledge that a boxer learns to jab more effectively with his left than with his right hand. A stenographer will be just as proficient with one hand as the other. In a large number of instances, work stations can be designed to do "two at a time." This is a good slogan for the methods analyst to keep in mind. By providing dual fixtures to hold two components, it is often possible to have both hands working at the same time and making symmetrical moves in opposite directions. (See Figure 5–24.)

For example, a production increase of 100 percent was made possible by developing a fixture that utilized two-handed operation and permitted grinding two motor brushes at a time. The old method involved a one-handed operation, for only one piece was done during each grinding cycle.

Each hand should go through as few motions as possible

It is just common sense that the more motions the hands make while performing a task, the longer it will take to do the work. All hand motions are a series of reaches, moves, grasps, positions, and releases, and the

FIGURE 5–24

Work station and fixture designed to allow productive work with both hands

General Electric Co.

more of these fundamental motions that can be eliminated or reduced, the more satisfactory will be the work station.

For example, by providing drop delivery and gravity chutes, it is possible to eliminate certain moves and positions and reduce release time. Likewise, installation of a belt conveyor to bring material to the work station and carry away the processed part will usually result in reduced "move" time. Position is usually a time-consuming basic division of accomplishment that in many instances can be minimized through well-designed fixtures. By using tapered channels and pilots, two mating parts can readily be assembled with considerable reduction or elimination of the positioning element.

The workplace should be arranged to avoid long reaches

The time required to pick up an article depends to a great extent on the distance the hand must move. Likewise, move time is definitely related to distance. If at all posible, the workplace should be arranged so all parts are in easy reach of the operator. If all components can be reached while both elbows are close to the body, then the work will be performed in the "normal" working area. This normal area represents the space within which work can be accomplished in a minimum time.

The work, tools, and parts should not be located beyond the reach of the hand when the arms are fully extended. The area encompassed with the arms fully extended in both the horizontal and vertical planes represents the maximum working area, and the analyst should be on the alert for work stations that demand work to be performed beyond this area.

Avoid using hand as a holding device

If either hand is ever used as a holding device during the processing cycle of a part, then useful work is not being performed by that hand.

FIGURE 5–25

Ideal assembly work station with all components arranged to avoid long reaches and moves

Alden Systems Co.

Invariably, a fixture can be designed to hold the work satisfactorily, thus allowing both hands to do useful work. Many times foot-operated mechanisms can be introduced which permit utilizing both hands for productive work. The therblig, "hold," represents an ineffective basic division of accomplishment and should be eliminated, if practically possible, from all work stations.

Summary: principles of motion economy

It is not necessary for the methods analyst to make a frame-by-frame analysis, characteristic of the micromotion procedure, to analyze a work station from the standpoint of applying principles of motion economy. He will be able to introduce many improvements by carefully watching the operator perform at the work station and subjecting each phase of the operator's work cycle to the questions related to motion economy. These principles should be kept in mind when "tooling up" any new job. If this is done, the work station will inevitably be quite proficient, and the necessity of restudying to effect improvements will be diminished.

Summary: 10 primary approaches to operation analysis

The 10 primary approaches to operation analysis represent a systematic approach to analyzing the facts presented on the operation and flow process chart. To visualize how the various steps in methods engineering are integrated, a general flow of the entire analysis is illustrated in Figure 5–26. Other tools of analysis used in developing a method include the man and machine process chart, the operator process chart and micromotion study. These subjects will be discussed in subsequent chapters.

Regardless of the nature of the work, whether continuous or intermittent, process or job shop, soft or hard goods, when systematic operation analysis is applied by competent personnel, real savings will result. It must be remembered that these principles are just as applicable in planning new work as in improving work already in production.

Increased output is the primary outcome of operation analysis, but it also distributes the benefits of improved production to all workers and helps develop better working conditions and methods, so the worker can do more work at the plant, do a good job, and still have energy to enjoy life.

A representative case history, which follows the method of analysis referred to, was that of the production of an Auto-Starter, a device for starting AC motors by reducing the voltage through a transformer. A subassembly of the Auto-Starter is the Arc Box. This part sits in the bottom of the Auto-Starter and acts as a barrier between the contacts so

FIGURE 5-26

The principal steps in a methods engineering program

SYSTEMATIC PROCEDURE FOR METHODS AND WORK MEASUREMENT

SELECTION OF PROJECT

NEW PLANTS & PLANT EXPANSION
NEW PRODUCTS
PRODUCTS WITH HIGH COST-LOW PROFIT
PRODUCTS UNABLE TO MEET COMPETITION
MANUFACTURING DIFFICULTIES
APPLICATION OF NEW METHODS

GATHER & PRESENT DATA

OBTAIN PRODUCTION REQUIREMENTS
PROCURE ENGINEERING DATA
PROCURE MANUFACTURING & COST DATA
DESCRIPTION AND SKETCHES OF WORK STATION & TOOLS
CONSTRUCT OPERATION PROCESS CHARTS
CONSTRUCT FLOW PROCESS CHART FOR INDIVIDUAL ITEMS

ANALYZE

USE TEN PRIMARY APPROACHES
TO OPERATION ANALYSIS
QUESTION EVERY DETAIL
USE: WHY, WHERE, WHAT, WHO,
WHEN, HOW

DEVELOP IDEAL WORK CENTER

MAN AND MACHINE PROCESS CHARTS
OPERATOR PROCESS CHARTS
MATHEMATICAL MODELS
ELIMINATE UNNECESSARY DETAILS
COMBINE DETAILS WHEN PRACTICAL
SIMPLIFY NECESSARY DETAILS
REARRANGE FOR BETTER SEQUENCE

PRESENT & SELL METHOD

WRITTEN PRESENTATION
FLOW PROCESS CHART OF PROPOSED METHOD
ORAL PRESENTATION
SELL METHOD TO OPERATOR, FOREMAN, AND
MANAGEMENT

INSTALL THE WORK CENTER

PUT METHOD TO WORK
WORK THROUGH CHANNELS
ESTABLISH SCHEDULES
KEEP EVERYONE SOLD
GIVE CREDIT WHERE CREDIT IS DUE

ESTABLISH JOB ANALYSIS & TIME STANDARDS

JOB DESCRIPTIONS
STOP WATCH TIME STUDY
STANDARD DATA
FORMULAS
FUNDAMENTAL MOTION DATA

FOLLOW UP THE METHOD

VERIFY SAVINGS
ASSURE INSTALLATION IS CORRECT
KEEP EVERYONE SOLD

there will be no short circuits. The present design consists of the following components:

> Asbestos barriers with three drilled holes.............. 6
> Spacers of insulating tubing 2″ long.................. 15
> Steel rods threaded at both ends.................... 3
> Pieces of hardware................................ 18
> Pieces Total..................................... 42

In assembling these components the operator places a washer, lock washer, and nut on one end of each rod. The rods are then inserted through the three holes in the first barrier. Then one spacer is placed on each of the rods (three in all), and another barrier added. This is repeated until six barriers are on the rods and separated by the tubing.

It was suggested that the six barriers be made with two slots—one at each end—and that two strips of asbestos for supporting the barriers be made with six slots in each.

These would be slipped together and placed in the bottom of the Auto-Starter as needed. The manner of assembly would be the same as that used in putting together the separator in an egg box.

A total of 15 suggested improvements occurred after the analysis was completed, with the following results:

Old method	New method	Savings
42 parts...............	8	34
10 work stations........	1	9
18 transportations.......	7	11
7,900 feet of travel.......	200	7,700
9 storages..............	4	5
0.45 hours time.........	0.11 hours time	0.34 hours
$1.55 costs.............	$0.60	$0.95

A program of operation analysis resulted in a 17,496-ton annual saving for one Ohio company. By forming a mill section into a ring and welding it, an original rough-forged ring weighing 2,198 pounds was replaced. The new mill section blank weighed but 740 pounds. The saving of 1,458 pounds of high-grade steel, amounting to twice the weight of the finished piece, was brought about by the simple procedure of reducing the excess material that had been cut away in chips.

An analytical laboratory in a New Jersey plant has applied the principles of operation analysis with gratifying results. New workbenches have been laid out in the form of a cross so each chemist has an L-shaped worktable. This arrangement allows the chemist to reach any part of his work station by taking but one stride.

The new workbench has consolidated equipment, thus saving space and duplication of facilities. One glassware cabinet services two chemists. A large four-place fume head allows multiple activity in this area that formerly was a bottleneck. All utility outlets are relocated for maximum efficiency.

A state government activity, in an effort to streamline its organization, developed a program of operation analysis that resulted in an estimated annual savings of more than 50,000 hours. This was brought about by combining, eliminating and redesigning all paper work activities, improving the plant layout, and developing paths of authority.

Application of method improvement is equally as effective in office procedures as in production operations. One industrial engineering department of a Pennsylvania company[9] was given the problem of simplifying the paper work necessary for shipping molded parts manufactured in one of their plants to an outlying plant for assembly. A new method was developed that reduced the average daily shipment of 45 orders from 552 sheets of paper forms to 50 sheets. The annual savings in paper alone brought about by this change was $366.60.

Methods improvement can and should be a continuing program. For example, in the early 1940's the average savings in the Procter & Gamble Company per member of management was approximately only $500. In order to improve the situation and to maintain the acceptable level of cost reduction, a methods program was inaugurated, giving manufacturing management appreciation sessions in the concepts of operation analysis. Also, a special course was conducted for methods engineers, men who were college graduates with one to five years of company experience. After completion of the operation analysis course, these men returned to their respective plants to work as methods specialists. The effect of this training was apparent in a very short time. Annual savings increased to approximately $700 per year per member of factory management. Since the program was a success, additional personnel were similarly trained and the program was extended to more plants.

By 1950, the position of the industrial engineer had changed from method specialist to method coordinator. It had been the practice for the engineer to suggest method improvements to the line foreman. Since it was only natural for the foreman to take the suggested changes as criticism, frequently he did not actively participate.

Functioning as a method coordinator, the engineer spent approximately two thirds of his time helping the factory supervisors on their projects, and the other third of his time working individually on special

---

[9] From a talk by Lynell Cooper, Manufacturing Engineer of Westinghouse Electric Corporation, to the central Pennsylvania chapter of the Society for Advancement of Management.

factory projects. Each member of plant management was assigned several selected projects where the cost was to be reduced, and each was encouraged to solicit assistance as required from the methods engineer.

The methods coordinator also periodically conducted training courses at his plant both for other staff members and for members of the line organization. With the active participation of plant management, the rate of savings had increased to $2,300 per year per member of factory management by 1950.

Subsequently, teams of four to eight men, made up equally of line foremen and staff were formed to work on selected projects having a high potential savings. More enthusiasm on the part of management resulted. Opportunities for recognition of good work were increased. There was a friendly rivalry for first place in plant standing between teams. Display boards were set up in the front office to show team standings. Factory goals for cost reduction were established. By 1954, companywide savings amounted to approximately $4,000 per member of management.

These results convinced top management that the cost reduction or profit improvement program should be plantwide and that all costs should be challenged. Consequently, the program was extended to all plants, and a summary sheet showing comparison of results of the program in each plant was circulated, which further stimulated the desire of individual plants to make a good showing.

The Director of Industrial Engineering for Procter & Gamble made the following statement concerning the program:

Early in the program, plants tended to think that they had "skimmed the cream." The easy projects had all been picked off. Next year would be harder, they thought; consequently a lower goal was in order. We had to sell some people on the reasonableness of a higher goal each year.

Higher goals were reasonable because of increased experience at cost reduction. The growth in business was another factor. Getting the less active team members to do more offered real potential for increased savings.

Although we had concluded that the goal setting process should be democratic, some guides were useful. The teams were encouraged to compare themselves with others on a dollars-saved-per-member-of-management basis. Comparisons were also made in terms of goal as a per cent of operating expense and as a per cent of production value. The desire of plant management groups to show up well in all-plant comparisons was a strong factor in motivating teams to choose goals which required their best efforts for attainment.

The annual savings continued to increase each year, and by 1970 they amounted to $27,000 per member of management. This is conservative in that no credit is given for savings which continue beyond the first year. See Figure 5–27.

FIGURE 5–27

Progressive annual savings per member of management resulting from methods engineering in the Procter & Gamble Company

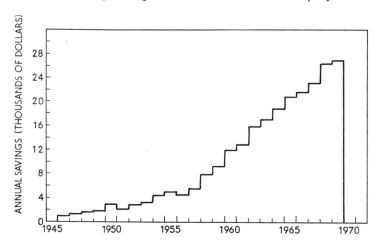

TEXT QUESTIONS

1. Can nickel be spot welded to lead? To Monel? To zinc?
2. In what four ways should investigation be made to improve process of $p\,83$ manufacture?
3. Explain how rearranging operations can result in savings.
4. What process is usually considered the fastest for forming and sizing operations? *Press operation (dies, stamped pieces)*
5. How should the analyst investigate the setup and tools to develop better $p\,88$ methods?
6. Why should the methods analyst accept as part of his responsibility the $p\,97$ provision of good working conditions?
7. Give the requisites of effective guarding. *P 103*
8. What are the two general types of plant layout? Explain each in detail. *P121*
9. To what scale are templates usually constructed? $\frac{1}{4}'' = 1'$ or $\frac{1}{8}'' = 1'$
10. What is the best way to test a proposed layout? *p127*
11. What questions should the analyst ask himself when studying work per- *p131* formed at a work station?
12. For what purpose is operation analysis used?
13. Explain the advantage of using a checklist.
14. What are the primary approaches to operation analysis? *P 134*
15. On what does the extent of tooling depend? *Amount of production*
17. Do working conditions appreciably affect output? Explain. *Yes*

16. How can planning and production control affect setup time?

18. How can you best handle a material? *mechanically*
19. Explain the effect of humidity on the operator. *burns wirn out*
20. What are some of the physical effects on the workmen when exposed to intermittent noise?
21. What is meant by work physiology?
22. What are the main factors to be considered in plant relocation?
23. Explain the meaning of the term footlambert.   *light*
24. In a certain work center the reflectance was considered to be approximately 50 percent and the category of seeing was estimated to be "ordinary." What footcandle intensity range would you recommend?
25. What colors would you advocate in a work center in order to increase the reflectance factor?
26. In your company's planing mill it is found that for periods up to four hours per day sound levels of 100 dBA are recorded. What recommendations would you make?

GENERAL QUESTIONS

1. Where would you find application for a hydraulic elevating table?
2. What is the difference between a skid and a pallet?
3. Explain the significance of the colored code for stock templates.
4. When would you recommend using three-dimensional models in layout work?
5. What is the general flow of analysis procedure when applied to a product that has never been manufactured?
6. In a process like operation analysis is it necessary to determine the point of diminishing returns? Why?
7. Select five work stations and measure the footcandle intensity at these stations. How do these values compare with recommended practice?

CHAPTER 6

Man and machine relationships

Once an operation has been found necessary through analysis of the operation and flow process chart, it may frequently be improved through further analysis. The three process charts discussed in this chapter are helpful tools for development of the ideal method. While the operation and flow process charts present facts and are used as tools of analysis, the man and machine process chart, gang process chart, and operator process chart are tools used to assist in the development of the ideal work center.

Man and machine process charts

While the operation and flow process charts are used primarily to explore a complete process or series of operations, the man and machine process chart is used to study, analyze, and improve but one work station at a time. This chart shows the exact relationship in time between the working cycle of the man and the operating cycle of his machine. With these facts clearly presented, possibilities for a fuller utilization of both man and machine time and better balance of work cycle exist.

Today, many of our machine tools are either completely automatic, such as the automatic screw machine, or are partially automatic, such as the turret lathe. In the operation of these types of facilities, the operator is often idle a portion of the cycle. The utilization of this idle time can increase operator earnings and improve production efficiency.

The practice of having one employee operate more than one machine is known as "machine coupling." Machine coupling is not new. One plant, during the depression of the middle 1930's, was unable to justify the amount of incentive earnings being turned in by the second shift in one of the machining departments. Investigation revealed that the operators were practicing machine coupling on their own initiative.

Today, some industries have encountered resistance from organized labor to the practice of machine coupling. The idea of "one operator for each machine" is to some extent a holdover from early World War II days when an acute scarcity of machine tools existed. At that time, it was essential that each machine tool be run to its full capacity every shift each day of the week. To accomplish this, one operator per machine was the logical answer.

The best way to sell machine coupling is to demonstrate the opportunity for added earnings. Since machine coupling will increase the percentage of "effort" time during the operating cycle, the opportunity for greater incentive earnings is enhanced. Also, higher base rates will result when machine coupling is practiced since the operator will have greater responsibility in operating more than one machine and he will exercise more mental and physical effort under multiple-machine operation.

Construction of the man and machine process chart

In the construction of the man and machine process chart, the analyst should first identify the chart in the usual fashion by indicating at the top of the sheet "Man and Machine Process Chart." Immediately below this heading, the following information should be included: part number, drawing number, description of operation being charted, present or proposed method, date, and name of person doing the charting.

Since man and machine charts are always drawn to scale, the analyst should next select a distance in inches to conform with a unit of time so that his chart can be neatly arranged on his paper. The longer the cycle time of the operation being charted, the shorter the distance will be per decimal minute of time. Once exact values have been established for distance in inches per unit of time, the analyst can begin his charting. On the left-hand side of the paper, the operations and time for the man are shown, and to the right of the man time is shown graphically the working and idle time of the machine or machines as the case may be. Working time on the part of the man is represented by a solid line drawn vertically. A break in the vertical man-time line signifies idle time. Likewise, a solid vertical line under each machine heading indicates machine operating time, and a break in the vertical machine line designates idle machine time. Loading and unloading machine time is shown by a dotted line under the machine column, indicating that the machine is neither idle nor is production work being accomplished at the moment (see Figure 6–1).

All elements of occupied and idle time for both the man and the machine he operates are charted until the termination of the cycle. At the foot of the chart is shown the total working time of the man plus his total idle time. Likewise, the total working time of each machine plus each

FIGURE 6–1

Man and machine process chart for milling machine operation

FIGURE 6–2

Man and machine process chart of thread-grinding operation with one man operating one machine

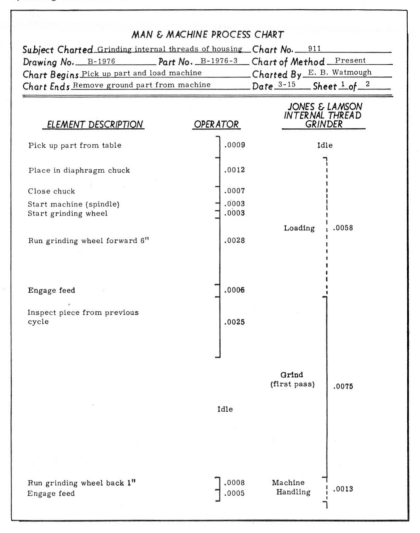

MAN & MACHINE PROCESS CHART

Subject Charted Grinding internal threads of housing   Chart No. 911
Drawing No. B-1976   Part No. B-1976-3   Chart of Method Present
Chart Begins Pick up part and load machine   Charted By E. B. Watmough
Chart Ends Remove ground part from machine   Date 3-15   Sheet 1 of 2

ELEMENT DESCRIPTION	OPERATOR	JONES & LAMSON INTERNAL THREAD GRINDER
Pick up part from table	.0009	Idle
Place in diaphragm chuck	.0012	
Close chuck	.0007	
Start machine (spindle)	.0003	
Start grinding wheel	.0003	
		Loading .0058
Run grinding wheel forward 6"	.0028	
Engage feed	.0006	
Inspect piece from previous cycle	.0025	
		Grind (first pass) .0075
	Idle	
Run grinding wheel back 1"	.0008	Machine Handling .0013
Engage feed	.0005	

machine idle time is posted. The productive time of the man plus idle man time must equal the productive time plus idle time of each machine he operates.

It will be noted that accurate elemental time values are necessary before the man and machine chart can be constructed. These time values should represent standard times[1] which include an acceptable manufac-

[1] See Chapter 17.

FIGURE 6-2 (Continued)

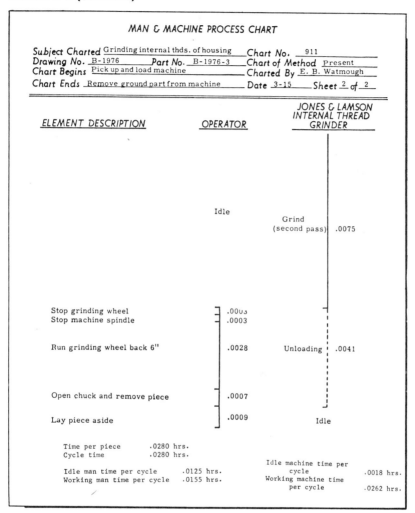

MAN & MACHINE PROCESS CHART

Subject Charted Grinding internal thds. of housing   Chart No. ___911___
Drawing No. _B-1976_____ Part No. _B-1976-3____ Chart of Method _Present____
Chart Begins _Pick up and load machine_____ Charted By _E. B. Watmough___
Chart Ends _Remove ground part from machine_____ Date _3-15____ Sheet _2_ of _2_

ELEMENT DESCRIPTION	OPERATOR	JONES & LAMSON INTERNAL THREAD GRINDER
	Idle	Grind (second pass) .0075
Stop grinding wheel	.0005	
Stop machine spindle	.0003	
Run grinding wheel back 6"	.0028	Unloading .0041
Open chuck and remove piece	.0007	
Lay piece aside	.0009	Idle

Time per piece   .0280 hrs.
Cycle time   .0280 hrs.

Idle man time per cycle   .0125 hrs.
Working man time per cycle   .0155 hrs.

Idle machine time per cycle   .0018 hrs.
Working machine time per cycle   .0262 hrs.

turing allowance to take care of fatigue, unavoidable delays, and personal delays. In no case should overall stopwatch readings be used in the construction of the chart.

The completed man and machine process chart clearly shows both idle machine and man time. These areas are generally a good place to start effecting improvements.

The analyst must be careful not to be deceived by what looks like an appreciable amount of idle man time. In many instances, it is far more economical to have a man idle a portion of a cycle rather than chance an expensive piece of equipment or process being idle even a small portion

FIGURE 6–3

Man and machine process chart of thread-grinding operation with one man operating two machines

MAN & MACHINE PROCESS CHART

Subject Charted Grinding internal threads of housing   Chart No. 912
Drawing No. B-1976   Part No. B-1976-3   Chart of Method Proposed
Chart Begins Pick up part and load machine   Charted By E. B. Watmough
Chart Ends Remove ground part from machine   Date 3-17   Sheet 1 of 3

ELEMENT DESCRIPTION	OPERATOR	JONES & LAMSON INTERNAL THREAD GRINDER NO.1	JONES & LAMSON INTERNAL THREAD GRINDER NO.2
Stop grinding wheel mch. #1	.0003		
Stop machine spindle machine #1	.0003		
Run grinding wheel back 6" machine #1	.0028	Unloading .0041	
Open chuck and remove part machine #1	.0007		Grind (second pass) .0075
Lay aside part	.0009	Idle	
Pick up new part from table	.0009		
Place part in diaphragm chuck machine #1	.0012		
Close diaphragm chuck mch. #1	.0007		
Start mch. (spindle) mch. #1	.0003		
Start grinding wheel mch. #1	.0003	Loading .0058	
Run grinding wheel forward 6"	.0028		Idle
Engage feed	.0005		
Walk to machine #2	.0011		
Stop grinding wheel mch. #2	.0003		
Stop machine spindle mch. #2	.0003		
Run grinding wheel back 6" machine #2	.0028	Grind (first pass) .0075	Unloading .0041

of the time. In order to be sure that his proposal is the best solution, the analyst must know the cost of the idle facility as well as the cost of the idle man. It is only when total cost is considered that one can safely recommend one method over another. Figure 6–3 illustrates a man and machine chart that represents economies over the one shown in Figure 6–2.

FIGURE 6–3 (Continued)

MAN & MACHINE PROCESS CHART

Subject Charted Grinding internal threads of housing   Chart No. 912
Drawing No. B-1976   Part No. B-1976-3   Chart of Method Proposed
Chart Begins Pick up part and load machine   Charted By E. B. Watmough
Chart Ends Remove ground part from machine   Date 3-17   Sheet 2 of 3

ELEMENT DESCRIPTION	OPERATOR	JONES & LAMSON INTERNAL THREAD GRINDER NO. 1	JONES & LAMSON INTERNAL THREAD GRINDER NO. 2
Open chuck and remove part machine #2	.0007		
Lay aside part	.0009		
Pick up new part from table	.0009		Idle
Place part in diaphragm chuck machine #2	.0012		
Close diaphragm chuck Mch. #2	.0007		
Start machine (spindle) mch. #2	.0003		
Start grinding wheel mch. #2	.0003		
			Loading .0058
Run grinding wheel forward 6" machine #2	.0028	Idle	
Engage feed	.0005		
Walk to machine #1	.0011		
Run grinding wheel back 1" machine #1	.0008	Machine Handling .0013	
Engage feed machine #1	.0005		
Inspect pieces from machine #1 and machine #2 previous cycle	.0050		Grind (first pass) .0075
		Grind (second pass) .0075	

Using the man and machine process chart

The analyst will construct a man and machine process chart when his preliminary investigation reveals that the working cycle of the operator is somewhat shorter than the operating cycle of the machine. Once he has completed the chart, the logical place to consider improvement possibilities is during the idle portion of the man's cycle. Considering the amount of this time, he should investigate the possibility of (1) operating a second machine during this idle time, and (2) performing some bench

FIGURE 6–3 (Continued)

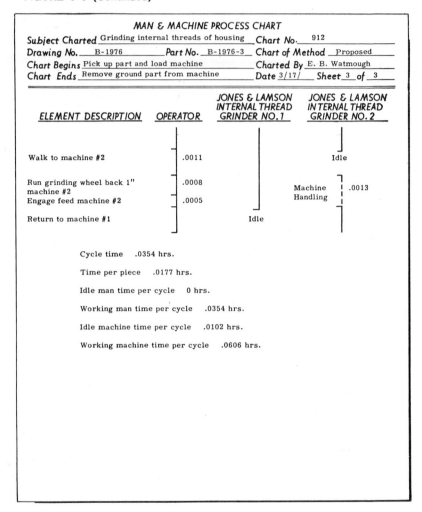

MAN & MACHINE PROCESS CHART

Subject Charted Grinding internal threads of housing Chart No. 912

Drawing No. B-1976 Part No. B-1976-3 Chart of Method Proposed

Chart Begins Pick up part and load machine Charted By E. B. Watmough

Chart Ends Remove ground part from machine Date 3/17/ Sheet 3 of 3

ELEMENT DESCRIPTION	OPERATOR	JONES & LAMSON INTERNAL THREAD GRINDER NO. 1	JONES & LAMSON INTERNAL THREAD GRINDER NO. 2
Walk to machine #2	.0011		Idle
Run grinding wheel back 1" machine #2	.0008		Machine Handling .0013
Engage feed machine #2	.0005		
Return to machine #1		Idle	

Cycle time   .0354 hrs.

Time per piece   .0177 hrs.

Idle man time per cycle   0 hrs.

Working man time per cycle   .0354 hrs.

Idle machine time per cycle   .0102 hrs.

Working machine time per cycle   .0606 hrs.

or manual operation such as filing burrs or gaging part during the idle time.

Sometimes more available operator time can be obtained by reducing the speed and feed of the machine. This may permit machine coupling where otherwise it would not have been possible, and thus reduce total costs. As mentioned earlier, it is not always advisable to practice machine coupling, as idle machine time introduced may more than offset the idle operator time saved. The only sure way to make the analysis is on a total cost basis.

Man and machine charts are effective in determining the extent of coupling justified in order to assure a "fair day's work for a fair day's pay." They are valuable for determining how idle machine time may be more fully utilized.

Gang process charts

The gang process chart, in a sense, is an adaptation of the man and machine chart. After completing a man and machine process chart, the analyst should be able to determine the most economical number of machines to be operated by one man. However, several processes and facilities are of such magnitude that it is not a question of how many machines should a man operate, but a problem as to how many men should it take to man the machine effectively. The gang process chart shows the exact relationship between the idle and operating cycle of the machine and the idle and operating time per cycle of the men who service it. This chart shows clearly the possibilities for improvement by reducing both idle man and machine time.

Construction of the gang process chart

After heading the gang process chart, "Gang Process Chart," and completely identifying the process being plotted with part number, drawing number, description of operation being charted, present or proposed method, date, and name of person doing the charting, the analyst should select a time scale to give a neat-appearing chart on the paper being used. As in the man and machine process chart, the gang process chart is always drawn to scale.

On the left-hand side of the paper are shown the operations being performed on the machine or process. Immediately to the right of the operation description, the loading, operating, and idle time of the machine is represented graphically. Further to the right, the operating and idle time of each operator manning the process is illustrated by flow lines in a vertical direction. A solid vertical line indicates productive work being done, while a dotted vertical line in connection with the facility shows that either loading or unloading operations are taking place. A void in the vertical flow line reveals idle time, and the length of the void determines the duration of the idle time. In the case of the operators, solid vertical lines show that work is being done, while breaks in the solid lines demonstrate that idle time is prevailing. Figure 6–4 illustrates a gang process chart, and it is apparent that a large number of idle man-hours exist. A better loading of the same process is shown on the gang process chart illustrated in Figure 6–5. The saving of 16 hours per shift was easily developed through the use of the gang process chart.

FIGURE 6-4

GANG PROCESS CHART OF PRESENT METHOD

HYDRAULIC EXTRUSION PRESS DEPT. 11 BELLEFONTE PA. PLANT

CHARTED BY B.W.N. 4-15- CHART NO. G-85

MACHINE		PRESS OPERATOR		ASSISTANT PRESS OPERATOR		FURNACE MAN		DUMMY KNOCKER		ASSISTANT DUMMY KNOCKER		PULL-OUT MAN	
OPERATION	TIME	OPERATION	TIME	OPERATION	TIME	OPERATION	TIME	OPERATION	TIME	OPERATION	TIME	OPERATION	TIME
Elevate Billet	.07	Elevate Billet	.07	Grease Die & Position Back in Die Head	.12			Position Shell on Small Press	.10	Move Away from Small Press and Lay Aside Tongs	.12	Pull Rod toward Cooling Rack	.20
Position Billet	.08	Position Billet	.08					Press Dummy Out of Shell	.12				
Position Dummy	.04	Position Dummy	.04										
Build Pressure	.05	Build Pressure	.05					Dispose of Shell	.18			Walk Back toward Press	.15
						Rearrange Billets in Furnace	.20						
Extrude	.45	Extrude	.45	Idle Time	.68	Idle Time	.51	Dispose of Dummy and Lay Aside Tongs	.12	Idle Time	.68	Grab Rod with Tongs and Pull Out	.45
Unlock Die	.06	Unlock Die	.06					Idle	.43				
Loosen & Push Out Shell	.10	Loosen & Push Out Shell	.10	Run Head & Shell Out	.11	Open Furnace Door & Remove Billet	.19			Guide Shell from Shear to Small Press	.20	Straighten Rod End with Mallet	.11
Withdraw Ram & Lock Die In Head	.15	Withdraw Ram & Lock Die in Head	.15	Shear Rod from Shell	.04	Ram Billet from Furnace & Close Furnace Door	.10	Grab Tongs & Move to Position	.05			Hold Rod while Die Removed at Press	.09
				Pull Die Off End of Rod	.05								
WORKING TIME	1.00 MIN.	WORKING TIME	1.00 MIN.		.32 MIN.		.49 MIN.		.57 MIN.		.32 MIN.		1.00 MIN.
IDLE TIME	0 "	IDLE TIME	0 "		.68 "		.51 "		.43 "		.68 "		0 "

IDLE TIME = 2.30 MAN-MINUTES PER CYCLE = 18.4 MAN-HOURS PER EIGHT-HOUR DAY

Using the gang process chart

The analyst usually constructs the gang process chart when his initial investigation of a given operation indicates that more men are being used to operate a facility or process than is necessary. If he suspects this, he will find that the gang process chart is a useful tool for determining the exact number of operators needed to service a machine or process effectively. Once the chart has been constructed, the hours of idle man time can be analyzed to determine the possibility of utilizing one man to perform the work elements currently performed by two or more.

For example, in the gang process chart shown in Figure 6–4, the company is employing two more men than needed. This is apparent when it is shown that under this process, 18.4 idle man-hours are involved in every 8-hour turn.

By relocating some of the controls of the process, it was possible to reassign the elements of work so that four, rather than six, men effectively operated the extrusion press.

Figure 6–5 illustrates a gang process chart of the proposed method

FIGURE 6–5

Gang process chart of proposed method of operation of hydraulic extrusion process

GANG PROCESS CHART–PROPOSED METHOD

Hydraulic Extrusion Press Dept. 11 Bellefonte, Pa. Plant

Charted by B.W.N.   4-15-58   Chart G-85

MACHINE OPERATION	TIME	PRESS OPERATOR OPERATION	TIME	ASSISTANT PRESS OPERATOR OPERATION	TIME	DUMMY KNOCKER OPERATION	TIME	PULL-OUT MAN OPERATION	TIME
Elevate Billet	.07	Elevate Billet	.07	Grease Die & Position Back in in Die Head	.12	Position Shell on Small Press	.10	Pull Rod toward Cooling Rack	.20
Position Billet	.08	Position Billet	.08	Walk to Furnace	.05	Press Dummy Out of Shell	.12		
Position Dummy	.04	Position Dummy	.04						
Build Pressure	.05	Build Pressure	.05	Rearrange Billets in Furnace	.20	Dispose of Shell	.18	Walk Back toward Press	.15
				Return to Press	.05	Dispose of Dummy and Lay Aside Tongs	.12		
Extrude	.45	Extrude	.45	Idle Time	.09			Grab Rod with Tongs and Pull Out	.45
					.19	Idle Time	.23		
Unlock Die	.06	Unlock Die	.06		.10	Grab Tongs & Move to Position	.05		
Loosen & Push Out Shell	.10	Loosen & Push Out Shell	.10	Run Head & Shell Out	.11	Guide Shell from Shear to Small Press	.20		.11
Withdraw Ram & Lock Die in Head	.15	Withdraw Ram & Lock Die in Head	.15	Shear Rod from Shell	.04				.09
				Pull Die Off End of Rod	.05				
Working Time	1.00 Min.		1.00 Min.		.91 Min.		.77 Min.		1.00 Min.
Idle Time	0		0		.09 Min.		.23 Min.		0

using but four operators and so making savings of 16 man-hours per shift. Without the gang process chart, this solution would have been quite difficult.

From the example given in Figures 6–4 and 6–5, it can be seen that the gang process chart aids in dividing the available work among the members of the team that operate the equipment, and then clearly determines the job assignment of all involved. Through the construction and use of the gang process chart, equipment will be operated to capacity, labor costs will be reduced, and employee morale will be improved as a result of equitable distribution of work assignments.

Quantitative techniques for man and machine relationships

Although the man and machine process chart can be used to determine the number of facilities to be assigned to an operator, this can often be computed through the development of a mathematical model in much less time.

Man and machine relationships are usually one of three types such as (1) synchronous servicing, (2) completely random servicing, and (3) combination of synchronous and random servicing.

Assigning more than one machine to an operator seldom results in the ideal case where both the man and the machine he is servicing are occupied the whole cycle. Ideal cases such as this are referred to as synchronous servicing and the number of machines to be assigned can be computed as:

$$N = \frac{O + M}{O}$$

where

N = Number of machines the operator is assigned
O = Total operator servicing time per machine
M = Total machine running time

For example, if the total operator servicing time would be equal to one minute, while the cycle time of the machine was four minutes, synchronous servicing would result in the assignment of five machines:

$$N = \frac{1 + 4}{1}$$
$$= 5$$

Graphically, this assignment would appear as follows:

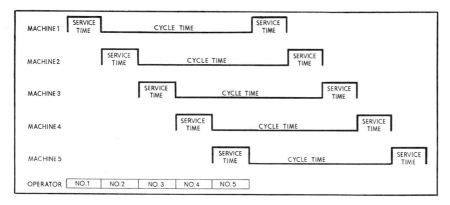

If the number of machines in the above example is increased, machine interference will take place, and we have a situation where one or more of the facilities the operator operates is idle a portion of the work cycle. If the number of machines is reduced to some figure less than five, then the operator will be idle a portion of the cycle.

In such cases, minimum total cost per piece usually represents the criteria for optimum operation. The best method will need to be established, considering the cost of each idle machine and the hourly rate of the operator. Quantitative techniques can be used to establish the best arrangement. The procedure is first to estimate the number of facilities the operator should be assigned by establishing the lowest whole number from the equation:

$$N_1 \leqq \frac{l + m}{l + w}$$

where

N_1 = Lowest whole number
l = Normal loading and unloading time of the facility in hours
m = Machine time in hours (power feed)
w = Normal walking time to the next facility in hours

It can be seen from the above, the cycle time with the operator servicing N_1 machines is $l + m$ since in this case, the operator will not be busy the whole cycle, while the facilities he is servicing will be occupied during the entire cycle.

Using N_1, the total expected cost may be computed as follows:

$$\text{T.E.C.}_{N_1} = \frac{K_1(l + m) + N_1 K_2(l + m)}{N_1}$$
$$= \frac{(l + m)(K_1 + N_1 K_2)}{N_1}$$

where

> T.E.C. = Cost of production per cycle from one machine
> K_1 = Operator rate in dollars per hour
> K_2 = Cost of machine in dollars per hour

After this cost is computed, a cost should be calculated with $N_1 + 1$ machines assigned to the operator. In this case the cycle time will be governed by the working cycle of the operator, since there will be some idle machine time. The cycle time now will be $(N_1 + 1)(l + w)$. Let $N_2 = N_1 + 1$. Then the total expected cost with N_2 facilities is:

$$\text{T.E.C.}_{N_2} = \frac{(K_1)(N_1 + 1)(l + w) + (K_2)(N_1 + 1)(N_1 + 1)(l + w)}{(N_1 + 1)}$$
$$= [(l + w)][K_1 + K_2(N_1 + 1)]$$

The number of machines to be assigned will depend upon whether N_1 or $N_1 + 1$ gives the lowest total expected cost per piece.

"Completely random servicing situations" refer to those cases in which it is not known when a facility will need to be serviced or how long it will take. Mean values are usually known or can be determined; with these averages, laws of probability can provide a useful tool in determining the estimated number of machines to assign the operator.

The successive terms of the binomial expansion will give a useful approximation of the probability of 0, 1, 2, 3, . . . n machines down (where n is relatively small), assuming that each machine is down at random times during the day and that the probability of running time is p and the probability of down time is q.

For example, let us determine the minimum proportion of machine time lost for various numbers of turret lathes assigned to an operator where it has been estimated that on the average the machines operate 60 percent of the time unattended. Operator attention time at irregular intervals will be on the average 40 percent. The analyst estimates that three turret lathes should be assigned per operator on this class of work. Under this arrangement, the combinations of machine running (p) or down (q) expressed as probabilities would be:

$$(p + q)^n = (p + q)^3$$
$$= p^3 + 3p^2q + 3pq^2 + q^3$$
$$= (0.60)^3 + (3)(0.60)^2(0.40) + 3(0.60)(0.40)^2 + (0.40)^3$$
$$1.00 = 0.216 + 0.432 + 0.288 + 0.064$$

In tabular form this would appear as follows:

Machine 1	Machine 2	Machine 3	Probability
	$R = 0.60$	$R = 0.60$ $D = 0.40$	$(0.60)(0.60)(0.60) = 0.216$ $(0.60)(0.60)(0.40) = 0.144$
$R = 0.60$	$D = 0.40$	$R = 0.60$ $D = 0.40$	$(0.60)(0.40)(0.60) = 0.144$ $(0.60)(0.40)(0.40) = 0.096$
$D = 0.40$	$R = 0.60$	$R = 0.60$ $D = 0.40$	$(0.40)(0.60)(0.60) = 0.144$ $(0.40)(0.60)(0.40) = 0.096$
	$D = 0.40$	$R = 0.60$ $D = 0.40$	$(0.40)(0.40)(0.60) = 0.096$ $(0.40)(0.40)(0.40) = \underline{0.064}$ 1.000

Thus, the proportion of time that some machines will be down may be determined and the resulting lost time of one operator per three machines may be readily computed. In this example we have:

No. of machines down	Probability	Machine hours lost per 8-hour day
0	0.216	0
1	0.432	0*
2	0.288	$(0.288)(8) = 2.304$
3	0.064	$(2)(0.064)(8) = \underline{1.024}$
	$\overline{1.000}$	3.328

* Since only one machine is down at a time, the operator can be attending the down machine.

$$\text{Proportion of machine time lost} = \frac{3.328}{24.0} = 13.9 \text{ percent}$$

Similar computations can be made for more or less machine assignments to determine the assignment resulting in the least machine down time. Decision on the most satisfactory arrangement is usually based on the arrangement showing the least Total Expected Cost per piece. The Total Expected Cost per piece of a given arrangement can be computed by the expression:

$$\text{T.E.C.} = \frac{K_1 + NK_2}{\text{Pieces from } N \text{ machines per hour}}$$

where

$K_1 = $ Hourly rate of the operator
$K_2 = $ Hourly rate of the machine
$N = $ Number of machines assigned

The pieces per hour from N machines can be computed knowing the mean machine time required per piece, the average machine servicing time per piece and the expected machine down or lost time per hour.

For example, under a five machine assignment to one operator, it was determined that the machining time per piece was 0.82 hours, the machine serving time per piece was 0.17 hours and the machine down time averaged 0.11 hours per machine per hour. Thus, each machine was available for production work only 0.89 hours each hour. The time to produce one piece per machine on the average would be $\dfrac{0.82 + 0.17}{0.89} = 1.11$. Therefore, the five machines would produce 4.5 pieces per hour. With an operator hourly rate of $2.80 and a machine hourly rate of $6, we have a total expected cost per piece of:

$$\frac{\$2.80 + 5(\$6.00)}{4.5} = \$7.29$$

Perhaps the most common type of man and machine relationships are combinations of synchronous and random servicing. Here the servicing time is constant, but the machine down time is random. Winding, coning, and quilling operations used in the textile industry are characteristic of this type of man and machine relationship. As in the former examples, algebra and probability can establish the mathematical model that will enhance a realistic solution. (See queueing theory, Chapter 22.)

Line balancing

The problem of determining the ideal number of workers to be assigned to a production line is analogous to the problem of the number of workers to be assigned to a production facility where the use of the gang process chart was recommended. Perhaps the most elementary line balancing situation, yet one that is very often encountered, is where several operators, each performing consecutive operations, are working as a unit. In such a situation, it is obvious that the rate of production coming off the line is dependent upon the slowest operator. For example, we may have a line of five operators assemblying bonded rubber mountings prior to the curing process. The specific work assignments might be as follows: Operator 1—0.52 minutes; Operator 2—0.48 minutes; Operator 3—0.65 minutes; Operator 4—0.41 minutes; Operator 5—0.55 minutes. Operator 3 establishes the pace as evidenced by the following:

Operator	Standard minutes to perform operation	Wait time based on slowest operator	Allowed standard minutes
1..............	0.52	0.13	0.65
2..............	0.48	0.17	0.65
3..............	0.65	—	0.65
4..............	0.41	0.24	0.65
5..............	0.55	0.10	0.65

The efficiency of this line can be computed as the ratio of the total standard minutes to the total allowed standard minutes or:

$$E = \frac{\sum\limits_{1}^{5} S.M.}{\sum\limits_{1}^{5} A.M.} \times 100 = \frac{2.61}{3.25} \times 100 = 80 \text{ percent}$$

where

E = Efficiency
$S.M.$ = Standard minutes per operation
$A.M.$ = Allowed standard minutes per operation

It is apparent that a real-life situation similar to the above example provides the opportunity for significant savings on the part of the methods analyst. If he can save 0.10 minute on Operator 3, the net savings per cycle is not 0.10 minute but 0.10 × 5 or 0.50 minutes.

Only under the most unusual situations would a line be perfectly balanced; that is, where the standard minutes to perform an operation would be identical for each member of the team. The reader should recognize at this time that the "standard minutes to perform the operation" is really not a standard. It is only standard in the eyes of the individual who established it. Thus, in our example where Operator 3 was shown to have a standard time of 0.65 minutes to perform the first operation, it should be recognized that a different work measurement analyst may have allowed as little as 0.61 minutes or as much as 0.69 minutes. The range of standards established by different work measurement analysts on the same operation might even be more than what has been suggested. The point is that no matter if the issued standard is 0.61, 0.65, or 0.69, the typical conscientious operator will have little difficulty in meeting the standard. In fact, he will probably better the standard in view of the performance of the operators on the line with less work content in their assignments. It should also be recognized that those operators who have a wait time based on the output of the slowest operator, seldom will be observed as actually waiting. They will, instead, reduce the tempo of their movements so as to utilize the number of standard minutes established by the slowest operator.

The number of allowed standard minutes to produce one unit of the product will be equal to the summation of the standard minutes required times the reciprocal of the efficiency. Thus,

$$\Sigma A.M. = \Sigma S.M. \times \frac{1}{E}$$

It is apparent then that the number of operators needed is equal to the required rate of production times the total allowed minutes or where

N = The number of men needed in the line
R = Desired rate of production
$N = R \times \Sigma\, A.M.$

For example, let us assume that we had a new design for which we were establishing an assembly line. Eight distinct operations were involved. The line must produce 700 units per day and since it is desirable to minimize storage, we do not want to produce many more than 700 units per day. The eight operations involve the following standard minutes based on existing standard data:

Operation 1—1.25 minutes; Operation 2—1.38 minutes; Operation 3—2.58 minutes; Operation 4—3.84 minutes; Operation 5—1.27 minutes; Operation 6—1.29 minutes; Operation 7—2.48 minutes; and Operation 8 —1.28 minutes. The analyst wishes to plan this assembly line for the most economic setup. He is able to estimate the number of operators required at 100 percent efficiency as follows:

$$\sum_{1}^{8} S.M. = 15.37 \text{ minutes}$$

$$N = \frac{700}{480} \times \frac{15.37}{E} = \frac{22.4}{E}$$

If the analyst plans for 95 percent efficiency, he would estimate the number of operators to be: $\dfrac{22.4}{0.95} = 23.6.$

Since it is impossible to have six tenths of an operator, the analyst will endeavor to set up the line utilizing 24 operators.

The next step will be to estimate the number of operators to be utilized at each of the eight specific operations.

Since 700 units of work are required a day, it will be necessary to produce one unit in about 0.685 minutes $\left(\dfrac{480}{700}\right)$. We can estimate how many operators will be needed on each operation by dividing the number of minutes in which it is necessary to have one piece produced into the standard minutes of each operation.

Operation	Standard minutes	Standard minutes / Minutes/unit	No. of operators
Operation 1.............	1.25	1.83	2
Operation 2.............	1.38	2.02	2
Operation 3.............	2.58	3.77	4
Operation 4.............	3.84	5.62	6
Operation 5.............	1.27	1.86	2
Operation 6	1.29	1.88	2
Operation 7.............	2.48	3.62	4
Operation 8.............	1.28	1.87	2
Total.............	15.37		24

In order to determine which is the slowest operation, we divide the estimated number of operators into the standard minutes for each of the eight operations.

Operation 1.................... 1.25/2 = 0.625
Operation 2.................... 1.38/2 = 0.690
Operation 3.................... 2.58/4 = 0.645
Operation 4.................... 3.84/6 = 0.640
Operation 5.................... 1.27/2 = 0.635
Operation 6.................... 1.29/2 = 0.645
Operation 7.................... 2.48/4 = 0.620
Operation 8.................... 1.28/2 = 0.640

Thus, Operation 2 will determine the output from the line. In this case it will be:

$$\frac{2 \text{ men} \times 60 \text{ min.}}{1.38 \text{ standard minutes}} = 87 \text{ pieces per hour or 696 pieces per day}$$

If this rate of production is inadequate, we must increase the rate of production of Operator 2. This can be accomplished by:

1. Working one or both of the operators at the second operation over-time, thus accumulating a small inventory at this work station.
2. Utilizing the service of a third man (on a part-time basis) at the work station of Operation 2.
3. Reassigning some of the work of Operation 2 to Operation 1 or Operation 3. (It would be preferable to assign more work to Operation 1.)
4. Improving the method at Operation 2 so as to diminish the cycle time of this operation.

In the preceding example, we have been given a cycle time and operation times and have determined the number of operators needed for each operation in order to meet a desired production schedule.

The production line work assignment problem can also be to minimize the number of work stations, given the desired cycle time; or, given the number of work stations, to assign work elements to the work stations, within restrictions established, so as to minimize the cycle time.

The following procedure, for assisting in the solution of the assembly line balancing problem is based on the General Electric Assembly Line Balancing publication. General Electric engineers have prepared a program, written for the GE-225 computer, for assigning work elements to stations on an assembly line.

The method established for the solution of the assembly line problem is based on the following:

1. Operators are not able to move from one work station to another in order to help maintain a uniform work load.
2. Work elements of such magnitude have been established that further division would substantially decrease the efficiency of performing the work element. (Once established, the work elements should be identified with a code.)

The first step in the solution of the problem is the determination of the sequence of the individual work elements. As can easily be recognized, the fewer the restrictions on the order in which the work elements can be done, the greater the probability for a favorable balance in the work assignments. In order for the analyst to determine the sequence of the work elements, he must ask and answer the question: "What other work elements (if any) must be completed before this work element can be started?"

FIGURE 6–6

Partially completed precedence chart

Note that work elements 002 and 003 may be done in any sequence with respect to any of the other work elements. Also that 032 cannot be started until 005, 006, 008, and 009 have been completed. Note that after 004 has been finished we may start either 033, 017, 021, 007, 008, or 009.

It is recommended that a precedence chart be completed for the production line under study. (See Figure 6–6.) The analyst should recognize that not only functional design, but available production methods, floor space, etc., can introduce constraints as far as the work element sequence is concerned.

A second consideration in the production line work assignment problem is the recognition of zoning restraints. A zone represents a subdivision, which may or may not be physically separated or identified from other zones in the system. Confining certain work elements to a given zone may be justified in order to congregate similar jobs, working conditions, or pay rates. Or again, it may be desirable to introduce zoning restraints in order physically to identify specific stages of a component, such as the keeping of it in a certain position while work elements are being performed. Thus, all work elements related to one side of a component may be performed in a certain zone prior to turning the component over.

Obviously, the more zoning restraints that are placed on the system, the fewer the combinational possibilities open to investigation. It is helpful for the analyst to make a sketch of the system and code the applicable zones. Within each zone should be shown the work elements that may be done in this area.

The next step is to estimate the production rate. This is done with the expression:

$$\text{Production per day} = \frac{\text{Working minutes/day}}{\text{Cycle time of system (min./unit)}} \times \text{rating factor}$$

For example, assuming a 15 percent allowance, we would have $480 - 72$ or 408 working minutes per day. The rating factor would be based on experience with the type of line under study. It could be either more or less than standard (100 percent). The cycle time of the system is the cycle time of the limiting station. Since we know the production requirements per day, we are able to compute the allowed cycle time of the limiting station.

The reader should recognize that the computer-generated assignment does not necessarily represent the optimum. It should be regarded as a good base from which the methods analyst can work and upon which he can hopefully improve. For example, the analyst may be able to divide an element and thus bring about a more efficient overall arrangement. Or again, he may see fit to modify zoning restrictions, or alter precedence relationships.

The computer can be used to select the assignments for each operator, taking into account the cycle time of the system, precedence, and zoning.

In order to illustrate the logic of the computer routine, the following precedence graph will be described:

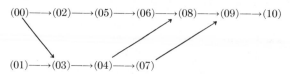

It can be seen from this precedence graph that work unit (00) must be completed before (02), (03), (05), (06), (04), (07), (08), (09), and (10); and work unit (01) must be completed before (03), (04), (07), (08), (09), and (10). Either (00) or (01) can be done first or concurrently. Work unit (03) cannot be started until both work units (00) and (01) are completed, etc.

In order to describe these relationships, the computer uses a precedence matrix as illustrated in Figure 6–7. Here the numeral 1 signifies a "must precede" relationship. For example, work unit (00) must precede

FIGURE 6–7

Precedence matrix as used by digital computer for line-balancing problem

Estimated work unit time (minutes)	Work unit	00	01	02	03	04	05	06	07	08	09	10
0.46	00			1	1	1	1	1	1	1	1	1
0.35	01				1	1			1	1	1	1
0.25	02						1	1		1	1	1
0.22	03					1			1	1	1	1
1.10	04								1	1	1	1
0.87	05							1		1	1	1
0.28	06									1	1	1
0.72	07										1	1
1.32	08										1	1
0.49	09											1
0.55	10											
6.61												

work units (02), (03), (04), (05), (06), (07), (08), (09), and (10). Also work unit (09) must precede only work unit (10).

Now a "positional weight" must be computed for each work unit. This is done by computing the summation of each work unit and all work units that must follow it. Thus, the "positional weight" for work unit (00) would be: Σ 00, 02, 03, 04, 05, 06, 07, 08, 09, 10 = 0.46 + 0.25 + 0.22 + 1.10 + 0.87 + 0.28 + 0.72 + 1.32 + 0.49 + 0.55 = 6.26.

Listing the positional weights in decreasing order of magnitude gives the following:

Unsorted work elements	Sorted work elements	Positional weight	Immediate predecessors
00	00	6.26	—
01	01	4.75	—
02	03	4.40	(00), (01)
03	04	4.18	(03)
04	02	3.76	(00)
05	05	3.56	(02)
06	06	2.64	(05)
07	08	2.36	(04), (06)
08	07	1.76	(04)
09	09	1.04	(07), (08)
10	10	0.55	(09)

Work elements must now be assigned to the various work stations. This is based on the positional weights (those work elements with the highest positional weights are first assigned) and the cycle time of the system. Thus, the work element with the highest positional weight is assigned to the first work station. The unassigned time for this work station is determined by subtracting the sum of the assigned work element times from the estimated cycle time. If there is adequate unassigned time, then the work element with the next highest positional weight may be assigned providing that the work elements in the "immediate predecessors" column have already been assigned.

The procedure is continued until all of the work elements have been assigned.

For example, let us assume that the required production per day was 300 units and that it was anticipated a 1.10 rating factor would prevail. Then:

$$\text{Cycle time of system} = \frac{(480 - 72)(1.10)}{300}$$
$$= 1.50 \text{ minutes}$$

	Work			Work element time	Station time		Remarks*
Sta-tion	Ele-ment	Positional weight	Immediate predecessors		Cumula-tive	Un-assigned	
1	00	6.26	—	0.46	.46	1.04	—
1	01	4.75	—	0.35	.81	0.69	—
1	03	4.40	(00), (01)	0.22	1.03	0.47	—
1	~~04~~	~~4.18~~	~~(03)~~	~~1.10~~	(2.13)		N.A.
1	02	3.76	(00)	0.25	1.28	0.22	—
1	~~05~~	~~3.56~~	~~(02)~~	~~0.87~~	(2.05)		N.A.
2	04	4.18	(03)	1.10	1.10	0.40	—
2	~~05~~	~~3.56~~	~~(02)~~	~~0.87~~	(1.97)		N.A.
3	05	3.56	(02)	0.87	.87	0.63	—
3	06	2.64	(05)	0.28	1.15	0.35	—
3	~~08~~	~~2.36~~	~~(04), (06)~~	~~1.32~~	(2.47)		N.A.
4	08	2.36	(04), (06)	1.32	1.32	0.18	—
4	~~07~~	~~1.76~~	~~(04)~~	~~0.12~~	(2.04)		N.A.
5	07	1.76	(04)	0.72	.72	0.78	—
5	09	1.04	(07), (08)	0.49	1.21	0.29	—
5	~~10~~	~~.55~~	~~(09)~~	~~0.55~~	(1.76)		N.A.
6	10	.55	(09)	0.55	.55	0.95	—

* N.A. means not acceptable.

With six work stations under the arrangement illustrated, we have a cycle time of 1.32 minutes (work station No. 4). This arrangement will more than meet the daily requirement of 300. It will produce:

$$\frac{(480 - 72)(1.10)}{1.32} = 341 \text{ units}$$

However, with six work stations, we have considerable idle time. The idle time per cycle is:

$$\sum_1^6 = 0.14 + 0.22 + 0.17 + 0 + 0.11 + 0.77 = 1.41 \text{ minutes}$$

The problem can be solved for cycle times less than 1.50 minutes for more favorable balancing. This may result in more operators and more production per day which may have to be stored. Another possibility includes operation of the line under a more efficient balancing for a limited number of hours per day.

Operator process chart

The operator process chart, sometimes referred to as a "left- and right-hand" process chart is, in effect, a tool of motion study. This chart shows all movements and delays made by both right and left hands, and the relationship between the relative basic divisions of accomplishment as performed by the hands. The purpose of the operator process chart is to present a given operation in sufficient detail so that by means of an analysis the operation can be improved. Usually it is not practical to make a detailed study through the operator process chart unless a highly repetitive manual operation is involved. Through motion analysis of the operator chart, inefficient motion patterns become apparent and violation of the laws of motion economy (see Chapter 7) is readily observed. This chart will facilitate changing a method so a balanced two-handed operation can be achieved and ineffective motions either reduced or eliminated. The result will be a smoother, more rhythmic cycle which will keep both delays and operator fatigue to a minimum.

Constructing the operator process chart

Although Frank and Lillian Gilbreth state that there are 17 fundamental motions, and that every operation consists of a combination of some of these elements, the methods analyst will find it practical when plotting operator process charts to use but eight basic divisions of accomplishment. These elemental motions with their symbols are:

Reach	Re	Use	U
Grasp	G	Release	Rl
Move	M	Delay	D
Position	P	Hold	H

See Chapter 7 for detailed description of each of these basic divisions of human work.

Although there are several different delay types,[2] such as unavoidable delay, avoidable delay, rest to overcome fatigue, and "balancing delay," the methods analyst need only indicate in the operator process chart a cessation of work with the identification "delay." Often, delays will not occur to both hands simultaneously. Thus, an operator hand-feeding the cross slide of his lathe would be performing "use" with his right hand while his left hand would be delayed. Other examples of delays would be interruptions of work due to a coughing spell of the operator or his sitting down to rest. In both of these examples, the right hand as well as the left hand would be shown as being delayed. Delays should be investigated with thought of eliminating or minimizing them.

The operator process chart should be headed "Operator Process Chart" and this should be followed with all necessary identifying information which would include part number, drawing number, operation or process description, present or proposed method, date, and the name of

[2] S. M. Lowry, H. B. Maynard, and G. J. Stegemerten, *Time and Motion Study and Formulas for Wage Incentives* (3d ed.; New York: McGraw-Hill Book Co., 1940).

the person doing the charting. Immediately below the identifying information should be a sketch of the work station drawn to scale. The sketch will materially aid in presenting the method under study. A typical operator process chart form, with a section of the sheet laid out in coordinate form to facilitate sketching is shown in Figure 6–8.

After the analyst has completely identified the operation and made a sketch of the work station showing dimensional relationships, he is ready to begin constructing the operator process chart. Since this chart is drawn

FIGURE 6–8

Operator process chart of assembly of cable clamps

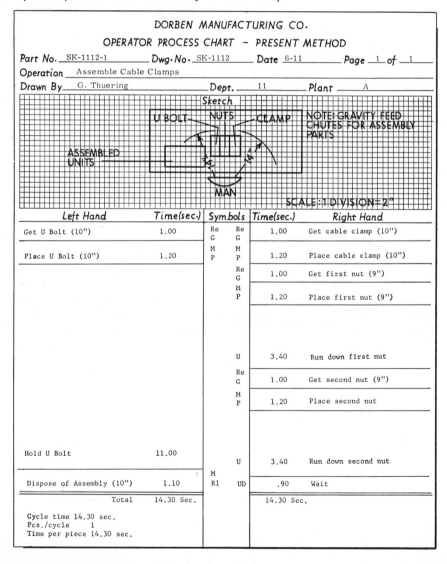

Left Hand	Time(sec.)	Symbols		Time(sec.)	Right Hand
Get U Bolt (10")	1.00	Re G	Re G	1.00	Get cable clamp (10")
Place U Bolt (10")	1.20	M P	M P	1.20	Place cable clamp (10")
			Re G	1.00	Get first nut (9")
			M P	1.20	Place first nut (9")
			U	3.40	Run down first nut
			Re G	1.00	Get second nut (9")
			M P	1.20	Place second nut
Hold U Bolt	11.00		U	3.40	Run down second nut
Dispose of Assembly (10")	1.10	M Rl	UD	.90	Wait
Total	14.30 Sec.			14.30 Sec.	

Cycle time 14.30 sec.
Pcs./cycle   1
Time per piece 14.30 sec.

to scale, the analyst should determine by observation the duration of the cycle. Then he can readily determine the amount of time represented by each ¼ inch of vertical space on the chart. For example, if it developed that the operation to be studied had a cycle time of 0.70 minutes and there were 7 vertical inches of available charting space, then each ¼ inch of chart space would equal 0.025 minutes.

It is usually less confusing to chart completely the activities of one hand, and then chart all the basic divisions of accomplishment performed by the other hand. Although there is no fixed rule on what part of the work cycle should be used as a starting point, it is usually best to start plotting immediately after the "release" of the finished part. If this release is done with the right hand, the next movement that would normally take place would be the first motion shown on the operator process chart. This, for the right hand, probably would be "reach for new part." If the analyst observed that the "reach" element took about 0.025 minutes to perform, he would indicate this duration by drawing a horizontal line across the right-hand side of the paper ¼ inch from the top. Under the symbol column, he would indicate a "Re" for "reach" and this would be shown in black pencil, indicating that an effective motion had been accomplished. Immediately to the right of the symbol would be a brief description of the event, such as "Reach 20 inches" for a ½-inch nut. Immediately below, the next basic division would be shown, and so on until completion of the cycle. The analyst would then proceed to plot the activity of the left hand during the cycle. While plotting the left hand, it is a good idea to verify that end points of the therbligs actually occur at the same point as indicated—a check for overall plotting errors.

It should be noted that elements must be large enough to be measured, since it is not possible in most instances to obtain with the stopwatch the time required for individual therbligs. For example, in Figure 6–8, the first element performed by the left hand was classified as "get U bolt." This element was comprised of the therbligs, "reach" and "grasp." It would not have been possible with a stopwatch to determine the time required to perform either of these therbligs. Only the moving-picture camera could disclose time values as short as these (see Chapter 9).

The observer in Figure 6–8 was using a decimal second watch and, by observing an element at a time, he could break them into one-second periods.

After the activities of both the right and the left hand are charted, a summary should be shown at the bottom of the sheet, indicating the cycle time, pieces per cycle, and time per piece.

Using the operator process chart

After the operator process chart of an existing method has been completed, the analyst should see what improvements can be introduced.

The "delays" and "holds" are good places to begin. For example, in Figure 6–8 it can be seen that the left hand was used as a holding device for almost the entire cycle. An analysis of this condition would suggest the development of a fixture to hold the U bolt. Further consideration of how to get balanced motions of both hands would suggest that, when the fixture holds the U bolts, then the left hand and the right hand would each assemble completely a cable clamp. Additional study of this chart might result in the introduction of an automatic ejector and gravity chute to eliminate the final cycle element "dispose of assembly."

The best way of doing a job is through systematic analysis of all the detailed elements constituting that job. The operator process chart clearly reveals the work done by each hand in performing an operation and shows the relative time and relationships of all motions performed by the hands. The operator process chart is an effective tool to:

1. Balance motions of both hands and reduce fatigue.
2. Eliminate and/or reduce nonproductive motions.
3. Shorten the duration of productive motions.
4. Train new operators in the ideal method.
5. Sell the proposed method.

The methods analyst should learn to make and use operator process charts to bring about improvements.

Summary: man-machine, gang, and operator process charts

The methods analyst should know the specific functions of the man and machine, gang, and operator process charts so he can select the appropriate one for improving operations. The operator chart is adapted to all work where the operator goes through a series of manual motions. The man and machine and gang process charts are used only when machines or facilities are used in conjunction with the operator or operators. Frequently, where an operator is employed in running a machine, it will be worthwhile to make a study both from the standpoint of possible coupling and improvement of motion pattern. Thus, it may be helpful to construct both a man and machine and an operator process chart. In summary, the functions of these three charts are:

1. Man and Machine Chart—Used to analyze idle man and idle machine time. Ideal for determining the amount of machine coupling to be practiced. Used as a training tool to show relation of work elements in a multimachine work center.
2. Gang Process Chart—Used to analyze idle facility time and idle time of operators servicing the facility or process. Ideal for determining labor requirements of a production facility. Used as training tool to

show work elements of several operators working with a production facility.

3. Operator Process Chart—Used to analyze work station for proper layout, proper operator motion pattern, and best sequence of elements. Best chart to use for improving repetitive manual motions.

Quantitative techniques can be used to determine the optimum arrangement of random servicing work centers. The analyst should be acquainted with sufficient algebra and probability theory so he can develop a mathematical model to provide the best solution to the problem of machine-facility assignment.

TEXT QUESTIONS

1. When is it advisable to construct a man and machine process chart? *p147*
2. Why will higher base rates result when machine coupling is practiced?
3. How does the gang process chart differ from the man and the machine process chart? *gang chart has multi man a one machine*
4. What is the purpose of the operator process chart? *p165*
5. What symbols are used in constructing the operator process chart? *p165*
6. Explain how you would sell machine coupling to union officials strongly opposed to the technique.
7. In what way does an operator benefit through machine coupling? *increased pay*
8. What is the difference between synchronous and random servicing?
9. How many machines should be assigned to an operator when:
    a) Loading and unloading time one machine 1.41 minutes.
    b) Walking time to next facility 0.08 minutes.
    c) Machine time (power feed) 4.34 minutes.
    d) Operator rate $2.20 per hour.
    e) Machine rate $3 per hour.
10. What proportion machine time would be lost in operating four machines when the machine operates 70 percent of the time unattended and the operator attention time at irregular intervals will be on the average 30 percent? Is this the best arrangement on the basis of minimizing the proportion of machine time lost?
11. In an assembly process involving six distinct operations, it is necessary to produce 250 units per eight-hour day. The measured operation times are as follows:

    1. —7.56 minutes   4. —1.58 minutes
    2. —4.25 minutes   5. —3.72 minutes
    3. —12.11 minutes   6. —8.44 minutes

    How many operators would be required at 80 percent efficiency? How many operators will be utilized at each of the six operations?
12. What is the principal application of the operator process chart?

p.165 13. What eight basic divisions of accomplishment are used in connection with the construction of the operator process chart?

GENERAL QUESTIONS

1. In the process-type plant which of the following process charts has the greatest application: man and machine, gang, operator? Why?
2. In the operation of some plant with which you are familiar, outline the "zoning restraints" and discuss how these influence the production line work assignment problem.

CHAPTER 7

Motion study

Both motion study and micromotion study techniques are used to analyze a given method and are used to help develop an efficient work center. These two techniques are used in conjunction with the principles of operation analysis when there is sufficient volume to justify the additional study and analysis required.

Motion study is the careful analysis of the various body motions employed in doing a job, to eliminate or reduce ineffective movements, and facilitate and speed effective movements. Through motion study, the work is performed more easily and the rate of output is increased. The Gilbreths pioneered the study of manual motion and developed basic laws of motion economy that today are considered fundamental. They were also responsible for the motion-picture technique for making detailed motion studies known as micromotion studies, which have proved invaluable in studying very highly repetitive manual operations.

Motion study, in the broad sense, covers two degrees of refinement that have wide industrial application. These are visual motion study and micromotion study.

Visual motion study has considerably the broader application, because the activity of the work need not be as great to justify its use economically. This type of study involves a careful observation of the operation and construction of an operator process chart, and a probing analysis of the chart, considering the laws of motion economy.

The micromotion procedure (see Chapter 8), in view of its much higher cost, is usually practical only on extremely active jobs where the life and repetitiveness are great. The two types of studies may be compared to viewing a part under a magnifying glass and viewing it under a microscope. The added detail revealed by the microscope finds application on only the most productive job.

The fundamental motions

The basic division of accomplishment concept, developed by Frank Gilbreth in his early work, applied to all production work performed by

TABLE 7–1

THERBLIG NAME	SYMBOL	COLOR DESIGNATION	SYMBOL
Search	S	Black	⬯
Select	SE	Gray, Light	→
Grasp	G	Lake Red	∩
Reach	RE	Olive Green	‿
Move	M	Green	⌣
Hold	H	Gold Ochre	⌒
Release	RL	Carmine Red	⌒
Position	P	Blue	9
Pre–position	PP	Sky–Blue	8
Inspect	I	Burnt–Ochre	0
Assemble	A	Violet, Heavy	#
Disassemble	DA	Violet, Light	#
Use	U	Purple	∪
Unavoidable Delay	UD	Yellow Ochre	⌒
Avoidable Delay	AD	Lemon Yellow	⌐o
Plan	PL	Brown	β
Rest to Overcome Fatigue	R	Orange	ę

the hands of the operator. He called these fundamental motions "therbligs" (Gilbreth spelled backward), and concluded that any and all operations are made up of a series of these 17 basic divisions. These 17 fundamental hand motions modified somewhat from Gilbreth's summary, and their symbols and color designations are shown in Table 7–1.

Definitions of basic divisions of accomplishment

The Management Research and Development Division of the Society for Advancement of Management in its "Glossary of Terms Used in Methods, Time Study, and Wage Incentives" has provided definitions of the various therbligs. These definitions, in part, are included in the following summary.

1. Search. Search is the basic operation element employed to locate an object. It is that part of the cycle during which the eyes or hands are groping or feeling for the object. It begins the instant the eyes move in an effort to locate an object and ends the instant they are focused on the found object.

Search is a therblig that the analyst should always endeavor to eliminate. Well-planned work stations allow work to be performed continuously so it is not necessary for the operator to perform this element. Providing an exact location for all tools and parts is the typical way to eliminate search from a work station.

A new employee, or one that is not familiar with his job, will find it necessary to use search periodically until his skill and proficiency develop.

The well-trained motion analyst will ask himself the following questions to eliminate or reduce "search" time:

1. Are articles properly identified? Perhaps labels or color could be utilized.
2. Can transparent containers be used?
3. Will a better layout of the work station eliminate searching?
4. Is proper lighting being used?
5. Can tools and parts be pre-positioned?

2. Select. Select is the therblig that takes place when the operator chooses one part over two or more analogous parts. This therblig usually follows search and even with a detailed micromotion procedure, it is difficult to determine the exact ending of search and the beginning of select. Select does occur without search when selective assembly is being encountered. In this case, it is usually preceded by inspect. Select can also be classified as an ineffective therblig and should be eliminated from the work cycle by better layout of the work station and control of parts.

To eliminate this therblig, the analyst should ask:

1. Are common parts interchangeable?
2. Can tools be standardized?
3. Are parts and materials stored in the same bin?
4. Can a rack or tray be used so parts will be pre-positioned?

3. Grasp. Grasp is the elemental hand motion of closing the fingers around a part in an operation. Grasp is an effective therblig and usually cannot be eliminated, but in many instances it can be improved. It occurs the instant the fingers of either or both hands begin to enclose around an object to maintain control of it and ends the moment control has been obtained. Grasp is usually preceded by reach and followed by move. Detailed studies have concluded that there are many types of grasp, some taking three times as much time to perform as others. The number of grasps occurring during the work cycle should be kept to a minimum and the parts to be picked up should be arranged so the most simple type of grasp can be used. This is done by having the object by itself in a fixed location and positioned so no interference takes place with the worktable, bin, or surrounding environment.

These therblig check questions may help improve the "grasps" performed during a cycle:

1. Would it be advisable for the operator to grasp more than one part or object at a time?
2. Can a contact grasp be used rather than a pickup grasp? In other words, can objects be slid instead of carried?
3. Will a lip on the front of bins simplify grasping small parts?
4. Can tools or parts be pre-positioned for easy grasp?
5. Can a vacuum, magnet, rubber fingertip, or other device, be used to advantage?
6. Can a conveyor be used?
7. Has the jig been designed so the part may easily be grasped when removing it?
8. Can previous operator pre-position tool or work thus simplifying grasp for the following operator?
9. Can tools be pre-positioned on a swinging bracket?

4. Reach.   Reach represents the motion of an empty hand, without resistance, toward or away from an object. The basic division reach was known as "transport empty" in Gilbreth's original summary. However, the shorter term is generally accepted by methods men today. Reach begins the instant the hand moves toward an object or general location and ends the instant hand motion stops upon arrival at the object or destination. Reach is usually followed by grasp and preceded by a release. Obviously, the time required to perform a reach depends on the distance of the hand movement. The time to perform reach also depends to some extent upon the type of reach. As in grasp, reach can be classified as an objective therblig, and usually cannot be eliminated from the work cycle. However, it can be reduced by shortening the distances required for reaching and providing fixed locations for objects that are reached for during the operator's work cycle. By keeping this elementary principle in mind, work stations can be developed that will keep reach time to a minimum.

5. *Move.* Move is the basic division to signify a hand movement with a load. The load can be in the form of pressure. Move was originally known as "transport loaded." This therblig begins the instant the hand under load moves toward a general location and ends the moment motion stops upon arrival at the destination. Move is usually preceded by a grasp and is usually followed by either a release or a position.

The time required to perform move depends on distance, weight to be moved, and type of move. Move is an objective therblig, and it is difficult to remove this basic division from the work cycle. Nevertheless, the time to perform move can be diminished by reducing the distances to be moved, lightening the load, and improving the type of move by providing gravity chutes or a conveyor at the terminal point of the move, so it will not be necessary to bring the object being moved to a specific location. Experience has proved that moves to a general location are performed more rapidly than to an exact location.

Both reach and move therbligs may be improved by asking and answering the following questions:

1. Can either of these therbligs be eliminated?
2. Can distances be shortened to advantage?
3. Are the best means being used? that is, conveyors, hand, tongs, tweezers, and so on.
4. Is the correct body member used? that is, fingers, wrist, forearm, shoulder.
5. Can a gravity chute be employed?
6. Can transports be effected through mechanization and foot-operated devices?
7. Will time be reduced by transporting in larger units?
8. Is time increased because of the nature of the material being moved or because of a subsequent delicate positioning?
9. Can abrupt changes in direction be eliminated?

6. *Hold.* Hold is the basic division of accomplishment that occurs when either hand is supporting or maintaining control of an object while the other hand does useful work. Hold is an ineffective therblig and can usually be removed from the work cycle by designing a jig or fixture to hold the work rather than using the hand. The hand is seldom considered an efficient holding device, and the methods analyst should always be on the alert to prevent hold from being a part of any work assignment.

Hold begins the instant control is exercised by the hand on the object and ends at the instant the other hand completes its work on the object. A typical example of hold would occur when the left hand holds a stud while the right hand runs a nut on the stud. During the assembly of the nut to the stud, the left hand would be utilizing the therblig hold.

Hold can often be eliminated by asking and answering these questions:

1. Can a mechanical jig such as a vise, pin, hook, rack, clip, or vacuum be used?
2. Can friction be used?
3. Can a magnetic device be used?
4. Should a twin holding fixture be used?

7. *Release.* Release is the basic division that occurs when the object of the operator is to relinquish control of the object. Release takes the least amount of time of all the therbligs, and little can be done to influence the time required for this objective therblig.

Release begins the instant the fingers begin to move away from the part held and ends the instant all fingers are clear of the part. This therblig is usually preceded by a move or a position and is usually followed by a reach.

1. Can the release be made in transit?
2. Can a mechanical ejector be used?
3. Are the bins that will contain the part after release of the proper size and design?
4. At the end of the therblig release load, are the hands in the most advantageous position for the next therblig?
5. Can multiple units be released?

8. *Position.* Position is an elment of work consisting of locating an object so it will be properly oriented in a specific location.

The therblig position occurs as a hesitation while the hand or hands are endeavoring to place the part so further work may be more readily performed. Actually, position may be a combination of several very rapid motions. Locating a contoured piece in a die would be a typical example of position. Position is usually preceded by a move and followed by a release. Position begins the instant the controlling hand or hands begin to agitate, twist, turn, or slide the part to orient it to the correct place and ends as soon as the hand begins to move away from the part.

Position frequently can be eliminated or improved through answering these and similar check questions:

1. Can such devices as a guide, funnel, bushing, stop, swinging bracket, locating pin, recess, key, pilot, or chamfer be used?
2. Can tolerances be changed?
3. Can the hole be counterbored or countersunk?
4. Can a template be used?
5. Are burrs increasing the problem of positioning?
6. Can the article be pointed to act as a pilot?

9. *Pre-position.* Pre-position is an element of work consisting of positioning an object in a predetermined place so it may be grasped in the position in which it is to be held when needed.

Pre-position often occurs in conjunction with other therbligs, one of which is usually move. It is the basic division that arranges a part so it can be conveniently placed upon arrival. The time required to pre-position is difficult to measure since the therblig itself can seldom be isolated. Pre-position would take place if a screwdriver was being aligned while being moved to the screw it was going to drive.

These check questions will assist the analyst in studying pre-position therbligs.

1. Can a holding device be used at the work station so that tools may be kept in proper position and the handles kept in upright position?
2. Can tools be suspended?
3. Can a guide be used?
4. Can a magazine feed be used?
5. Can a stacking device be used?
6. Can a rotating fixture be used?

10. *Inspect.* Inspect is an element included in an operation to assure acceptable quality through a regular check by the employee performing the operation.

Inspect takes place when the predominant purpose is to compare some object with a standard. It usually is not difficult to detect when inspect is encountered, since the eyes are focused upon the object and a delay between motions is noted while the mind decides either to accept or reject the piece in question. The time taken for inspect is determined primarily by the severity of the standard and the amount of deviation of the part in question. Thus, if an operator were sorting out all blue marbles from a bin, little time would be consumed in deciding what to do with a red marble. However, if a purple marble were picked up, there would be a longer hesitation for the mind to evaluate the marble and decide if it should be accepted or rejected.

These questions, when answered by the analyst, may result in improvements on inspect therbligs:

1. Can inspection be eliminated or combined with another operation or therblig?
2. Can multiple gages or tests be used?
3. By increasing the illumination, will inspection time be reduced?
4. Are the articles being inspected the correct distance from the workmen's eyes?
5. Will a shadowgraph facilitate inspection?
6. Does an electric eye have application?
7. Does the volume justify automatic electronic inspection?
8. Would a magnifying glass facilitate the inspection of small parts?
9. Is the best inspection method being used? Has consideration been

given to polarized light, template gages, sound tests, performance tests, and so on?

11. *Assemble.* Assemble is the basic division that occurs when two mating parts are brought together. This is another objective therblig and can more readily be improved than eliminated. Assemble is usually preceded either by a position or a move and is usually followed by a release. It begins the instant the two mating parts come in contact with one another and ends upon completion of the uniting element.

12. *Disassemble.* Disassemble is just the reverse of assemble and occurs when two mating parts are disunited. The basic division is usually preceded by a grasp and is usually followed by either a move or a release. Disassemble is objective in nature, and improvement possibilities are more likely than complete elimination of the therblig. Disassemble begins the moment either or both hands have control of the object after grasping it, and ends as soon as the disassembly has been completed, usually evidenced by the beginning of a move or the beginning of a release.

13. *Use.* Use is a completely objective therblig and occurs when either or both hands have control of an object during that part of the cycle when productive work is being performed. When both hands are holding a casting up against a grinding wheel, "use" would be the therblig that would correctly indicate the action of the hands. After a screwdriver had been positioned in the slot of the screw, use would occur as the screw is being driven home. The duration of this therblig depends on the operation as well as the performance of the operator. It is quite easily detected, as this therblig "always advances the operation toward the ultimate objective."[1]

In studying the three objective therbligs, assemble, disassemble, and use, thought should be given to the following questions:

1. Can a jig or fixture be used?
2. Does the activity justify automated equipment?
3. Would it be practical to make the assembly in multiple units?
4. Can a more efficient tool be used?
5. Can stops be used?
6. Is the tool being operated at the most efficient feeds and speeds?
7. Should a power tool be employed?

14. *Unavoidable delay.* Unavoidable delay is an interruption beyond the control of an operator in the continuity of an operation. It represents idle time in the work cycle experienced by either hand or both hands because of the nature of the process. Thus while an operator is hand feeding a drill with his right hand to a part held in a jig, the left hand would be

---

[1] L. P. Alford and J. R. Bangs, *Production Handbook* (New York: Ronald Press Co., 1944).

unavoidably delayed. Since the operator has no control over unavoidable delays, to remove them from the cycle the process will have to be changed in some manner.

15. Avoidable delay. Any idle time that occurs during the cycle for, which the operator is solely responsible, either intentionally or unintentionally, is classified as an avoidable delay. Thus, if an operator developed a coughing spell during a work cycle, this delay would be avoidable, for normally it would not appear in the work cycle. The majority of avoidable delays encountered can be avoided by the operator without changing the process or method of doing the work.

16. Plan. The therblig plan is a mental process, when the operator pauses to determine the next action. Plan may take place during any part of the work cycle and is usually readily detected as a hesitation after all components have been located. This therblig is characteristic of a new employee and usually can be removed from the work cycle through proper operator training.

17. Rest to overcome fatigue. This delay seldom appears in every cycle, but is evidenced periodically for the operator to recover from fatigue caused by his work. The duration of rest to overcome fatigue will vary not only with the class of work but also with the individual performing the work.

To reduce the number of occurrences of the therblig rest, the analyst should consider:

1. Is the best order-of-muscles classification being used?
2. Are temperature, humidity, ventilation, noise, light, and other working conditions satisfactory?
3. Are benches the proper height?
4. Can the operator alternately sit and stand while performing his work?
5. Does the operator have a comfortable chair of the right height?
6. Are mechanical means being used for heavy loads?
7. Is the operator aware of his average intake requirements in calories per day? The approximate calories required for sedentary activities is 2,400; for light manual labor 2,700; for medium labor 3,000; for heavy manual labor 3,600.

Therblig summary

The 17 basic divisions can be classified as either effective or ineffective therbligs. Effective therbligs are those that directly advance the progress of the operation. These therbligs can frequently be shortened, but it is difficult to eliminate them completely. Ineffective therbligs do not advance the progress of the work and should be eliminated by applying the principles of operations analysis and motion study.

A further classification breaks the therbligs into physical, semimental or mental, objective, and delay groups. Ideally, a work center should be comprised of only the physical and objective therbligs.

A. Effective
   1. Physical basic divisions.
     a) Reach
     b) Move
     c) Grasp
     d) Release
     e) Pre-position
   2. Objective basic divisions
     a) Use
     b) Assemble
     c) Disassemble

B. Ineffective
   1. Mental or semimental basic divisions
     a) Search
     b) Select
     c) Position
     d) Inspect
     e) Plan
   2. Delay
     a) Unavoidable delay
     b) Avoidable delay
     c) Rest to overcome fatigue
     d) Hold

Principles of motion economy

Beyond the basic division of accomplishment concept, as first set forth by the Gilbreths, are the principles of motion economy also developed by them and added to by others, notably Ralph M. Barnes. These laws of motion economy are not all applicable to every job, and several find application only through the tool of micromotion study as discussed in Chapter 8. However, those that apply to visual motion study, as well as the micromotion technique, that should always be considered are broken down into three basic subdivisions: (1) use of the human body, (2) arrangement and conditions of the workplace, and (3) design of tools and equipment.[2]

The methods analyst should become familiar with the visual laws of motion economy so he will be able to detect inefficiencies in the method

---

[2] *Ibid.*

by briefly inspecting the workplace and the operation. These basic principles under their respective divisions are as follows:

I.   Use of the human body
  a)   Both hands should begin and end their basic divisions of accomplishment simultaneously and should not be idle at the same instant, except during rest periods.
  b)   The motions made by the hands should be made symmetrically and simultaneously away and toward the center of the body.
  c)   Momentum should be employed to assist the worker wherever possible, and it should be reduced to a minimum if it must be overcome by muscular effort.
  d)   Continuous curved motions are preferable to straight-line motions involving sudden and sharp changes in direction.
  e)   The least number of basic divisions should be used, and these should be confined to the lowest possible classifications. These classifications, summarized in ascending order of time and fatigue expended in their performance, are:
    1.   Finger motions.
    2.   Finger and wrist motions.
    3.   Finger, wrist, and lower arm motions.
    4.   Finger, wrist, lower arm, and upper arm motions.
    5.   Finger, wrist, lower arm, upper arm, and body motions.
  f)   Work that can be done by the feet should be arranged so that it is done simultaneously with work being done by the hands. It should be recognized, however, that simultaneous moving of the hand and foot is difficult to perform.
  g)   The middle finger and the thumb are the strongest working fingers. The index finger, fourth finger, and little finger are not capable of handling heavy loads over extended periods.
  h)   The feet are not capable of efficiently operating pedals when the operator is in a standing position.
  i)   Twisting motions should be performed with the elbows bent.
  j)   To grip tools, use the segments of the fingers closest to the palm of the hand.

II. Arrangement and conditions of the workplace
  a)   Fixed locations should be provided for all tools and material so as to permit the best sequence and to eliminate or reduce the therbligs search and select.
  b)   Gravity bins and drop delivery should be used to reduce reach and move times; also ejectors should be provided wherever possible to remove finished parts automatically.
  c)   All materials and tools should be located within the normal area in both the vertical and horizontal planes.

    d) A comfortable chair should be provided for the operator and the height so arranged that the work can be efficiently performed by the operator alternately standing and sitting.

    e) Proper illumination, ventilation, and temperature should be provided.

    f) Visual requirements of the workplace should be considered so eye fixation demands are minimized.

    g) Rhythm is essential to the smooth and automatic performance of an operation, and the work should be arranged to permit an easy and natural rhythm wherever possible.

III. Design of tools and equipment

    a) Multiple cuts should be taken whenever possible by combining two or more tools in one, or by arranging simultaneous cuts from both feeding devices if available (cross slide and hex turret).

    b) All levers, handles, wheels, and other control devices should be readily accessible to the operator and should be designed so as to give the best possible mechanical advantage and utilize the strongest available muscle group.

    c) Holding parts in position should be done by fixtures.

    d) Always investigate the possibility of powered or semiautomatic tools, such as power nut and screwdrivers, speed wrenches, etc.

EXPLANATION OF LAWS OF MOTION ECONOMY

Both hands should begin and end their basic divisions of accomplishments simultaneously and should not be idle at the same instant except during rest periods.

When the right hand is working in the normal area to the right of the body and the left hand is working in the normal area to the left of the body, there is a feeling of balance that tends to induce rhythm in the performance of the operator that leads to maximum performance. When one hand is working under load and the other hand is idle, the body exerts an effort to put itself in balance. This usually results in greater fatigue than if both hands were employed doing useful work. This law can readily be demonstrated by reaching out with the right hand about 14 inches, picking up an object weighing about a half pound and moving it 10 inches toward the body before releasing it. The operation should then be immediately repeated, only this time the part is moved away from the body. Repeat the cycle about 200 times and note the discomfort in the body induced by "balance fatigue." Now repeat the operation using both hands simultaneously. Have the left hand reach out radially to the left of the body and the right hand reach out radially to the right of the body, grasp the objects, move both objects toward the body, and release them simultaneously. Repeat the cycle 200 times and note that the body feels less fatigued, even though twice as much load was handled.

The motions made by the hands should be made symmetrically and simultaneously away and toward the center of the body.

It is natural for the hands to move in symmetrical patterns: deviations from symmetry in a two-handed work station result in slow, awkward movements of the operator. The difficulty of patting the stomach with the left hand while rubbing the top of the head with the right hand is familiar to many. Another experiment that can readily be tried to illustrate the difficulty of performing nonsymmetrical operations is to draw a circle with the left hand while the right hand is drawing a square. Figure 7–1

FIGURE 7–1

An ideal work station that permits the operator to assemble two products by going through two series of symmetrical motions made simultaneously away from and toward the center of the body

General Electric Co.

illustrates an ideal work station that allows the operator to assemble two products by going through a series of symmetrical motions made simultaneously away and toward the center of the body.

Momentum should be employed to assist the worker wherever possible, and it should be reduced to a minimum if it must be overcome by muscular effort.

As the hands progress through the elements of work constituting the operation, momentum will be developed during reach and move therbligs and will be overcome during position and release therbligs. To make full use of the momentum built up, work stations should be designed so a finished part can be released in a delivery area while the hands are on their way to get component parts or tools to begin the next work cycle. This allows the hands to perform their reaches with the aid of momentum and makes the therblig easier and faster to perform.

Detailed studies have proven conclusively that both reaches and moves are performed faster if the hand is in motion at the beginning of the therblig.

Continuous curved motions are preferable to straight-line motions involving sudden and sharp changes in direction.

This law is very easily demonstrated by moving either hand in a rectangular pattern, and then moving it in a circular pattern of about the same magnitude. The greater amount of time required to make the abrupt 90° directional changes is quite apparent. To make a directional change, the hand must decelerate, change direction, accelerate until it is time to decelerate preparatory to the next directional change. Continuous curved motions do not require deceleration, and consequently are performed faster per unit of distance.

The least number of basic divisions should be used and these should be confined to the lowest practicable classifications.

To become fully aware of the significance of this fundamental law of motion economy, it is first necessary to be able to identify the various classifications of motions.

1. The finger motion is the fastest of the five motion classes and is readily recognized, for it is made by moving the finger or fingers while the remainder of the arm is kept stationary. Typical finger motions are running a nut down on a stud, depressing the keys of a typewriter, grasping a small part, and so on. Usually there is a significant difference in time required to perform finger motions with the various fingers. The index finger in most cases will be able to move considerably faster than the other fingers, and in designing work stations this should be taken into consideration. Although with practice the fingers of the left hand (in right-handed people) can be trained to move with the same rapidity as the fingers of the right hand, detailed studies have shown that the fingers

of the left hand will move somewhat slower. R. E. Hoke made a study of the "universal" keyboard used on typewriters and found that 88.9 taps could be made with the fingers of the left hand for every 100 made with the right hand.[3]

The analyst should recognize that the finger motion is the weakest of the five motion classes. Consequently, care should be exercised in designing work stations involving great manual effort so higher classifications than finger motion may be employed.

2. Finger and wrist motions are made by movements of the wrist and fingers while the forearm and upper arm are stationary. In the majority of cases, finger and wrist motions consume more time than strictly finger motions. Typical finger and wrist motions occur when positioning a part in a jig or fixture or when assembling two mating parts. Reach and move therbligs usually cannot be performed by motions of the second class unless the transport distances are very short.

3. The finger, wrist, and lower arm motions are commonly referred to as "forearm" motions and include those movements made by the arm below the elbow while the upper arm is stationary. Since the forearm includes a strong muscle, this motion is usually considered efficient, since it is not fatiguing. The time required to make forearm motions for a given operator depends on the distance moved and the amount of resistance overcome during the movement. By designing work stations so these third-class motions will be used to perform the transport therbligs rather than fourth-class motions, the analyst will minimize cycle times.

4. The finger, wrist, lower arm, and upper arm motion, commonly known as the fourth-class or shoulder motion, is probably used more than any one single motion class. The fourth-class motion for a given distance takes considerably more time than the three lower classes just described. Fourth-class motions are required to perform transport therbligs of parts that cannot be reached without extending the arm. The time required to perform fourth-class motions depends primarily on the distance of the move and the resistance to the move.

5. Fifth-class motions include body movements and those, of course, are the most time consuming. Body motions include ankle, knee, and thigh motions as well as body trunk motions.

It will be noted that the first-class motion requires the least amount of effort and time, while the fifth class is considered the least efficient. Therefore, the analyst should always endeavor to utilize the lowest practicable motion classification with which to perform the work properly. This will

---

[3] R. E. Hoke, *The Improvement of Speed and Accuracy in Typewriting* (The Johns Hopkins University Studies in Education No. 7) (Baltimore: The Johns Hopkins Press, 1922).

involve careful consideration of the location of tools and materials so ideal motion patterns can be arranged.

Work that can be done by the feet should be arranged so it is done simultaneously with work done by the hands.

Since the majority of work cycles are performed by the hands, it follows that it is economical to relieve the hands of work that can be done by the feet, if this work is being performed while the hands are occupied.

FIGURE 7–2

This foot-operated press permits the operator's hands to procure parts in preparation for the next cycle while the press is in operation

General Electric Co.

Since the hands are more dexterous than the feet, it would be folly to have the feet perform elements while the hands were idle. Foot pedal arrangement allowing clamping, ejection of parts, feeding, and so on, can often be arranged, thus freeing the hands for useful work and consequently reducing the cycle time (see Figure 7–2). When the hands are moving, the feet should not be moving although they can be applying pressure such as on a foot pedal. In the development of work stations involving the coordination of the hands and feet, care should be exercised so that simultaneous movements of the hands and feet are not required.

The middle finger and the thumb are the strongest working fingers.

The index finger, fourth finger, and little finger are not capable of handling heavy loads over extended periods.

Although the index finger is usually the finger that is capable of moving the fastest, it is not the strongest. Where a relatively heavy load is involved, it usually will be more efficient to use the middle finger or a combination of the middle finger and the index finger.

FIGURE 7–3

Fixed locations for all materials and tools are provided in this work station, minimizing search and select hesitations

General Electric Co.

Twisting motions should be performed with the elbows bent.

When the elbow is extended, tendons and muscles in the arm are stretched. If in this position the arm is obliged to perform twisting motions, there can be an overstressing of both muscle groups and tendons.

To grip tools, use the segments of the fingers closest to the palm of the hand.

The segments of the hand closest to the palm are not only stronger than other segments but, being closer to the load held in the hand, do not induce as great a bending moment as the more remote segments.

Fixed locations should be provided for all tools and materials to permit the best sequence and to eliminate or reduce the therbligs search and select.

In driving an automobile, we are all familiar with the shortness of time required to apply the foot brake. The reason is obvious; since the brake pedal is in a fixed location, no time is required to decide where the brake is located. The body responds instinctively and applies pressure to the area where the driver knows the foot pedal will be. If the location of the brake foot pedal varied from time to time, considerably more time would be needed to apply braking to the car. By providing fixed location for all tools and materials at the work station, the short hesitations required to search and select the various objects needed to do the work will be eliminated or at least minimized (see Figure 7–3).

Gravity bins and drop delivery should be used to reduce reach and move times.

The time required to perform both of the transport therbligs, reach and move, is proportional to the distance that the hands must move in performing these elements. By utilizing gravity bins, components can be continuously brought to the normal working area, thus eliminating long reaches to get supplies of parts. Likewise, gravity chutes allow disposal of parts within the normal area, thus eliminating the necessity for long moves to dispose of the completed part or parts. Gravity chutes make possible a clean workplace area, as finished material will be carried away from the work area rather than stacked up all around the workplace (see Figure 7–4).

All materials and tools should be located within the normal area in both the vertical and horizontal plane.

The normal working area in the horizontal plane of the right hand includes the area generated by the arm below the elbow when moving in an arc pivoted at the elbow. This area will represent the most convenient zone within which motions may be made by that hand with a normal expenditure of energy.

In a similar manner the normal area may be established by the left hand.

Since movements are made in the third dimension as well as in the horizontal plane, the normal working area applies to the vertical plane as well. The normal area relative to height for the right hand includes the area made by the lower arm in an upright position hinged at the elbow moving in an arc. In like manner there is a normal area for the left hand in a vertical plane (see Figures 7–5 and 7–6).

The maximum working area represents that portion of the workplace within which all tools and materials should be located and where work may be performed without excessive fatigue. This area is formed by drawing arcs with the arms fully extended and, as in the normal working area, both the horizontal and vertical planes are considered.

FIGURE 7–4

Work station utilizing gravity bins and belt conveyor to reduce reach and move times. Note the conveyor in the background carrying other parts by this particular work station. Operator is feeding on to the conveyor from under the platform by merely dropping assembled parts on to feeder belt.

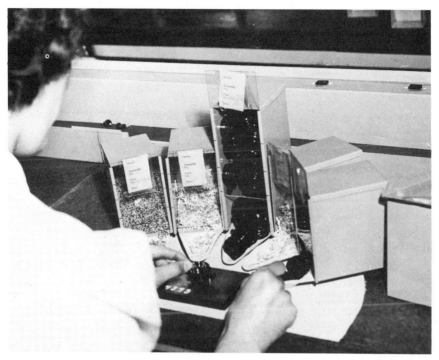

Alden Systems Co.

FIGURE 7–5

Normal and maximum working areas in the horizontal plane for women (for men, multiply by 1.09)

In the design of both facilities and work stations, consideration should be given to such factors as arm reach, leg clearance, and body support since these human dimensions are important criteria in developing worker environment that is comfortable and efficient. The human dimensions shown in Figures 7–7 and 7–8 should be used as a basis for the design of operation work stations.

A comfortable chair should be provided for the operator and the height arranged so the work can be efficiently performed by the operator alternately standing and sitting.

FIGURE 7–6

Normal and maximum working areas in the vertical plane for women (for men, multiply by 1.09)

MAXIMUM FOR EXTENDED ARM

28"

NORMAL FOR FOREARM

16.7"

The stool or chair used by the operator should receive careful attention to reduce operator fatigue. It should accommodate the 1st to 98th percentile of workers. This is equivalent to providing a work-surface height from 36.5 inches to 44.7 inches. In general, the chair or bench seats should be broad and long enough to support the thighs, yet not so long as to cut into the back of the knees of shorter operators. The contour of the seat should be slightly saddle-shaped and the front end should be chamfered. Sixteen inches by 16 inches with the curved portion beginning about 3 inches back from the front edge is considered a good size. The seat should be lightly padded and aerated. Whenever possible, backs should be provided for all chairs, and these should be designed so they

FIGURE 7–7

Dimensions of the average adult male based on the 2½ to
97½ percent range of measured subjects

Memorize all dimensions

Average weight is 153.1 lb,
ranging from 118 to 202 lb.

Product Engineering

do not interfere with movements of the arms. The backrest should not
result in undue pressure against the pelvis or ribs, nor should it cause interference with shoulder blade movement. It should be slightly curved
with dimensions of approximately 5 inches in height and 10 inches in

width. Some padding on the backrest is desirable in order to eliminate sharp edges. A tilting feature is desirable.

Good chair design should permit several effective working postures. The seats should be adjustable in height within the range of 15 to 21 inches. One-half inch increments of height adjustment should be provided. If the operator is working at benches higher than 30 inches in

FIGURE 7–8

Seating depends on reach, vision, and work load on the operator (dimensions shown are based on the small man, which will accommodate the reach limitations of 95 percent of all men)

Product Engineering

height, chair adjustment should permit a range of seat heights from 18 inches to 27 inches. Chair manufacturers supply industrial chairs adjustable in height from the floor to the top edge of the seat. In recent years both industrial and medical experts have collected data that in many instances prove that production costs have been lowered by using chairs and benches of proper height (see Figure 7–8).

If the height of the work station and chair is made so the operator can alternately work in a standing and a sitting position, fatigue and job monotony will be substantially reduced. Monotony is definitely an important factor in producing fatigue, and with the present-day tendency toward specialization and resulting increases in fatigue accidents, everything possible should be done to reduce monotony.

FIGURE 7–9

Better illumination releases energy for useful work

From *National Safety Council Bulletin No. 50, p. 9.*

In the event it is not practical to have the operator work alternately in a standing and sitting position, it has been found desirable to have a seat which can slightly tilt the body forward.

Proper illumination, ventilation, and temperature should be incorporated when possible.

As explained in Chapter 5, good, comfortable working conditions are fundamental for peak production and operator satisfaction. Defective illumination has long been recognized as an important factor in causing operator fatigue, poor quality of product, and low production output. The National Safety Council, in its *Safe Practices Pamphlet No. 50*, mentions that eyes are used in "serious" work about 70 percent of the time and that failure to provide proper lighting will increase consumption of body energy (see Figure 7–9).

Ventilation and temperature are also important considerations in maintaining good working conditions by controlling fatigue and accident causes. Laboratory data recorded in diversified industries are in agreement that atmospheric conditions exert an appreciable influence upon physical activity.

Members of the medical profession, industrialists, and psychologists have realized that colors are effective in stimulating or depressing. By

FIGURE 7–10

Effective visual areas for average employee

Product Engineering

having physical surroundings that relieve eyestrain and stimulate the worker by creating a more cheerful atmosphere, the industry will have fewer injuries and less absenteeism.

Visual requirements of the workplace should be considered so eye fixation demands are minimized.

Certain visual requirements are characteristic of all work centers. Some equipment or controls may be scanned from nearby or remote points.

Other areas will require more concentrated attention. By pre-positioning those components requiring more concentrated observation, such as instruments and dials, not only will less eye fixation time be required but less eye fatigue on the part of the operator will result. Visual control areas are illustrated in Figure 7–10.

Rhythm is essential to the smooth and automatic performance of an operation, and the work should be arranged to permit an easy and natural rhythm wherever possible.

If the sequence of basic motions performed can be arranged so there is a regular recurrence of like therbligs, or a regular alternation in the therbligs, the hands will instinctively work with a rhythmical effect. When

FIGURE 7–11

4AC single spindle automatic chucking machine

Warner & Swasey Co.

work is performed with such a regularity or flow of movement, the operator appears to be working effortlessly yet invariably production is high and operator fatigue is low.

Multiple cuts should be taken whenever possible by combining two or more tools in one, or by arranging simultaneous cuts from both feeding devices if available (cross slide and hex turret).

FIGURE 7–12

Forming cut and drilling operation on a single spindle automatic chucking machine

Warner & Swasey Co.

Production planning in advance for the most efficient manufacture will include taking multiple cuts through combination tools and simultaneous cuts from different tools. Of course, the type of work to be processed and the number of parts to be produced will determine the desirability of combining cuts such as from the square turret and the hexagon turret. Figures 7–11 and 7–12 illustrate typical combined and multiple cuts that can be utilized in turret lathe work (see also Figure 7–13).

Figure 7–11 shows combined cuts from the cross slide and from the multiple turning head on the pentagon turret being performed on a Warner & Swasey 4AC single spindle automatic chucking machine. Two overhead turning tools and one boring tool are cutting from the multiple turning head while a facing cut is being made from the cross slide.

Figure 7–12 shows a forming cut being made from the cross slide while a drilling operation is being performed from the turret.

In Figure 7–13, combined cuts are being made from the square turret cross slide and overhead turning tool mounted in a multiple turning head with an overhead pilot bar for extra support. Also an internal boring operation is simultaneously being made.

All levers, handles, wheels, and other control devices should be readily accessible to the operator and should be designed to give the best possible mechanical advantage and utilize the strongest available muscle group.

Many of our machine tools and other devices are mechanically perfect,

FIGURE 7–13

Combined cuts and an internal boring operation simultaneously being made

Warner & Swasey Co

yet are incapable of effective operation because the designer of the facility overlooked the various human factors in the operation of the equipment. Handwheels, cranks, and levers should be of such size and placed in such positions that operator manipulation can be done with greatest proficiency and with a minimum of fatigue.

Those controls that are used most often should be placed between elbow and shoulder height. For seated operators, maximum force can be applied to levers located at elbow level and at shoulder level for standing operators. Handwheel and crank diameters depend upon both the torque to be expected as well as the mounting position. Maximum diameters of handgrips depend on the forces to be exerted. For example, if a 10- to 15-pound force is required, the diameter should be no less than ¼ inch and preferably larger; for 15 to 25 pounds, a minimum of ½ inch should be used; and for 25 or more pounds, a minimum of ¾ inch.

Maximum diameters should not exceed 1½ inches and the grip length should be at least 3¾ inches in order to accommodate the breadth of the hand.

Guidelines for crank and handwheel radii are: light loads radii from 3 to 5 inches; medium to heavy loads, radii of 4 to 7 inches; very heavy loads radii more than 8 inches but not to exceed 20 inches.

Knob diameters of ½ to 2 inches are usually satisfactory. It should be recognized that the diameter of knobs should be increased as greater torques are needed.

The hand is seldom an efficient holding device because, when it is occupied in holding the work, it cannot be free to do useful work. Parts to be held in position while being worked on should be supported by a fixture, freeing the hands for productive motions. Fixtures not only save time in processing parts, but they permit better quality, in that the work can be held more accurately and firmly.

Investigate the possibility of powered or semiautomatic tools, such as power nut and screwdrivers, speed wrenches, and so on.

Power hand tools will not only perform work faster than manual tools but will do the work with considerably less operator fatigue. Greater uniformity of product can be expected when power hand tools are used. For example, a power nut driver will drive nuts consistently to a predetermined tightness in inch-pounds, while a manual nut driver cannot be expected to maintain constant driving pressure in view of operator fatigue.

PRACTICAL USE OF MOTION STUDY IN THE PLANNING STAGE

Motion analysis as applied in planning

Production men in general agree that it is better to concentrate thinking about method improvement in the planning stage, rather than depend entirely on trying to correct manufacturing methods after they have been introduced.

Insufficient volume may make it impossible to consider later many improvement proposals that might have been introduced in the planning stage with substantial saving over existing methods.

For example, let us take an operation that was done on a drill press in which a ½-inch hole was reamed to the tolerance of 0.500/0.502 inches. The activity of the job was estimated to be 100,000 pieces. The time study department established a standard of 8.33 hours per thousand to perform the reaming operation and the reaming fixture cost $500. Since a base rate of $1.80 per hour was in effect, the money rate per thousand pieces was $15.

Now let us assume that a method analyst suggests broaching the inside diameter because his calculations reveal that the part can be broached at the rate of five hours per thousand. This would be a saving of 3.33 hours per thousand pieces, or a total saving of 333 hours. At our $1.80 base rate this would mean a direct labor savings of $599.40. However, it would not be practical to go ahead with this idea, since the tool cost for broaching is $700. Thus, the change would not be sound unless the labor savings can be increased to $700 to offset the cost of the new broaching tools.

Since the labor savings in a new broaching setup would be 3.33 × $1.80 per thousand, it can be calculated that 116,800 pieces would have to be ordered before the change in tooling would be justified.

$$\frac{\$700 \times 1,000}{\$1.80 \times 3.33} = 116,800 \text{ pieces}$$

However, if the broaching method had been used originally instead of the reaming procedure, it would have paid for itself in

$$\frac{\$700 - \$500}{\$1.80 \times 3.33/M} = 33,400 \text{ pieces}$$

With production requirements of 100,000 pieces, 3.33 × $1.80 × 66.6 thousands (difference between 100,000 and 33,400) = $398 in labor would have been saved over the present reaming method. Had a motion analysis been made in the planning stage this saving might have been realized. Figure 7–14 illustrates these relationships with the customary crossover (break-even chart).

By keeping the laws of motion economy in mind, and breaking the proposed method into its basic divisions, it is possible to develop a right-hand, left-hand analysis prior to starting production. Then by assigning synthetic time values to the various elements of the operator process chart (see Chapter 19), the practicability of the proposed method can be determined. Let us see how this technique is practiced on a simple manufacturing job. The job involves (1) a light blanking operation, (2) low annual production requirements (200,000 pieces per year), and (3) competitive price.

FIGURE 7–14

Crossover chart illustrating fixed and variable costs of two competing methods

With these requirements in mind, the methods analyst proposes performing the job on an arbor press with accompanying die to do the trimming. He then breaks the job down in the form of a right- and left-hand process chart as shown in Figure 7–15.

A review of this operator process chart reveals that several of the laws of motion economy have been violated. Motions of the right hand and the left hand are not balanced, unavoidable delays occur in the pattern of the left hand, and both hands do not finish their work simultaneously.

Analysis of the poor setup discloses that the first wait of the left hand is during the period the right hand raises the handle of the arbor press.

The left hand is then kept idle while the right hand removes the part from the die, and finally, is unavoidably delayed while the right hand reaches out to gain control of the arbor press handle.

It can also readily be seen that the right hand must grasp the arbor press handle every cycle as a result of relinquishing it earlier in the cycle to remove the finished part from the die. Therefore, if the operator did

FIGURE 7–15

Right- and left-hand analysis of a proposed method of a blanking operation

THE AIRFELT MFG. CORP.

RIGHT AND LEFT HAND ANALYSIS

Operation_____ Blank supporting strip on hand arbor press _____

Part No.___ P-1107-7 ___ Dwg. No.___ PB-1107 ___ Date ___ 1-12- ___

Drawn By___ W. Eitele ___ Dept.___ 13 ___ Plant Bellefonte Sheet 1 of 1

Sketch

Left Hand	Symbols		Right Hand	
1. Pick up part from hopper			Pull arbor press handle down	1.
Reach for part	Re	H	Hold handle	
Grasp part	G	H	Hold handle	
Move part adjacent to die	M	M	Move press handle down	
2. Wait for right hand			Raise arbor press handle	2.
Unavoidable delay	UD	M	Move arbor press handle back	
Unavoidable delay	UD	R1	Release press handle	
			Get part from die	3.
3. Wait for right hand		Re	Reach for part in die	
Unavoidable delay	UD	G	Grasp part	
Unavoidable delay	UD			
			Aside part to chute	4.
4. Place part in fixture		M	Move part to chute	
Move part to fixture	M	R1	Release part	
Position part in fixture	P	UD	Wait for left hand	
Release part	R1			
5. Wait			Get arbor press handle	5.
Unavoidable delay	UD	Re	Reach for handle	
Unavoidable delay	UD	G	Grasp handle	

not have to remove the finished piece from the die, he would also be freed of the element "grasp arbor press handle." The improved method in the form of an operator process chart is shown in Figure 7–16.

If this method should be put in operation, we should have a balanced setup with considerably shorter cycle time. It is possible to develop a fixture to include leaf springs that will lift the part clear of the die on the return stroke of the arbor press. The piece can then be automatically ejected through the back of the press by an air blast actuated from the ram of the press.

This motion analysis in the planning stage allows the part to be blanked in the most economical manner.

FIGURE 7–16

Right- and left-hand analysis of a proposed method of a blanking operation in which unavoidable delays have been omitted

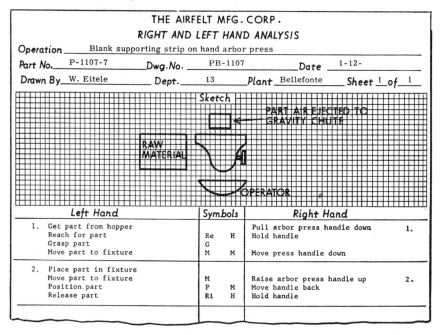

THE AIRFELT MFG. CORP.

RIGHT AND LEFT HAND ANALYSIS

Operation _____ Blank supporting strip on hand arbor press _____

Part No. ___P-1107-7___ Dwg. No. ____PB-1107____ Date ___1-12-___

Drawn By ___W. Eitele___ Dept. ____13____ Plant ___Bellefonte___ Sheet _1_ of _1_

Left Hand	Symbols		Right Hand	
1. Get part from hopper			Pull arbor press handle down	1.
Reach for part	Re	H	Hold handle	
Grasp part	G			
Move part to fixture	M	M	Move press handle down	
2. Place part in fixture				
Move part to fixture	M		Raise arbor press handle up	2.
Position part	P	M	Move handle back	
Release part	Rl	H	Hold handle	

Let us take another example and see how motion study in the planning stage helps determine the ideal method. The operation under study is the assembly of the components going into the upper jaw of a pipe vise. The parts involved are the jaw, brace, two lock washers, and two machine screws (see Figure 7–17). The production schedule called for assembly of 10,000 of these units per year and the item must be priced to meet stiff competition.

Since the parts are all small and can be readily controlled with either hand, the method analyst may first consider hand assembly at a bench, with the operator seated and all parts fed to the normal work area by gravity bins. This method in the form of a right- and left-hand analysis would appear as shown in Figure 7–18.

A quick review of this method discloses that the left hand is ineffectively employed the majority of the cycle, since it is occupied by the therblig "hold" in five distinct areas. To alleviate this condition, the analyst considers making a fixture to hold the part. To eliminate the element "dispose of part" he introduces an ejector pin actuated by a foot pedal (see Figure 7–19). This ejects the part into an accompanying gravity chute.

FIGURE 7–17

Components of upper jaw of pipe vise. Parts in order of assembly (left to right) are shown in upper panel and assembled parts in lower panel

To dispose of the element "lay aside yankee screwdriver," he suspends the tool overhead. To permit a balanced two-handed motion pattern throughout the cycle, an additional yankee screwdriver is suspended overhead for the left hand. Thus both screws can be driven home simultaneously with the aid of self-aligning sleeves incorporated in the fixture. Through the use of fundamental motion data, it can be estimated that the improved

FIGURE 7–18

Right- and left-hand analysis of assembly of pipe vise jaw

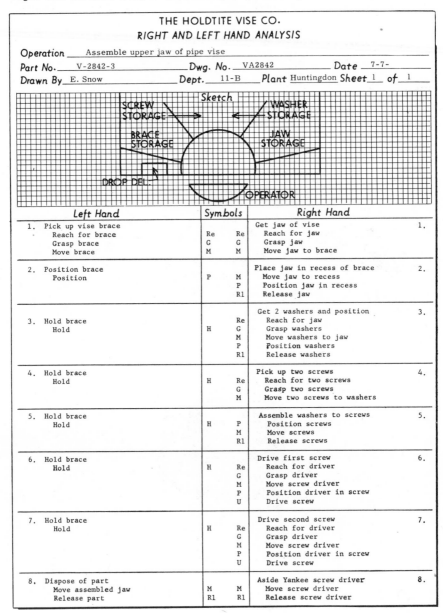

THE HOLDTITE VISE CO.
RIGHT AND LEFT HAND ANALYSIS

Operation ___ Assemble upper jaw of pipe vise ___
Part No. ___ V-2842-3 ___ Dwg. No. ___ VA2842 ___ Date ___ 7-7- ___
Drawn By ___ E. Snow ___ Dept. ___ 11-B ___ Plant ___ Huntingdon ___ Sheet 1 of 1

Left Hand	Symbols		Right Hand	
1. Pick up vise brace			Get jaw of vise	1.
Reach for brace	Re	Re	Reach for jaw	
Grasp brace	G	G	Grasp jaw	
Move brace	M	M	Move jaw to brace	
2. Position brace			Place jaw in recess of brace	2.
Position	P	M	Move jaw to recess	
		P	Position jaw in recess	
		Rl	Release jaw	
			Get 2 washers and position	3.
3. Hold brace		Re	Reach for jaw	
Hold	H	G	Grasp washers	
		M	Move washers to jaw	
		P	Position washers	
		Rl	Release washers	
4. Hold brace			Pick up two screws	4.
Hold	H	Re	Reach for two screws	
		G	Grasp two screws	
		M	Move two screws to washers	
5. Hold brace			Assemble washers to screws	5.
Hold	H	P	Position screws	
		M	Move screws	
		Rl	Release screws	
6. Hold brace			Drive first screw	6.
Hold	H	Re	Reach for driver	
		G	Grasp driver	
		M	Move screw driver	
		P	Position driver in screw	
		U	Drive screw	
7. Hold brace			Drive second screw	7.
Hold	H	Re	Reach for driver	
		G	Grasp driver	
		M	Move screw driver	
		P	Position driver in screw	
		U	Drive screw	
8. Dispose of part			Aside Yankee screw driver	8.
Move assembled jaw	M	M	Move screw driver	
Release part	Rl	Rl	Release screw driver	

FIGURE 7–19

Guide and ejector pin details for foot-operated mechanism

method will increase the productivity by at least 50 percent. A right- and left-hand analysis of this proposed method would appear as shown in Figure 7–20.

Figure 7–21 shows a work station for a "doffing yarn" operation. Figure 7–22 illustrates the motion pattern that the operator was following. The operation in this case was not planned and by means of stroboscopic photography, it can be seen that the operator was going through an elaborate body motion pattern. The planned method shown in Figure 7–23 reduced the number and difficulty of the motions so the operator is less fatigued and his production is greatly improved.

The application of the laws of motion economy and an understanding of the therblig concept will prove to be valuable in establishing ideal methods in the planning stage, as well as improving existing methods.

FIGURE 7–20

Right- and left-hand analysis of proposed setup for assembly of pipe vise jaw

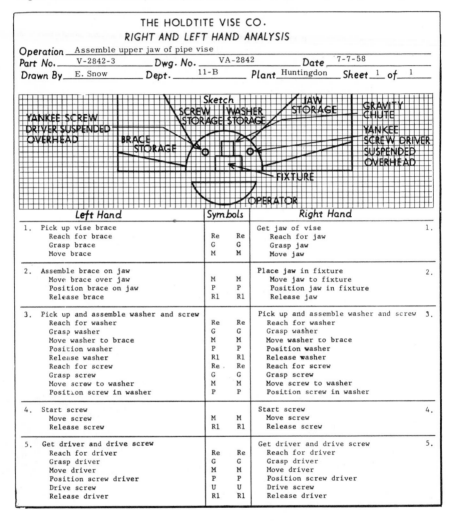

THE HOLDTITE VISE CO.

RIGHT AND LEFT HAND ANALYSIS

Operation __Assemble upper jaw of pipe vise__

Part No. __V-2842-3__ Dwg. No. __VA-2842__ Date __7-7-58__

Drawn By __E. Snow__ Dept. __11-B__ Plant __Huntingdon__ Sheet __1__ of __1__

Left Hand	Symbols		Right Hand
1. Pick up vise brace			Get jaw of vise 1.
Reach for brace	Re	Re	Reach for jaw
Grasp brace	G	G	Grasp jaw
Move brace	M	M	Move jaw
2. Assemble brace on jaw			Place jaw in fixture 2.
Move brace over jaw	M	M	Move jaw to fixture
Position brace on jaw	P	P	Position jaw in fixture
Release brace	R1	R1	Release jaw
3. Pick up and assemble washer and screw			Pick up and assemble washer and screw 3.
Reach for washer	Re	Re	Reach for washer
Grasp washer	G	G	Grasp washer
Move washer to brace	M	M	Move washer to brace
Position washer	P	P	Position washer
Release washer	R1	R1	Release washer
Reach for screw	Re	Re	Reach for screw
Grasp screw	G	G	Grasp screw
Move screw to washer	M	M	Move screw to washer
Position screw in washer	P	P	Position screw in washer
4. Start screw			Start screw 4.
Move screw	M	M	Move screw
Release screw	R1	R1	Release screw
5. Get driver and drive screw			Get driver and drive screw 5.
Reach for driver	Re	Re	Reach for driver
Grasp driver	G	G	Grasp driver
Move driver	M	M	Move driver
Position screw driver	P	P	Position screw driver
Drive screw	U	U	Drive screw
Release driver	R1	R1	Release driver

FIGURE 7–21

Work station for doffing yarn

E. I. du Pont de Nemours & Co.

FIGURE 7–22

Stroboscopic photograph showing motion pattern prior to motion planning on yarn doffing operation

E. I. du Pont de Nemours & Co.

FIGURE 7–23

Stroboscopic photograph showing motion pattern after motion planning on yarn doffing operation

E. I. du Pont de Nemours & Co.

TEXT QUESTIONS

1. When is micromotion study practical? *extremely active jobs where life & repetitiousness are great*

[7 (

2. Define and give examples of the 17 fundamental motions, or therbligs. *p172*
3. How may the basic motion "search" be eliminated from the work cycle?
4. What basic motion generally precedes reach? *release   p174*
5. What three variables affect the time for the basic motion "move"? *p175: Distance, weight & type*
6. How does the analyst or observer determine when the operator is per- *p177* forming the element "inspect"? *operator solely responsible — method is responsible*
7. Explain the difference between avoidable and unavoidable delays.
8. Why should fixed locations be provided at the work station for all tools and materials? *To avoid search Therblig*
9. Which of the five classes of motion is the one most used by industrial *physical* workers?
10. Why is it desirable to have the feet working only when the hands are *p86* occupied? *Hands are more dextrous than feet*
11. Explain the significance of human dimensions.
12. What are the approximate number of calories required by the typical

operator per day for sedentary activities? For light manual labor? For medium labor? For heavy manual labor?

13. What is the range of work-surface height that would accommodate all workers through the 98th percentile?

14. Outline the principal guidelines in the design of operators handgrips, handwheels, and knobs.

GENERAL QUESTIONS

1. Which of the 17 therbligs are classed as effective, and usually cannot be removed from the work cycle?

2. Take an operation out of your daily routine such as dressing, analyze it through the operator process chart, and try to improve the efficiency of your movements.

3. Explain why effective visual areas are reduced where concentrated attention will be required.

4. Why does a broach usually cost more than a reamer to perform the same sizing operation?

CHAPTER 8

Micromotion study

This chapter deals with the most refined technique for analysis of an existing work center. The cost of conducting a micromotion study is approximately four times as great as the cost of conducting a visual motion study of the same operation. Consequently, it is only when the activity of a specific job or class of work is high that it is economically sound to utilize moving pictures for motion study. The term "micromotion study" is used to signify the making of a detailed motion study employing the motion-picture technique. Here each space occupied by a single picture on the moving-picture film, known as a frame, is projected and studied independently, and then collectively with successive frames.

The basic division-of-motion or therblig concept is usually more important in making a micromotion study than in conducting a visual motion study, in that a work assignment can more readily be broken down into basic elements with the frame-by-frame analysis than when visual motion studies are made. Since the object of the micromotion procedure is to uncover every possible opportunity for improvement, down to the performance of each therblig, it is fundamental that the analyst be able to identify each basic division as performed.

The laws of motion economy cited in Chapter 7 are again summarized with several important corollaries so the reader will be cognizant of these laws in their application to micromotion study.

I. Use of the human body
  a) Both hands should begin and end their basic divisions of accomplishment simultaneously and should not be idle at the same instant, except during rest periods.

211

b) The motions made by the hands should be made symmetrically and simultaneously away and toward the center of the body.

c) Momentum should be employed to assist the worker wherever possible, and it should be reduced to a minimum if it must be overcome by muscular effort.

d) Continuous curved motions are preferable to straight-line motions involving sudden and sharp changes in direction.

e) The least number of basic divisions should be used, and these should be confined to the lowest possible classifications. These classifications, summarized in ascending order of time and fatigue expended in their performance, are:
1. Finger motions.
2. Finger and wrist motions.
3. Finger, wrist, and lower arm motions.
4. Finger, wrist, lower arm, and upper arm motions.
5. Finger, wrist, lower arm, upper arm, and body motions.

f) Work that can be done by the feet should be arranged so that it is done simultaneously with work being done by the hands. It should be recognized, however, that simultaneous moving of the hand and foot is difficult to perform.

g) The middle finger and the thumb are the strongest working fingers. The index finger, fourth finger, and little finger are not capable of handling heavy loads over extended periods.

h) The feet are not capable of efficiently operating pedals when the operator is in a standing position.

i) Twisting motions should be performed with the elbows bent.

j) To grip tools, use the segments of the fingers closest to the palm of the hand.

k) Important corollaries
1. Habits of best sequences of therbligs should be established.
2. Any substantial variation in time required for a given therblig should be investigated and the cause determined.
3. Hesitations should be carefully examined and analyzed so as to determine causes and then to eliminate them.
4. Cycles and portions of cycles completed in the least amount of time should be used as a goal to attain. Deviations from these minimum times should be studied in order to determine cause.

II. Arrangement and conditions of the workplace
a) Fixed locations should be provided for all tools and materials so as to permit the best sequence and to eliminate or reduce the therbligs search and select.

b) Gravity bins and drop delivery should be used to reduce reach and move times; also ejectors should be provided wherever possible to remove finished parts automatically.

c) All materials and tools should be located within the normal area in both the vertical and horizontal planes.

d) A comfortable chair should be provided for the operator and the height so arranged that the work can be performed efficiently by the operator alternately standing and sitting.

e) Proper illumination, ventilation, and temperature should be provided.

f) Visual requirements of the workplace should be considered so that eye fixation demands are minimized.

g) Rhythm is essential to the smooth and automatic performance of an operation, and the work should be arranged to permit an easy and natural rhythm wherever possible.

h) Important corollary. Tools and materials should be located to allow the best possible sequence of therbligs, thus automatically building up rhythm in ballistic type movements that are faster, easier, and more accurate.

III. Design of tools and equipment

a) Multiple cuts should be taken whenever possible by combining two or more tools in one, or by arranging simultaneous cuts from both feeding devices if available (cross slide and hex turret).

b) All levers, handles, wheels, and other control devices should be readily accessible to the operator and should be designed so as to give the best possible mechanical advantage and utilize the strongest available muscle group.

c) Holding parts in position should be done by fixtures.

d) Always investigate the possibility of powered or semiautomatic tools, such as power nut and screwdrivers, speed wrenches, etc.

Preparing for the micromotion study

It is usually advisable to take motion pictures of the operation or operations to be studied in the laboratory provided for the purpose. This allows making the study without the interferences that would be encountered on the production floor, and permits taking adequate time to assure first-class pictures. Also, difficulty in providing such aids as adequate light, three-dimensional background (see Figure 8–1), and timing devices in the factory make taking pictures in a laboratory more satisfactory.

Of course, at times it will be necessary to take the pictures outside the laboratory, as for certain machine operations when it would be impractical to provide the facility in the laboratory. In fact, in the interest of economy, several industries today take all their studies at the regular workplace in the factory. Satisfactory pictures can be made in this manner, but they will be assured if taken in the laboratory.

In making a micromotion study, it is wise to study either the best or, preferably, the best two operators. This procedure is quite different from time study where usually an average operator is selected for study (see

FIGURE 8–1

Schematic drawing of camera, overhead mirror, and workbench used for film analysis of operator movements

Advanced Management

Chapter 14). It is not always possible because the operation might be performed by only one person. In such instances, if past performance indicates that the individual is only a fair or a poor operator, then a competent, skilled, cooperative employee should be trained in the operation before the pictures are taken. Only first-class, proficient operators should be selected for filming. This is fundamental for a number of reasons: the proficient employee is usually a dexterous individual who will instinctively follow the laws of motion economy related to the use of the human body; this type of operator is usually cooperative and willing to be photographed; extra effort put forth by this operator will show greater results than when similar effort is employed by the mediocre person.

If the best two operators have been studied, analysis will indicate proficiency in different areas of the cycle for the two men. This may lead to greater improvement than if only one individual is studied.

The people who are being studied should be given at least a day's notice prior to taking the motion picture. This allows them to make any personal preparations they may wish and also permits them to choose wearing apparel that will be conducive to making clear pictures.

To secure the cooperation of the foreman, it is essential that he be advised of the plans several days in advance. This is necessary so he will be able to adjust his personnel to assure that his projected production schedules will be maintained. Interruptions brought about by film analysis work may cause a given section to lose several valuable man-hours, and if the foreman is not given advance notice of contemplated motion study work involving his section, he can hardly be expected to be cooperative.

Micromotion study as a training aid

In addition to being used as a method improvement tool, micromotion study is finding increasing use as a training aid. The world of sports has used this tool for many years, to develop timing of movement, rhythm, and smoothness of performance in various athletes. Motion pictures are made of outstanding performers in a given sport, and then the pictures are enlarged several times and projected on the screen to facilitate detailed analysis of their motions. Less proficient performers are then able to pattern their efforts after the experts.

Industry is finding that it can attain the same results accomplished in the area of athletics. By filming highly skilled workmen and showing the pictures in slow motion and highly enlarged, it is possible to train new employees in a minimum of time to follow the ideal motion-method pattern.

One Pennsylvania concern engaged in the manufacture of loose-leaf notebooks, writing paper, envelopes, tablets, and similar paper items continually takes motion pictures for training purposes, not only in its own plant but in affiliated plants. By continually exchanging motion pictures taken at the different plants, they can take advantage of method improvements introduced throughout the corporation, and they are able to train their employees in following the new method in a minimum of time.

Management should take full advantage of the industrial movies, once a micromotion program is launched. By showing all pictures taken of the various operations to the operators involved and to their fellow workers, immeasurable goodwill and individual interest are established throughout the organization. Once operators understand the usefulness and need of micromotion study, their assistance can be enlisted in the working out of improved methods.

Micromotion equipment

To be able to do an acceptable job in micromotion study, it will be necessary to budget a minimum of $3,000 for camera, projection equipment, and the other facilities necessary to carry out a complete program. This figure is only a rough approximation based on current prices and can fluctuate appreciably in either direction as market conditions change.

Today, industrial pictures are almost altogether confined to 16 mm. and this size equipment will prove to be quite satisfactory. It offers an excellent alternative to the high-cost 35-mm. equipment and the lack of detail experienced with 8-mm. facilities.

The motion-picture camera

The most important piece of equipment in micromotion work is the camera. Several acceptable cameras are on the market today, each having certain desirable features. Some cameras are equipped with spring drive, others with electric motor drive, and some provide both of these drives in the same camera. Straight spring-driven cameras are on the average about 30 percent lower in cost than constant speed, motor-driven cameras, and offer the additional advantage of not requiring a nearby power source. In general, the film capacity of the spring-driven camera is as large or larger than that of its motor-driven companion.

FIGURE 8–2

Bell & Howell 70 TMR Time and Motion Study Camera

The principal disadvantage of the spring-driven camera is that re-winding is a periodic necessity. The operator may forget to do this and have to stop and rewind at a critical point in the job being studied. A decade ago these cameras sometimes failed to maintain an even speed, but the better spring-driven cameras on the market today run at a speed sufficiently constant to offer no problem in this respect.

FIGURE 8–3

The Paillard Bolex, Model H-16; a 16-mm. camera with three standard lenses

Electric, synchronous, motor-driven cameras assure constant speed exposure, and thus it is not necessary to include a microchronometer or other timing device in the background of the pictures being taken. Standard models are available that allow speeds of either 1 frame per second, 10 frames per second, or 1,000 frames per minute. The latter, being the most popular for motion study work, is slightly faster than the normal camera speed of 960 frames per minute (see Figures 8–2 and 8–3).

The lens

In selecting a camera, one must consider the matter of "picture-making scope."[1] This depends almost entirely on the lens and the shutter.

The larger a lens is in relation to its focal length, which is the distance from the lens to the film, the more light will be admitted during a given period, and the more light per interval, the greater the scope given to the camera.

---

[1] *How to Make Good Pictures,* Eastman Kodak Company, Rochester, N.Y.

Ofter we hear the term "speed" referred to when describing the lens of the camera. By "speed" is meant the comparison of the diameter to the focal length of the lens. Thus, an $f/16$ lens is one whose diameter is one sixteenth of its focal length. Likewise, an $f/3.5$ lens is one in which the diameter is $1/3.5$ of its focal length. From this, it can readily be seen that the larger the f number, the slower the lens and the smaller the f number, the faster the lens. Actually the f number of a lens is determined by the ratio of the focal length and the aperture (diameter of the largest diaphragm opening) at which the lens will be most effective.

The faster a lens, the greater its cost. To be assured of good pictures throughout a plant, an $f/1.9$ lens should be provided. This lens will give the versatility needed for almost all industrial pictures. To compare the speeds of two lenses, keep in mind that the speeds will vary inversely as the square of their f numbers. Thus an $f/4$ lens would be 16 times as fast as an $f/16$ lens (see Figure 8–4).

To be assured of getting good pictures in all situations, three lenses should be provided: one of standard focal length with a field width of approximately 10 feet at a 25-foot distance; a wide-angle lens giving a 15-foot field width at a 25-foot distance; and a long-focus lens with a field width of about 3 feet at a 25-foot distance (see Figure 8–5).

Often it is not possible to move the camera equipped with only standard lens far enough away from the scene to secure all of the details required. The size of the room or work area may be such that it limits positioning the camera. In cases like this, a wide-angle lens is necessary to broaden and heighten the field of view, so analysis can be made of the complete work station and all of the operator's movements.

The long-focus lens is employed when it becomes desirable to obtain greater detail, through larger images, than is possible with the standard lens. This situation may frequently arise when studying the finger motions of the operator performing a delicate manipulative operation. In such situations, it would be disturbing to the operator to move the camera as close as would be necessary if only a standard lens were available.

It is well to remember that the wide-angle lens will minimize camera movement, and rock-steady pictures can readily be taken by holding the camera against the head. However, when the long-focus or telephoto lens is put into use, camera movements will be accentuated. Therefore, a tripod must be used to get steady pictures when filming with this lens.

The shutter

It is important that shutter speeds do not vary: all the good effects of a fine lens can be nullified through lack of control of the shutter. The

FIGURE 8–4

The larger the relative size of the lens, the greater is its speed, or ability to collect light and transmit it to the film—and the shorter the exposure needed under any given light conditions (notice, also, that as size and ability increase, the lens in general becomes more complex, hence more expensive to make)

A KEY TO LENS ABILITY

Relative Sizes of Various Lenses	Relative Exposure Times Required	Approximate Relative Speeds	Glass Elements Used in Lenses
MENISCUS		1	
DOUBLET		1½	
ANASTIGMAT f/8.8		3	
ANASTIGMAT f/6.3		6	
ANASTIGMAT f/4.5		11	
ANASTIGMAT SPECIAL f/3.5		18	
EKTAR f/1.9		62	

camera purchased must be of such quality that shutter speeds can be depended upon.

Black-and-white versus color film

There is usually the consideration of whether or not to use color film. The obvious advantage of color film is its universal appeal when projected on the screen. If the films are shown to members of the production floor for industrial relations purposes, the extra cost of colored film is well justified. Colored film generally costs about one third more than black-and-white reversible film.

FIGURE 8–5

Relationship of focal length of lens to object size and distance and image size

Eastman Kodak Co.

To obtain good pictures using colored film requires greater care because lighting is considerably more critical. With the fast lenses and high-speed films available, excellent black-and-white movies can be made with regular industrial lighting fixtures. However, if colored film is used, it is necessary to introduce photographic flood or reflector-type flood lamps. In addition to the high illumination level needed for proper exposure of colored film, it is important that the light be sufficiently dispersed so all colors are uniformly lighted. This requirement should be met, since contrast in colored photography is provided by differences between colors.

Since less care relative to lighting need be exercised, and the film costs less, it is wise to begin a motion study program by taking black-and-white pictures. As further use of the pictures becomes advisable and experience is gained, it may be well to use colored film.

Light meter

Even though a broad latitude is given in XX reversible film, judgment should not be relied upon to determine the intensity of the light being cast upon the subject to be photographed. A light meter is the only tool that assures an accurate recording of the light intensity. Since the light that strikes the film in the camera is reflected light, it is necessary that this light be measured rather than incident light, which is the light cast upon the subject.

It must be remembered that the exposure should be constant for the

FIGURE 8–6

Exposure meter for measuring intensity of reflected light

Weston Electrical Instrument Corp.

film being used. Since exposure equals light times time, it is essential that the quantity of light be known. If the quantity of light is small, the time will be great; conversely, if the amount of light is great, the time will be short.

A photoelectric cell exposure meter is shown in Figure 8–6. A light reading is made by aiming the meter toward the scene and pointing the instrument downward. It is important that the meter is not pointed toward a floodlight or, for outdoor pictures, toward the sky. If this is done, an inflated reading will result in improper setting of the *f*-stop number and consequent underexposure of the film. Reflected brightness from the scene energizes the light-sensitive photoelectric cell, and intensity is read on the scale in candles per square foot.

Tripod

If the camera is carefully supported against the head, it is possible to get fairly steady pictures. However, more satisfactory pictures will result if the camera is rigidly supported during the picture-taking process.

Rather than construct a homemade tripod to support the camera, it is advisable to purchase one that gives versatility as well as assures rock-steady pictures. The head of the tripod illustrated in Figure 8–2 can be rotated on both a horizontal and vertical axis and when required can be locked in any given position for multiple exposure filming. The legs are adjustable so pictures can be taken while supporting the camera at heights ranging from 2½ to 5 feet.

Floodlights

With the high-speed films and fast lenses available today, black-and-white pictures can be made satisfactorily in a good share of the factory without the aid of supplementary lighting. There will, however, be cases where it may be desirable to take pictures in areas away from windows and light fixtures; then supplementary lighting will be needed to assure good pictures.

When additional light is called for, two floodlights will take care of the job. One should be placed close to either side of the camera, while the second should be located so a 45° angle is made between the floodlight and the axis running through the camera and the subject. Figure 8–7

FIGURE 8–7

Convenient method of holding floodlight reflector or other accessory (can be clamped on table or stand and allows positioning of light at any angle)

S.O.S. Cinema Supply Corp.

FIGURE 8–8

16-mm projector equipped with stop action, slow motion (1–12 frames per second), illuminated frame counter, and self-contained control box for forward, reverse, cine-stop, or pulse control

Traid Corporation

illustrates a photographic flood lamp and reflector equipped with a ball-and-swivel socket to allow positioning at any angle.

Projection equipment

Many styles of projection equipment are available today and care should be exercised in selecting a projector that will allow (1) counting frames; (2) stop action; (3) variable speed projecting; and (4) clear pictures.

If the projector is equipped with a frame counter, it will save the analyst the laborious, monotonous operation of counting frames while analyzing elemental motions.

Stop action is necessary so that each frame may be projected as a still slide for extensive analysis.

Variable speed is a characteristic that makes the projector more versatile. When this feature is incorporated in the projector, it will be useful for training operators in following the correct method. Also, it will be helpful in training time study men to performance rate or level (see Chapter 15). Figure 8–8 illustrates a 16-mm. projector that gives all the fundamental characteristics required to do a good job of projecting for both motion study and micromotion study work.

Microchronometer

Frank Gilbreth designed a fast-moving, spring-driven clock that recorded time to 0.0005 minute. He called his clock a microchronometer and used it for determining elapsed elemental times when viewing his films taken with a hand-cranked camera.

The microchronometer shown in Figure 8–9 is driven by a synchronous motor, thus assuring constant speed. There are 100 divisions on the face of the clock, each having a value of 0.001 minute. The large sweep hand makes a complete revolution in six seconds, while the smaller hand takes 10 minutes to circle the dial.

By placing the microchronometer within the viewing area, the analyst can determine the elapsed time from one frame to the next. It also serves to identify specific cycles or points within a cycle.

Splicer and viewer

Once the pictures have been taken and developed, they will need to be reviewed for specific titling, removal of certain substandard parts, adjustment of sequence, and so forth. A combination splicer, viewer, and rewinder, as illustrated in Figure 8–10, has been designed to aid in performing the editing function. As the film is passed through the viewer, it can be decided where the cut should be made. After removal of the censored film, the fixture permits immediate splicing and continued inspection of the film.

Optical screen

In the analysis of the films, it is not always convenient to set up a screen and then view in darkness or semidarkness the films projected

FIGURE 8–9

Microchronometer

Lafayette Instrument Co.

some distance away. To allow the analyst to view films at a desk or table and under normal daylight conditions, an optical screen, as illustrated in Figure 8–11, is available. This unit has a recessed area for placing the projector, and the pictures are shown against a mirror inside the enclosed cabinet and placed at an angle of about 45° to the lens of the projector. The mirror then reflects the image to an opal glass pane located in the unit directly in front of the analyst. This arrangement permits viewing the pictures at extremely close range so all details of each frame are clearly observed. Since the pictures are quite sharp even in bright daylight, the analyst can record and plot his data as he goes along without the inconvenience of working in darkness.

Storage of films

Damage to films is a result of use or misuse, rather than storage. In the United States the storage of films represents no major problem, since temperatures and humidities in this country do not deviate greatly from the most desirable storage conditions for films, which is around 40 percent relative humidity at about 75° F. If stored films begin to show mold growth and fungus, then it is certain that the humidity is too high, and steps should be taken to reduce it. On the other hand, if the films become brittle after being stored a short while, it will be necessary to raise the humidity of the air in the storage area to the proper level.

FIGURE 8–10

Combination splicer, viewer, and rewinder makes a convenient tool in editing

Craig, Inc.

The 16-mm. films available today are produced on a safety base and present no particularly dangerous fire hazard. In fact, the hazard induced is no more severe than that of any newsprint paper stored in the same quantity and form.

Ideally, films should be placed in cans and stored on edge in metal cabinets. The cabinets should not be located in basements or top building floors, since basements invariably are too damp and top floors frequently become too hot in summer. In locating the cabinets, make sure that they are not placed up against a source of heat such as a radiator or steampipe.

Many metal storage cabinets available today allow controlled humidification. When the humidity drops below 25 percent, the proper

FIGURE 8–11

Observer is analyzing a film under normal daylight conditions (note clarity of image an optical screen)

amount of moisture can be added and the air circulated by mechanical humidifiers.

Summary

In summary, the following equipment is recommended to carry on a first-rate program of micromotion study and achieve resulting labor relation benefits.

1. One motion-picture camera with film capacity of 100 feet.
2. One $f/1.9$ lens.
3. One wide-angle lens.
4. One telescopic lens.
5. One tripod with head that can be rotated on both a horizontal and vertical axis.
6. One exposure meter.

7. Two photoflood lamps with swivel-type reflectors.
8. One projector with hand-crank and frame counter attachment adapted for showing films at normal speed to audiences.
9. One portable screen.
10. One optical screen.
11. One titling kit.
12. One splicer and viewer.
13. One steel cabinet for film storage.
14. One microchronometer.

TEXT QUESTIONS

1. How does micromotion study differ from motion study?
2. For micromotion study, what additional considerations should be given to "use of human body" and "arangement and conditions of workplace"?
3. What advantage is there in taking micromotion pictures in the laboratory provided for that purpose as compared to the production floor?
4. Why is the best operator usually selected in the micromotion procedure?
5. What consideration should be given the foreman relative to taking micromotion pictures in his department?
6. How can micromotion study be helpful in training?
7. What types of cameras have been used for micromotion study? What are the advantages and disadvantages of each?
8. Why are the lens and shutter important in micromotion photography?
9. Why isn't color film used more often in micromotion study? Summarize the advantages of color film.
10. Why is "stop action" an important feature on projection equipment?
11. What "extra" devices should be included with a projector to make it ideal for film analysis work?
12. Where should the microchronometer be placed during the picture taking process?
13. What is an optical screen? What are the advantages of using one?
14. How does humidity affect stored films?
15. What is meant by the "speed" of the lens?
16. How fast would an $f/1.8$ lens be as compared to an $f/5.6$ lens?
17. Would an $f/16$ lens be considered a fast lens? Why?
18. Explain how multiple cuts can be accommodated on an engine lathe. On a turret lathe.

GENERAL QUESTIONS

1. Make a sketch of your desk or work station and show arrangement and conditions that would agree with the laws of motion economy and their corollaries.

2. Interview at least two factory workmen and get their reaction to micro-motion study through the film analysis technique.
3. What activity within an industrial organization other than methods analy-sis might include the use of micromotion equipment? How?
4. Discuss the relative merits of the telephoto and the wide-angle lens.

CHAPTER 9

Taking motion pictures for micromotion study and film analysis

In general, the fundamental steps in making a micromotion study, in order of their chronological sequence, are:

1. Take moving pictures of two of the most superior operators.
2. Analyze the film on a frame-by-frame basis, plotting the results on a simo chart (simultaneous motion chart).
3. Consider the laws of motion economy and their corollaries and create an improved method.
4. Teach and standardize the new method.
5. Take moving pictures of the new method.

Taking the moving pictures

Several factors should be checked before taking moving pictures on the production floor or in the laboratory. First, be sure that the selected operators have had a reasonable advance notice that pictures are to be taken. This is important so that they can be properly groomed and attired. It is also necessary to be sure that clearance has been obtained from the departmental foreman for the use of his operators. In some plants, it is necessary to obtain clearance from the union before proceeding with the picture taking. Even if this is not required, it is always wise,

in the interests of healthy labor relations, to keep the union officers completely informed as to the intent relative to all phases of the moving-
picture procedure. This is important since some plants have misused the
data developed by the micromotion technique to the detriment of organized labor, and thus have caused suspicion and resentment toward
the filming technique. Every effort should be made to avoid creating the

FIGURE 9–1

Three-dimensional view of operator at work station allows all motions to be in clear
view for analysis purposes

Advanced Management

same reaction to the micromotion procedure that developed toward the
stopwatch during the 1920's.

Then make sure that there is an adequate inventory of material so that
it will not be necessary to replenish various suppplies during the picture-
taking process. The camera should be carefully checked to ascertain that
it is in good working order and that the lens is clean. After this, the
cameraman should be ready to place the camera in the most advantageous position for taking pictures.

As has been pointed out, it is possible to get fairly steady pictures by
holding the camera in the hand while supported against the head; however, it is advisable to use a good, sturdy tripod. The camera should be
placed as close to the work area as conveniently possible so as to give
clear detail of the most remote areas of the work station within which the

operator performs. When the camera is placed at a sufficient height the operator motions in the horizontal plane will tend to be perpendicular to the line of sight and, consequently, will be easily analyzed upon projection of the developed film. When pictures are filmed in the laboratory, a mirror can be placed close to the work station at an angle of about 45°. This will give a top view as well as front view when pictures are taken with the line of sight parallel to the plane of the work station (see Figure 9–1).

By placing a grid background behind the operator and perpendicular to the work station, and incorporating a similar cross section with 2-inch scribed squares on the work area, it will be possible for the micromotion analyst to record true distances of the elemental therbligs when analyzing the film. Depending on the position of the grids and the position of the hand relative to the grid, grid distances will have to be corrected in order to obtain true distances. The correction factor may be determined by ordinary triangulation.

Upon completing the arrangement of the scene, loading the camera, and checking the illumination with the exposure meter, the analyst should set the lens to the correct opening as determined by the exposure meter for the emulsion speed of the film being used. Next, the distance between the subject and the film plane should be measured and the lens focused while precision-framing the subject. Pertinent information relative to the various camera adjustments should then be recorded on the micromotion study data sheet (see Figure 9–2).

After the above has been done, the camera film meter should be set to zero so that it will be possible to detect at all times the number of feet of exposed film and the remaining feet of unexposed film in the camera. This procedure is not necessary on some modern cameras, as reloading automatically sets the dial at zero feet of exposed film. At this point make sure that the speed required has been established and that the camera has been wound. (This of course is not necessary in electric-driven cameras.) About 35 feet of film at normal speed of 16 frames per second can be exposed before it is necessary to rewind the camera. Modern cameras have a warning bell that sounds when they are nearly run down. After the bell rings, about 3 additional feet of film can be exposed without fear of variation in the film exposure speed.

Upon completion of several practice cycles so as to relieve the operator of any nervousness he may have developed while being "put under the spotlight," he is requested to give his best performance, and then the film is exposed. Several cycles, depending on their duration, should be taken for analysis. Often, the first cycle is unsatisfactory, as the operator may develop a case of nerves when he hears the camera begin to operate. This reaction is usually short in duration, and he will soon acquire his normal feel for the work. Usually, operators enjoy being photographed,

FIGURE 9–2

Micromotion study data sheet

MICROMOTION STUDY DATA SHEET

Operation _____

Operator _____ No. _____ Part No. _____ Dwg. _____

Film No. _____ Date _____ Method _____

Camera _____ Lens _____

Frames per Min. _____ Exposure _____ Film Type _____

Light Reading _____ Aperture "f" _____ Focus _____

Performance Factor _____ Time of Day _____

SKETCH OF WORKPLACE & CAMERA ARRANGEMENT

SCALE 1/4" = ——

and little difficulty is encountered in getting excellent cooperation from them.

Analyzing the film

Before analyzing the film, the analyst should run the pictures through several times in order to determine the cycle that represents the best performance. If the projector is equipped with a frame counter, this can readily be done by noting the transpired frames of each cycle. If a microchronometer was included in the scene, then it is a simple matter to observe the "winks" required to perform the cycle from the projected pictures. The shortest cycle usually is the best one to study.

Once the cycle that is to be studied is determined, the analyst can begin the frame-by-frame analysis procedure. Although the study can be made at any point in the cycle, it is customary to begin the analysis at the frame after "release of finished part" of the previous cycle. Thus, the first basic operation employed in most instances would be reach, in order to pick up a part or tool so as to begin production on the cycle being studied.

Once the starting point of the cycle has been determined, then the analyst should set the frame counter to zero so as to facilitate recording elapsed elemental times.

After the therblig being employed by the operator is noted, the film should be advanced a frame at a time until termination of the basic division. The number of frames exposed is then read off the frame counter and recorded on the micromotion data sheet.

Reach and move motions are considered as beginning at the frame preceding the frame in which noticeable movement occurs, and as ending in the frame where noticeable motion ceases. In motions where only minor movements occur, such as grasp, release, and position, the beginning point is considered to be the frame in which the preceding motion ended, and the ending point is the frame preceding the one in which the following motion showed noticeable movement.

While reviewing the film, the analyst carefully observes the motion class being used while performing the basic division, and records this information on his data sheet. At all times, the analyst must have an open and probing mind so as to determine the possibilities of either eliminating or improving each basic division.

After briefly describing the basic division in the space provided (as "move to fixture" in Figure 9–3), the analyst draws a horizontal line across the portion of the paper representing the body member being studied. For the most part, only the arms and hands of the operator are studied, although sometimes it is desirable to analyze foot motions as well as the body motions.

The motion symbol should be recorded in the space provided, and in combined motions, symbols of the elements occurring simultaneously should be noted. Thus, a pre-position may occur during a move, such as when the hand aligns a bolt while transporting it. In this case, the element description would be "Move bolt —— inches," and the symbols recorded would be "P.P. and M."

In the motion class columns, it is helpful to differentiate the productive

FIGURE 9–3

Film analysis of vise clamp assembly

DATE: JANUARY 9	DEPT. I.E. 320	DRAWING: SEE REPORT	PART NO. 114

PART DESCRIPTION: VISE CLAMP

OPERATION: ASSEMBLY   FILM SPEED: 16 FRAMES/SEC.

CLOCK READINGS	LEFT HAND	SYMBOL	MOTION CL.	TIME (IN WINKS)	MOTION CL.	SYMBOL	RIGHT HAND	CLOCK READINGS
2059								2059
2089	MOVE TO JAW BIN 14"	RE	3	0030	3	RE	MOVE TO BRACE BIN 14"	2089
2105	PICK UP JAW	G	1	0016				
2125	MOVE TO FIXTURE 8"	M	3	0020 / 0036		UD	IDLE	2125
2184	PLACE IN FIXTURE	U	1	0059	1	G	PICK UP BRACE	2184
				0038	3	M	MOVE TO FIXTURE 8"	2222
2451	MOVE TO FIXTURE 12"	M	3	0037	3	M	MOVE TO FIXTURE 12"	2451
2579	SCREW IN SCREWS	U	1	0128	1	U	SCREW IN SCREWS	2579

elements from the nonproductive elements. This is usually done through color; thus, the elements reach, grasp, move, use, and assemble would be shown as solid black, and the remainder of the therbligs would be shown in red or by crosshatching if the charts are to be duplicated. Delay times are signified as Class 1 motions in red. All other therbligs are identified on the chart by the motion class utilized in performing the operation.

The time scale selected should provide enough room to identify clearly the shortest basic divisions so as to give a neat-appearing chart that can be easily studied and diagnosed for improvement. Release is the shortest of all the therbligs, taking but one frame at normal camera speed. Thus, if each division of the time scale should be equated to 0.002 of a minute or four "winks," a neat-appearing chart would result.

After the first basic division of one hand has been studied, analyzed, and the method recorded, the film should be slowly advanced, and the next basic division should likewise be studied and so on until completion of the cycle. To avoid confusion, one hand should be completely studied before beginning to study the other hand. As the second hand is being considered, periodic check should be made to verify that the motions recorded are occurring in the same relationship with the other hand as indicated in the analysis sheet. The analyst must remember that when the projected picture is reviewed the left arm is on the right side of the picture. In fact, all directions are reversed.

After both hands have been completely charted, a summary should be included at the bottom of the chart showing the cycle time, pieces made per cycle, productive time per cycle, and nonproductive time per cycle. Sometimes a sketch of the workplace is helpful and this can be included at the bottom of the chart. The sketch usually is not necessary, since the film will give a pictorial presentation of the work area.

Create an improved method

After the simo chart has been completed, the next step is to use it. The nonproductive sections of the chart represent a good place to start. These sections will include the therbligs hold, search, select, position, pre-position, inspect, and plan, and all the delays. The more of these that can be eliminated, the better will be the proposed method. However, the analysis should not be confined to the red sections of the chart, since possibilities for improvement exist in the productive portions as well. For example, the productive element "reach 24" can be improved by reducing the distance and, consequently, lowering the motion class.

A micromotion checklist is helpful for the analyst so he does not forget to consider all the feasible possibilities for improvement. Table 9–1 illustrates a checklist that covers most of the considerations that apply to the laws of motion economy and their corollaries.

TABLE 9–1

Checklist for simo chart

1. Are both hands beginning their therbligs simultaneously?
2. Are both hands ending their therbligs at the same time?
3. Can delay or idle times be removed from the cycle?
4. Is the motion pattern of the arms symmetrical?
5. Are motions made radially from the body in opposite directions?
6. Can a fixture be incorporated to eliminate hold?
7. Are all materials and tools within the normal work area in both the horizontal and vertical planes?
8. Does the chair and work station allow the operator to get close enough to the work?
9. Has the overhead space been utilized to suspend tools and store inventory components?
10. Are motions confined to lowest possible classifications?
11. Are tools and materials located to permit best sequence of motions?
12. Can foot-operated mechanisms be advantageously introduced?
13. Have gravity chutes and drop delivery been provided for?
14. Are all tools pre-positioned to minimize grasp time and reduce the search and select therbligs?
15. Has an automatic ejector been incorporated in the fixture?
16. Can position times be reduced by providing "pilots" or some other device for mating parts?

Figure 9–4 illustrates a completed simo chart of the assembly of a variable resistor. This chart was constructed after a new fixture was developed to facilitate assembly and represents a method considerably improved over the original method of assembly. Yet an analysis of this chart will disclose several areas for further improvement. The right- and left-hand movements are not balanced in many parts of the cycle, and there are 10 ineffective motions performed by the left hand and 11 ineffective motions executed by the right hand. Several of the moves and reaches appear to be unduly long, suggesting shortening of distances at the work station layout.

The micromotion technique should be used to uncover every inefficiency regardless of its apparent insignificance. Sufficient numbers of minute improvements in total will result in an appreciable annual savings.

Teach and standardize the new method

To be assured that full benefits are realized from the micromotion study, it is important that the improved method be put into practice as soon as possible and that it be followed in exact detail by all operators to whom it applies. Verbal explanations on the motion pattern to be followed are usually inadequate: both time and effort will be saved if an instruction chart is completed giving specific information on the "how" of the improved method.

The typical micromotion instruction sheet, in form, is similar to the

FIGURE 9–4

Simo chart assembly of variable resistor

MICROMOTION DATA

NAME OF PART. VARISTOR   NO. 30 A   FILM NO. 5209

OPERATION. ASSEMBLY OF VARISTOR   OPERATOR. MAYHEW

TIME SCALE	E.T.		LEFT-HAND DESCRIPTION		MOTION CLASS 1 2 3 4 5	MOTION CLASS 5 4 3 2 1		RIGHT-HAND DESCRIPTION	NO.	WINKS	TIME SCALE
0163	WINKS	NO.					RL	RELEASE ASSEMBLY	NO.	WINKS	0163
0170	7	1	MOVING TOWARD BINS	RE			RE	MOVE TO BIN	1	10	0173
0182	12	2	GRASP SPRING WASHER	G			G	GRASP BOLT	2	9	0182
0201	18	3	MOVE TO FIXTURE	M			M	MOVE TO FIXTURE POSITION BOLT	3	19	0201
0250	49	4	WAIT FOR RIGHT HAND	UD			P		4	49	0250
0254	4	5	POSITION WASHER	P			RL	RELEASE BOLT	5	4	0254
0272	18	6	PLACE ON BOLT	A			UD	WAIT FOR LEFT HAND	6	19	0273
0276	4	7	RELEASE WASHER	RL							
0295	19	8	MOVE TO BINS	RE			RE	MOVE TO BIN	7	18	0291
0310	15	9	GRASP TUBE	G			G	GRASP BRASS WASHER	8	11	0302
0340	30	10	MOVE TO FIXTURE	M			M	MOVE TO FIXTURE	9	43	0345
0343	3	11	POSITION	P			P	POSITION WASHER	10	4	0349
0349	6	12	PLACE TUBE ON BOLT	A							
0354		13	HOLD	H							
0356	2	14	RELEASE TUBE	RL							
			MOVE TO BIN AND	RE			A	PLACE WASHER ON BOLT	11	30	0379
0385	29	15	GRASP FIBER WASHER	G			RL	RELEASE WASHER	12	2	0381
0402	17	16	MOVE TO FIXTURE	M			RE	MOVE TO BIN	13	19	0400
							G	GRASP CONTACT	14	6	0406
							M	MOVE TO FIXTURE	42	21	1122
							P	POSITION DRIVER	43	5	1127
1184	100	40	HOLD POSITIONER UP	H			U	TIGHTEN NUT	44	57	1184
1186	2	41	RELEASE POSITIONER	RL			RL	RELEASE DRIVER	45	2	1886
							RE	MOVE TO FIXTURE	46	11	1197
1205	19	42	MOVE TO BINS	RE			G	GRASP ASSEMBLY	47	4	1201
							M	MOVE TOWARD BINS	48	11	1212

TIME PER PIECE

1049 WINKS

OR

0.5245 MIN.

R. E. Call

operator process chart discussed in Chapter 6. A layout of the work area drawn to scale heads the instruction sheet and following this is shown the motion sequence of both the right hand and the left hand. These elements appear in relationship to each other. Special tools such as form cutters, gages, jigs, and fixtures are identified after the element in which they are used. Also, speeds, feeds, depth of cut, and other pertinent manufacturing information will be shown. Usually, a time summary will accompany the instruction sheet, so the operator will be able to measure his performance against standard while being trained in the new method. A typical instruction sheet appears in Figure 9–5.

It is important that the foreman or line supervisor be well versed in the proposed method so he will be able to assist in training the workmen.

FIGURE 9–5

Instruction card

TURRET LATHE INSTRUCTION SHEET

LEFT HAND	BASE TIME	RIGHT HAND
Pick up chuck wrench and tighten chuck	.20 min.	Pick up casting, place in chuck
Start machine and engage feed	.05 min.	Present facing tool
Face casting	.52 min.	Face casting-plug gage (F-1112) part from previous cycle
Back-off facing tool, change speed	.06 min.	Present center drill and center drill
Change feed	.05 min.	Index hex turret
Drill 33/64" H.S.S.	.20 min.	Drill 33/64" H.S.S.
Change speed and feed	.07 min.	Index hex turret
Drill 13/16" H.S.S.	.15 min.	Drill 13/16" H.S.S.
Change feed	.05 min.	Index hex turret
Bore to .865	.22 min.	Bore to .865"
Change feed and speed	.07 min.	Index hex turret
Ream to .868 (F-1102)	.32 min.	Ream to .868 (F-1102)
Stop machine	.08 min.	Double index
Hold chuck	.08 min.	Pick up chuck wrench and open chuck
Lay aside piece for inspection	.03 min.	Lay aside chuck wrench

Usually, instruction sheets are run off in Ditto or some other rapid duplicating process so copies can be filed in the methods section, time study section, and foremen's office, as well as given to each operator performing the operation. A hanger for the instruction sheet should be provided at the operator's work station so it can readily be referred to at all times during the operating cycle. If a clear plastic envelope is provided to hold the instruction sheet, it will remain readable for a considerably longer period.

The foreman, with the methods engineer, should periodically check each operation on the production floor to be sure the new method is being followed, and to answer any question that may come up on the new procedure. Installation and follow-up are two very important phases in micromotion methods improvement. Often it is difficult for the average operator to justify the new method because the changes may appear so insignificant. Consequently, it will be necessary for both the foreman and the methods engineer to do a real job of selling the improved system.

Unless periodic checks are made for at least several weeks, operators may go back to their old way of doing the job and disregard completely the new technique. One of the added benefits of the written instruction sheet is getting the operator to conform to the established instructions.

As soon as one of the better operators has become skilled in the new method, moving pictures can be taken and a simo chart constructed to illustrate the improvements resulting from the study. The same operators selected in making pictures of the unimproved method should be used. This will give a better comparison for evaluating the savings than if different operators were used in the final pictures. Once the new pictures have been taken, they should be used as a training tool for all other operators performing the same operation. Seeing how the operation should be done is much more helpful than reading or hearing how it should be done. The psychological impact of seeing a fellow worker perform the new method is a force in breaking down the inherent human resistance to change.

The completed simo chart of the improved method when compared to the one drawn of the old method will clearly present the savings. Figure 9–6 illustrates a proposed method after a complete micromotion study. Note that this tool not only shows the amount of savings but vividly explains how these results were made possible.

Other motion study techniques involving photographic methods

There are two motion study techniques that give more detail than visual motion study and less than micromotion study. Both of these have application under certain conditions. These are memomotion study, and cycle graphic and chronocycle graphic study.

FIGURE 9–6

Simo chart of improved method for the assembly of lace finger in textile machinery

SIMO CHART

OPERATOR: Ken Reisch
DATE: May 21,
OPERATION: Assembly
PART: Lace Finger
METHOD: Proposed
CHART BY: Joseph Riley

TIME SCALE (winks)	ELEMENT TIME	LEFT-HAND DESCRIPTION	SYMBOL	MOTION CLASS	SYMBOL	RIGHT-HAND DESCRIPTION	ELEMENT TIME	TIME SCALE (winks)
4548	12	Reach for finger	RE		RE	Reach for finger	12	4548
4560	19	Grasp finger	G		G	Grasp finger	19	4560
4579	31	Move finger	M		M	Move finger	31	4579
4610	75	Position and release finger	P RL		P RL	Position and release finger	75	4610
4685	15	Reach for clamp	RE		RE	Reach for clamp	15	4685
4700	15	Grasp clamp	G		G	Grasp clamp	15	4700
4715								4715
7541	12	Grasp assembly	G		G	Grasp assembly	12	7541
7559	18	Move and release assembly	M RL		M RL	Move and release assembly	18	7559

SUMMARY

%	TIME	LEFT HAND SUMMARY	SYM.	RIGHT HAND SUMMARY	TIME	%
8.56	249	Reach	RE	Reach	245	8.4
7.49	218	Grasp	G	Grasp	221	7.5
12.16	354	Move	M	Move	413	14.2
30.45	887	Position	P	Position	1124	38.7
39.3	1145	Use	U	Use	876	30.1
1.03	30	Idle	I	Idle	0	0.0
.96	28	Release	RL	Release	32	1.1
100.0	3011	TOTALS			3011	100.0

FIGURE 9–7

Portion of memomotion study of four men operating hydraulic extrusion press (film exposed at rate of one frame per second)

Memomotion study is a moving-picture technique developed by Marvin Mundel several years ago to analyze the principal movements in an operation to improve methods, define problem areas, and establish standards.

Memomotion study usually uses a filming speed of 60 frames per minute with an accurate rate time interval between pictures to provide a record for frame-by-frame analysis. However, equipment is available to provide much greater flexibility in the rate of film exposure. For example, the equipment illustrated in Figure 9-8 allows exposure from two frames per second to one frame every three seconds or greater.

I have standardized on 60 frames per minute or 1 frame per second. This speed gives measurement of elapsed elements with adequate precision for establishing standards, and still exercises significant economy over regular camera speeds which are 960 frames per minute for 16-mm. silent film. Thus under memomotion, pictures are being exposed just $\frac{1}{16}$ as fast as under normal speed (see Figure 9-7). For example, in the study of a three-minute cycle job, the exposure and the analysis of only 4.5 feet of film is required as compared with 72 feet when the micromotion procedure is used.

$$\frac{3 \text{ min.} \times 60 \text{ frames/min.}}{40 \text{ frames/foot}} = 4.5 \text{ feet}$$

Frequently, it is advantageous to employ memomotion study in the following areas of work:

1. Multiman activities
2. Multifacility operations
3. Irregular cycle studies
4. Long-cycle operations
5. Plant layout
6. Recorded picture histories
7. Work sampling studies

Memomotion finds application on the above areas of study because:

1. It provides a more accurate record than visual means for analysis and film appraisal.
2. It will record interrelated events more accurately than visual techniques.
3. It provides a basis for work measurement since the camera operates at a constant speed.
4. It focuses the attention on the major movements taking place at a work center.
5. It reduces the film to be purchased and analyzed to about 6 percent of the costs experienced when operating at normal speed.

In the study of multiman or crew activities, memomotion is particularly helpful. Terminal points in elements of various operators within a group and the relation of terminal points to each other is almost impossible to

FIGURE 9–8

Time lapse controller permits exposures from two frames per second to one frame every three seconds or greater

Si-Con Signal Control, Inc.

recognize by visual methods. Through frame-by-frame analysis, the relationship of the various work elements performed by the members of the crew is easily determined. Consequently, memomotion study lends itself for studies such as crew balance and gang process chart work. (See Chapter 6.)

Multifacility operation studies are quite similar to multiman studies from the standpoint of adaptability to memomotion study work. Here it is desirable to follow not only the activities of the man but also the facilities he services. Factors such as interference delays, machine breakdowns, and so on are very difficult to study by visual means and yet they are easily observed through the frame-by-frame procedure. The study of irregular cycles, such as periodic replenishing of stock supplies, sharpening tools, and moving completed work by visual means is quite difficult. To begin, the analyst does not know when they are going to take place and consequently he is obliged to record the element and measure its duration while it is taking place. This is most difficult. The memomotion procedure records pictorially all the facts: the method employed and the time consumed so an analysis of the facts may be conveniently and leisurely made by frame-by-frame analysis.

Long-cycle operations employing many short elements are usually too costly to study by micromotion techniques and too difficult to study in adequate detail by visual methods. Memomotion provides the ideal alternative to both these procedures.

Memomotion studies of work areas will highlight the major moves of all personnel coming into that area. Such long moves as backtracking, trips for tools, raw materials, and supplies are emphasized and inefficient areas of the layout are pointed out. Frequently, a work area that appears satisfactory under a conventional micromotion film will indicate areas for improvement under memomotion.

Filing a permanent record of a method is frequently helpful. The permanent record simplifies setting up for the same job at a later date; it is useful also for method improvement studies. at later dates, for settling labor disputes, and for operator training.

Another important use of the memomotion camera is in preparing work sampling studies. (See Chapter 21.) By using memomotion equipment, unbiased work sampling studies may be made. To the typical memomotion camera is attached a timer that permits taking random observations during the eight-hour day. The "observation times" can be preset by placing small metal clips around the circumference of the timer dial. A random number table may be used in locating the clips. Also, the timer can be set to take pictures at regular intervals during the day if this is desired. An electric motor driven timer operates the synchronous motor that drives the camera.

Another mechanism that the author developed (see Figure 9–9) provides a means for randomly triggering the camera. Here random punchings on a constant speed tape energize the switching mechanism. The roll of tape can allow operation of the equipment for 160 working hours based on a minimum of 10 seconds between random observations. A timer can be preset to allow the exposure of 1 to 10 frames at each triggering of the camera. Thus, at random times during the work period, observations of 1 to 10 seconds are taken of the work area.

FIGURE 9–9

Triggering equipment for randomly exposing a predetermined number of frames of 16-mm. film

By using memomotion equipment adapted as mentioned above, the operator can make work sampling studies that will give unbiased results. Work sampling studies made by an observer recording data at random intervals tend to be biased because of the following reasons.

1. The mere presence of the observer arriving at the work scene will influence the operator to become productively engaged in work which normally he would not be doing at the time of the observation.

2. There is a natural tendency for the observer to record what just has happened or what will be happening at the exact moment of the observation.

FIGURE 9–10

Time-lapse TV system shown studying a group activity

Timelapse, Inc.

The use of memomotion to make work sampling studies is a labor savings in the collection of the data, since it is only necessary to remove the film at the end of the work period rather than periodically going to the work scene for the recording of data.

The reader should recognize that for the most part, micromotion study will allow the same analysis that memomotion study does. However, memomotion offers the kind of economies that opens the door to frame-by-frame analysis of activities that normally would not justify the cost of a micromotion study.

Time-lapse TV is available today that provides the added feature of instantaneous replay. After taking pictures on video tape, the analyst can observe immediately the operation under study. Tapes may be used over and over again for different time-lapse studies. Figure 9–10 illustrates equipment that is available in compression ratios of 15 hours of activity to 1 hour of viewing to 2 hours of activity to 1 hour of showing.

A cyclegraph is a photographic record of a body motion. "Still" film is used, but a light is attached to the body member, so the path of the motion is revealed when the picture is developed.

A chronocyclegraph is similar to the cyclegraph, except that speed as well as path of the motion is determined from the resulting photograph. In the chronocyclegraph, the light attached to the body member flickers. Speed is determined by the length of the alternate streaks of light and dark voids. Consequently, it is possible for the analyst to determine hesitations that may develop because of some obstacle in the existing motion pattern. Likewise, the influence on time of directional change can be determined. It is also possible to determine if rhythm is being developed by taking a series of chronocyclegraphs of different cycles and noting the similarity in the movement paths.

The practical uses of the cyclegraph and chronocyclegraph are confined to operations of short cycle and those requiring skill. For such work, this type of study is particularly helpful in operator training.

It is especially helpful in those work areas where no fixtures or tool stations exist to direct the motion pattern. For example, in the operation of wrapping fixative and turban, or folding a garment, or making a bed no definite motion pattern is established by equipment to shape the movements of the hands. The chronocyclegraph will provide a record of the ideal motion pattern for the trainee to follow.

It can be appreciated that, on complex motion patterns, the chronocyclegraph is a helpful supplement to the right- and left-hand process chart. With the chronocyclegraph giving a pictorial presentation of the motion pattern and the right- and left-hand chart a description of the motion pattern, a complete record is obtained.

Both the chronocyclegraph and the cyclegraph were originally developed by Gilbreth, but they have not been used extensively in this country.

TEXT QUESTIONS

1. What are the important steps in making a micromotion study?

2. What precautionary procedures should be observed before beginning the actual filming?
3. How does the simo chart differ from the operator process chart?
4. Which motions are classified as ineffective on the simo chart?
5. What class of motion is signified on the simo chart when plotting any of the delays?
6. What is the purpose of the micromotion instruction sheet?
7. In film analysis, why is it not advisable to analyze both hands simultaneously?
8. What advantages does memomotion study have over micromotion study?
9. How much film would be required to study a cycle 13.5 minutes in duration using a memomotion speed of 50 frames per minute?
10. What advantages does the chronocyclegraphic study have over the cyclegraphic study?
11. What is the filming speed usually used in making memomotion studies? What range of speeds is possible in memomotion study work?
12. Explain when you would advocate the use of time-lapse TV facilities.

GENERAL QUESTIONS

1. Why do some unions require permission before moving pictures are taken on the production floor?
2. In general, what is the operator's attitude on being filmed?
3. How can industrial relations be improved with the micromotion procedure?
4. Investigate the work done by Anne Shaw of England in conjunction with chronocyclegraphic studies.
5. Explain what impact, if any, that today's philosophy of "throw-away" type designs has on the use and application of micromotion study.
6. What influence does international competition have on the application of micromotion study?

CHAPTER 10

Presentation and installation of proposed method

Selling the proposed method is the step following development in the systematic procedure for methods and work measurement. This step is as important as any of the preceding steps since a method not sold will not be installed.

The analyst must keep in mind that it is natural for humans to resent the attempts of others to influence their thinking. When someone approaches us with a new idea, our instinctive reaction is to put up a defense against it. We feel that we must protect our own individuality— preserve the sanctity of our own ego. And all of us are just egotistical enough to convince ourselves that our ideas are better than those of anyone else. It is natural for us to react in this manner even if the idea is for our own advantage. If the idea has merit, there is a tendency to resent it because we did not think of it first.

Some suggestions that the successful analyst frequently uses to help sell his ideas include:

1. Introduce the idea in the other person's mind, so that he feels it really is his idea to a large extent. For example, begin by, "You recently gave me the idea that. . . ."

2. Do not appear overly anxious to have your ideas accepted. Introduce your thoughts with such statements as: "Do you think this idea has possibilities?" or "Have you considered this?"
3. Present your own objections to your idea. This can get the other person arguing for the support of your idea.

Presentation of the proposed method should emphasize savings. Savings in material (both direct and indirect) and savings in direct and indirect labor should highlight the analyst's report. The second most important part of the report is that dealing with the recovery of capital investment.

Once the proposed method has been properly presented and sold, installation can take place. Installation, like presentation, requires sales ability. During installation, the successful analyst will continually be selling the proposed method to engineers and technicians on his own level, to subordinate executives and supervisors, and to labor and representatives of organized labor. The analyst's job during presentation and installation of the proposed method will involve "selling up," "selling down," and "selling sideways."

The proposed method report

It is important that the analyst make his presentation in both written and oral form. Even if the company involved does not require a written report, it is good practice to make one in writing for record purposes and for future applications. A well-written report is a major step in selling the proposed method.

The elements of a well-written report are:

1. Title page
2. Table of contents
3. Letter of transmittal
4. Summary
5. Body
6. Appendix

From the standpoint of presentation, the summary is the most important section of the report, since it will be the only part read by the busy executive. The summary is based upon the report body, and consequently is usually not written until after the body has been completed. However, it is presented early in the report so those who must pass or disapprove the proposal can obtain the facts quickly in order to make a decision.

The summary should contain three elements: an abstract explaining briefly the nature of the problem; conclusions outlining the results of the analysis; and recommendations setting forth the proposed method and summarizing estimated savings and recovery of capital expenditures.

The body elements include a section on the nature of the problem followed with details relative to gathering the data and methods of analysis. In this section will be the operation and flow process charts used to present the facts and the man and machine, gang, and operator process charts used in developing the proposed work center. This section will contain the reasons for the conclusions and recommendations given in the summary.

The entire report should have the qualities of correctness, clearness, conciseness, completeness, and accuracy. It should be prepared so it can be easily read and studied.

Reporting recovery of capital investment

The three most used appraisal techniques for determining the desirability of investing in a proposed method are (1) return on sales, (2) return on investment, and (3) cash flow.

The return on sales method involves a computation of the ratio of average yearly profit brought about through using the method, to average yearly sales or increase in dollar value added to the product, based on the estimated pessimistic life of the product. Although this ratio provides information on the effectiveness of the method and resulting sales efforts, it does not consider the original investment required to get started on the proposed method.

The return on investment method gives the ratio of the average yearly profit brought about through using the method, based on the estimated pessimistic life of the product, to the original investment. Of two proposed methods that would result in the same sales and profit potential, management would prefer obviously to use the one requiring the investment of least capital.

The cash flow method computes the ratio of the present worth of cash flow based on a desired percentage return, to the original investment. This method introduces the rate of flow of money in and through the company and the time value of money. To compute the time value of money, we have the relationship:

$$S = P(1 + i)^n$$

where

i = Interest rate for a given period
n = Number of interest periods
P = Present worth of principal
S = Worth of sum n periods later

Under the cash flow calculation, an assumed return rate (i) is the basis of the computation. Then all cash flows following the initial investment for the new method are estimated and adjusted to their present worth based on the assumed return rate (i). The total estimated cash flows for the estimated pessimistic life of the product are then summed up as a profit or loss in terms of cash on hand today. This total is then compared with the initial investment.

An illustrative example will help clarify the use of these three appraisal methods for prognosticating the potential of a proposed method.

Investment for proposed method: $10,000.
Return on investment desired: 10 percent.
Salvage value of jigs, fixtures, and tools: $500.
Estimated life of product for which proposed method will be used: 10 years.

End of year	Increase in sales values due to proposed method	Cost of production with proposed method	Gross profit due to proposed method
1	$ 5,000	$ 2,000	$ 3,000
2	6,000	2,200	3,800
3	7,000	2,400	4,600
4	8,000	2,600	5,400
5	7,000	2,400	4,600
6	6,000	2,200	3,800
7	5,000	2,000	3,000
8	4,000	1,800	2,200
9	3,000	1,600	1,400
10	2,000	1,500	500
Totals	$53,000	$20,700	$32,300
Average	$ 5,300	$ 2,070	$ 3,230

$$\text{Return on sales} = \frac{3,230}{5,300} = 61\% \qquad \text{Return on investment} = \frac{3,230}{10,000} = 32.3\%$$

Present worth of cash flow:

$(3,000)(0.9091) = \$2,730$		$(3,800)(0.5645) =$	2,140
$(3,800)(0.8264) = 3,140$		$(3,000)(0.5132) =$	1,540
$(4,600)(0.7513) = 3,460$		$(2,200)(0.4665) =$	1,025
$(5,400)(0.6830) = 3,690$		$(1,400)(0.4241) =$	595
$(4,600)(0.6209) = 2,860$		$(\;\;500)(0.3855) =$	193
			$21,373

Salvage value of tools:

$$(500)(0.3855) = \$193$$

Total present worth of anticipated gross profit and tool salvage value: $21,566. Ratio of present worth to original investment:

$$\frac{21,566}{10,000} = 2.16$$

The new method has satisfactorily passed all three of these appraisal methods. Sixty-one percent return on sales and 32.3 percent return on capital investment certainly represent attractive returns. The cash flow analysis reveals that the original investment of $10,000 will be recovered in four years while earning 10 percent. During the 10-year anticipated life of the product, $11,566 more than the original investment will be earned.

The analyst must recognize that product demand estimates for 10 years hence may deviate considerably from reality. Thus the element of chance is introduced and the probabilities of success tend to diminish with increased length of the payoff period.

Oral presentation

Frequently, the analyst will be asked to present his method proposal orally. To help assure that approval is given the proposal, the analyst should be prepared to present the benefits and advantages accurately and forcefully. He should be prepared to give estimates of the resulting increase in productivity and/or decrease in cost. If quality will be improved or customer service enhanced, this information should be given.

It is important that the analyst plan his presentation in advance. He should have data relative to all the advantages of the proposed method as well as cost information and facts giving the expected savings and recovery of capital investment. It is a good idea to make a list in advance of all the information that one's superior may ask for, and then be prepared to supply this information.

The analyst should also be prepared to answer objections raised to the proposal. These are usually centered around initial cost, time to adopt the method, and inconvenience while installation is taking place. He should point out that these objections have been carefully considered and plans made to cope with them.

The oral presentation of the proposed method requires much study, preparation, and salesmanship. A good method will not sell itself; it must be sold.

Installation

After a proposed method has been approved, the next step is installation. Too frequently the analyst does not stay close enough to the job during installation. He tends to feel that installation will take place automatically according to his proposal. Often this is not the case. The maintenance man, mechanic, or workman will make a slight change or modification on his own initiative without considering the consequences. This may mean that the proposed method will not give the results anticipated.

The analyst should stay with the job during installation to assure all details are carried out in accordance with the proposed plans. During installation, he should verify that the work center being established is equipped with the facilities proposed, that the planned working conditions are provided, that the tooling is in accordance with that recommended, and that the schedule of work progresses satisfactorily.

During installation, the analyst will have opportunity to sell the new method to the operator, foreman, setup man, and so on. Then by the time the installation is complete, these men will be more ready to give the new method an enthusiastic try.

Once the new work center has been installed, the analyst should check all aspects to see if it conforms to the specifications established. In particular, he should verify that the "reach" and "move" distances the operator must perform are the correct length; that the tools are correctly sharpened; that the mechanisms function soundly; that stickiness and sluggishness have been worked out; that safety features are operative; that material will be available in quantities as planned; that working conditions associated with the work center are as anticipated; and that all parties have been informed of the new method.

After the analyst is sure that every aspect of the method is ready for operation, he should have the foreman assign the operator who will be working with the method. The analyst should stay with the operator as long as necessary to break him in on the new assignment. This period may be a matter of a few minutes or may be a matter of several hours or even days depending on the complexity.

Once the operator begins to get a feel for the method and works along systematically, the analyst can proceed with other work. However, he should not consider the installation phase complete until he has checked back several times during the first few days after installation to assure the proposed method is working out as planned.

TEXT QUESTIONS

1. What are some of the communication skills that are important in selling a new method? *256*

2. What are the principal elements of a well-written report? *256*

3. What is meant by the "cash flow" appraisal technique?

4. How much capital could be invested in a new method if it was estimated that $5,000 would be saved the first year, $10,000 the second year, and $3,000 the third year? Management expects at least a 30 percent return on invested capital.

5. What are the principal concerns of management relative to a new proposal that is relatively costly to install?

GENERAL QUESTIONS

1. What is the relationship between return on capital investment and risk associated with anticipated sales of the product for which the new method will be used?
2. When do you feel the oral report would be more important, on getting the approval of a new method project, than the written report?

CHAPTER 11

Making the job analysis
and the job evaluation

Closely associated with installation of the proposed method, is the job analysis of the work center and the resulting job evaluation. Every time a method is changed, the job description should be altered to reflect the conditions, duties, and responsibilities of the improved method. When a new method is introduced, it is important that a job analysis be made so a qualified operator may be assigned to the work center and so an appropriate base rate may be considered.

Factory cost of a product includes the cost of direct labor, direct material, and factory expense. Factory expense consists of items such as light, heat, rent, service supplies, and factory supervision. A close review of expense or overhead items will show that these costs are made up of but two components: material and labor, or a combination of the two. So, in effect, factory cost is made up of just labor and material. Therefore:

Factory cost = Cost of labor + cost of material

Material cost is easily determined, no matter what the product may be. In every instance, it is determined by multiplying the cost per unit of measure by the number of measures involved. Thus, some yardstick always governs its basis of cost. Steel is bought by the ton, castings and forgings by the piece, water and gas by the cubic foot, electricity by the kilowatt-hour, tubing by the foot, silver by the ounce, cloth by the square yard, oil by the gallon, and so forth. In every case, material cost can be prorated so it is possible to determine the proportional share each product item should absorb.

The only other item of cost entering into factory cost is the cost of labor either direct or indirect. Labor cost, in most commodities, represents the major portion of total costs. To have some conception of true costs of specific products, standards must be established on labor elements. Hourly monetary rates mean nothing unless they are supplemented with performance standards. If an operator running a No. 2 Brown & Sharpe Universal Mill is paid a base rate of $2.10 per hour while milling a profile on a forging, there is no conception of the unit milling cost until a standard has been established on the job in terms of time. If a standard allows six minutes per piece, then a labor cost of $0.21 can be

assigned to the operation. However, time standards alone do not give the entire story with regard to labor costs. They do form one side of the rectangle whose area may be thought of as equitable and competitive costs of labor. The other side of the rectangle is sound base rates.

Base rates that are sound must assure money rates commensurate with area rates for similar work; they must allow adequate differentials for jobs requiring higher skills and responsibilities; they must be based on techniques that can be explained and justified.

Job analysis

Appropriate base rates are a result of job evaluation, which was defined in Chapter 1 as a technique for equitably determining the relative worth of the different work assignments within an organization. The basis of job evaluation is job analysis, which is the procedure for making a careful appraisal of each job and then recording the details of the work so it can be evaluated fairly by a trained analyst. Figure 11–1 illustrates an analysis of a clerical job for use in a point job evaluation plan. It should

FIGURE 11–1

Job analysis for shipping and receiving clerk

JOB TITLE____Shipping and Receiving Clerk_____DEPT.____Shipping_____

MALE_X_FEMALE____DATE_____TOTAL POINTS_280_CLASS 5

JOB DESCRIPTION

Directs and assists in loading and unloading, counting, and receiving or rejecting purchased parts and supplies, and later delivers to proper departments.
Examines receivals out of line with purchase orders. Maintains file on all purchase
orders and/or shipping orders and keeps open orders up to date. Maintains daily and
weekly shipping reports and monthly inventory reports.
Assists in packing of all foreign and domestic shipments. Makes up request for inspection form on certain materials received and rejection form for all items rejected.
Job requires thorough knowledge of parking, shipping, and receiving routine, knowledge
of plant layout, shop supplies and finished parts. Needs to have a knowledge of
simple office routine. Ability to work with other departments, as a service department,
and to deal effectively with vendors. Job requires considerable accuracy and dependability.

JOB EVALUATION	DEGREE	POINTS
EDUCATION	1	15
EXPERIENCE AND TRAINING	2	50
INITIATIVE AND INGENUITY	3	50
ANALYTICAL ABILITY	3	50
PERSONALITY REQUIREMENTS	2	30
SUPERVISORY RESPONSIBILITY	1	25
RESPONSIBILITY FOR LOSS	1	10
PHYSICAL APPLICATION	6	25
MENTAL OR VISUAL APPLICATION	1	5
WORKING CONDITIONS	5	20
		280

be clearly understood that before a job description is developed, all aspects of the opportunity should be carefully studied to assure that the
best methods are being used and that the operator is thoroughly trained
in the prescribed method.

Job evaluation

The main purpose of any job evaluation plan is to determine the proper compensation for work performed on each job. A well-conceived job evaluation plan includes the following factors:

1. It provides a basis for explaining to employees why one job is worth more or less than another job.
2. It provides a reason to employees whose rate of pay is adjusted because of a change in method.
3. It provides a basis for assignment of personnel with specific abilities to certain jobs.
4. It helps determine criteria for a job when employing new personnel or making promotions.
5. It provides assistance in the training of supervisory personnel.
6. It provides a basis for determining where opportunities for method improvement exist.

There are four principal methods of job evaluation being practiced in this country today. These are the classification method, point system, factor comparison method, and the ranking method.

The classification method, sometimes called the grade description plan, consists of a series of definitions designed to differentiate jobs into wage groups. Once the grade levels have been defined, each job is studied and assigned to the appropriate level on the basis of the complexity of duties and responsibilities. This plan is used extensively in the United States Civil Service.

When using this method of job evaluation, the following steps must be considered:

1. Prepare a grade description scale for each type of job, e.g., machine operations, manual operations, skilled (craft) operations, inspection.
2. Write the grade descriptions for each grade in each scale, using factors such as:
   a) Type of work and complexity of duties,
   b) Education necessary to perform job,
   c) Experience necessary to perform job,
   d) Responsibilities,
   e) Effort demanded.
3. Prepare job descriptions for each job. Classify each job by "slotting" (placing in a specific category) the job description into the proper grade description.

Both the point system and the factor comparison method are more objective and thorough in their evaluations of the various jobs involved, in that both of these two plans make a study of the basic factors common to most jobs and influence their relative worth. Of the two plans, the point plan is generally considered the more accurate method for occupational rating. In this method, all the different attributes of a job are compared directly with these attributes in other jobs.

When a point system is to be installed, the following procedure should be followed:

1. Establish and define basic factors which are common to most jobs and which indicate the elements of value in all jobs.
2. Specifically define the degrees of each factor.
3. Establish the points to be accredited to each degree of each factor.
4. Prepare a job description of each job.
5. Evaluate each job by determining the degree of each factor contained in it.
6. Sum points for each factor to get total points for job.
7. Convert the job points into a wage rate.

The factor comparison method of job evaluation usually has the following elements:

1. Factors are determined that will establish the relative worth of all jobs.
2. An evaluation scale is established which is usually similar to a point scale except that the units are in terms of money.
3. Job descriptions are prepared.
4. Key jobs are evaluated factor by factor by ranking each job from the lowest to the highest for each factor.
5. The wages paid on each key job are allocated to the various factors. The money allocation automatically fixes the relationship between jobs for each factor, and therefore establishes the ranks of jobs for each factor.
6. On the basis of the monetary values assigned the various factors in the key jobs, other jobs are evaluated factor by factor.
7. By adding the money value for each factor, a wage is determined.

The ranking method arranges the jobs in their order of importance or according to their relative worth. This method became popular in the United States during World War II because of its simplicity and ease of installation. It was at this time that the National War Labor Board set up the requirements that all companies working on government contracts must have some type of wage classification system. This ranking method satisfied this requirement. Generally speaking, the ranking method is less objective than the other techniques; consequently, greater knowledge of all jobs is necessary. For this reason, it has not been extensively used in recent years but has been superseded by the other plans. The following steps are followed when installing the ranking plan:

1. Prepare job descriptions.
2. Rank jobs (usually departmentally first) in order of their relative importance.
3. Determine the class or grade for groups of jobs using a bracketing process.
4. Establish the wage or wage range for each class or grade.

Selection of factors

It is generally considered preferable to use a small number of factors. Under the factor comparison method, most companies use five factors. In some point programs, 10 or more factors may be used. The objective is to use only as many factors as are necessary to provide a clear-cut difference between the jobs of the particular company. The elements of any job may be classified as to:

1. What the job demands the employee to bring in the form of physical and mental factors.
2. What the job takes from the employee in the form of physical and mental fatigue.
3. The responsibilities that the job demands.
4. Conditions under which the work is done.

The selection of factors is usually the first basic task to be undertaken when introducing job evaluation.

The National Electrical Manufacturers Association states that the relative value of a job is considered to depend on the following factors:

1. Education
2. Experience
3. Initiative and ingenuity
4. Physical demand
5. Mental and/or visual demand
6. Responsibility for equipment or process
7. Responsibility for material or product
8. Responsibility for safety of others
9. Responsibility for work of others
10. Working conditions
11. Hazards

These factors are present in varying degrees in the various jobs, and any job under consideration will fall under some one of the several degrees of each factor. The various factors are not of equal importance. To give recognition to these differences in importance, weights or points are assigned to each degree of each factor as shown in Table 11–1. Figure

11–2 illustrates a job rating and substantiating data sheet based on the National Electrical Manufacturers Association plan.

Each degree of each factor is carefully defined so that it is evident what degree characterizes the work situation under study.

For example, education may be defined as appraising the requirements for the use of shop mathematics, drawings, measuring instruments, or trade knowledge. First-degree education may require only the ability to read and write, and to add and subtract whole numbers. Second-degree education could be defined as requiring the use of simple arithmetic, such as addition and subtraction of decimals and fractions, to-

TABLE 11–1

Points assigned to factors and key to grades

Factors	1st Degree	2nd Degree	3rd Degree	4th Degree	5th Degree
Skill					
1. Education	14	28	42	56	70
2. Experience	22	44	66	88	110
3. Initiative and ingenuity	14	28	42	56	70
Effort					
4. Physical demand	10	20	30	40	50
5. Mental or visual	5	10	15	20	25
Responsibility					
6. Equipment or process	5	10	15	20	25
7. Material or product	5	10	15	20	25
8. Safety of others	5	10	15	20	25
9. Work of others	5	10	15	20	25
Job Conditions					
10. Working conditions	10	20	30	40	50
11. Unavoidable hazards	5	10	15	20	25

SOURCE: National Electrical Manufacturers Association

gether with simple drawings and some measuring instruments, such as calipers and scale. It would be characteristic of two years of high school. Third-degree education may require the use of fairly complicated drawings, advanced shop mathematics, handbook formulas, and variety of precision measuring instruments, plus some trade knowledge in a specialized field or process. It could be thought of as being equivalent to four years of high school plus short-term trades training. Fourth-degree education could require the use of complicated drawings and specifications, advanced shop mathematics, wide variety of precision measuring instruments, broad shop knowledge. It may be equivalent to four years of high school plus four years of formal trades training. Fifth-degree education may require a basic technical knowledge sufficient to deal with complicated and involved mechanical, electrical, or other engineering problems.

FIGURE 11–2

JOB RATING – SUBSTANTIATING DATA
DORBEN MFG. CO.
UNIVERSITY PARK, PA.

JOB TITLE: Machinist (General)   CODE: 176   DATE: Nov. 12

FACTORS	DEG.	POINTS	BASIS OF RATING
Education	3	42	Requires the use of fairly complicated drawings, advanced shop mathematics, variety of precision instruments, shop trade knowledge. Equivalent to four years of high school or two years of high school plus two to three years of trades training.
Experience	4	88	Three to five years installing, repairing, and maintaining machine tools and other production equipment.
Initiative and Ingenuity	3	42	Rebuild, repair, and maintain a wide variety of medium-size standard automatic and hand-operated machine tools. Diagnose trouble, disassemble machine and fit new parts, such as antifriction and plain bearings, spindles, gears, cams, etc. Manufacture replacement parts as necessary. Involves skilled and accurate machining using a variety of machine tools. Judgment required to diagnose and remedy trouble quickly so as to maintain production.
Physical Demand	2	20	Intermittent physical effort required tearing down, assembling, installing, and maintaining machines.
Mental or Visual Demand	4	20	Concentrated mental and visual attention required. Laying out, setup, machining, checking, inspecting, fitting parts on machines.
Responsibility for Equipment or Process	3	15	Damage seldom over $300. Broken parts of machines. Carelessness in handling gears and intricate parts may cause damage.
Responsibility for Material or Product	2	10	Probable loss due to scrapping of materials or work, seldom over $150.
Responsibility for Safety of Others	3	15	Safety precautions are required to prevent injury to others; fastening work properly to face plates, handling fixtures, etc.
Responsibility for Work of Others	2	10	Responsible for directing one or more helpers a great part of time. Depends on type of work.
Working Conditions	3	30	Somewhat disagreeable conditions due to exposure to oil, grease, and dust.
Unavoidable Hazards	3	15	Exposure to accidents, such as crushed hand or foot, loss of fingers, eye injury from flying particles, possible electric shock, or burns.

REMARKS: Total 307 Points--assign to job class 4.

Fifth-degree education could be thought of as being equivalent to four years of technical university training.

Experience appraises the length of time that is usually required by an individual, with the specified education, to learn to perform the work satisfactorily from the standpoint of both quality and quantity. Here, first degree could involve up to three months. Second degree, three months to one year; third degree, one to three years; fourth degree, three to five years; and fifth degree, over five years.

In a similar manner each degree of each factor is identified with a clear definition and with specific examples when applicable.

A score range is assigned to each labor grade. The number of labor grades within a given plant is a function of the range of points characteristic of the jobs within the plant. For example, if the point range of all the jobs within a plant ranged from 110 to 365 the following grades could be established:

Grade	Score range points	Grade	Score range points
12	100–139	6	250–271
11	140–161	5	272–293
10	162–183	4	294–315
9	184–205	3	316–337
8	206–227	2	338–359
7	228–249	1	361 and above

The hourly rate of each grade would be based on area rates for similar work, cost-of-living index, and company policy. A rate range can be established for each labor grade. The total performance of the operator will determine his pay rate within the established range. Total performance refers to quality, quantity, safety, attendance, suggestions, etc.

It has been seen how one side of the rectangle whose area is competitive cost of labor can be determined. Job evaluation will provide the means for compensating all employees within an organization in proportion to their responsibilities and to the difficulty of their work. At the same time, it will lead to base pay rates in line with remuneration for similar work in the community. The benefits effected through job evaluation will enhance ideal personnel relations.

Conclusion

Job analysis and job evaluation are important steps after "installation." These procedures will help the analyst be assured that the proposed work center will be acceptable to labor, that the anticipated savings will be realized, and that harmonious labor relations will prevail.

To predetermine factory cost, so necessary from the standpoint of submitting bids and quotations, it is essential that cost of the various direct and indirect materials and the cost of all labor be precisely predetermined.

Predetermined material costs can easily be calculated. Predetermined labor costs also can be readily computed if good labor standards developed by one of the work measurement techniques prevail. Standards determined by estimates and historical records usually will not be sufficiently accurate to meet competitive prices or will not allow manufacture at a necessary profit.

Although labor standards determine "how long," it is necessary to have sound base rates to measure fairly the "how much" in terms of dollars and cents. Of the various methods of job evaluation used in establishing sound base rates, the point plans tend to give the most reliable results. Point job evaluation systems patterned after the National Metal Trades and the National Electrical Manufacturers Association techniques represent a logical approach toward developing the relative worth of the different work assignments within an organization.

To compensate equitably for total performance a range of rates should be established for each labor grade. George Fry & Associates undertook a comprehensive survey of job evaluation practices involving over 500 companies. Some significant results from this survey follow:

Firms using a standard job evaluation plan....		66%
Plan used:		
Ranking............................	3.5%	
Grade description......................	1.0%	
Factor comparison.....................	10.5%	
Point system.........................	85.0%	
Average of hourly employees covered........		65%
Job Evaluation function reports to:		
Industrial Relations....................	69.0%	
Industrial Engineering..................	16.0%	
Results used in employment...............		87%
Results used in employee placement........		88%
Results used in wage rate bargaining........		68%
Job Evaluation program is recognized in union contract......................		83%
Job Evaluation is an issue during negotiations........................		59%
Job Evaluation has gone to arbitration (of these cases, management won 74%).....		27%

Understanding and acceptance:	*Good*	*Average*	*Poor*	*None*
Employee understanding.................	7%	39%	49%	5%
Top-management understanding..........	50%	36%	13%	1%
Middle-management understanding.......	48%	47%	5%	0%
First-line supervision..................	35%	52%	13%	0%

TEXT QUESTIONS

1. What are the three basic components of cost?
2. Is time a common denominator of labor cost? Why? *p 258*   *No, also need stds.*
3. What is job analysis? *p 258*
4. What four methods of job evaluation are being practiced in this country *p.260* today?
5. Explain in detail how a "point" plan works.
6. What factors influence the relative worth of a job?
7. Why are estimates unsatisfactory for determining direct labor time standards?
8. What is the weakness of using historical records as a means to establish standards of performance?
9. What work measurement techniques will give valid results when undertaken by competent trained analysts?
10. What are the principal benefits from a properly installed job evaluation plan?
11. Explain why a range of rates rather than just one rate should be established for every labor grade.
12. Explain what is meant by total operator performance.

GENERAL QUESTIONS

1. When plotting area rates against job point values, it is necessary that the resulting curve be a straight line. Why?
2. Should cost-of-living increases be given as a percentage of base rates or as a straight hourly increment? Why?
3. Why would be a consulting firm such as George Fry and Associates undertake a comprehensive survey of job evaluation practices?

CHAPTER 12

Time study requirements

The eighth step in the systematic procedure for developing the work center to produce the product is establishing time standards. Three techniques have been used to determine labor standards: estimates, historical records, and work measurement procedures.

Estimates as a means of establishing standards were used to a greater extent in years past than today. With increasing competition from foreign producers, there has been an increasing effort to establish standards based on facts rather than judgment. Experience has shown that no individual can establish consistent and fair standards of production by the simple procedure of taking a look at a job and then judging the amount of time required to produce it. Where estimates are used, standards will be out of line on an average of about 25 percent. Compensating errors sometimes will diminish this figure, but over a period, experience has shown that estimated values deviate substantially from measured standards. Both historical records and work measurement techniques will give much more accurate values than will the use of estimates based on judgment alone.

Under the historical method, production standards are based on the records of previously produced, similar jobs. In common practice, the worker "punches in" on a time clock every time he begins a new job, and then "punches out" on the job when he has completed it. This technique tells us how long it took to do a job, but never indicates how long it should have taken. Since operators wish to justify their entire working day, some jobs carry personal delay time, unavoidable delay time, and avoidable delay time to a much greater extent than they should, while other jobs will not carry their appropriate share of delay time. I have seen historical records deviate consistently as much as 50 percent on the same operation of the same job. Historical records as a basis of determining labor standards are better than no records at all. This method will give more reliable results than using estimates based on judgment alone, but it does not provide sufficiently valid results to assure equitable and competitive cost of labor.

Any of the work measurement techniques—stopwatch time study, standard data, time formulas or work sampling studies—represents a better way to establish fair production standards. All of these methods are based on facts. All of these techniques consider each detail of the work and its relation to the normal time required to perform the entire cycle. Accurately established time standards make it possible to produce more within a given plant, thus increasing the efficiency of equipment and operating personnel. Poorly established standards, although better than no standards at all, will lead to high costs, labor dissension, and eventually possible failure of the enterprise.

In Chapter 1, time study was defined as a technique for establishing an allowed time standard to perform a given task. This technique is based upon measurement of work content of the prescribed method, with due allowance for fatigue and personal and unavoidable delays. Frequently, time study is defined by the layman as a method of determining a "fair day's work," and this concept will be discussed before the requirements and responsibilities of those associated with time study are explained. It is necessary to have a clear understanding of what is involved in a fair day's work.

A fair day's work

Practically everyone connected with industry in any way has heard many times the expression, "a fair day's work," yet if asked to define just what is a fair day's work, he is immediately perplexed to establish a sound definition. The intraplant wage rate inequities agreements of the basic steel industries[1] contain the provision that "the fundamental principle of the work and wage relationship is that the employee is entitled to a fair day's pay in return for which the company is entitled to a fair day's work." A fair day's work is defined in these agreements as the "amount of work that can be produced by a qualified employee when working at a normal pace and effectively utilizing his time where work is not restricted by process limitations." This definition is limited on what is exactly meant by "qualified employees," "normal pace," and "effective utilization." Although all of these terms have been defined by the steel industries, a certain amount of flexibility prevails because firm bench marks cannot be

---

[1] With United Steelworkers of America.

established on such broad terminology. For example, a "qualified employee" is defined as "a representative average of those employees who are fully trained and able satisfactorily to perform any and all phases of the work involved, in accordance with the requirements of the job under consideration." This definition leaves a doubt as to what is meant by a "representative average employee."

Then the term "normal pace" is defined as "the effective rate of performance of a conscientious, self-paced, qualified employee when working neither fast nor slow and giving due consideration to the physical, mental, or visual requirements of the specific job." The intraplant wage rate inequities agreements specify as an example "a man walking without load, on smooth, level ground at a rate of three (3) miles per hour." Although the three miles an hour concept tends to tie down what is meant by normal pace, still a notable amount of latitude can prevail, when we think of normal pace on the thousands of different jobs in American industry.

Again, a feeling of uncertainty arises when one considers the definition of "effective utilization." This is explained in the agreements as "the maintenance of a normal pace while performing essential elements of the job during all portions of the day except that which is required for reasonable rest and personal needs, under circumstances in which the job is not subject to process, equipment or other operating limitations."

In general, a fair day's work is one that is fair to both the company and the employee. This means that the employee should give a full day's work for the time that he gets paid, with reasonable allowances for personal delays, unavoidable delays, and fatigue. He is expected to operate in the prescribed method at a pace that is neither fast nor slow, but one which may be considered representative of all-day performance by the experienced, cooperative employee.

Time study requirements

Certain fundamental requirements need to be realized before the time study should be taken. If the standard is required on a new job, or if it is required on an old job on which the method or part of the method has been altered, the operator should be thoroughly acquainted with the new technique before the operation is studied. Also, it is important that the method to be studied has been standardized at all points where it is to be used. Unless all details of the method and working conditions have been standardized, the time standards will have little value and will be a continual source of mistrust, grievances, and internal friction.

It is also important that the union steward, the departmental foreman, and the operator are cognizant of the fact that the job is to be studied. Each of these parties will then be able to make any specific plans in advance and take the necessary steps to allow a smooth, coordinated study. The operator should verify that he is performing the correct method and endeavor to acquaint himself with all details of the operation. The foreman should check the method to make sure that feeds, speeds, cutting tools, lubricants, and so forth, conform to standard practice as established by the methods department. Also, the foreman must investigate the amount of available material so no shortage will take place during the study. If several operators are available for study of the operation in question, the foreman should determine to the best of his ability which operator will be likely to give the most satisfactory study. The union steward should then make sure that only trained competent operators are selected for time study observation. He should explain to the operator why the study is being taken and answer pertinent questions that come to the operator's attention from time to time.

Responsibilities of the time study man

All work involves varying degrees of skill and physical and mental effort to accomplish the task satisfactorily. In addition to the variations in job content, there are differences in aptitude, physical application, and dexterity of the workmen. It is an easy matter for the analyst to observe an employee at work and measure the actual time taken to perform a task. It is a considerably more difficult problem to evaluate all variables and determine the time required for the "normal" operator to perform the job.

Because of the many human interests and reactions associated with the time study technique, it is essential that there be a full understanding of the foremen, the employee, the union steward, and the time study analyst.

In general, the time study analyst is charged with these responsibilities:

1. To probe, question, and examine the present method to assure that it is correct in all respects before the standard is established.
2. To discuss equipment, method, and operator's ability with the foreman before studying the operation.
3. To answer questions relating to time study practice or to a specific time study that may be asked by the union steward, the operator, or the foreman.
4. To cooperate with the foreman and the operator at all times to obtain maximum help from both.
5. To refrain from any discussion with the operator or other operators that might be construed as criticism of the individual being studied.
6. To show on each time study, complete and accurate information, thus specifically identifying the method under study.

7. To record accurately times taken to perform the individual elements of the operation being studied.
8. To evaluate the performance of the operators honestly and fairly.
9. To conduct himself at all times so he obtains and holds the respect and confidence of the representatives of both labor and management.

The qualifications of a time study man that are necessary for him to meet successfully the responsibilities of his position are similar to those required for success in any field in which the major efforts are directed toward establishing ideal human relations.

First of all, a good time study man must have the mental ability to analyze diversified situations and make rapid, sound decisions. He should have an inquisitive, probing, and open mind that seeks to improve and always to be cognizant of the "why" as well as the "how."

Supplementing a keen mind, it is essential that the time study analyst have practical shop training in the areas in which he will be establishing standards. If he is to be associated with the metal trades, he should have a background as a journeyman machinist or the equivalent knowledge of machines, hand tools, jigs, fixtures, gages, and their correct use and application. This would include specific knowledge of cutting feeds, speeds, and depths of cut to get the maximum results consistent with desired quality of the product and ultimate tool life.

Since the time study man directly affects the pocketbook of the worker and the profit and loss statement of the company, it is essential that his work be completely dependable and accurate. Inaccuracy and poor judgment will not only affect the operator and the company financially but may also result in complete loss of confidence by the operator and the union, which may undo harmonious labor relations that have taken management years to build up.

To achieve and maintain good human relations, the following personal requirements can be considered essential for the successful time study man:

1. Honesty
2. Tact, human understanding
3. Resourcefulness
4. Self-confidence
5. Good judgment, analytical ability
6. Pleasing, persuasive personality, supplemented with optimism
7. Patience with self-control
8. Bountiful energy tempered with a cooperative attitude
9. Well-groomed, neat appearance
10. Enthusiasm for the job

A review of all of the qualifications essential for a successful time study man may give the reader the opinion that he should be on a staff level with the president of the company. In fact, it is questionable if all of these attributes would be required of top executives of a concern. However, when one considers the magnitude of the labor relations problem today, it is essential that only the most competent people enter the field of time study. No other one individual within a company comes in contact with as many personnel from different levels of the organization as the time study analyst. Therefore, it is imperative that he have the best qualifications.

In the time study man's approach to various employees, he should learn to recognize the human qualities in a man and then be guided by a realization of the limitations of human nature. Thus, to receive cooperation he must determine and follow through with the best method of approach to the workman. This calls for analysis of the employee's attitude toward his job, his fellow workmen, the company, and toward the time study man himself.

Foreman's responsibility

Any and all foremen are management's representatives throughout the plant. Next to the operator, the foreman is closer to specific jobs than any other man in the plant. In view of this, he must accept certain responsibilities in connection with the establishment of time standards.

To begin, the foreman, in the interest of harmonious labor relations within the department in which he supervises, finds it mandatory that equitable time standards prevail. Both "tight" and "loose" standards are the direct cause of endless personnel problems, and the more of these that can be avoided, the easier and more pleasant will be his job. Of course, if all standards were loose, he would find his supervisory responsibilities relatively easy. However, this situation could not exist practically, since competition would not be met where all standards are loose.

The foreman should notify the operator in advance that his work assignment is to be studied. This clears the way for both the time study analyst and the operator. The operator has the assurance that his direct superior is cognizant of the fact that a rate is to be established on the job and will have the opportunity to bring out speciffic difficulties that he feels should be corrected before a standard is set. The time study analyst will of course feel considerably more at ease, knowing that his presence has been anticipated.

It should be the foreman's responsibility to see that the proper method established by the methods department is being utilized and that the operator selected is competent and has adequate experience on the job. Although the time study analyst is required to have a practical background in the area of work he is studying, he can hardly be expected to be infallible in specifications of all methods and processes. Thus, he should consider the foreman as his ally to verify that the cutting tools are properly ground, the correct lubricant is being used, and that proper selection of feeds, speeds, and depths of cut have been considered.

If, for any reason, conditions are such that the operation will be so affected that it is questionable whether a fair time study can be taken, the foreman should immediately make this fact known to the time study analyst.

In general, the foreman is responsible for assisting and cooperating with the time study man in any way that will aid in defining or clarifying an operation. He should carefully consider any suggestions for improvement brought out by the time study man, and fully utilize his own background and influence to establish an ideal method in conjunction with the methods department, prior to stopwatch study.

The foreman is responsible for seeing that his men use the prescribed method, and he should conscientiously assist and train all those employees coming under his jurisdiction in perfecting this method. He should freely answer any questions asked by the operator regarding the operation.

Any time a methods change takes place within his department, the foreman should notify the time study department immediately so an appropriate adjustment of the standard can be made. This procedure should be followed regardless of the degree of the methods adjustment. It would include such things as changes in material handling to and from the work station, changes in inspection procedure, changes in feeds and speeds, changes in work station layout, and process changes.

Upon completing a time study, the foreman should be required to sign the original study, thus indicating that he has complied with all his responsibilities on the study taken. Foremen who accept and carry out their responsibilities toward time study practice can be assured of operating harmonious departments that will be looked on with favor by management, the union, and the employees themselves. Foremen who fall short of these responsibilities can contribute to the establishment of inequitable rates that will result in numerous labor grievances, pressure from management, and considerable dissatisfaction from the union.

The union's responsibility

As every union steward knows, poor time standards are just as much of a problem to him as they are to the management of the company. In the interests of operating a healthy union within a profitable business, the union must accept certain responsibilities toward time study.

Through training programs, the union should educate all of its members in the principles, theories, and economic necessity of time study practice. All of us tend to fear anything on which we are poorly informed. Operators can hardly be expected to be enthusiastic about time study if they know nothing about it. This is especially true in view of its background (see Chapter 2). Therefore, the union should accept the responsibility of helping to clarify and sell this important tool of management.

The union should accept the responsibility of seeing that adjusted standards are put into effect whenever a methods change is made. When methods are revised, the union should see that the time study department is notified through specified lines of authority.

The union should encourage its members to cooperate with the time study analyst and have the operators refrain from practices that would tend to place their performances at the low end of the rating scale. Encouraging operators to deceive the time study man will, in the final analysis, add up to but one thing: a poor standards structure, which will include both loose and tight rates.

Unions that train their members relative to the elements of time study, encourage cooperativeness, and stay abreast of management's program will benefit by more cooperation at the bargaining table, fewer work stoppages, and better satisfied members. Those unions that encourage distrust of time study, and facilitate a program of "keeping the operator in the dark," will be faced with a multitude of grievances from their members, a balky management team to negotiate with, and over a period, sufficient work stoppages to create a hardship on all parties concerned.

Operator's responsibility

Every employee should be sufficiently interested in the welfare of his company to give his wholehearted support to every practice and procedure inaugurated by management. Unfortunately, this situation is seldom realized, but it certainly can be approached if a company's management demonstrates its desire to operate with fair standards, fair base rates, good working conditions, and adequate employee benefits in the form of insurance and retirement programs. Once management has taken the initiative in these areas, every employee can be expected to cooperate in all operations and production control techniques.

The individual operators should be responsible for giving new methods a fair trial when introduced. They should wholeheartedly cooperate in helping to work out the "bugs" characteristic of practically every innovation. Suggestions for further improvement of the method should be accepted as a part of each operator's responsibilities. The operator is closer to the job than anyone else, and he can make a real contribution to the company and to himself by doing his part in establishing ideal method procedures.

The operator should be responsible for assisting the time study analyst in breaking down the job into elements, thus assuring that all details of the job are specifically covered. He should also be responsible for working at a steady, normal pace while the study is being taken and should introduce as few foreign elements and extra movements as possible. He should be responsible for using the exact prescribed method and make no effort to deceive the time study analyst by introducing an artificial method with the thought of lengthening the cycle time and receiving a more liberal standard.

Conclusion

To many practicing time study men, the responsibilities of the operator, the union, and the foreman may be considered a utopian approach which can never be realized. However, as stated, if management takes the initiative, these conditions can be approximated and the result will be a competitive, profitable business for all parties. For example, Howard M. Hinkel, personnel director of American Type Founders, Inc., reports that by establishing an "appreciation" course in time study and incentive techniques for union stewards and committeemen in his company, they have almost eliminated rate discussions that go beyond the operator's initial complaint.[2]

Time study procedures are the only known methods for supplying accurate information on standard times that are so essential for the profitable, efficient operation of industry and business. To assure the most valid results from time study practice, the time study analyst must receive complete cooperation from the foreman, the union steward, the operator, and company management.

Time study represents one of the most important and exacting forms of work in any industrial, commercial, or governmental enterprise. When intelligently used and fully understood by all parties, it offers marked benefits to workmen, management, and the general public.

TEXT QUESTIONS

1. What type of reliability can we expect with estimates?
2. How is a fair day's pay determined by the intraplant wage rate inequities agreements of the basic steel industries?
3. What bench mark for normal pace is given under these agreements?
4. Why should the foreman sign the time study?
5. Why should the time study man have excellent personal qualities?
6. Explain how poor time standards increase the difficulties of the union steward.

---

[2] "Time Study Training for Stewards and Committeemen," *Factory Management and Maintenance*, August, 1947.

7. How can management increase the cooperation of the union steward, the foreman, and the operator in their dealings with the time study analyst?

GENERAL QUESTIONS

1. Is it customary for the union to cooperate with the time study department to the extent recommended in this text? Is this cooperation likely to occur?

2. If the requirements for a time study man are so high, why is it that industry does not pay more for time study work?

3. How does the walking pace of three miles per hour agree with your concept of a normal performance?

CHAPTER 13

Time study equipment

The minimum equipment that is required to carry on a time study program includes a stopwatch, a time study board, time study forms, and a slide rule.

In addition to the above, time-recording devices that are being used successfully and that offer some advantages over the stopwatch are time-recording machines and a motion-picture camera.

It will be noted that the equipment needed for time study or work measurement is not nearly as elaborate or costly as that required for micromotion study work. In general, the ability and personality of the time study analyst represent the criteria of success rather than the equipment he chooses to use.

The Stopwatch

There are several types of stopwatches in use today, the majority of which are included in one of the following classifications:

1. Decimal minute watch (0.01 minute)
2. Decimal minute watch (0.001 minute)
3. Decimal hour watch (0.0001 hour)

The decimal minute watch (0.01 minute shown in Figure 13–1) has 100 divisions on its face, and each division is equal to 0.01 minute. Thus, a complete sweep of the long hand would require one minute. The small dial on the watch face has 30 divisions, and each division here is equal to one minute. For every revolution of the sweep hand, the small hand will move one division or one minute.

FIGURE 13–1

Decimal minute watch

FIGURE 13–2

Decimal minute split (double-action) watch

FIGURE 13–3

Decimal hour watch

Meylan Stopwatch Co.

To start this watch, the side slide is moved toward the crown. In order to stop the watch and have the hands retain their respective positions, the side slide is moved away from the watch crown. To continue operation of the watch from the point where the hands stopped, the slide is moved toward the crown. In order to move both the sweep hand and the small hand back to zero, the crown is depressed. Releasing the crown will put the watch back into operation unless the side slide is moved away from the crown.

The decimal minute watch tends to be a favorite with time study men because of its ease of reading and ease of recording. The sweep hand moves only 60 percent as fast as the long hand of the decimal hour watch, and thus terminal points are more discernible. In recording the time values, the analyst's task is simplified by the fact that the elemental readings are in one hundredths of a minute, eliminating the need for the ciphers that are registered when using the decimal hour watch, which is read in ten thousandths of an hour.

The decimal minute watch (0.001 minute) is similar to the decimal minute watch (0.01 minute). In the former, each division of the larger hand is equal to one thousandth of a minute. Thus, it takes 0.10 minute for the sweep hand to circle the dial rather than one minute as in the 0.01 decimal minute watch. This watch is used primarily for timing short elements for standard data purposes (see Chapter 18). In general, the 0.001 minute watch has no starting slide on its side, but is started, stopped, and returned to zero by successive depressions of the crown.

A special adaptation of the decimal minute watch that many time study men find convenient to use is illustrated in Figure 13–2. The two long hands indicate decimal minutes and will complete one turn of the dial in one minute. The upper small dial is graduated in minutes, and a complete sweep of its hand represents 30 minutes.

To start this watch, the crown is depressed and both sweep hands will simultaneously start from zero. At the termination of the first element, the side pin is depressed and this will stop the lower sweep hand only. The time study man can then observe the elapsed time for the element without the difficulty of reading a moving hand. He then depresses the side pin, and the lower hand will rejoin the upper hand which has been moving uninterruptedly. At the end of the second element the side pin is depressed and the procedure is repeated.

The decimal hour stop watch has 100 divisions on its face also, but each division on this watch represents 1 ten thousandth (0.0001) of an hour. Thus a complete sweep of the large hand on this watch would represent 1 one hundredth (0.01) hour or 0.6 minute. The small hand registers each turn of the long hand, and a complete sweep of the small hand would take 18 minutes or 0.30 hour (see Figure 13–3).

The decimal hour watch is started, stopped, and its hands are returned to zero in the same manner as in the decimal minute (0.01) stopwatch.

Since the hour represents a universal unit of time in measuring output, the decimal hour watch is a practical timer and is widely used. Somewhat more skill is required to read this watch while timing short elements on account of the speed of the sweep hand. For this reason, some time study men prefer the decimal minute watch with its slower moving hand.

It is possible to mount four watches on a board, with linkage between them, so that the analyst, during the course of a study, can always read one watch which has stopped hands. Figure 13–4 illustrates such an ar-

FIGURE 13–4

Time study board with four watches and form mounted, placed in proper position

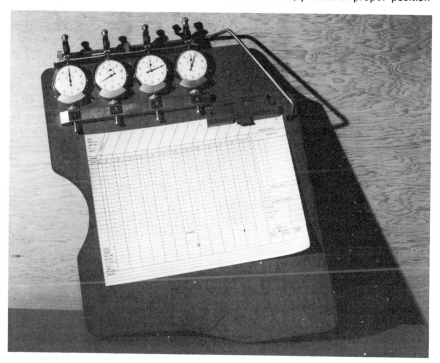

rangement. Here are shown four crown action watches which are actuated by a lever shown at the right. First pressure on lever starts Watch 1 (far left), cocks Watch 2, stops Watch 3 and starts Watch 4. At end of first element, a clutch activating Watch 4 is disengaged and the lever is again pressed. This will stop Watch 1, start Watch 2, reset Watch 3 to zero, while Watch 4 continues to run as it will measure the overall time as a check. Watch 1 is now waiting to be read, while the next element is being timed by Watch 2.

The more common practice is to use but one watch attached to the observation board as illustrated in Figure 13–6.

Most stopwatches are produced so as to record times with accuracies of plus or minus 0.025 minutes over 60 minutes of operation. Government specifications of stopwatch equipment allow a deviation of 0.005 minutes per 30-second interval. All stopwatches should be checked periodically to verify that they are not providing "out-of-tolerance" readings. To help assure continued accuracy of reading, it is essential that stopwatches be maintained properly. They should be protected from moisture, dust, and abrupt temperature changes. Regular (about once a year is adequate) cleaning and lubrication should be provided. If the watches are not used regularly, they should be wound and allowed to run down periodically.

Time-recording machines

Several versatile time study machines are on the market today which facilitate the accurate measurement of time intervals. These machines may be used advantageously for measurement of the time that a facility is productive without the presence of the time study analyst. For example, Figure 13–5 illustrates an eight-channel recorder where any two terminals may be connected to any normally open sensor which closes only when the machine or activity is productive. A stylus records on the chart paper the state of the facility continuously. In the model illustrated,

FIGURE 13–5

Eight-channel time study machine

Meylan Stopwatch Co.

the activity of eight separate facilities can be recorded. Chart speeds ranging from 6 inches per hour to 480 inches per hour are available depending upon the precision of measurement desired.

An adaptation of this equipment is its use with push-button control and where each channel can be used in connection with a specific work element. This adaptation is especially useful in work sampling type studies where a professional wishes to self-evaluate the distribution of his time. For example, he may choose to assign the following to the eight channels:

Channel 1.   Creative development
Channel 2.   Conference
Channel 3.   Dictation
Channel 4.   Incoming phone calls
Channel 5.   Outgoing phone calls
Channel 6.   Supervision and assigning work
Channel 7.   Read mail
Channel 8.   Personal and interruptions

By pushing a button related to the appropriate channel, he continuously accounts for the time expended during his workday.

Motion-picture camera

The motion-picture camera is ideal for recording operator methods and elapsed time. Unfortunately, the cost of film and the delay necessitated by having to send the films out to be developed, prohibit the use of the method in a great many instances.

More and more industries are resorting to the motion-picture camera for establishment of standards with the development of synthetic motion-time values. By taking pictures of the operator and then studying them a frame at a time, the analyst can record exact details of the method used and assign time values. It is also possible to establish standards by projecting the exposed films at the same speed that the pictures were taken and then performance rating the operator. All the facts necessary to accomplish a fair and accurate job of rating are available by observing the exposed film. Then, too, potential method improvements are revealed through the camera eye that would never be uncovered with the stopwatch or time study machine.

These advantages, supplemented with the "memomotion" procedure, which allows longer cycle filming with minimum exposure of film, have increased the popularity of the camera as an effective tool of the time study analyst (see Chapter 9). Figure 9–7 illustrates a portion of a memomotion film taken at the rate of one frame per second.

The motion-picture camera described and illustrated in Chapter 8 will also do an excellent job when filming for the purpose of establishing time standards.

Time study board

When the stopwatch is being used, it will be necessary to provide a suitable board to hold the time study form and the stopwatch. The board should be light, so as not to tire the arm, and yet strong and hard enough to provide a suitable backing for the time study form. One-quarter-inch plywood or a smooth plastic make suitable materials. The board should have arm and body contacts (see Figure 13–6) for comfortable fit and ease of writing while it is being held.

In the upper right-hand corner of the board (for right-handed people) is mounted the watch, and to the left, a spring clip holds the time study

FIGURE 13–6

Time study board for right-handed observer, (note alignment chart on board to assist observer in determining performance rating factor. See page 346 for explanation of this alignment chart)

form. By standing in the proper position, the time study analyst can look over the top of his watch to the work station, and follow the operator movements while keeping both the watch and the time study form in his immediate field of vision.

In order to assist the analyst in performance rating the operation under study, an alignment chart, developed by the author, may be attached to the board (see Figure 13–6). This chart permits the analyst to determine synthetically the allowed time for several of the effort elements comprising the study. The ratio of the synthetic value for a particular element to the mean value actually taken by the operator serves as a guide for determining the performance factor. This chart establishes standards for the therbligs reach, grasp, move, position, and release when performed collectively.

Time study forms

On the time study form is recorded all details of the study. To date there has been little standardization of the design of forms used by various industries. It is important that the form provide space to record all pertinent information concerning the method being studied. This is often done by constructing an operator process chart (see Chapter 6) on one side of the form. In addition to making a permanent record of the relative location of the tools and materials in the work area, the analyst should record such method data as feeds, depth of cut, speeds, and inspection specifications. Of course, it is also necessary to identify completely the operation being studied by including information such as the operator's name and number, operation description and number, machine name and number, special tools used and their respective numbers, department where operation is performed, and the prevailing working conditions. It is always better to provide too much information on the job being studied than too little. This will be discussed in a subsequent chapter.

The time study form should also include space for the signature of the foreman, indicating his approval of the method under observation. Likewise, the inspector should sign every study taken, acknowledging his acceptance of the quality of the parts being produced during the time study.

The form should be designed so that the analyst can conveniently record watch readings, foreign elements (see Chapter 14), rating factors (see Chapter 15), and still use the sheet to calculate the allowed time. Figures 13–7 and 13–8 illustrate a time study form that has been developed by the author which allows sufficient flexibility to study practically any type of operation.

In this form, the various elements comprising the operation are recorded horizontally across the top of the sheet and the cycles studied are recorded vertically row by row.

FIGURE 13-7

Time study form (front) designed for either elemental or overall rating

FIGURE 13-8

Time study form (back). Note space for operator chart (act breakdown) so that all details of method under study may be recorded

SKETCH		STUDY NO._____DATE_____
		OPERATION_____
		DEPT._____OPERATOR_____NO._____
		EQUIPMENT_____
		_____MCH. NO._____
		SPECIAL TOOLS, JIGS, FIXTURES, GAGES_____
		_____
		_____
		CONDITIONS_____
		MATERIAL_____
		PART NO._____DWG. NO._____
		PART DESCRIPTION_____

ACT BREAKDOWN		ELEM. NO.	SMALL TOOL NUMBERS, FEEDS, SPEEDS, DEPTH OF CUT, ETC.	ELEMENTAL TIME	OCC. PER CYCLE	TOTAL TIME ALLOWED
LEFT HAND	RIGHT HAND					

EACH PIECE_____		TOTAL _____
SET-UP		HRS. PER C
FOREMAN	INSPECTOR	
OBSERVER	APPROVED BY	

The "R" column is divided into two sections. The large area is for recording the watch readings and in the small section marked "F" is shown the element performance factor if elemental rating is used. The "T" column is provided for elemental elapsed values (see Chapter 14).

Auxiliary equipment

The time study analyst will find it necessary to provide certain additional equipment to facilitate calculation of studies rapidly and accurately. Foremost of these items is the slide rule by means of which calculation of the time study involving multiplication, division, and proportion can be solved correctly and rapidly in a small fraction of the time required to work it out by longhand arithmetical procedures.

FIGURE 13–9

Speed indicator for use in determining speeds in revolutions per minute

Brown & Sharpe Manufacturing Co.

It is recommended that the time study analyst use a slide rule with a 10-inch scale, as this will give results correct to within about 1 part in 1,000 or 0.10 percent. The shorter the rule, the less accurate will be the readings, and of course the larger the scales, the more precise will be the results.

Although, in most cases, modern machine tools, being self-powered, show their speeds in an obvious place, there will be occasions when the running speed will not be evident. Then too, speeds indicated by the manufacturer are based on certain pulley diameters which may have been altered during the setup or changed during maintenance or overhaul of the machine.

In order to determine the speed being used, the time study analyst will find it convenient to use a speed indicator. This instrument has few parts, is simple in operation, and will give relatively accurate revolutions of shafting, wheels, and spindles in either direction. Figure 13–9 illustrates a typical speed indicator. To use the speed indicator, it is merely necessary to place the point of the indicator on the spindle or shaft and watch the dial for a given period of time. In the illustration, the figures showing through the small, round windows on the dial read every five revolutions. The inside dial reads every 100 revolutions. The dials may be quickly returned to zero for repeated use by turning a knob on the back of the indicator.

FIGURE 13–10

Checking spindle speed with speed indicator

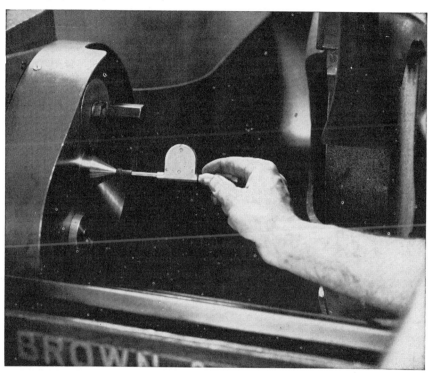

Training equipment

Two inexpensive pieces of equipment should be available to assist in the training of time study men. The first of these, a random elapsed time describer is illustrated in Figure 13–11. This device can be programmed (by means of a specially contoured cam) so that successive elements, in this case one through nine are completed and each is accomplished in a known period. At the end of each element, a buzzer may sound and a bulb on the panel will light. The elements duration are recorded by the

,trainee as they take place. The trainee is signaled by the lighting of the bulb and by the buzzer at the end of each element. Either the buzzer or the light may be made inoperative if desired.

This exercise provides practice in reading the watch at terminal points and recording the elapsed time. As an operator becomes proficient with data generated through the given cam, he is challenged by changing to a new cam capable of generating shorter elemental cycles. This device

FIGURE 13–11

Random elapsed time describer for training time study analysts

teaches the trainee the technique of using both sound and sight to identify terminal points. It also provides practice in handling two or more short elements that occur successively and are followed by a relatively long element.

A second helpful training tool is the metronome as used by students of music. This device can be set to provide a predetermined number of beats per minute. For example, the metronome can be set to provide 104 beats per minute (the number of cards dealt per minute when operating at a normal pace). By synchronizing the delivery of a card at a four-hand bridge table so that a card is delivered with each beat of the metronome, we are able to demonstrate normal pace. This speed of movement involving a series of reaches, grasps, moves, and releases can be easily identified with practice. To illustrate 80 percent performance, the instructor needs only to set his metronome to 83 beats per minute and then synchronize his card dealing accordingly. The instructor will find this device very helpful in demonstrating various levels of performance in card dealing. Once a new time study trainee becomes proficient in accurately rating hand movements involving the dealing of cards, he can make the transition of evaluating shop operations more easily.

TEXT QUESTIONS

1. What equipment is needed by the time study analyst to carry on a program of time study?
2. What features of the decimal minute watch make it attractive to time study men?
3. Where does the decimal minute watch (0.001 minute) have application?
4. How does the duration of one division on the decimal hour watch compare to one division on the decimal minute watch?
5. What is the principal advantage of the time-recording machine?
6. What is the "memomotion" procedure? What are its advantages and limitations?
7. Why is it desirable to provide space for an operator process chart on the time study form?
8. Describe the speed indicator and how it is used.
9. How many feet of film would be exposed on a five-minute cycle while using the memomotion technique?
10. How do government specifications of stopwatch equipment compare with the accuracy to which most stopwatches are produced?
11. Explain how a "random elapsed time describer" can be used to train new work measurement analysts.
12. How can the metronome be used as a training tool for performance rating?

GENERAL QUESTIONS

1. Explain the statement, "the ability and personality of the time study engineer represent the criteria of success rather than the equipment he chooses to use."
2. Why has there not been a standardized time study form adopted by industry?
3. Do you feel that the typical shop workman would favor the time study machine? Why?
4. What would be the advantages of having a time study machine that would be able to record and play back sound as well as record end points of progressive elements?

CHAPTER 14

Elements of time study

The actual taking of a time study is both an art and a science. In order to be sure of success in this field the analyst must have developed the art of being able to inspire confidence, exercise judgment, and create a personable approach to all with whom he comes in contact. In addition, it is essential that his background and training have been such that he thoroughly understands and is able to perform the various functions related to each step in the taking of the study. These elements include selecting the operator, analyzing the job and breaking it down into its elements, recording the elapsed elemental values, performance rating the operator, assigning appropriate allowances, and working up the study.

Choosing the operator

The first approach to beginning a time study is made through the departmental foreman or line supervisor. Upon review of the job in operation, both the foreman and the time study man should agree that the job is ready to be studied. If more than one operator is performing the work assignment on which the standard is to be established, several things should be taken into consideration in selecting just which operator to use in taking the study. In general, the operator who is average or somewhat above average in performance will give a more satisfactory study than the low-skilled or highly superior operator. The average operator usually will perform the work consistently and systematically. His pace will tend to be in the approximate range of normal (see Chapter 15), thereby making it easier for the time study analyst to apply a correct performance factor.

Of course, the operator should be completely trained in the method being used and should possess a liking for his work and an interest in doing a good job. He should be familiar with time study procedures and practice, and have confidence in time study methods as well as in the time study analyst. It is desirable that the operator have a cooperative spirit, so that he will follow through willingly with suggestions made by both the foreman and the time study analyst.

At times, the analyst will have no choice as to whom he studies, in that the operation is performed by only one man. In cases of this nature, the analyst must be very careful when he establishes his performance rating because the operator may be performing at either of the extreme ends of the rating scale. In one-man jobs, it is also especially important that the method being used is correct and that the analyst approach the operator tactfully.

Approach to the operator

The technique used by the time study man in approaching the selected operator will have much to do with the extent of cooperation received. The operator should be approached in a friendly manner and be informed that the operation is to be studied. He should then be given the opportunity to ask any questions relative to such matters as the timing technique, method of rating, and application of allowances. In some instances, the operator may have never before been studied, and the time study man will find it worthwhile to answer all his questions frankly and patiently. He should encourage the operator to offer suggestions and, when the operator does so, should receive them willingly, thus recognizing that he respects the skill and trade knowledge of the operator.

The time study man should show interest in the workman's job, and at all times be fair and straightforward in his behavior toward the workman. This approach will establish the workman's confidence in the time study man's ability, and the analyst will find the respect and goodwill resulting will not only help in establishing a fair standard, but will also make his future work assignments on the production floor more pleasant.

Analysis of materials and methods

Perhaps the most common mistake made by time study analysts is neglecting to make sufficient analysis and records of the method being studied. The time study form illustrated in Chapter 13 allows space for a sketch or photograph of the work area. If a sketch is made, it should be drawn to scale and should show all pertinent details that affect method. The sketch should clearly show the location of the raw material and finished parts bins with respect to the work area. Thus, distances that the operator must move or walk are clearly recorded. The location of all tools involved in the operation should be indicated, thus illustrating the motion pattern utilized in performing successive elements.

Immediately below the pictorial presentation of the method, space frequently is allotted for an operator process chart (see Chapter 6) of the method being studied. On high-activity work, it is recommended that this chart be completed before the actual timing of the operation begins. By completing this right- and left-hand chart, the analyst can entirely identify the method under study and can observe opportunities for methods improvement. Elemental breakdown of the study to be taken will be facilitated, and the analyst will be able to acquire a better conception of the skill being executed.

The value of completely identifying the method under study cannot be overemphasized. Since management usually guarantees a standard as long as the method studied is in effect, it is mandatory that the method studied be completely known. For example, after machining a casting, the operator may have been studied as placing the casting in a tote box on a pallet 4 feet from the work station. The element "lay aside finished casting" may have consumed 0.05 minute. Let us assume that sometime after the standard was established the location of the skid was changed so that a chute and drop delivery could be used to remove the completed part. This could reduce the "lay aside finished casting" element to 0.01 minute. The savings of 0.04 minute per cycle would be substantial if the job could be completed in 0.40 minute or less. This small method change could result in a loose rate that would be troublesome to the union, the company, and the worker's fellow employees. Unless a complete record of the method originally used to "lay aside finished casting" had been established, the time study department would have no authority to restudy the job.

More pronounced methods changes are often made without informing the time study department, such as changing the job to a different machine, increasing or decreasing feeds and speeds, or using different cutting tools. Changes of this nature, of course, seriously affect the validity of the original standard. Often the first time it is brought to the time study department's attention is when a grievance has been submitted that a rate is too tight, or the cost department complains about a loose standard. Investigation will frequently reveal that a change in method has been the cause of this inequitable standard. In order to know what part or parts of the job should be restudied, the analyst must have information as to method used when the job was initially studied. If this information is not available and the rate appears too loose, the only recourse the analyst has is to let the loose rate prevail for the life of the job—a situation that will be resented by management—or to change the method again and then immediately restudy the job—a program that will be strongly criticized by the operator.

Information as to the type of material being used should be recorded, as well as material used in cutting tools (ceramic, high-speed, carbide). A design change calling for a part to be made from "60–40 brass" rather than "70–30 brass" could have a pronounced effect on cycle time. Likewise, a change from high-speed tools to carbide tools could decrease machining time by more than 50 percent.

It has continually been emphasized that a job should not be time studied until it is *ready* to be studied; that is, until the method employed is correct. However, it has also been shown that methods must be continually improved in order to progress. A plant that does not continually emphasize methods improvement will fall into the doldrums and will eventually be unable to operate profitably. Since methods changes are continually taking place, it is necessary that complete analysis of the existing materials and methods be made and recorded prior to beginning the actual watch readings.

Recording the significant information

Complete information should be recorded concerning the machines, hand tools, jigs or fixtures, working conditions, materials used, operation performed, name of operator and clock number, department, date of study, and the time study observer's name. Perhaps all this detail will seem unimportant to the novice, but through experience he will realize that the more pertinent information recorded, the more useful will the study be over the years to come. The time study will be a source of establishing standard data (see Chapter 18) and the development of formulas (see Chapter 20). It also will be useful in methods improvement, operator evaluation, tool evaluation, and machine performance.

When machine tools are used, the name, size, style, capacity, and serial or inventory number should be specified. For example "No. 3 Warner & Swasey Ram Type turret lathe, Serial No. 111408, equipped with 2-jaw S.P. air chuck," would identify the facility under use. Cutting tools should be described completely as "½-inch, two-flute, high-speed, 18–4–1, gun drill." Likewise, description of general facilities should be complete and well defined, such as "2-pound ball-peen hammer," "1-inch micrometers," "combination square," "12-inch bastard file."

Dies, jigs, gages, and fixtures can be identified by their number and a short description. For example, "flange trimming die F–1156," "progressive trimming, piercing, forming die F–1202," "Go-No-Go Thread Plug Gage F–1101."

The working conditions should be noted for several reasons. First, the prevailing conditions will have a definite relationship to the "allowance" added to the leveled or normal time. If conditions improve in the future, the allowance for personal time as well as fatigue may be diminished.

Conversely, if for some reason, it becomes necessary to alter the working conditions so that they become poorer than when the time study was first taken, it would follow that the allowance factor should be raised.

If working conditions prevailing during the study are different from the normal conditions that exist on that job, then they would have an effect on the usual performance of the operator. For example, in a drop forge shop, if a study were taken on an extremely hot summer day, it can be readily understood that working conditions would be poorer than they usually are, and operator performance would reflect the effect of the intense heat. The following examples will illustrate the description that should be included when recording the job conditions: "Normal for job, wet, hot (90° F.), operator standing," or "poor, temperature 85° F., operator seated, clean, noisy."

It will be noted that it is customary to indicate first the working conditions as they compare with the average conditions for that job. This description is then followed by a short account of the exact conditions which were observed.

Raw materials are identified completely, giving such information as heat number, size and shape, weight, quality, and previous treatments.

The operation being performed is specifically described. For example, "broach ⅜ inch × ⅜ inch keyway in 1-inch bore" is considerably more explicit than the description "broach keyway." There could be several inside diameters on the part, each having a different keyway, and unless the hole that is being broached is specified and the keyway size is shown, misinterpretation may result.

The operator being studied should be identified by name and clock number. There could easily be two John Smiths in one company. Then, too, the clock number does not completely identify an employee, as labor turnover results in assignment of the same clock numbers to more than one employee over a period of years.

Observer's position

Once the time study analyst has made the correct approach to the operator and has recorded all the significant information, he is ready to record the time consumed by each element.

The time study observer should take a position a few feet to the rear of the operator so as not to distract or interfere with him. It is important that the time study analyst stand while taking the study. A time study man who takes his studies while seated will be subject to criticism from the operators and will soon lose the respect of the production floor. Then, too, when standing, the observer is better able to move about and follow the movements of the operator's hands as he goes through his work cycle. Figure 14–1 illustrates the correct position of the observer with respect to

FIGURE 14–1

Time study observer studying a radial drill press operation

the operator while studying a radial drill operation. It can be seen that the observer is in a position to have a simultaneous view of his watch, his time study form, and the hands of the operator.

During the course of the study, the observer should avoid any conversation with the operator, as this would tend to upset the routine of both the analyst and the workman.

Dividing the operation into elements

For ease of measurement the operation is divided into groups of therbligs known as "elements." So the operation may be divided into its individual elements, the observer should watch the operator for several cycles. However, if the cycle time is relatively long (over 30 minutes), the observer should write the description of the elements while taking the study. If possible, the elements into which the operation is to be divided should be determined in advance of the start of the study. Elements should be broken down into divisions as fine as possible and yet not so small that accuracy of reading will be sacrificed. Elemental divisions of about 0.04 minute are about as fine as can be read consistently by the experienced time study analyst. However, if the preceding and succeeding elements are relatively long, an element as short as 0.02 minute can be readily timed.

To identify end points completely and develop consistency in reading the watch from one cycle to the next, elemental breakdown should consider sound as well as sight. Thus, terminal points of elements can be associated with the sounds made, such as when a finished piece hits the container, when a facing tool bites into a casting, when a drill breaks through the part being drilled, and when a pair of micrometers are laid on a bench.

Each element should be recorded in its proper sequence and include a basic division of work terminated by a distinctive motion or a sound. Thus, the element "up part to manual chuck and tighten" would include the basic divisions of reach for part, grasp part, move part, position part, reach for chuck wrench, grasp chuck wrench, move chuck wrench, position chuck wrench, turn chuck wrench, and release chuck wrench. The point of termination of this element would be evidenced by the sound of the chuck wrench being dropped on the head of the lathe. The element "start machine" could include reach for lever, grasp lever, move lever, and release lever. Rotation of the machine with accompanying sound would identify the point of termination so readings could be made at exactly the same point in each cycle.

Frequently, a standard elemental breakdown is adopted by the different time study analysts within a company for given classes of facilities to assure uniformity in establishing terminal points. For example, all single spindle bench-type drill press work may be broken down into standard elements and all lathe work may be composed of a series of predetermined elements. Having standard elements as a basis for operation breakdown is especially important in the establishment of standard data (see Chapter 18).

The principal rules for accomplishing the elemental breakdown are:

1. Ascertain that all elements being performed are necessary. If it develops that some are unnecessary, the time study should be discontinued and a methods study should be made to develop the proper method.
2. Keep manual and machine time separate.
3. Do not combine constants with variables.
4. Select elements so terminal points can be identified by a characteristic sound.
5. Select elements so they can be readily and accurately timed.

When dividing the job into elements, the analyst should keep machine or cutting time separate from effort or handling time. Likewise, constant elements (those elements for which the time will not deviate within a specified range of work), should be kept separate from variable elements (those elements for which the time will vary within a specified range of work).

Once the proper breakdown is made of all the elements constituting the operation, it is then necessary that each element be accurately described. The termination of one element is automatically the beginning of the succeeding element and is referred to as the "breaking point." The description of this terminal point or breaking point should be such that it will be readily recognized by the observer. This is especially important when the element does not include sound at its ending. On cutting elements, the feed, speed, depth, and length of cut should be recorded immediately after the element description. Typical element descriptions are: "Pk. up pt. from table & pos. in vise" and "Dr. $\frac{1}{2}$" D. .005" F 1200 R.P.M." It will be noted that the analyst, in the interest of brevity, abbreviates and uses symbols to a great extent. This system of notation is acceptable only if the element is completely described in terminology and symbols meaningful to all who may come in contact with the study. Some companies use standard symbols throughout their plant, and all connected with the plant are familiar with the terminology.

When elements repeat themselves, it is not necessary to describe the element a second time, but only necessary to indicate in the space provided for a description of the element, the identifying number of the element that was used when it first occurred.

The time study form offers the flexibility required by diversified studies. For example, occasionally, it will not be possible to record an element that successively repeats itself, due to the space limitations of the time study form. This can be handled by recording the watch readings of the repeating elements in the same column as the one in which the first occurrence of the element was recorded. Figure 14–2 illustrates this method of recording.

When more than 15 elements constitute the study, a second sheet should be used to record those elements in excess of 15. If more than 20 cycles are to be observed and the study is comprised of seven or less elements, then the right-hand half of the form can be utilized by repeating the elements and continuing the study in the open spaces. However, if more than seven elements occur and more than 20 cycles are to be recorded, a second sheet should be used. Figure 14–3 illustrates a 60-cycle study constituting four elements.

Taking the study

There are two techniques of recording the elemental time while taking the study. The continuous method, as the name implies, allows the stopwatch to run for the entire duration of the study. In this method the

FIGURE 14–2

Method of recording an element that successively repeats itself

DATE / /
STUDY NO.__
SHEET NO.__
OF
SHEETS

NUMBER	1			2			3			4			5			6			7			8			9			10			11			12			13			14			15		
NOTES / CY.NO	T	R	F	T	R	F	T	R	F	T	R	F	T	R	F	T	R	F	T	R	F	T	R	F	T	R	F	T	R	F	T	R	F	T	R	F	T	R	F	T	R	F	T	R	F
1		5			12			16			26			35																																	
2								39			48			57																																
3								62			71			80			101			9			19			48			57			62			68			201			11			32	
4		37			44			49			60			71																																	
5								75			83			92																																
6								97			307			17			36			43			52			81			90			93			400			35			44			63	
7		89			77			82			91			501																																	
8								6			16			24																																
9								27			38			47			66			78			89			608			17			23			29			59			69			88	
10		93			701			5			14			24																																	
11								9			29			40																																
12								44			52			64			84			93			806			35			46			52			58			85			94			920	
13		25			33			37			47			56																																	
14								60			69			78																																
15								83			96			1005			25			33			43			70			81			86			91			1125			35			55	
16		60			68			73			82			91																																	
17								96			1206			15																																
18								19			29			30			59			67			77			1302			11			17			23			54			64			84	
19		90			97			1401			11			22																																	
20								26			37			47																																

SUMMARY

	1	2	3	4	5	6	7	8	9	10	11	12	13	14	15
TOTALS															
OBSER.															
AVE. T.															
LEV. FACT															
L.F. & AV. T.															
% ALL.															
TIME ALLOWED															

FOREIGN ELEMENTS			GENERAL RATING CHECK	SYN. VAL. __ = %	REMARKS:
	R	T		OBS. VAL.	
A				STUDY STARTED	STUDY FINISHED	OVERALL TIME
B				__ A.M. __ P.M.	__ A.M. __ P.M.	__ MIN.
C				F		
D				G		
E				H		

FIGURE 14–3

Time study form showing recording of four-element 60-cycle study

DATE / /
STUDY NO.___
SHEET NO.___
OF
SHEETS

NUMBER	1	2	3	4	1	2	3	4	1	2	3	4
CY. NO	R	R	R	R	R	R	R	R	R	R	R	R
1	4	14	20	23	64	73	80	83	53	65	72	75
2	27	36	42	46	87	97	503	6	80	91	97	1001
3	51	62	69	74	10	20	25	28	5	15	22	25
4	78	88	94	98	33	45	52	55	29	39	46	49
5	101	13	19	23	59	69	75	78	53	61	67	71
6	26	35	41	44	84	95	602	5	74	84	90	93
7	48	56	62	65	9	19	26	29	97	1106	13	16
8	69	79	85	88	34	43	49	52	20	30	37	40
9	91	200	5	9	55	63	68	72	44	54	60	63
10	13	22	28	31	76	91	98	702	67	76	82	85
11	35	45	51	54	5	15	21	24	89	99	1202	5
12	58	66	71	74	29	39	46	49	9	19	25	28
13	79	89	97	301	53	63	70	73	32	42	48	51
14	5	15	22	26	77	86	93	96	55	66	72	74
15	30	41	46	49	800	10	18	24	78	88	94	98
16	52	60	66	69	29	37	45	48	1302	12	18	21
17	73	83	89	92	52	62	69	72	25	35	41	44
18	96	406	12	15	76	85	91	94	49	61	68	71
19	19	29	35	38	98	908	15	18	75	85	91	95
20	42	51	57	60	23	35	45	48	1400	12	18	21

SUMMARY

TOTALS												
OBSER.												
AVE. T.												
LEV. FACT												
L.F. ĈAV. T.												
% ALL.												
TIME ALLOWED												

FOREIGN ELEMENTS		GENERAL RATING CHECK	SYN. VAL. ____ = %	REMARKS:
R	T		OBS. VAL.	
A		STUDY STARTED	STUDY FINISHED / OVERALL TIME	
B		____ A.M. P.M.	____ A.M. P.M. ____ MIN.	
C		F		
D		G		
E		H		

watch is read at the breaking point of each element while the hands of the watch are moving. In the snapback technique, the watch is read at the termination point of each element, and then the hands are snapped back to zero. As the next element takes place, the hands move from zero. The elapsed time is read directly from the watch at the end of this element, and the hands are again returned to zero. This procedure is followed throughout the entire study.

When starting the study, using either the continuous method or the snapback, the time study analyst should advise the operator that he is beginning his study, and also let him know the exact time of day at which the study is being taken so the operator will be able to verify the overall time. The time of day that the study is started is recorded on the time study form (see Figure 14–4), just prior to starting the stopwatch. Figures 14–4 and 14–5 illustrate a completed time study.

Snapback method

The snapback method has ceratin advantages and disadvantages compared with the continuous technique. These should be clearly understood before standardizing on one way of recording the values. In fact, some time study men find it desirable to use both methods, feeling that studies made up predominantly of long elements are adapted to snapback readings, while short-cycle studies are better studied with the continuous procedure.

Since elapsed elemental values are read directly in the snapback method, no clerical time is required for making successive subtractions, as is necessary with the continuous method. Then, too, elements that are performed out of order by the operator can be readily recorded without special notation. Proponents of the snapback method also bring out the fact that when using this procedure, it is not necessary to record delays, and since elemental values can be compared from one cycle to the next, a decision can be made as to the number of cycles to study. Actually, observations of the past few cycles, as a means of determining how many additional cycles should be studied is an erroneous procedure. This practice can lead to studying entirely too small a sample.

W. O. Lichtner[1] points out one accepted disadvantage of the snapback method, namely that individual elements should not be removed from the operation and studied independently because elemental times are dependent on preceding and succeeding elements. Consequently, by omitting such factors as delays, foreign elements, and transposed elements, erroneous values will prevail in the readings accepted.

One of the objections to the snapback method that has received con-

---

[1] W. O. Lichtner, *Time Study and Job Analysis* (New York: Ronald Press Co.).

FIGURE 14–4

Completed time study illustrating the continuous method of watch reading and overall performance rating (front of form)

	Pick up part from table & bring to vise & file edge		Position part in vise & tighten vise by hand, position table		Start machine & engage feed		Mill 3/4" slot		Return table eight inches, stop machine		Open vise & remove part		Brush out chips		Reposition part for second cut		Tighten vise & return table		Start machine		Run table forward 4" & engage feed		Mill second 3/4" slot		Return table eight inches		Stop machine & open vise		Brush chips & aside part	
NUMBER	1		2		3		4		5		6		7		8		9		10		11		12		13		14		15	
NOTES CY. NO	T	R	T	R	T	R	T	R	T	R	T	R	T	R	T	R	T	R	T	R	T	R	T	R	T	R	T	R	T	R
1	14	14	16	30	4	34	68	102	6	8	19	27	14	41	11	52	21	73	3	76	8	84	77	261	9	70	12	82	18	300
2	12	12	15	27	5	32	73	405	7	12	16	28	15	43	10	53	23	76	5	81	10	91	80	571	9	80	6	86	20	606
3	A 22	36	17	53	4	57	64	1021	5	26	21	47	18	65	10	75	21	96	3	99	11	1110	75	85	11	96	10	1206	16	22
Blow Nose 4	12	34	B 16	32	(10)	42	70	1512	8	20	21	41	14	55	11	66	19	85	4	89	9	98	82	1680	11	91	8	99	19	1718
5	12	30	12	42	4	46	70	1816	7	23	22	45	16	61	9	70	22	92	2	94	9	1903	71	74	9	83	8	91	19	2010
6	13	23	17	40	4	44	66	2110	5	15	20	35	15	50	10	60	20	80	5	85	10	95	80	2275	C 16	36	9	45	20	65
Drop Part 7	16	81	16	97	5	2402	73	75	5	80	(34)	2514	14	28	9	37	21	58	3	61	8	69	76	2645	(4)	49	10	59	18	77
Incomp. Brushing 8	15	92	17	2709	4	13	(50)	64	6	70	18	88	(7)	95	10	3005	20	25	5	30	11	41	80	3732	E 9	41	12	53	16	69
9	14	83	17	3800	4	4	71	75	6	81	21	3902	14	16	11	27	21	48	5	53	8	61	71	4032	10	42	14	56	15	71
10	17	88	12	4100	–	M	–	80	5	85	21	4206	14	20	11	31	22	53	–	M	–	M	–	4340	10	50	8	58	18	76
11	12	88	15	4403	5	8	70	78	6	84	20	4504	14	4528 4514	20	4514 4564	20	4548 4528	4	52	10	62	75	4637	9	46	7	53	17	70
12	15	85	18	4703	4	7	68	4775	6	81	17	98	15	4813	9	22	21	43	4	47	10	57	78	4935	10	45	8	53	20	73
13	11	94	17	5001	6	7	71	78	7	85	18	5103	16	19	10	29	20	49	4	53	9	62	80	5242	11	53	8	61	18	79
14	13	92	17	5309	5	14	73	87	6	93	16	5409	15	24	9	33	19	52	5	57	8	65	77	5542	9	51	9	60	20	80
15	20	5600	18	18	4	22	71	93	5	98	19	5717	13	30	9	39	19	58	6	64	10	74	80	5854	11	65	9	74	19	93
16	13	5906	14	20	4	24	66	90	6	96	18	6014	14	28	11	39	20	59	5	64	12	76	74	6150	9	59	7	66	17	83
17	11	94	19	6213	5	18	70	88	6	94	20	6314	12	26	10	36	19	55	5	60	11	71	79	6450	8	58	8	66	20	86
18	12	98	20	6518	6	24	71	95	5	6600	20	20	15	35	9	44	20	64	6	70	9	79	80	6759	8	67	10	77	18	95
19	14	6809	16	25	5	30	75	6905	4	9	15	24	17	41	11	52	23	75	5	80	10	90	81	7071	9	80	8	88	17	7105
20	12	7117	18	35	6	41	72	7213	5	18	19	37	15	52	9	61	21	82	6	88	11	99	80	7379	9	88	10	98	22	7420

SUMMARY

	1	2	3	4	5	6	7	8	9	10	11	12	13	14	15
TOTALS	2.80	3.27	.94	12.62	1.16	3.61	2.80	1.99	4.12	.85	1.84	14.76	1.81	1.81	3.67
OBSER.	20	20	18	18	20	19	18	20	20	19	19	19	19	20	20
AVE. T.	.140	.163	.047	.701	.058	.190	.147	.100	.206	.045	.097	.777	.095	.090	.184
LEV. FACT.	1.10	1.10	1.10	1.00	1.10	1.10	1.10	1.10	1.10	1.10	1.10	1.00	1.10	1.10	1.10
L.F.C AV.T.	.154	.179	.052	.701	.064	.208	.162	.110	.226	.050	.107	.777	.104	.099	.202
% ALL.	15	15	15	10	15	15	15	15	15	15	15	10	15	15	15
TIME ALLOWED	.177	.206	.060	.806	.711	.239	.186	.126	.260	.058	.123	.855	.120	.114	.232

FOREIGN ELEMENTS			GENERAL RATING CHECK	SYN. VAL. #2 $\frac{.164}{.150}$ = 109 %		REMARKS:
	R	T		OBS. VAL.		
A	914 606	308	Get drink	STUDY STARTED	STUDY FINISHED	OVERALL TIME
B	1416 1234	182	Interrupted by foreman	10:32 ~~A.M.~~ P.M.	11:46 ~~A.M.~~ P.M.	74 MIN.
C	2326 2275	51	Gage part	F		
D	2914 2713	201	Chip in eye	G		
E	3652 3041	611	Replace milling cutter	H		

FIGURE 14-5 Completed time study form (back of form)

STUDY NO. 132   DATE 9-15

OPERATION Mill diagonal slots in regulator clamp

DEPT. 11-5   OPERATOR B.V. Harvey NO. 14

EQUIPMENT #2 B. + S. Horizontal Mill

MCH. NO. 3-17694

SPECIAL TOOLS, JIGS, FIXTURES, GAGES Milling fixture
#F-14611, 18-4-1 high speed cutters

CONDITIONS Normal

MATERIAL X-4130 steel forging

PART NO. S-11694-1   DWG. NO. SA-11694

PART DESCRIPTION 2" clamp for series 411

SKETCH

Bin with Raw Forgings ←—3'—→ Operator ½' Finished Parts Bin on Pallet

#2 B. + S. Mill

ACT BREAKDOWN

ELEM. NO.	LEFT HAND	RIGHT HAND	SMALL TOOL NUMBERS, FEEDS, SPEEDS, DEPTH OF CUT, ETC.	ELEMENTAL TIME	OCC. PER CYCLE	TOTAL TIME ALLOWED
1	Reach 12", grasp (simple)	Reach 8", grasp file,		.186	1	.186
2	forging on mill bed, move	move file to forging,		.197	1	.197
3	12", hold.	file edge (3 strokes)		.054	1	.054
4	Position forging in vise	Move file 8", release.	95 R.P.M. 5½"/Min.	.763	1	.763
5		Reach 12" for vise handle,		.076	1	.076
6		grasp handle, turn handle		.252	1	.252
7		90 to 180 degrees		.189	1	.189
8				.129		.129

Motion and Time Study Sheet

Element Description	No.	Speed	Time		Time
Get new piece from bin. / for feed lever, grasp lever, Move lever	10		.266	1	.266
Reach for stop button, apply pressure. / Idle during mill cut / Move lever	11		.050 / .117	1 / 1	.050 / .117
Reach 8" grasp control wheel, Move 45° release wheel. / Idle during mill cut	12	95 R.P.M. 5⅜"/Min.	.846	1	.846
Reach 15" to part, grasp part, / Reach 16" for vise handle, grasp handle, turn handle 90-180°.	13		.124	1	.124
Move part 8" and release. / Reach 16" for vise handle	14		.117	1	.117
Idle / Reach 12" grasp brush, Move brush to vise 12" and brush chips.	15		.227	1	.227
Reach 8" to part, grasp, / Move brush to table 12", release brush, reach for vise handle					
Move 8" to vise, position / Grasp vise handle, turn handle 90 to 180 degrees.					
Idle / reach 8" grasp control wheel move 45 degrees and release					
Idle / Reach 14" for Start button, apply pressure.					
Idle / Reach 14" for control wheel, grasp wheel, turn wheel 15 degrees, release.					
Reach 18" grasp feed lever move lever / Lay aside finished piece.					
Idle during mill cut / Reach for control wheel 14", grasp wheel, turn 60 degrees.					
Idle / Release control wheel, reach 12" and grasp vise handle, move handle 90°.					
Reach 16" for stop button, apply pressure. / Reach 12", grasp brush, move brush to vise 12", brush chips, lay brush aside.					
Reach for part 12", grasp, Move part to table release.					

EACH PIECE 3.593 MIN.

TOTAL 3.593

HRS. PER C 5.988

SET-UP _____

FOREMAN W. H. Armstrong

OBSERVER George Thuring

INSPECTOR CA Anderson

APPROVED BY BUM.

siderable attention, particularly from labor groups, is the time that is lost while the hand is being snapped back to zero. Lowry, Maynard, and Stegemerten state: "It has been found that the hand of the watch remains stationary from 0.00003 to 0.000097 hour at the time of snapback, depending upon the speed with which the button of the watch is pressed and released."[2] This would mean an average loss of time of 0.0038 minute per element which would be a 3.8 percent error in an element, 0.10 of a minute in duration. Of course, the shorter the element, the greater the percent of error introduced, and the longer the element, the smaller the error. Although experienced time study men will tend in reading the watch to allow for the "snapback time" by reading to the next highest digit, it should be recognized that a sizable cumulative error can develop with the snapback method.

Another disadvantage of the snapback method is the tendency for the observer to become careless once he has established a value for the various elements. He may anticipate what the reading will be and record the corresponding value without close attention to the true elapsed time.

In summary, the snapback procedure has the following disadvantages:

1. Time is lost in snapping back; therefore, a cumulative error is introduced into the study.
2. Short elements (0.06 minute and less) are difficult to time.
3. Record of the complete study is not always given in that delays and foreign elements may not be recorded.
4. Carelessness on part of time study man is promoted.

The continuous method

The continuous method of recording elemental values is recommended for several reasons. Probably the most significant reason is that this type of study presents a complete record of the entire observation period and, as a result, appeals to the operator and his representatives. The operator is able to see that no time has been left out of the study and that all delays and foreign elements have been recorded. With all the facts clearly presented, it is easier to explain and sell this technique of recording times.

The continuous method is also better adapted to recording very short elements. Since no time is lost in snapping the hand back to zero, accurate values can be obtained on successive elements of 0.04 minute and on elements of 0.02 minute when followed by a relatively long element. With practice, a good time study man using the continuous method will

---

[2] S. M. Lowry, H. B. Maynard, and G. J. Stegemerten, *Time and Motion Study and Formulas for Wage Incentives* (3d ed.; New York: McGraw-Hill Book Co., 1940).

be able to catch accurately three successive short elements (less than 0.04 minute), if they are followed by an element of about 0.15 minute or longer. He does this by remembering the watch readings of the terminal points of the three short elements and then recording their respective values while the fourth longer element is taking place.

Of course, as previously pointed out, more clerical work is involved in calculating the study when using the continuous method. Since the watch is read at the breaking point of each element while the hands of the watch continue their movements, it is necessary to make successive subtractions of the consecutive readings to determine elapsed elemental times. For example, the following readings might represent the terminal points of a 10-element study: 4, 14, 19, 121, 25, 52, 61, 76, 211, 16, and the elemental values of this cycle would be 4, 10, 5, 102, 4, 27, 9, 15, 35, and 5.

Recording the time consumed by each element

When recording the watch readings, the analyst notes only the necessary digits and the decimal point is not indicated, thus giving as much

TABLE 14–1

Consecutive reading of watch in decimal minutes	Recorded reading
0.08	8
0.25	25
1.32	132
1.35	35
1.41	41
2.01	201
2.10	10
2.15	15
2.71	71
3.05	305
3.17	17
3.25	25

time as possible to observe the performance of the operator. Thus, if a decimal minute watch should be used and the terminal point of the first element occurred at 0.08 minute, the analyst would record only the digit 8 in the "R" (reading) column of the time study form. If the decimal hour watch is in use and the end point of the first element is 0.0052, the recorded reading would be 52. Table 14–1 illustrates the procedure of using a decimal minute watch.

The small hand on the watch will indicate the number of elapsed minutes so the observer can refer to it periodically to verify the correct first digit to record after the large hand sweeps past the zero. For example, after 22 minutes have passed in taking a given study, the observer may not recall whether the value to record after the termination of the element he is observing should be prefixed by "22" or "21." By glancing at the small hand of his watch, he will note that it has moved past the 22, thus letting him know that 22 is the correct prefix of the reading to be recorded.

All watch readings are recorded in consecutive order in the "R" column until the cycle is completed. Subsequent cycles are studied in a similar manner, and their elemental values are recorded.

Difficulties encountered

During the time study the observer will encounter variations from the sequence of elements that he originally established, and occasionally he himself will miss specific terminal points. These difficulties tend to complicate the study, and the less often they occur, the easier it will be to calculate the study.

When the observer misses a reading, he should immediately indicate an "M" in the "R" column of the time study form. In no case should he make an approximation and endeavor to record the missed value, because this practice can destroy the validity of the standard established for the specific element. If the element were used as a source of standard data, appreciable discrepancies in future standards may result. Occasionally, the operator will omit an element and this is handled by drawing a horizontal line through the space in the "R" column. This variation should happen infrequently, since it is a sign of an inexperienced operator or else an indication of lack of standardization of method. Of course, the operator can inadvertently omit an element such as forgetting to "vent cope" in making a bench mold or omitting the element "apply parting dust." If elements are repeatedly omitted, the analyst should stop the study and investigate the necessity of performing the omitted elements at all. This should be done in cooperation with the foreman and the operator so the best method can be established. The observer is expected to be constantly on the alert for determining better ways to perform the elements; as ideas come to his mind, he should jot them down in the "note" section of the time study form for future study and possible development.

Another variation in sequence with which the observer will be faced is the performance of elements out of order. This may happen fairly frequently when studying a new or inexperienced employee on a long-cycle job made up of many elements. To avoid as many of these disturbances as possible is one of the prime reasons for studying a competent, fully trained employee. However, when elements are performed out of order, the observer should immediately go to the element that is being performed and draw a horizontal line through the middle of its "R" space;

directly below this line is shown the time the operator began the element, and above it, the completion time is recorded. This procedure is repeated for each element performed out of order and for the first element that is performed back in the normal sequence. Figure 14–4 illustrates a typical study, and elements 2, 3, and 4 on Cycle 6 show how the analyst handled the elements performed out of order.

During the time study the operator may encounter unavoidable delays such as being interrupted by a clerk or a foreman or tool breakage. Furthermore, the operator may intentionally cause a change in the order of work by going for a drink or stopping to rest. Interruptions of this nature occurring in the work cycle are referred to as "foreign elements."

Foreign elements can occur either at the breaking point or else during the course of an element. The majority of foreign elements, particularly if they are controlled by the operator, occur at the termination of one of the elements constituting the study. When a foreign element occurs during an element, the observer will signify the event by an alphabetical designation in the "T" column of this element. If the foreign element took place at the breaking point, the alphabetical designation will be recorded in the "T" column of the work element which follows the interruption. The letter "A" is used to signify the first foreign element and "B" the second, and so on.

As soon as the foreign element has been properly designated with an alphabetical symbol, a short description is made of it in the space provided immediately after the corresponding reference letter. The time that the foreign element begins is shown in the lower part of the "R" block of the foreign element section, and the watch reading at the termination of the foreign element is recorded in the upper part. These values can then be subtracted at the time the study is calculated, to determine the exact duration of the foreign element. This value is then shown in the "T" column of the foreign element section. Figure 14–4 illustrates the correct handling of several foreign elements.

Sometimes elements occur during the course of a study which may be treated as foreign elements, but investigation reveals that they have a definite relation to the job being studied. In cases like this, the element should be considered irregular and the elapsed time should be leveled, the proper allowance added, and the result properly prorated to the cycle time so a fair standard can be achieved.

Occasionally, a foreign element will occur that will be of such short duration that it will be impossible to record it in the fashion outlined. Typical examples of this would be dropping a wrench on the floor and quickly picking it up, wiping one's brow with a handkerchief, or turning to speak briefly to the foreman. In cases similar to these examples where the foreign element may be 0.06 minute or less, the most satisfactory method of handling the interruption is to allow it to accumulate in the element where it occurs and immediately circle the reading, indicating that a "wild" value has been encountered. A short comment should also be made in the "note" section of the time study form across from the element where the interruption occurred, thus justifying the circling procedure.

Number of cycles to study

The number of cycles to be studied to arrive at an equitable standard is a subject that has caused considerable discussion among time study analysts. Since the activity of the job, as well as its cycle time, directly influences the number of cycles that can be studied from an economic standpoint, one cannot be completely governed by the sound statistical practice that demands a certain size sample based on the dispersion of the individual element readings.

The General Electric Company has established Table 14–2 as a guide to the number of cycles to be observed:

TABLE 14–2

Cycle time in minutes	Recommended number of cycles
0.10	200
0.25	100
0.50	60
0.75	40
1.00	30
2.00	20
2.00– 5.00	15
5.00–10.00	10
10.00–20.00	8
20.00–40.00	5
40.00–above	3

SOURCE: Information taken from the Time Study Manual of the Erie Works of the General Electric Company, developed under the guidance of Albert E. Shaw, Manager of Wage Administration.

The Westinghouse Electric Corporation has given consideration to activity as well as cycle time and has evolved the values shown in Table 14–3 as a guide for their time study men.

The mean of the sample of the observations should be reasonably close to the mean of the population. Thus the analyst should take sufficient readings so when their values are recorded a distribution of values with a dispersion characteristic of the population dispersion is obtained.

Some concerns,[3] in their training programs for time study analysts, have the observer take readings and plot the values to obtain a frequency distribution. Although there is no assurance that the population of elemental times is normally distributed, still experience has shown that the

---

[3] For example, the Kurt Salmon Company.

TABLE 14-3

When the time per piece of cycle is over (hours)	Minimum number of cycles to study (activity)		
	Over 10,000 per year	1,000 to 10,000	Under 1,000
8.000	2	1	1
3.000	3	2	1
2.000	4	2	1
1.000	5	3	2
0.800	6	3	2
0.500	8	4	3
0.300	10	5	4
0.200	12	6	5
0.120	15	8	6
0.080	20	10	8
0.050	25	12	10
0.035	30	15	12
0.020	40	20	15
0.012	50	25	20
0.008	60	30	25
0.005	80	40	30
0.003	100	50	40
0.002	120	60	50
under 0.002	140	80	60

variation of performance of a given operator will approximate the normal bell-shaped curve (see Figure 14–6).

The number of cycles to be studied to assure a reliable sample may be determined mathematically, and this value, tempered with sound judgment, will give the analyst a helpful guide in deciding the length of observation.

Statistical methods may be utilized as an aid in determining the number of cycles to study. It is known that averages of samples ($\bar{x}$) drawn from a normal distribution of observations are distributed normally about

FIGURE 14–6

The normal frequency distribution

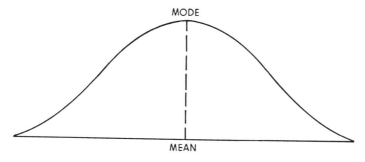

MODE

MEAN

the population mean μ. The variance of $\bar{x}$ about the population mean μ equals $\frac{\sigma^2}{n}$ where $n =$ the sample size and σ^2 equals the population variance.

Normal curve theory leads to the following confidence interval equation:

$$\bar{x} \pm z \frac{\sigma}{\sqrt{n}}$$

The above equation assumes the population standard deviation is known. This, in general, is not true but the population standard deviation may be estimated by the sample standard deviation s where:

$$s = \sqrt{\frac{\sum_{i=1}^{i=n} (x_i - \bar{x})^2}{n - 1}}$$

or for computational purposes:

$$s = \sqrt{\frac{\sum x_i^2}{n - 1} - \frac{(\sum x_i)^2}{n(n - 1)}}$$

When estimating σ in this way, we are dealing with the quantity:

$$\frac{\bar{x} - \mu}{\frac{s}{\sqrt{n}}}$$

which is not normally distributed except for large samples ($n > 30$). Its distribution is student's "t" distribution, which should be used in the formulas that follow. The confidence interval equation then is:

$$\bar{x} \pm t \frac{s}{\sqrt{n}} \tag{1}$$

For example, if 25 readings for a given element showed $\bar{x} = 0.30$ and $s = 0.09$ there would be 95 percent confidence that μ would be contained in the interval 0.337 to 0.263 or that $\bar{x}$ is within $\pm$ 12.3 percent of μ. (See Table A3–3, Appendix 3, for values of t.)

$$\bar{x} \pm t \frac{s}{\sqrt{n}}$$

$$0.30 + 2.06 \frac{0.09}{5} = 0.337$$

$$0.30 - 2.06 \frac{0.09}{5} = 0.263$$

$$\frac{0.037}{30} = 12.3 \text{ percent}$$

If the accuracy is deemed unsatisfactory when equation (1) is utilized in the above manner, it is possible to solve for N the required number of readings for a given accuracy by equating $\dfrac{t\,s}{\sqrt{N}}$ to a percentage of $\bar{x}$:

$$\frac{ts}{\sqrt{N}} = k\bar{x}$$

$$N = \left(\frac{st}{k\bar{x}}\right)^2$$

where $k =$ an acceptable percentage of $\bar{x}$.

In the above example, if $\bar{x}$ is required to be within ± 5 percent of μ with 95 percent confidence:

$$N = \left(\frac{st}{k\bar{x}}\right)^2$$
$$= \left(\frac{(0.09)(2.06)}{(0.05)(0.30)}\right)^2$$
$$= 152 \text{ observations}$$

If n readings have been taken on a time study, the selection of the most appropriate element for computing the desired number of readings may be a problem. It is recommended that the element having the greatest coefficient of variation $\dfrac{s}{\bar{x}}$ be selected for this purpose. It is also possible to solve for N in advance of taking the time study by interpreting historical data of similar elements or by actually estimating $\bar{x}$ and s from several snapback readings of certain elements to be studied.

One concern[4] has equated the number of observations in terms of the range of the cycle time and the average cycle time. This has been expressed as:

$$N = 205\frac{R}{\bar{x}} - 42$$

where

$$
\begin{aligned}
N &= \text{Number of observations required} \\
R &= \text{Range of cycle time} \\
\bar{x} &= \text{Mean cycle time}
\end{aligned}
$$

This has been derived as follows:

$$R = Ks$$

where

$$
\begin{aligned}
K &= \text{Average ratio between the range and the} \\
  &\quad \text{standard deviation in a succession of samples} \\
s &= \text{The standard deviation of the sample taken}
\end{aligned}
$$

---

[4] A. C. Spark Plug Division, General Motors Corporation.

To conform to the limits desired of 95 percent probability and 3 percent permissible error, the possible error, As and the permissible error, $.03\bar{x}$ are assumed to be equal.
Therefore:

$$As = 0.03\bar{x}$$
$$s = \frac{0.03\bar{x}}{A}$$

where

$$A = \text{Probability factor at 95 percent}$$

Substituting for s in the range formula:

$$R = \frac{(K)(0.03\bar{x})}{A}$$

The values of K and A vary with the number of observations (N) taken.

Substituting in the formula

$$R = \frac{(K)(0.03\bar{x})}{A}$$

the representative values in Table 14–4 are shown.

TABLE 14–4

N	$K*$	$A\dagger$	$\bar{x} = 0.10$ Minute	$\bar{x} = 0.20$ Minute
40	4.3216	0.3222	0.0402	0.0805
50	4.4982	0.2859	0.0472	0.0944
75	4.8060	0.2310	0.0624	0.1248
100	5.0152	0.1990	0.0756	0.1512
125	5.1727	0.1774	0.0875	0.1749
150	5.2985	0.1617	0.0983	0.1967
175	5.4029	0.1494	0.1085	0.2169
200	5.4921	0.1396	0.1180	0.2360

* K values obtained from *Biometrika* by L. H. C. Tippett.
† A values obtained from *Statistical Methods for Research Workers* by R. A. Fisher.

On graph paper, plotting R (range), against $\bar{x}$ (average time), for various samples (N), we find a straight-line relationship from the formula, $R = M\bar{x} + B$. Therefore, for sample sizes of 40, 150, 200, we get slope M:

$$N = 40 \qquad M = 0.402 \qquad B = 0$$
$$N = 150 \qquad M = 0.983 \qquad B = 0$$
$$N = 200 \qquad M = 1.180 \qquad B = 0$$

To introduce N into the above formula, N was plotted against M for various sample sizes and the resulting straight-line formula is:

$$N = M_1 M + B$$
$$N = 205M - 42 \text{ (approximate)}$$

From the formula, $R = M\bar{x} + B$, since $B = 0$, we get M in terms of R and $\bar{x}$ as:

$$M = \frac{R}{\bar{x}}$$

Substituting this expression from M in the formula: $N = M_1 M + B$, we get

$$N = 205 \frac{R}{\bar{x}} - 42$$

Having an equation involving N, number of observations, R, range of cycle time, and $\bar{x}$, average cycle time, an alignment chart may be designed to facilitate the solution of N. The N alignment chart illustrated in Figure 14–7 is evolved as follows:

Rearranging the equation to conform to the general N chart equation:

$$\frac{205R}{\bar{x}} - N = 42$$

N varies from 0 to 240
R varies from 0 to 0.30
$\bar{x}$ varies from 0 to 0.75

Comparing with the general alignment chart equation:

$$Af(u) + Bf(v) = Cf(w) + CK$$

Then:

$$R = f(u)$$
$$N = f(v)$$
$$0 = f(w)$$
$$A = \frac{205}{\bar{x}}$$
$$B = -1$$
$$C = 1$$
$$K = 42$$

Select chart width 8 inches, chart height 12 inches.
Develop scale modulus:

$$M_x = \frac{\text{Length of scale}}{\text{Range of } f(u)} = \frac{12}{0.30} = -40$$
$$\text{(when } B \text{ is negative, } M_x \text{ is negative)}$$
$$M_y = \frac{\text{Length of scale}}{\text{Range of } f(v)} = \frac{12}{240} = 0.05$$

FIGURE 14–7

N type alignment chart for determining the time study observations required (above 40) for 95 percent probability and 3 percent error

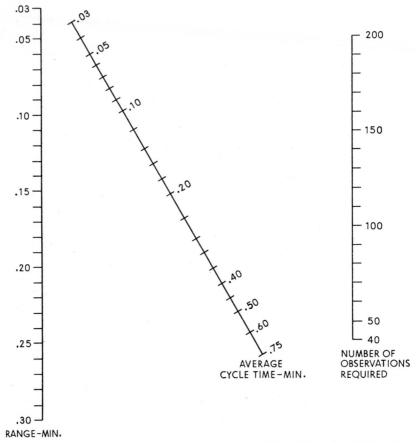

RANGE–MIN.

AVERAGE
CYCLE TIME–MIN.

NUMBER OF
OBSERVATIONS
REQUIRED

A. C. Spark Plug Division, General Motors Corp.

Calculate A:

$$A = \frac{BDM_x}{AM_y + BM_x} = \frac{(-1)(8)(-40)}{\dfrac{205}{\bar{x}}(0.05) + (-1)(-40)} = \frac{0.320}{\dfrac{10.25}{\bar{x}} + 40}$$

Calculate E:

$$E = \frac{CM_x M_y (f(w) + K)}{AM_y + BM_x} = \frac{(1)(-40)(0.05)(42)}{\dfrac{205}{\bar{x}}(0.05) + (-1)(-40)}$$

$$E = \frac{-84}{\dfrac{10.25}{\bar{x}} + 40}$$

The scale equations:

$$X = M_x f(u) = -40R$$
$$Y = M_y f(v) = 0.05N$$

Values are then developed in tabular form as shown in Table 14–5.

TABLE 14–5

Sample

R	$x = -40R$	N	$y = 0.05N$	$\bar{x}$	$A = \dfrac{320}{\dfrac{10.25}{\bar{x}} + 40}$	$E = \dfrac{-84}{\dfrac{10.25}{\bar{x}} + 40}$
0.......	0	0	0	0	....	....
0.05.......	−2	40	2	.05	1.306	−0.343
0.20.......	−8	150	7.5	.40	4.876	−1.280
0.30.......	−12	240	12.0	.75	5.963	−1.565

Using these values, the N chart is laid out and plotted.

As has been pointed out, these mathematical derivations represent only a guide to the analyst and do not replace common sense and good judgment, which are still fundamental if the time study analyst is to do a good job in a practical manner.

The reader might rightfully ask, "When should the recommended number of cycles be observed?" If 30 cycles are to be taken, should they be taken as one successive group, as two groups of 15, or as three groups of 10? The reader should intuitively recognize that the mean of three groups of 10 taken at random times during the day will probably give a better estimate of the population mean than one group of 30. The taking of a time study is a sampling procedure, and the average of several small samples usually provides more reliable estimates of parent parameters than one sample of a size equivalent to the total of the several small samples. For example, if we had a barrel of 10,000 bolts, we would be more confident of the quality of the entire 10,000 if we averaged the results from three independent samples. Thus, we might take one sample of 40 from one end, another sample of 40 from the middle, and a third sample of 40 from the other end. This would be a more reliable procedure than if we took a sample of 120 from one end.

The individual samples taken should be large enough so that their mean is somewhat stabilized. By being stabilized, we mean that the addition of one more cycle will not substantially alter the mean. For example, we might have the following averages given in Table 14–6.

In Table 14–6 it is apparent that the average was stabilizing at the end of the fourth cycle and there was really nothing practical accomplished by the analyst in observing more than six cycles.

TABLE 14–6

Average at the end of the	Average
1st cycle...................	0.22
2nd cycle...................	0.28
3rd cycle...................	0.24
4th cycle...................	0.27
5th cycle...................	0.273
6th cycle...................	0.271
7th cycle...................	0.272
8th cycle...................	0.273
9th cycle...................	0.270
10th cycle...................	0.272

Rating the operator performance

Before the observer leaves the work station, he should have given a fair performance rating to the study. On short-cycle, repetitive work, it is customary to apply one rating to the entire study. However, where the elements tend to be of long duration and entail diversified manual movements and motions, it is more practical to evaluate the performance of each element as it occurs during the study. The time study form illustrated in Figures 14–4 and 14–5 makes a provision for both the over-all rating and the individual element rating.

Since the actual time that was required to perform each element of the study was dependent to a high degree on the skill and effort of the operator, it is necessary to adjust the time of the good operator up to normal and the time of the poor operator down to normal.

In the performance rating or leveling system, the observer evaluates the effectiveness of the operator in terms of his conception of a "normal" man performing the same element. This effectiveness is given a value expressed as a decimal or percentage and assigned to the element observed. A "normal" operator is defined as a qualified, thoroughly experienced operator working under conditions as they customarily prevail at the work station, at a pace neither too fast nor too slow but representative of average. The normal man exists only in the mind of the time study analyst and has developed as a result of thorough and exacting training and experience in the technique of measuring wide varieties of work.

The basic principle of performance rating is to adjust the actual observed mean time for each acceptable element performed on the study to the time that would be required by the normal man to perform the same work. To do a fair job of rating, the time study man must be able to disassociate himself from personalities and other varying factors and consider only the amount of work being done per unit of time as compared to the amount of work that the normal man would produce. Chapter 15 explains more fully the performance rating or leveling techniques in common use.

Apply allowances

It would be impossible for an operator to maintain an average pace for every minute of the working day, just as it would be impossible for a football game to entail 60 minutes of actual, continuous play time. Three classes of interruptions take place occasionally for which extra time must be provided. The first of these is personal interruptions, such as trips to the rest room and drinking fountain; the second is fatigue, which, as we all know, affects the strongest individual even on the lightest type of work. Lastly, unavoidable delays take place for which some allowances must be made, such as tool breakage, interruptions by the foreman, and slight tool trouble.

Since the time study is taken over a relatively short period and since foreign elements have been removed in determining the normal time, an allowance must be added to the leveled or base time to arrive at a fair standard that can be achieved by the normal operator when exerting average effort. Chapter 16 outlines in detail means of arriving at realistic allowance values.

Calculate the study

Once the analyst has properly recorded all necessary information on the time study form, has observed an adequate number of cycles, and has properly performance rated the operator, he should thank the operator and proceed to the next step, which is computation of the study. In some plants, clerical help is used to compute the study, but in most cases the analyst himself does the work. The analyst usually prefers to analyze his own study because he is vitally interested in the resulting standard and does not care to let other individuals tamper with his calculations. Then, too, less chance of error will be risked if the analyst computes his own study, in that he will encounter no difficulty in interpreting his own notes and reading his own recorded values.

The initial step in computing the study is to verify the final stopwatch reading with the overall elapsed clock reading. These two values should check within plus or minus a half minute, and if a sizable discrepancy is noted, the analyst should check the study stopwatch readings for error.

When using the continuous method, a subtraction is made between the watch reading and the preceding reading, giving the elapsed time, and this is recorded in ink or red pencil. This procedure is followed throughout the study, each reading being subtracted from the succeeding one. It is important that the analyst be especially accurate in this phase.

Carelessness at this point can completely destroy the validity of the study. If elemental performance rating has been used, a supplementary work sheet will be required to record the elapsed elemental time, and these values, after being multiplied by the levling factor, will be recorded in ink or red pencil in the "T" spaces of the time study form.

Elements that have been missed by the observer are signified by placing an "M" in the "R" column as previously explained. When computing the study, the analyst must disregard both the missed element and the succeeding one, since the subtracted value in the study will include the time for performing both elements.

Elements missed by the operator may be disregarded, since they have no effect on the preceding or succeeding values. Thus, if the operator happened to omit element 7 of cycle 4 in a 30-cycle study, the analyst should have but 29 values of element 7 with which to calculate the mean observed time.

To determine the elapsed elemental time on out-of-order elements, it is merely necessary for the analyst to subtract the value appearing in the lower half of the "R" block from the value in the upper half for the element that was performed out of order.

For foreign elements, it is necessary to deduct the time required for the foreign element from the cycle time of the element in which it occurred. The time taken by the foreign element is obtained by subtracting the lower reading in the "R" space of the foreign element section of the time study form from the upper reading.

After all elapsed times have been calculated and recorded, they should be carefully studied for abnormality. There is no set rule for determining the degree of variation permitted to keep the value for calculation. If variations are broad on certain elements and can be attributed to some influence that was too brief to be handled as a foreign element, yet long enough to affect substantially the time of the element, such as dropping a tool or blowing the nose, or if the variation may be attributed to errors in reading the stopwatch, then these values should be immediately circled and excluded from further consideration in working up the study. However, if wide variations are due to the nature of the work, then it would not be wise to discard any of the values.

Elements that are "paced" by the facility or process will have little variation from cycle to cycle, while considerably wider variation in "operator controlled" elements would be expected. When unexplainable variations in time occur, the analyst should be quite careful before circling any such values. He must be aware that this is not a performance rating procedure, and by arbitrarily discarding high values or low values, he may end up with an incorrect standard. A good rule is, "When in doubt do not discard the value."

If elemental rating is being used, then after the elemental elapsed time values have been computed, the normal elemental time is determined by multiplying each elemental value by its respective performance factor. This normal time is then recorded for each element in the "T" columns. The mean elemental normal value is next determined by dividing the number of observations into the total of the times in the "T" columns.

After the analyst has determined all elemental elapsed times, he should make a check to assure that no arithmetic errors have been made. This can best be done by adding the "total" column for each element and the foreign element times and the abnormal element times. The total of these values must be equal to the last reading of the stopwatch. If this total does not equal the last watch reading, the study should be checked for arithmetic errors before proceeding with further computation of the study. This check applies only when the continuous method is being employed.

If the overall study is leveled, then the means of the elapsed elemental times are computed and the performance factor is applied to these values in the space provided to determine the various normal elemental time values.

After the normal elemental times have been evolved, the percentage allowance is added to each element to determine the allowed time. The nature of the job will determine the amount of allowance to be applied, as will be shown in Chapter 16. Suffice to say at this point that 15 percent is an average allowance for effort elements and 10 percent is representative of the allowance applied to mechanically controlled elements.

Upon determining the allowed time for each element, the analyst should then summarize these values in the space provided on the reverse side of the time study form to obtain the allowed time for the entire job. This is commonly referred to as the "standard" or the "rate" for the job.

Summary of computing the study

To summarize the steps taken in computing a typical study with continuous watch readings and overall performance rating, the following procedure in chronological sequence would be observed:

1. Make subtractions of consecutive readings to obtain elemental elapsed times and record in red pencil.
2. Circle and discard all abnormal or "wild" values where assignable cause is evident.
3. Summarize remaining elemental values.
4. Determine mean of the observed values of each element.
5. Determine elemental normal time by multiplying the performance factor by the mean elapsed time.
6. Add the appropriate allowance to the elemental normal values to obtain the elemental allowed times.

7. Summarize the elemental allowed times on the reverse side of the time study form to obtain the standard time. (Elements occurring more than once per cycle need be shown but once with the number of occurrences and the resulting product.)

If elemental leveling has been used on a continuous study, then the series of events in computing the study would be:

1. Make subtractions of consecutive readings to obtain elemental elapsed times.
2. Determine normal times of each individual element by multiplying performance factor by elapsed time value and record in red pencil in the "T" column.
3. Circle and discard all abnormal or "wild" values where assignable cause is evident.
4. Determine mean of the elemental normal times.
5. Add the appropriate allowance to the elemental normal values to obtain the elemental allowed times.
6. Summarize the elemental allowed times on the reverse side of the time study form to obtain the standard time. (Elements occurring more than once per cycle need be shown but once with the number of occurrences and the resulting product.)

TEXT QUESTIONS

1. Outline the characteristic that the operator should have if he is selected for time study.
2. What are the prinicpal responsibilities of the time study observer?
3. What are some of the qualifications for the successful time study analyst?
4. How does the time study analyst "directly affect the pocketbook of the worker"?
5. Explain the statement that all foremen are "management's representatives throughout the plant."
6. Why does the foreman require fair time standards in his department?
7. What are the main responsibilities of the foreman in relation to time study work?
8. What is the significance of the foreman's signature on the time study?
9. What is a fair day's work?
10. Explain how an appreciation course in the elements of time study made available to all employees will promote good labor relations.
11. What considerations should be given to choice of operator to be studied?
12. Of what use is the operator process chart on the time study form?
13. Why is it essential to record complete information on tools and facility on the time study form?

14. Why are working conditions important in identifying the method being observed?

15. Why would a time study analyst who is hard of hearing have difficulty in recording his stopwatch readings of terminal points?

16. Differentiate between constant and variable elements. Why should they be kept separate when dividing the job into elements?

17. Explain how repeating elements may be recorded on the time study form.

18. What advantages does the continuous method of watch recording offer over the snapback?

19. Why is the time of day recorded on the time study form?

20. What variations in sequence will the observer occasionally encounter during the course of the time study?

21. Explain what a foreign element is and how foreign elements are handled under the continuous method.

22. What factors enter into the determination of the number of cycles to observe?

23. Why is it necessary to performance rate the operator?

24. When should individual elements of each cycle be rated?

25. Define a "normal" operator.

26. For what reasons are allowances applied to the normal time?

27. What is the significance of a "circled" elapsed time? *world value*

28. What are the steps taken in computation of a time study conducted by the continuous overall performance rating procedure?

29. What would be the required number of readings if the analyst wanted to be 87 percent confident that the mean observed time is within ±5 percent of the true mean and he established the following values for an element after observing 20 cycles:
0.09, 0.08, 0.10, 0.12, 0.09, 0.08, 0.09, 0.12, 0.11, 0.12, 0.09, 0.10, 0.12, 0.10, 0.08, 0.09, 0.10, 0.12, 0.09?

30. Based upon the Westinghouse guide sheet, how many observations should be taken on an operation whose annual activity is 750 pieces and the cycle time is estimated at 15 minutes? What would be the number of observations needed according to the General Electric guide sheet?

GENERAL QUESTIONS

1. What do you feel the difference is between (a) a normal operator, (b) an average operator, (c) a standard operator?

2. Why are time study procedures the only techniques for supplying reliable information on standard times?

3. To what positions of importance does time study work lead?

4. In what way can "loose" time standards result in poor labor relations?

5. Why are poor time standards a "headache" to union officials?

6. How would you approach a belligerent operator if you were the time study analyst?

7. You were using the General Electric guide sheet to determine the number of observations to study. It developed that 10 cycles were required, and after taking the study you used the standard error of the mean statistic to estimate the number of observations needed for a given confidence level. The resulting calculation indicated 20 cycles should be studied. What would be your procedure? Why?

CHAPTER 15

Performance rating

While the time study observer is taking the study, he will carefully observe the performance of the operator during the entire course of the study. Seldom will the performance being executed conform to the exact definition of "normal," often referred to as "standard." Thus, it is essential that some adjustment be made to the mean observed time in order to derive the time required for the normal man to do the job when working at an average pace. The actual time taken by the above-standard operator must be increased to that required by the normal worker, and the time taken by the below-standard operator must be reduced to the value representative of normal performance. Only in this manner can a true standard be established in terms of a normal operator.

Performance rating is probably the most important step in the entire work measurement procedure. Certainly, it is the step most subject to criticism since it is based entirely on the experience, training, and judgment of the work measurement analyst. Because of its importance, this chapter will bring out not only the most accepted techniques used today but also will review some of the more important historical methods such as the Westinghouse system. An understanding of the historical philosophies and resulting methods will be helpful to the student and practitioner in developing an appreciation for this very important step in the systematic procedure for methods and work measurement.

Definition

Performance rating is a technique for equitably determining the time required to perform a task by the normal operator after the observed values of the operation under study have been recorded. In Chapter 12, a "normal" operator was defined as a qualified, thoroughly experienced operator who is working under conditions as they customarily prevail at the work station, at a pace that is neither fast nor slow, but representative of average.

There is no one universally accepted method of performance rating, although the majority of the techniques are based primarily on the judgment of the time study man. For this reason, the time study analyst must have the high personal characteristics discussed earlier in this text. No other component of the time study procedure is subject to as much controversy and criticism as the performance rating phase. Regardless of whether the rating factor is based on the speed or tempo of the output or based upon the performance of the operator when compared to that of the normal worker, judgment is still the criterion for the determination of the rating factor. Some attempts have been made to accumulate fundamental motion data and compare these values to the mean observed values so as to arrive at a factor that can be used for evaluation of the entire study. This technique known as "synthetic rating"[1] will be discussed later in this chapter.

Concept of normal

Just as there is no one universal method of performance rating, so there is no one universal concept of normal performance. In general, industries engaged in the manufacture of low-cost, highly competitive products will have a "tighter" conception of normal performance than that expected by a company producing a line of products protected by patents.

In defining what is meant by "normal" performance, it is helpful to enumerate bench mark examples that are familiar to all. When this is done, care must be taken that method and work requirements are carefully defined. Thus, if the bench mark of dealing 52 cards in 0.50 minute is established, complete and specific description relative to distance of the four hands dealt, with respect to the dealer and the technique of grasping, moving, and disposing of the cards should be given. Likewise, if the bench mark of 0.38 minute is established for walking 100 feet (3 miles per hour), it should be clearly explained whether this is walking on level ground or not, whether this is walking with or without load, and if with load, how heavy the load. Supplementing the bench mark examples should be a clear description of the characteristics of an employee carrying out a normal performance. A representative description of such an employee might be:

A workman who is adapted to the work, and has attained sufficient experience to enable him to perform his job in a workmanlike manner with little or

---

[1] Robert Lee Morrow, *Time Study and Motion Economy* (New York: Ronald Press Co., 1946).

no supervision. He possesses co-ordinated mental and physical qualities which enable him to proceed from one element to another without hesitation or delay, in accordance with the principles of motion economy. He maintains a good level of efficiency by his knowledge and proper use of all tools and equipment related to his job. He co-operates and performs at a pace best suited for continuous performance.

The more clear-cut and specific the definition of normal, the better it will be. It should clearly describe the skill and effort involved in the performance, so that all workers in the plant will have a comprehensive understanding of the concept of normal that prevails in the plant.

Uses and effects

Even though personnel departments endeavor to provide only "normal" or "above normal" employees for each position within the company, still individual differences do exist. These differences among a given group of employees within the plant can become more pronounced as time goes on. Differences in inherent knowledge, physical capacity, health, trade knowledge, physical dexterity, and training will cause one operator consistently and progressively to outperform another. The degree of variation in the performance of different individuals has been estimated to approximate the ratio of 1 to 2.25.[2] Thus, in a random selection of 1,000 employees, the frequency distribution of the output would approximate the normal curve with less than three cases on the average falling outside the three sigma limits (99.73 percent of the time). If 100 percent should be taken as normal, then based on a ratio of the slowest operator to the fastest as 2.25 to 1, $\bar{x} - 3\sigma$ could equal 0.61, and $\bar{x} + 3\sigma$ would then equal 1.39. This would mean that 68.26 percent of the people would be within plus or minus one sigma limit or between performance rating values of 0.87 and 1.13. Graphically, the expected total distribution of the 1,000 people would appear as shown in Figure 15–1.

Since employees are usually carefully screened by personnel departments before being assigned to specific jobs, the mean of any selected group may exceed the 100 percent figure representative of a sample taken arbitrarily from the population, and the dispersion of their output will probably be considerably less than the 2.25 to 1 ratio. In fact, by careful testing programs, some concerns feel that their selection of the right person for the job, supplemented by intensive training in the correct method of performance, will result in similar output within close limits by different operators assigned to the same job.

In the majority of cases, significant differences in output will prevail among those assigned to a given class of work, and it is necessary to

---

[2] Ralph W. Presgrave, *The Dynamics of Time Study* (2d ed.; New York: McGraw-Hill Book Co., 1945).

FIGURE 15–1

Normal distribution curve of the output of 1,000 people selected at random

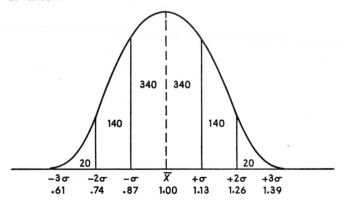

adjust the performance of the operator being studied to a predetermined concept of normal.

The learning curve

Industrial engineers, human engineers and other professionals interested in the study of human behavior have recognized that learning is time dependent. Even the simplest of operations may take hours to master. Complicated work may take days and even weeks before the operator can achieve coordinated mental and physical qualities enabling him to proceed from one element to another without hesitation or delay. A typical learning curve is illustrated by Figure 15–2.

FIGURE 15–2

Typical productivity increase graph

Once the operator reaches the flattening section of the learning curve (as pictured in Figure 15–2) the problem of performance rating is simplified. However, it is not always convenient to wait this long in the development of a standard. The analyst may be obliged to establish the standard at the point in the learning curve where the slope is the greatest. It is in these cases that the analyst must have acute powers of observation and be able to execute mature judgment based on thorough training so that an equitable normal time is computed.

FIGURE 15–3

Estimated unit times based on 20 percent reduction each time quantity doubles

It is helpful for the analyst to have learning curves available which are representative of the various classes of work being performed in the company. This information can be useful, not only in determining at what stage in the production it would be desirable to establish the standard, but also by providing a guide as to the expected level of productivity characteristic of the average operator with a known degree of familiarity of the operation achieved by producing a fixed number of parts.

By plotting learning curve data on logarithmic paper, the analyst may be able to linearize the data, and thus have it in a form that is easier to use. For example, by plotting both the dependent variable (unit time) and the independent variable (cumulative production) shown in Figure 15–2 on log-log paper, a straight line is obtained as shown in Figure 15–3.

The analyst must recognize that a new learning curve situation does not necessarily result every time a new design is put into production.

Former designs, similar to new designs, have a pronounced effect on the point when the learning curve begins to flatten. Thus, if a company introduces a new design of a complex electronic panel, the assembly of this panel by female workers would involve a much different learning curve than if a somewhat similar panel had been in production for the past five years.

The theory of the learning curve proposes that as the total quantity of units produced doubles, the time per unit declines at some constant percentage. For example, if it is expected that an 80 percent rate of improvement will be experienced, then, as production doubles, the average time per unit will decline 20 percent. Typical rates of learning that have been encountered are as follows: assembly work—70 to 80 percent; welding—80 to 90 percent; machining—90 to 95 percent.

Useful algebraic expressions for calculating the total man-hours required to produce a predetermined number of units and cumulative average hours per unit for any number of units may be readily determined if the learning curve percentage (slope) and man-hours to build the first unit can be estimated.

Thus we have the relations:

$$T_{c.a} = h \, n^c$$
$$T_t = h \, n^c \, n$$

where:

T_t = Total man-hours required to produce a predetermined number of units

$T_{c.a}$ = Cumulative average hours per unit for any number of units

h = Man-hours to produce the first unit

n = Number of complete units

c = Slope—equal to log (percent of learning curve) divided by log (2)

An example will help clarify the above relationships. Assume that 50 units are produced at a cumulative average of 20 man-hours per unit. It is desired to determine the learning curve percentage when 100 units are produced at a cumulative average of 15 man-hours per unit.

n_1 = Cumulative production to point one (50 units)

n_2 = Cumulative production to point two (100 units)

$\dfrac{n_2}{n_1}$ = 2 (when production quantity is doubled)

and

$$\frac{T_{c.a.2}}{T_{c.a.1}} = \frac{h \, n_2^c}{h \, n_1^c} = 2^c$$

in logarithmic form:

$$\log T_{c.a} = \log h + c \log n$$
$$\log 20 = \log h + (c) \log 50$$
$$\underline{\log 15 = \log h + (c) \log 100}$$
$$\log 20 - \log 15 = c \, (\log 50 - \log 100)$$
$$c = \frac{\log 20 - \log 15}{\log 50 - \log 100}$$
$$= \frac{1.30103 - 1.17609}{1.69897 - 2.00000}$$
$$= \frac{0.12494}{0.30103}$$
$$= -0.415$$

and

$$2^{-0.415} = \text{Learning curve percentage}$$
$$= 75 \text{ percent}$$

Table 15–1 gives the slope of various learning curve percentages:

TABLE 15–1

Learning curve percentage	Slope
70	−0.514
75	−0.415
80	−0.322
85	−0.234
90	−0.152
95	−0.074

The above derivation is based on the "cumulative average learning curve" since the relationships refer to the average hours to produce a unit based on all units produced up to a particular point.

When working with man-hours required to produce a specific unit, we are dealing with the "unit learning curve" which refers to the hours required to produce a specific unit. The (log) plot of the cumulative average is asymptotically parallel to the (log) plot of the unit curve. When n is large, then the cumulative average hours per unit approximate the man-hours to produce a specific unit.

Characteristics of a sound rating system

The first and most important characteristic of any rating system is accuracy. Since the majority of rating techniques rely on the judgment of the time study observer, perfect consistency in rating cannot be expected. However, rating procedures that readily permit the different time study analysts, within a given organization, to study different operators employing the same method, to arrive at standards that are not more than

5 percent in deviation from the average of the standards established by the group are considered adequate. The rating plan that carries variations in standards greater than the plus or minus 5 percent tolerance should be improved or replaced.

Other factors being similar, the rating plan that gives the most consistent results will be the most useful. Inconsistency in rating will do more than any other one thing to destroy the operator's confidence in the time study procedure. For example, if a standard should be developed through stopwatch study that allowed 7.88 hours to mill 100 castings, and at some later date a similar casting entailing a slightly longer cut should be studied, and a standard of 7.22 hours be established, considerable complaint would be registered by the operator, even though both studies were within the plus or minus 5 percent criterion of accuracy.

A rating plan that achieves consistency when used by the various time study analysts within a given plant and yet is outside the accepted definition of normal accuracy can be corrected. A rating procedure that gives inconsistent results when used by the different time study men will be sure to end in failure. Time study men who find difficulty in rating consistently after proper and thorough training will be better off if they seek some other means of livelihood. It is not difficult to correct the rating habits of an analyst who rates consistently high or consistently low, but it is most difficult to instill rating ability in the mind of the analyst who today is rating considerably too high and tomorrow may be rating considerably too low.

The rating system that is simple, concise, easily explained, and keyed to well-established bench marks will be more successful than complex techniques that require involved adjusting factors and similar mathematical computation techniques that confuse the average shop employee.

In view of the aforementioned accuracy limitations, every company will have, as time goes on, a number of standards which will be referred to as "tight" by the production floor, as well as those that will be known as "loose." If these inequities are within the 5 percent tolerance range, few grievances will develop. However, if it becomes possible for an operator to earn as much as 50 percent premium on one job, and he finds it difficult even to make standard on another, then general dissatisfaction can be anticipated for the whole rate program. At this point, it might be well to mention that inequalities in different rates are not necessarily entirely due to poor performance rating. Loose rates frequently are due to methods improvements inaugurated over a period of time without restudy of the job from the time study point of view.

Rating at the work station

There is only one time when the performance rating should be done and that is during the course of the observation of the elemental times.

As the operator progresses from one element to the next, the analyst carefully evaluates his speed, dexterity, freedom from false moves, rhythm, coordination, effectiveness, and all other factors influencing output by the prescribed method. It is at this time, and this time only, that the performance of the operator in comparison to normal performance is most clearly evident to the observer. Once the performance has been judged and recorded, it should not be changed. This does not imply that faulty judgment on the part of the observer is not possible. In case the leveling is questioned, the job or operation should be restudied to prove or disprove the recorded evaluation.

Immediately after completing the study and recording the final performance factor, the observer should advise the operator as to his performance rating. Even if elemental rating is used, the analyst will be able to approximate the operator's performance and so advise him. This practice will permit the analyst to defend his standard prior to its calculation, and will give the operator an opportunity to express his opinion as to the fairness of the performance factor directly to the man responsible for its development. Thus, an understanding can be achieved prior to computation of the standard. Where this procedure is practiced, time study men will find that they receive greater respect from the operators and will also find that they tend to be more conscientious in their rating of the operator's performance. Also, considerably fewer rate grievances will be submitted because most rates will have been agreed upon, or at least satisfactorily explained and sold, before they are issued.

Rating elements versus overall study

The question as to how frequently should the performance be evaluated during the course of a study often comes up. Although no set rule can be established as to the interval limit that permits concise rating, generally it can be said that the more frequently the study is rated, the more accurate the evaluation of the true normal performance will be.

On short-cycle repetitive operations, little deviation in operator performance will be realized during the course of the average length study (15 to 30 minutes). In cases like this, it will be perfectly satisfactory to evaluate the performance of the entire study and record the rating factor for each element in the space provided. Of course, power-fed or machine-controlled elements will be rated normal or 1.00, as their speed cannot be changed or modified at will by the operator. In short-cycle studies, if the observer endeavors to performance rate each successive element of the entire study, he will be so busy recording values that he will be unable to do an effective job of observation, analysis, and evaluation of the operator performance.

When the study to be taken is relatively long (over 30 minutes) or is made up of several long elements, then operator performance may be expected to vary during the course of the time study. In such studies, it is important that performance be periodically evaluated and rated. Elements longer than 0.10 minute in duration can be consistently and accurately rated as they occur. However, if a study is made of a series of elements shorter than 0.10 minute, then no effort should be made to evaluate each element of each cycle of the study, as time will not permit this operation. It will be satisfactory to rate the overall time of each cycle or perhaps each group of cycles.

METHODS OF RATING

Westinghouse system

One of the oldest and at one time most widely used systems of rating is the one developed by the Westinghouse Electric Corporation and outlined in detail by Lowry, Maynard, and Stegemerten.[3] In this method, four factors are considered in evaluating the performance of the operator. These are skill, effort, conditions, and consistency.

Skill is defined as "proficiency at following a given method" and can be further explained by relating it to craftsmanship, demonstrated by proper coordination of mind and hands.

The skill of an operator is determined by his experience and inherent aptitudes such as natural coordination and rhythm. Practice will tend to develop skill, but it cannot entirely compensate for deficiencies in natural aptitude. All the practice in the world could not make major league baseball pitchers out of most male athletes.

A person's skill increases on a given operation over a period of time because increased familiarity with the work brings speed, smoothness of motions, and freedom from hesitations and false moves. A decrease in skill is usually caused by impairment of ability brought about by physical or psychological factors such as failing eyesight, failing reflexes, and loss of muscular strength or coordination. From this, it can readily be appreciated that a person's skill can vary from job to job and even from operation to operation on a given job.

According to this system of leveling or rating, there are six degrees or classes of skill within which an operator can perform that represent an acceptable proficiency for evaluation. These are: poor, fair, average, good, excellent, and super. The skill displayed by the operator is evaluated by the observer and rated in one of these six classes. Table 15-2 illustrates the characteristics of the various degrees of skill together with their equivalent numerical values. The skill rating is then translated into

---

[3] S. M. Lowry, H. B. Maynard, and G. J. Stegemerten, *Time and Motion Study and Formulas for Wage Incentives* (3d ed.; New York: McGraw-Hill Book Co., 1940).

its equivalent percentage value, which ranges from plus 15 percent for superskill to minus 22 percent for poor skill. This percentage is then combined algebraically with the ratings for effort, conditions, and consistency to arrive at the final leveling, or performance rating factor.

Effort, according to this rating method, is defined as a "demonstration of the will to work effectively." It is representative of the speed with which skill is applied, and can be controlled to a high degree by the operator. The observer when evaluating the effort given must exercise care to rate only the effective effort demonstrated. Many times an operator will apply misdirected effort with high tempo in order to increase the

TABLE 15-2

Skill

+0.15	A1	Superskill
+0.13	A2	Superskill
+0.11	B1	Excellent
+0.08	B2	Excellent
+0.06	C1	Good
+0.03	C2	Good
0.00	D	Average
−0.05	E1	Fair
−0.10	E2	Fair
−0.16	F1	Poor
−0.22	F2	Poor

Source: S. M. Lowry, H. B. Maynard, and G. J. Stegemerten, *Time and Motion Study and Formulas for Wage Incentives*, (3d ed.; New York: McGraw-Hill Book Co., 1940).

cycle time of the study and yet retain a liberal rating factor. As for skill, six classes of effort can be exhibited that are representative of acceptable speed for rating purposes: poor, fair, average, good, excellent, and excessive. Excessive effort has been assigned a value of plus 13 percent and this figure diminishes to minus 17 percent, the value given to poor effort. Table 15–3 gives the numerical values for the different degrees of effort and also outlines the characteristics of the various categories.

The conditions referred to in this performance rating procedure are those which affect the operator and not the operation. In more than the majority of instances, conditions will be rated normal or average, as conditions are evaluated in comparison with the way in which they customarily are found at the work station. Elements that would affect the working conditions include temperature, ventilation, light, and noise. Thus, if the temperature at a given work station was 60° F. whereas it customarily was maintained at 68° to 74° F., the conditions would be rated lower than normal. Those conditions which affect the operation,

TABLE 15–3

Effort

+0.13.....................	A1	Excessive
+0.12.....................	A2	Excessive
+0.10.....................	B1	Excellent
+0.08.....................	B2	Excellent
+0.05.....................	C1	Good
+0.02.....................	C2	Good
0.00.....................	D	Average
−0.04.....................	E1	Fair
−0.08.....................	E2	Fair
−0.12.....................	F1	Poor
−0.17.....................	F2	Poor

SOURCE: S. M. Lowry, H. B. Maynard, and G. J. Stegemerten, *Time and Motion Study and Formulas for Wage Incentives* (3d ed.; New York: McGraw-Hill Book Co., 1940).

such as poor condition of tools or materials, would not be considered
when applying the performance factor for working conditions. Six general classes of conditions have been enumerated with values from plus 6
percent to minus 7 percent. These "general state" conditions are listed
as ideal, excellent, good, average, fair, and poor. Table 15–4 gives the
respective values for these different conditions.

The last of the four factors that influence the performance rating is the
consistency of the operator. Unless the snapback method is used, or
unless the observer is able to make and record successive subtractions as
he goes along, the consistency of the operator must be evaluated as the
study is being worked up. Elemental time values that repeat constantly
would, of course, have a perfect consistency. This situation occurs very
infrequently, as there always tends to be dispersion due to the many
variables, such as material hardness, tool cutting edge, lubricant, skill
and effort of operator, erroneous watch readings, and presence of foreign
elements. Those elements that are mechanically controlled would, of

TABLE 15–4

Conditions

+0.06.....................	A	Ideal
+0.04.....................	B	Excellent
+0.02.....................	C	Good
0.00.....................	D	Average
−0.03.....................	E	Fair
−0.07.....................	F	Poor

SOURCE: S. M. Lowry, H. B. Maynard, and G. J. Stegemerten, *Time and Motion Study and Formulas for Wage Incentives* (3d ed.; New York: McGraw-Hill Book Co., 1940).

course, have near perfect consistency values, but these elements are not rated. There are six classes of consistency: perfect, excellent, good, average, fair, and poor. Perfect consistency has been given the value of plus 4 percent and poor consistency is rated minus 4 percent, while the other categories fall in between these values. Table 15–5 summarizes these values.

No fixed rule can be cited as to the universal application of the consistency table. Some operations that are of short duration and tend to be free of delicate positioning manipulations will give relatively consistent results from one cycle to the next. Thus, operations of this nature would have a more exacting requirement of average consistency than a job of long duration, demanding high skill in view of the positioning,

TABLE 15–5

Consistency

+0.04	A	Perfect
+0.03	B	Excellent
+0.01	C	Good
0.00	D	Average
−0.02	E	Fair
−0.04	F	Poor

SOURCE: S. M. Lowry, H. B. Maynard, and G. J. Stegemerten, *Time and Motion Study and Formulas for Wage Incentives* (3d ed.; New York: McGraw-Hill Book Co., 1940).

engaging, and aligning elements. The determination of the justified range of variation for a particular operation must be based to a large extent on the time study analyst's knowledge of the work.

The observer should be cautioned against the operator who consistently performs poorly in an effort to deceive the observer. This is easily accomplished by counting to oneself, thereby setting a pace that can be accurately followed. Operators who familiarize themselves with this performance rating procedure sometimes will perform at a pace that is consistent and yet is below the effort rating curve. In other words, they may be performing at a pace that is poorer than poor. In cases like this, the operator cannot be leveled. The study must be stopped and the situation brought to the attention of the operator or foreman or both.

Once the skill, effort, conditions, and consistency of the operation have been assigned, and their equivalent numerical values established, the performance factor is determined by algebraically combining the four values and adding their sum to unity. For example, if a given job is rated C2 on skill, C1 on effort, D on conditions, and E on consistency, the performance factor would be evolved as follows:

Skill	C2	+.03
Effort	C1	+.05
Conditions	D	+.00
Consistency	E	−.02
Algebraic Sum		+.06
Performance Factor		1.06

The reader should again be cautioned that the performance factor is applied only to the effort or manually performed elements; all machine controlled elements are rated 1.00.

The Westinghouse method of performance rating is adapted to the leveling of the entire study rather than elemental evaluation. This method would prove cumbersome if used to level each element as soon as it took place. In fact, the time study form itself does not provide sufficient space to evaluate skill, effort, conditions, and consistency for each element of every cycle.

Many companies have modified the Westinghouse system so as to include only skill and effort factors entering into the determination of the rating factor. The contention is that consistency is very closely allied to skill, and conditions in most instances are rated average. If conditions would deviate substantially from normal, either the taking of the study could be postponed, or else the effect of the unusual conditions could be taken into consideration in the application of the allowance (see Chapter 16).

The Westinghouse Company itself in 1949 developed a new rating method which they termed their "performance rating plan" to distinguish it from the leveling procedure just discussed. The performance rating plan is being used in most of the Westinghouse plants added since then.

In developing the performance rating plan, in addition to using physical attributes displayed by the operator, the company made an attempt to evaluate the relationship between the physical attributes and the basic divisions of work. The characteristics and attributes that the Westinghouse performance rating technique considers are (1) dexterity, (2) effectiveness, and (3) physical application.

These three major classifications do not in themselves carry any numerical weight, but have in turn been assigned attributes that do carry numerical weight. Table 15–6 gives the numerical values of the nine attributes that are evaluated under this system.

The first major classification, dexterity, has been divided into three attributes; the first of which is: *1. Displayed ability in use of equipment and tools, and assembly of parts.*

When considering this attribute, the analyst is concerned primarily with the "do" portion of the work cycle after the "get" operations (reach, grasp, move) have taken place.

The second attribute under dexterity is: *2. Certainty of movement.*

In evaluating this attribute, the analyst is concerned with the number and degree of hesitations, pauses, or roundabout moves. The basic divisions of accomplishment performed by the operator that will tend to give a low rating for this attribute are change direction, plan, and avoidable delay. All of these affect certainty of movement.

The last attribute considered under dexterity is: *3. Coordination and rhythm.*

This attribute is evidenced by the degree of the displayed performance, by the smoothness of motions, and the freedom from spasmodic spurts and lags.

TABLE 15–6

	+ Above	0 Expected		– Below	
	+	**0**		**–**	
DEXTERITY:					
1. Displayed ability in use of equipment and tools, and assembly of parts.	6	3	0	2	4
2. Certainty of movement.	6	3	0	2	4
3. Co-ordination and rhythm.			2	0	2
EFFECTIVENESS:					
1. Displayed ability to continually replace and retrieve tools and parts with automaticity and accuracy.	6	3	0	2	4
2. Displayed ability to facilitate, eliminate, combine, or shorten motions.	6	3	0	4	8
3. Displayed ability to use both hands with equal ease.	6	3	0	4	8
4. Displayed ability to confine efforts to necessary work.			0	4	8
PHYSICAL APPLICATION:					
1. Work pace.	6	3	0	4	8
2. Attentiveness.			0	2	4

The second major classification, effectiveness, has been defined as efficient, orderly procedure. This classification has been divided into four individual attributes. The first of these is: *1. Displayed ability to replace continually and to retrieve tools and parts automatically and accurately.*

Here the analyst evaluates the ability of the workman to repeatedly place tools, materials, and parts in specified locations and positions, and to retrieve them with automatism and accuracy by eliminating such ineffective basic divisions of work as searching and selecting.

The second of the individual attributes in effectiveness is: *2. Displayed ability to facilitate, eliminate, combine, or shorten motions.*

Here the analyst evaluates the proficiency of the basic divisions: position, pre-position, release, and inspect. The transport therbligs are predetermined usually by the established method. However, a skilled workman will be able to eliminate or shorten the elements of pre-position, position, and inspect because of his manipulative ability.

The third attribute under effectiveness is: *3. Displayed ability to use both hands with equal ease.* Here the degree of effective utilization of both hands is rated.

The fourth and last attribute under effectiveness is: *4. Displayed ability to confine efforts to necessary work.*

This attribute is used to rate the presence of unnecessary work that could not be removed when taking the study. It carries only a negative weight, for when the work is confined to the necessary work, no percentage is added because this condition is expected.

The third major classification, physical demand, is defined as demonstrated rate of performance and has two attributes. The first of these is: *1. Work pace.*

Work pace is rated by the comparison of the speed of movement to preconceived standards for the particular type of work under consideration.

The second attribute for physical application is: *2. Attentiveness.*

Attentiveness is rated as the degree of displayed concentration.

Both of the Westinghouse rating techniques demand considerable training in order that the time study analysts recognize the different levels of each of the attributes. Their training entails a 30-hour course of which approximately 25 hours are spent rating films and discussing the attributes and the degree to which each is displayed. The procedure generally followed is:

1. A film is shown and the operation explained.
2. The film is reshown and rated.
3. The individual ratings are compared and discussed.
4. Film is reshown and attributes pointed out and explained.
5. Step 4 repeated as often as necessary to reach understanding and agreement.

Synthetic rating

In an effort to develop a method of rating that would not rely on the judgment of the time study observer and would give consistent results. R. L. Morrow established a procedure known "as synthetic leveling."[4]

The synthetic leveling procedure determines a performance factor for representative effort elements of the work cycle by comparing actual elemental observed times to times developed through the medium of fundamental motion data (see Chapter 19). Thus, the performance factor may be expressed algebraically as:

---

4 Morrow, *op. cit.,* p. 241.

$$P = \frac{F_t}{O}$$

where

P = Performance or leveling factor
F_t = Fundamental motion time
O = Observed mean elemental time for the
same elements as used in F_t

The factor thus determined would then be applied to the remainder of the manually controlled elements comprising the study. Of course, machine controlled elements would not be rated, as is the case in all rating techniques.

A typical illustration of the application of synthetic rating would be as shown in Table 15–7.

TABLE 15–7

Element no.	Observed average time in minutes	Element type	Fundamental motion time in minutes	Performance factor
1....................	0.08	Manual	0.096	123
2....................	0.15	Manual	. . .	123
3....................	0.05	Manual	. . .	123
4....................	0.22	Manual	0.278	123
5....................	1.41	Power Fed	. . .	100
6....................	0.07	Manual	. . .	123
7....................	0.11	Manual	. . .	123
8....................	0.38	Power Fed	. . .	100
9....................	0.14	Manual	. . .	123
10....................	0.06	Manual	. . .	123
11....................	0.20	Manual	. . .	123
12....................	0.06	Manual	. . .	123

It will be noted that for element 1,

$$P = \frac{0.096}{0.08} = 120 \text{ percent}$$

and that for element 4,

$$P = \frac{0.278}{0.22} = 126 \text{ percent}$$

The mean of these would be 123 percent, and this is the factor used for rating all of the effort elements. It can readily be seen that synthetic performance rating is a sampling technique.

It is essential that more than one element be used in establishing a synthetic rating factor because research has proven, especially in complex work, that operator performance will vary significantly from element to element.

Actually, all experienced time study men unconsciously follow the synthetic rating procedure to some extent. The time study man's mind is full of bench marks that have been established from past experience on similar work. Consequently, he knows that the normal performance of advancing the drill of a 17-inch single-spindle Delta drill is 0.03 minute, and of indexing the hex turret of a No. 4 Warner & Swasey turret lathe is 0.06 minute, and of blowing out a vise or fixture with an air hose and laying the finished part aside is 0.08 minute. These bench marks and many others, when compared to actual performance, certainly influence and even determine the rating factor given the operator.

Perhaps one of the major objections to the application of the synthetic leveling procedure is the time required to construct a left- and right-hand chart of the elements selected for the establishment of basic motion times. The reader may well consider the desirability of establishing a standard for the entire job synthetically. This would eliminate the laborious task of recording elemental times, making subtractions, determining the mean elapsed time, determining the normal time synthetically for several elements so as to arrive at a performance factor, and applying the performance factor. In order to arrive at synthetic values rapidly and accurately, for aiding in the determination of the performance factor, an alignment chart has been designed, which may be attached to the time study board (see Figure 13–6). The application of this tool by the analyst will be discussed later in this chapter. This technique permits the analyst to utilize synthetic values as a guide toward the establishment of a valid performance factor.

Speed rating

Speed rating is a method of evaluating the performance in which consideration is given only to the rate of accomplishment of the work per unit time. In this method, the observer measures the effectiveness of the operator against the conception of a normal man doing the same work, and then assigns a percentage to indicate the ratio of observed performance to normal performance. Particular emphasis is placed on the observer having complete knowledge of the job before taking the study. It is evident that the pace for machine work in a plant which produces aircraft engine parts would appear considerably slower to the novice than would the pace executed by machine workers who produce farm machinery components. The greater precision requirements of the aircraft work would require such care that the movements of the various operators would appear unduly slow to one who was not completely familiar with the work being performed.

In speed rating, 100 percent is usually considered normal. Thus a rating of 110 percent would indicate that the operator was performing at a speed 10 percent greater than normal and a rating of 90 percent would mean that he was performing 90 percent of normal. Some concerns using the speed rating technique have chosen to call 60 standard or normal. This is based on the standard hour approach; that is, producing 60 minutes of work every hour. On this basis, a rating of 80 would mean that the operator was working at a speed of 80/60 which equals 133 percent or 33 percent above normal. A rating of 50 would indicate a speed of 50/60 or 83⅓ percent of normal or standard.

In the speed rating method, the analyst first makes an appraisal of the performance to determine if it is above or below his conception of normal. He then executes a second judgment in an effort to place the performance in the precise position on the rating scale, which will correctly evaluate the numerical difference between standard and performance being demonstrated.

A form of speed rating referred to as "pace rating" has received considerable attention from the basic steel industry. In effect, pace rating is speed rating. However, in an effort to identify completely a normal pace on different jobs, bench marks have been provided on a broad range of work. Thus, in addition to card dealing, such effort operations as shoveling sand, coremaking, brick handling, and walking have been clearly identified as to method, and quantified as to normal rate of production. Once the time study analyst familiarizes himself with a series of bench marks closely allied to the work he is going to study, he will be much better equipped to evaluate the speed being performed.

Objective rating

The rating procedure known as "objective rating," a method developed by M. E. Mundel,[5] endeavors to eliminate the difficulty of establishing a normal speed criterion for every different type of work. In this procedure, a single work assignment is established to which all other jobs are compared as to pace. After the judgment of pace, a secondary factor is assigned to the job to take care of its relative difficulty. The factors that influence the difficulty adjustment are: (1) amount of body used, (2) foot pedals, (3) bimanualness, (4) eye-hand coordination, (5) handling or sensory requirements, and (6) weight handled or resistance encountered.

Numerical values, resulting from experiments, have been assigned for a range of degrees of each factor. The sum of the numerical values for

---

[5] M. E. Mundel, *Motion and Time Study* (New York: Prentice-Hall, Inc., 1950).

each of the six factors comprises the secondary adjustment. By this method the normal time can be expressed as follows:

$$T_n = (P_2)(S)(O)$$

where

T_n = Computed established normal time
P_2 = Pace rating factor
S = Job difficulty adjustment factor
O = Observed mean elemental time

This performance rating procedure will tend to give consistent results since the comparison of pace of the operation under study to an operation that is completely familiar to the observer can more readily be achieved than judging simultaneously all the attributes of an operation to a concept of normal for that specific job. The secondary factor will not effect inconsistency since this factor merely adjusts the rated time by the application of a percentage. This percentage value used is taken from a table that gives values for the effect of various difficulties present in the operation being performed.

OPERATOR SELECTION

In an effort to eliminate the performance rating step entirely in the calculation of the standard, some concerns select the operators to be studied and then consider the average observed time as the normal time. When this method is utilized, usually more than one operator is studied and enough cycles are observed so that a reliable average time (within plus or minus 5 percent of the population average) is calculated. Of course, the success of this method is dependent on the selection of the employees who are to be studied and their performance during the study. If the performances of the operators being observed are slower than normal, then too liberal a standard will result; conversely, if the observed operators produce at a pace more rapid than normal, then the standard will be unduly tight. There is always the possibility of having but one or two available operators and the chance that they may differ from normal. Then, in an effort to avoid delay in establishing a standard, the time study observer will make the study; the result will be a poor time standard.

Analysis of rating

As is true of all procedures requiring the exercise of judgment, the simpler and more concise the plan, the easier it will be to use, and, in general, the more valid the results will be.

The performance rating plan that is the easiest to apply, the easiest to explain, and the one that tends to give the most valid results is straight speed or pace rating augmented with synthetic bench marks. As has been explained, in this procedure, 100 is considered normal, and performance greater than normal is indicated by values directly proportional to 100. Thus, a rating of 120 would indicate that a performance of 20 percent higher than normal was being exhibited. A rating of 60 would indicate that the operator was performing at a pace of only 0.60 of normal. The speed rating scale usually covers a range from 0.50 to 1.50. Operators performing outside this productivity range of 3 to 1 may be studied, but it is not recommended. The closer the performance is to normal, the better will be the chance of achieving the true normal time.

The time study analyst using speed rating will have four considerations which when properly followed will allow him consistently to establish values not more than 5 percent above or below the true normal. These are:

1. Experience in the class of work being performed.
2. Synthetic bench marks on at least two of the elements being performed.
3. Selection of an operator who has from past experience given performances somewhere between 115 and 85 percent of normal.
4. Use the mean value of three or more independent studies.

Certainly, the most important of these four criteria is experience in the class of work being performed. This does not necessarily mean that the analyst must have at one time been an actual operator in the work being studied, although this would be desirable. He should be sufficiently familiar with the work from his past personal experience, either by observation or operation, that he understands every detail of the method being used. Thus, on a job being performed on a turret lathe, he should recognize the tooling, have knowledge of the correct speeds and feeds, the correct rake and clearance angles, lubricant, horsepower requirements, method of holding the work, and so on. On an assembly job taking place in a fixture, the time study man should be familiar with the difficulty in positioning the components in the fixture; he should know the class of fit between all mating parts and have a clear understanding of the relationship between time and class of fit. He should know the proper sequence of events and the weights of all parts being handled.

It has often been said that experience is the key to accurate performance rating, and this statement certainly is true. An analyst with 10 years' experience in the metal trades would find considerable difficulty in establishing standards in a woman's shoe factory, and of course the reverse would be true: a time study man with years of experience in the fabrication of shoes would be unable to establish equitable standards in a machine shop until he had acquired some experience in the line of work being performed.

Although it has been proven that operator performance does vary from element to element, the average performance of two or more elements of the study will give a reasonably good estimate of the cycle performance. If the time study analyst has available information that allows him to preestablish synthetically the normal time required to perform several of the elements involved in the study, he has an indication of the overall performance being executed.

The alignment chart[6] shown on the time study board (see Figure 13–6) permits the analyst to establish synthetically the normal time for the elements: "pick up pc. & position in fixture, jig, or die," "pick up pc. & bring to work station," "pick up pc. & lay aside." Since very few work assignments can be performed without utilizing at least one of these elements, the time study analyst has at his disposal a useful guide for establishing a "correct" performance factor. For example, if a 10-pound casting is picked up and placed in a 3-jaw chuck of a turret lathe, and the element entailed a reach of 30 inches and a move of 20 inches and a class 4 grasp (see Chapter 19 on M.T.M.) and a P3SE position, the synthetic time could be determined graphically. By going from 20 inches on scale 1 vertically to 10 pounds on scale 2 and then moving horizontally to scale 3, a time of 0.017 minute for the move and release is shown. This point connected to the G4 grasp of 0.005 minute (scale 4) gives a turning point on scale 5. This turning point on scale 5 connected with a reach of 30 inches on scale 6 gives a time of 0.04 minute for the reach, grasp, move, and release. This point connected with a P3SE position entailing 0.025 minute on scale 8 gives the time to perform the complete element 0.065 minute on scale 9.

It is not intended to infer that the synthetic value will establish a rating that is to have application for every element of each cycle of the study. The analyst through his experience and training in performance rating will be able to evaluate the operator quite precisely; the alignment chart and resulting synthetic standards will provide an additional check and guide to the analyst, giving him more confidence in his ability to establish fair normal times.

Whenever more than one operator is available to be studied, the one who is thoroughly experienced on the job, who has a reputation of being receptive to time study practice, and who consistently performs at a pace near standard or slightly better than standard should be selected. The closer the operator performs to a normal pace, the easier will he be to level. Sizable errors in judgment during rating are invariably a result of

---

[6] The data used in the design of this alignment chart were developed in part by the author after analyzing over 600 feet of film. The remainder of the data used was taken from Methods-Time Measurement tables.

improper evaluation of an operator who is performing at either extremity of the rating scale. For example, if 0.50 minute is considered normal for dealing a deck of cards into four bridge hands, it will be found that performance within plus or minus 15 percent of this conception of normal will be fairly easy to identify. However, once the performance runs 50 percent faster or 50 percent slower than normal, considerably more difficulty is encountered in establishing an accurate rating factor indicative of the rate of performance being demonstrated.

It is good practice to take several (three or more) studies before arriving at the standard. The total error, due to rating and the determination of a mean elemental elapsed time that deviates from the population mean, is minimized when averages of several independent studies are used for computing the time standard. The independent studies can be made on the same operator at different times of the day, or on different operators. The point is, as the number of studies increase, compensating errors will diminish the overall error. A recent example will clarify the point. The author, along with two other trained industrial engineers, reviewed performance rating training films involving 15 different operations. The results are tabulated in Table 15–8. The standard ratings were

TABLE 15–8

Performance ratings of three different engineers observing 15 different operations

	Standard rating	Engineer A		Engineer B		Engineer C		Average of Engineer A, B, C	
Operation		Rating	Deviation	Rating	Deviation	Rating	Deviation	Rating	Deviation
1.....	110	110	0	115	+5	100	−10	108	−2
2.....	150	140	−10	130	−20	125	−25	132	−18
3.....	90	110	+20	100	+10	105	+15	105	+15
4.....	100	100	0	100	0	100	0	100	0
5.....	130	120	−10	130	0	115	−15	122	−8
6.....	120	140	+20	120	0	105	−15	122	+2
7.....	65	70	+5	70	+5	95	+30	78	+13
8.....	105	100	−5	110	+5	100	−5	103	−2
9.....	140	160	+20	145	+5	145	+5	150	+10
10.....	115	125	+10	125	+10	110	−5	120	+5
11.....	115	110	−5	120	+10	115	0	115	0
12.....	125	125	0	125	0	115	−10	122	−3
13.....	100	100	0	85	−15	110	+10	98	−2
14.....	65	55	−10	70	+5	90	+25	72	+7
15.....	150	160	+10	140	−10	140	−10	147	−3
Average of 15 operations........	112	115		112.3		111.3		112.9	
Average deviation....	0	+3.0		+0.3		−0.7		+0.9	

not disclosed until all 15 operations had been rated. The average deviation of all three engineers for the 15 different operations was only 0.87 of a point on a speed rating scale with a range from 50 points to 150 points. Yet Engineer C was 30.0 high on operation 7, and Engineer B was 20.0 low on operation 2. In only one case (operation 3), when the known ratings were within the 70 to 130 range, did the average rating of the three analysts exceed ±5 points of the known rating.

The normal time for the operation should then be determined by averaging the normal times of the independent studies. This procedure will not only reduce the error inherent in the performance rating process, but will result in the determination of a mean measured time with less deviation from the population mean measured time.

Performance rating, like any other form of work involving judgment, must be accomplished by competent, well-trained individuals. If this caliber of person is doing the work, and if he is equipped with a background of experience, has access to reliable synthetic time values, and uses sound judgment in operator selection, then reasonably accurate results can be assured.

Training for rating

To be successful, the time study man must develop a record for setting standards correctly so that they will be accepted by both labor and management. Furthermore, his rates must be consistent so that he will maintain the respect of all parties. In general, the time study analyst is expected to be able regularly to establish standards within plus or minus 5 percent of the true rate, when studying operators that are performing somewhere in the range of 0.70 to 1.30 of normal. Thus, if several operators are performing the same job and different time study men establish time standards on the job, each analyst studying a different operator, then the resulting standard from each individual study should be within plus or minus 5 percent of the mean of the group of studies.

To assure consistency in rating, not only to keep agreement with former rates which he himself has established, but also to maintain accordance with the other time study analysts in his plant, the time study man should continually participate in organized training programs. Of course, the training in performance rating should be more intense with the neophyte time study analyst.

One of the most widely used methods for training in performance rating is the observation of moving-picture films illustrating diversified operations performed at different productivity levels. Each film has a known level of performance, and after it is shown on the screen, the correct rating is compared with the values established independently by the various trainees. If any of the time study analysts' values deviate substantially from the correct value, then specific information is given so as to justify the rating. For example, the observer may have been misled because of high performance in the handling of the material to and from the work station, while poor performance prevailed during the cycle at the work station. Then, too, the analyst may have underrated the operator because of his apparently effortless sequence of motions, whereas his

FIGURE 15–4

Chart showing record of seven studies with analyst tending to rate a little on studies 1, 2, 4, and 6, and a little low on studies 3 and 7. Only study 1 was rated outside the range of desired accuracy

smooth, rhythmic blending of movements is really an indication of high dexterity and manipulative ability.

The operations selected should be simple, yet should contain a number of fast motions. The observations of short elements cultivates both speed and concentration in the observer and trains the "second sight."

As successive films are shown, it is helpful for the analyst to plot his rating against the known values (see Figure 15–4). A straight line would indicate perfection, whereas high irregularities in both directions would indicate inconsistency as well as inability to evaluate performance.

In the example shown, the analyst rated the first film 75, whereas the correct rating was 55. In the second case, he rated 80 while the proper performance was 70. In all but the first case, the analyst was within the company's established area of correct rating. It is interesting to note that this concern indicates that only at the 100 percent or normal level of performance is the plus or minus 5 percent criterion of accuracy valid. When performance is below 70 percent of normal or above 130 percent of normal a much larger than 5 percent error can be expected by the experienced time study analyst.

It is also helpful to plot successive ratings on the X axis and indicate the magnitude of deviation either positive or negative from the known normal on the Y axis (see Figure 15–5). The closer the time study man comes to the X axis with his rating, the more correct he will be.

FIGURE 15–5

Record of an analyst's rating factors on 15 studies

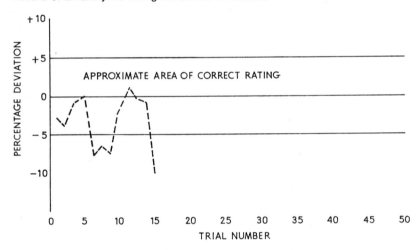

To determine quantitatively the ability of the analyst to performance rate, it is helpful to compute the percentage of the analyst's rating contained within specified limits of the known ratings. This can be done as follows:

1. Compute the mean difference ($\bar{x}_d$) between the rater's rating and the actual rating for n tests. (n should be at least 15 observations.)
2. Compute the standard deviation s_d of the differences in rating.
3. Compute the normal deviate z_1 where:

$$z_1 = \frac{5(\text{or some other figure of accuracy}) - \bar{x}_d}{s_d}$$

4. Compute the normal deviate z_2 where:

$$z_2 = \frac{-5(\text{or some other figure of accuracy}) - \bar{x}_d}{s_d}$$

5. Compute the area under the normal distribution between ± 5 (or some other figure of accuracy) centered at $\bar{x}_d$ which is assumed equal to μ_d and s_d is assumed equal to σ_d.

For example, suppose that, after reviewing 15 rating films, a given analyst had the achievement shown in Table 15–9.

TABLE 15-9

Film no.	Correct rating	Analyst's rating	Difference (d)	Difference squared
1............	115	105	-10	100
2............	125	120	-5	25
3.........	85	95	$+10$	100
4.........	105	105	0	0
5.........	100	105	$+5$	25
6.........	95	110	$+15$	225
7.........	120	125	$+5$	25
8.........	140	150	$+10$	100
9.........	100	105	$+5$	25
10.........	60	75	$+15$	225
11.........	100	100	0	0
12.........	110	105	-5	25
13.........	90	90	0	0
14.........	130	125	-5	25
15.........	80	90	$+10$	100

The following computations would be made:

$$\bar{x}_d \text{ (mean difference)} = \frac{\Sigma d}{n} = \frac{50}{15} = 3.33$$

$$s_d \text{ (standard deviation)} = \sqrt{\frac{\Sigma d^2 - \dfrac{(\Sigma d)^2}{n}}{n-1}} = 7.7$$

$$z_1 = \frac{5.00 - 3.33}{7.7} = 0.217$$

and

$$P(z_1) = \int_0^{z_1} \frac{1}{\sqrt{2\pi}} e^{-\frac{z^2}{2}}\, dz = 0.0859$$

$$z_2 = \frac{-5 - 3.33}{7.7} = -1.08$$

and

$$P(z_2) = \int_0^{z_2} \frac{1}{\sqrt{2\pi}} e^{-\frac{z^2}{2}}\, dz = 0.3597$$

$$P(z_1) + P(z_2) = 0.4456$$

In this example, the analyst would be given a rating of 0.4456. This represents the portion of his ratings that would lie within plus or minus 5 rating points of the ideal ratings. This area of correct rating together with the distribution of the difference between the analyst's rating and the correct rating is shown in Figure 15–6. It would be advisable for the analyst to use the student's "*t*" distribution if the number of films observed is less than 15.

A recent statistical study involving the performance rating of 6,720 individual operations by a group of 19 analysts over a period of approximately two years confirmed several facts that had been accepted by most

FIGURE 15–6

Graphic presentation of portion of analyst's correct rating (±5) and distribution of all his ratings

industrial engineers. This study concluded that the "level of performance" is a factor that affects significantly the error in rating performance. Time study men tend to overrate low levels of performance and to underrate high levels of performance.

It also was concluded that the operation studied has an effect on the error of rating performance. Thus complex operations tend to be more difficult to performance rate, even by the experienced analyst, than simpler operations. At low levels of performance, overrating is greater for difficult operations than for simple operations, while at high levels of performance, the underrating is larger for the easy to perform operations.

Today, no known tests are available that can accurately evaluate the ability of a person to rate performance. Experience, however, has shown that unless an analyst shows a tendency toward consistency and proficiency after a brief training in rating, he may never be able to do an acceptable job in rating.

A survey made by one large manufacturer disclosed that the industrial engineering employee who was older in point of service did not level any more accurately than the newer man, that those in the higher work classifications did not level better than the lower men, that those in machining areas did no better than those in assembly areas and vice versa.

A group of undergraduate engineers were given 15 minutes instruction in rating and then were requested to performance rate a film illustrating a series of heavy labor operations. The students were given no orientation in the class of work, and the operations observed were substantially varied from the operations used in giving them a concept of proper performance. It was interesting to note that the students were extremely successful in adjusting the concepts learned on light operations to those on heavy labor operations.

In another instance, 34 undergraduate engineering students were asked to performance rate five industrial films involving operations rang-

TABLE 15–10

Known rating	Number of students in each rating bracket					
	85–90	91–95	96–100	101–105	106–110	111–125
1.15...................	0	3	4	12	6	9
1.00...................	4	5	19	2	3	1
1.00...................	2	3	7	12	5	5
1.00...................	7	5	14	8	0	0
1.00...................	1	2	26	4	1	0

ing from mold making to bench assembly. Four of these films were established as being representative of normal performance and one was rated as 1.15 or 15 percent above normal. The results are shown in Table 15–10.

Note that the majority of the students did not deviate greatly from the known values.

One division of the General Electric Company upon request checked the validity of the performance rating technique on three different occasions. After brief training in their rating methods, the union steward and the foreman were requested to rate a given operation in conjunction with a time study analyst and the time study supervisor. At the completion of the study, the time study man rated the study without advising the other three men on the values he used, so they would not be influenced by his opinion. These three men then went into their respective offices so they would not be influenced by each other's opinions and independently and secretly rated the operation. The results were as follows: time study man 100; planning and wage payment supervisor 99; foreman 103; union steward 103.

At a later date involving an entirely different class of work, a similar test case was undertaken. These results were: time study man 100; planning and wage payment supervisor 99; foreman 103; union steward 103.

On the third occasion an entirely new set of conditions prevailed and in this instance all four men rated identically—109!

The foregoing studies bring out that (1) a conception of normal performance can be quickly taught, and (2) the concept of normal is transferable to some degree to dissimilar operations.

By actual observation of different work assignments throughout a plant under the guidance of the time study supervisor, it is possible to achieve excellent training in rating. The supervisor will explain in detail the "why" of his values after the trainees have already written their ratings independently. The independent values should be recorded to determine the consistency of the group and the necessity for additional, and perhaps more intensive, training.

It has been proven that companies that have extensive and well-designed programs of training in rating have been successful in largely eliminating the tendency to overrate and underrate.

TEXT QUESTIONS

1. Why has industry been unable to develop a universal conception of "normal performance"?
2. What factors enter into large variances in operator performance?
3. What are the characteristics of a sound rating system?
4. When should the performance rating procedure be accomplished? Why is this important?
5. What governs the frequency of performance rating during a given study?
6. Explain the Westinghouse system of leveling.
7. How does the Westinghouse performance rating method differ from the leveling method?
8. Under the Westinghouse rating system, why are "conditions" evaluated?
9. What is synthetic rating? What is its principal weakness?
10. What is the basis of speed rating and how does this method differ from the Westinghouse system?
11. What is the purpose of the "secondary adjustment" in the objective rating technique? What factors are considered in the "secondary adjustment"?
12. What four criteria are fundamental for doing a good job in speed rating?
13. Why is training in performance rating a continuous process?
14. Using the data illustrated in Figure 15–4, determine the average percentage of correct rating within plus or minus 5 rating points.
15. Why is performance rating the most important step in the entire work measurement procedure?
16. Why should more than one element be used in the establishment of a synthetic rating factor?

GENERAL QUESTIONS

1. Would there be any objection to studying an operator who was performing at an excessive pace? Why?

2. In what ways can an operator give the impression of high effort and yet produce at a mediocre or poor degree of performance?

3. If an operator strongly objected to his performance rating factor upon completion of the study, what would your next step be if you were the time study analyst?

4. How would you go about maintaining a uniform concept of normal performance with an enterprise involving a multiplant complex where the various plants are located in different sections of the country?

CHAPTER 16

Allowances

After the calculation of the normal time, sometimes referred to as the "rated" time, one additional step must be performed in order to arrive at a fair standard. This last step is the addition of an allowance to take care of the many interruptions, delays, and slowdowns brought on by fatigue which enter into every work assignment. For example in planning a motor car trip of 1,000 miles, we know that the trip cannot be made in 20 hours when driving at a speed of 50 miles per hour. An allowance to take care of periodic stops for personal needs, for driving fatigue, for unavoidable stops brought on by traffic congestion and stoplights, for possible detours and resulting rough roads, for car trouble, and so forth must be added. Thus we may estimate making the trip in 25 hours since we feel that 5 additional hours would be necessary to take care of all delays. Similarly, an allowance must be provided for the workman in order that the resulting standard will be fair and readily maintainable by the average workman who is performing at a steady, normal pace.

It must be remembered that the watch readings of any time study are taken over a relatively short period of time, and abnormal readings, unavoidable delays, and time for personal needs are removed from the study in the determination of the average or selected time. Therefore, the normal time has not provided for unavoidable delays and other legitimate lost time; consequently, some adjustment must be made to compensate for such losses.

In general, allowances are made to cover three broad areas. These are personal delays, fatigue, and unavoidable delays. The application of allowances in some concerns is considerably broader than in others. For example, a survey of 42 firms relative to what was ordinarily included in their allowances revealed the information shown in Table 16–1.

Allowances are frequently carelessly applied because they have not been established on sound time study data. This is especially true of allowance for fatigue, where it is difficult if not impossible to establish values based on rational theory. Many unions, well aware of this situation, have endeavored to bargain for additional fatigue allowance as if it were a "fringe" issue. (Fringe benefits are those which are expenses to the company but are not proportional to employee output, such as insurance and pensions.) Allowance must be determined as accurately and correctly as possible; otherwise, all the care and precision that has been put into the study up to this point will be completely nullified.

TABLE 16–1

Allowance factor	No. of firms	Percent
1. Fatigue	39	93
A. General	19	45
B. Rest periods	13	31
Did not specify A or B	7	17
2. Time required to learn	3	7
3. Unavoidable delay	35	83
A. Man	1	2
B. Machine	7	17
C. Both, man and machine	21	50
Did not specify A, B, or C	6	14
4. Personal needs	32	76
5. Setup or preparation operations	24	57
6. Irregular or unusual operations	16	38

SOURCE: J. O. P. Hummel, "Motion and Time Study in Leading American Industrial Establishments" (master's thesis, Pennsylvania State University).

Allowances are applied to three categories of the study. These are: (1) allowances applicable to the total cycle time, (2) allowances that need be considered on machine time only, and (3) allowances applicable to effort time only.

Allowances applicable to the whole cycle time are usually expressed as a percentage of the cycle time and include such delays as personal needs, cleaning the work station, and oiling the machine. Machine time allowances include time for tool maintenance and power variance, while representative delays covered by effort allowance are fatigue and certain unavoidable delays.

There are two methods of developing standard allowance data that are frequently used. One is the production study which requires an observer to study two or perhaps three operations over a long period of time. The observer records the duration and reason for each idle interval (see Figure 16–1), and upon establishing a reasonably representative sample, summarizes his findings to determine the percent allowance for each applicable characteristic. The data obtained in this fashion must be adjusted to the level of normal performance as for any time study.

Since the observer must spend a long period of time in direct observation of one or more operations, this method is exceptionally tedious, not

FIGURE 16–1

Lost time analysis chart

LOST TIME ANALYSIS OF TIME STUDY

Dwg._____ Part _____ Date _____

Operation _____

Symbol _____

A. Personal _____
B. Start work late _____
C. Stop work early _____
D. Talk with foreman or instructor _____
E. Talk with other persons _____
F. Search for tools _____
G. Search for drawings _____
H. Rework fault of operator _____
I. Rework fault of another operator _____
J. Rework fault of machine or fixtures _____
K. Idle-wait for crane (excess over allowed) _____
L. Idle-wait for inspector (excess over allowed) _____
M. Wait in line at tool crib (excess over allowed) _____
N. Wait in line at dispatch office (excess over allowed) _____
O. Wait in line at B/P station _____
P. Tool maintenance _____
Q. Oil machine _____
R. Clean work station _____
S. Circled readings (circled reading minus ave. for ele.) _____
T. Miscellaneous minor delays _____
U. Lost time developing methods during study _____
V. _____
W. _____
X. _____
Y. _____
Z. _____

                                                    Total_____

1. Gross over-all _____Mins. _____ Hrs.
2. Total lost _____ " _____ "
3. % lost time compared with net actual (2 ÷ 4)   _____
4. Net actual or productive _____Mins. _____ Hrs.
5. Allowed time   _____ " _____ "

_____
_____
_____

Note--Place lost time symbol alongside description of lost time on study and staple this card
      to study.

only to the analyst but also to the operator or operators as well. It has further disadvantages in that there is a tendency to take too small a sample, which may result in biased results.

The second technique of establishing allowance percentage is through work sampling studies (see Chapter 21). This method involves the taking of a large number of random observations, thus requiring only part-time, or at least intermittent, services of the observer. In this method, no stopwatch is used, as the observer merely walks through the area under study at unscheduled times and makes a brief notation as to what each operator is doing.

The number of delays recorded divided by the total number of observations during which the operator is engaged in productive work will tend to equal the allowance required by the operator to accommodate the normal delays encountered.

In using work sampling studies for the determination of allowances, the observer must practice several precautionary measures. First the observer must be careful that he does not anticipate his observations and that he records only the actual happenings. Then, a given study should not cover dissimilar work, but should be confined to similar operations on the same general type of equipment. The larger the number of observations and the longer the period of time over which the data were taken, the more valid will be the results. Studies taken by R. L. Morrow indicate that fairly reliable results were obtained with 500 observations while 3,000 observations gave very accurate results.[1] Daily observations should be taken over a span of at least two weeks.

Personal delays

Under the item of personal delays will come those cessations in work necessary for maintaining the general well-being of the employee. This will include periodic trips to the drinking fountain and the rest room. The general working conditions and class of work will influence the time necessary for personal delays. Thus, working conditions involving heavy work performed at high temperatures, such as that done in the press-room of a rubber-molding department or in a hot-forge shop, would require greater allowance for personal needs than light work performed in comfortable temperature areas. Detailed production checks have demonstrated that a 5 percent allowance for personal time, or approximately 24 minutes in eight hours, is appropriate for typical shop working conditions. The amount of time needed for personal delays will, of course, vary to some extent with the person as well as the class of work. The 5 percent figure cited appears to be adequate for the majority of male and female workers.

Fatigue

Closely associated with allowance for personal needs is allowance for fatigue, although this allowance is usually applied only to the effort portions of the study. Fatigue allowances have not reached the state where

---

[1] R. L. Morrow, *Time Study and Motion Economy* (New York: Ronald Press Co., 1946).

their qualifications are based on sound, rational theories, and they probably never will. Consequently, next to performance rating, the fatigue allowance is the least defensible and the most open to argument of all the factors making up a time standard. However, fair fatigue allowances for different classes of work can be approximated by empirical means. Fatigue is not homogeneous in any respect; it ranges from strictly physical to purely psychological and includes combinations of both the physical and the psychological. It has a marked influence on some people, and apparently has little or no effect on others.

Whether the fatigue that sets in is physical or mental, the results are similar: there is a lessening in the will to work. The major factors that affect fatigue are well known and have been clearly established. Some of these are:

1. Working conditions:
   a) Light
   b) Temperature
   c) Humidity
   d) Air freshness
   e) Color of room and environment
   f) Noise
2. Repetitiveness of work:
   a) Monotony of similar body movements
   b) Muscular tiredness due to stressing of some muscles
3. General health of the worker, physical and mental:
   a) Physical stature
   b) Diet
   c) Rest
   d) Emotional stability
   e) Home conditions

It is evident that fatigue can be reduced, but can never be eliminated. In general, heavy work is diminishing in industry because of the marked progress in mechanization of both material handling and processing elements. As industry becomes more automated, there will be less muscular tiredness due to stressing of muscles. Thus, we have made real progress toward the decreasing of physical fatigue. The major problem of fatigue today is not physical but psychological, and industry through its scientific selection programs is substantially reducing this factor by putting the right people on the right jobs. A person who has an unfavorable reaction to monotony is not placed on a monotonous job. Since it is not customary to provide fatigue allowance for those general health factors that influence the degree of fatigue that sets in, such conditions as emotional stability, rest, diet, and physical stature are usually considered in employee selection.

Because fatigue cannot be eliminated, proper allowance must be made for working conditions and repetitiveness of work that influence the degree to which it sets in. Experiments have shown that fatigue must be plotted as a curve, not as a straight line. Figure 16–2 illustrates a typical work curve showing the relationship between load in pounds and time for handling each load.

Figure 16–3 shows the effect of fatigue in an assembly operation. After 80 blocks of work were completed (1 block involved 1,296 cycles) an experiment of exhaustion was performed where the work load was increased by allowing only one five-minute break after the completion of

FIGURE 16–2

Typical work curve

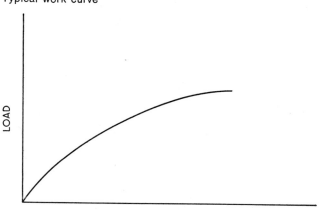

TIME PER UNIT LOAD

SOURCE: Redrawn from "Fatigue Allowances in Industry," Thesis by J. W. Siphron, The Pennsylvania State College.

a block of work. Many industrial studies have shown a drop in production toward the end of the working period which is attributable to fatigue alone. Usually, the rate of production tends to increase during the early part of the day and then falls after the third hour. There is a short period of increased production after the lunch period, but this begins to taper off and output usually continues to decline for the balance of the working day.

Perhaps the most widely used method of determining fatigue allowance is that of measuring the decline in production throughout the working period. Thus, the production rate for every quarter of an hour may be measured during the course of the working day. Any decline of production that cannot be attributed to method change or personal or unavoidable delays may be attributed to fatigue and expressed as a percentage. It must be recognized, however, that many outside factors can

FIGURE 16–3

Learning curve for assembly work showing impact of financial incentive and effect of fatigue after flattening of learning
curve

SOURCE: Redrawn from W. Rohmert and K. Schlaich, "Learning of Complex Manual Tasks," *The International Journal of Production Research*, Vol. 5,
No. 2 (1966), p. 137.

influence the fatigue factor, such as state of health or outside interference. Thus, many studies should be made in order to obtain a reasonable
sample before deciding upon the final fatigue allowance for a given
facility. Eugene Brey[2] has expressed the coefficient of fatigue as follows:

$$F = \frac{(T - t)\ 100}{T}$$

where

F = Coefficient of fatigue
T = Time required to perform operation at
the end of continuous work
t = Time required to perform operation at
beginning of continuous work

---

[2] Eugene E. Brey, "Fatigue Research in Its Relation to Time Study Practice,"
Proceedings, Time Study Conference, Society of Industrial Engineers.

Many attempts have been made to measure fatigue, none of which has been completely successful. The tests of fatigue may be classified into three groups: (1) physical, (2) chemical, and (3) physiological.

Physical tests include the various dynamometer tests of changes in the rate of working, such as the hand dynamometer, the mercury dynamometer, the water dynamometer, and the Martin spring balance for registering force exerted by six different sets of large body muscles.

Chemical tests include the various techniques for analysis of the blood and the body secretions, such as the saliva, so as to note changes resulting from fatigue.

TABLE 16–2

Factor	Percent decrease	Percent increase
1. Pulse count		113.5
2. Pulse pressure		77.0
3. Respiratory rate		60.5
4. CO_2 combining power	41.0	...
5. Metabolism		43.0
6. White blood cells		57.0
7. Red blood cells		6.0
8. Blood pressure; diastolic	28.0	...
9. Blood pressure; systolic		20.5
10. Blood sugar		12.0

SOURCE: Moss and Roe, *Physiological Reactions Due to Fatigue.*

The physiological tests of fatigue include pulse count, blood pressure, respiratory rate, oxygen consumption, and production of carbon dioxide. Table 16–2 shows the rate of change in physiological reactions due to fatigue.

In recent years, considerable attention has been directed to the physiological requirements of various work assignments. This branch of the scientific study of the worker and his environment is being recognized as "occupational physiology." Here, the effort per unit of time plus the physiological recovery time is measured for the different work assignments within a plant. As these studies progress, more quantitative data will inevitably result for estimating fatigue allowances. It is also expected that laws of physiological economy will result which will supplement and may even supersede some of the laws of motion economy.

In the development of equitable fatigue allowance, one of the foremost problems of time study is to determine at which portion of the fatigue curve a time study was made, and then derive a fatigue allowance which can be used as a constant for work performed at the given work station in the future.

For most industrial operations, fatigue allowances have been arbitrarily broken into three elements, each of which has a spread of influence on the total fatigue allowance. These are: operations involving strenuous work, operations involving repetitive work, and operations performed under disagreeable working conditions. Of course, it is possible for more than one of these conditions, in varying degrees, to apply in any specific operation.

By taking controlled production studies from an adequate sample of work it is possible to arrive at fatigue allowance values that will prove equitable for the various degrees of each of the above-enumerated factors. The apparent adequacy of fatigue allowances determined by measuring the decline in production through all-day production studies is due to the fact that the fatigue allowance for a given job is not a critical value but may be safely established within a rather broad range.

The International Labour Office has tabulated the effect of working conditions in order to arrive at an allowance factor for personal delays and fatigue. This tabulation is shown in Table 16–3. The factors considered include: standing while working, abnormal positions demanded, use of force, illumination, atmospheric conditions, job attention required, noise level, mental strain, monotony, and tediousness.

In using this table the analyst should determine an allowance factor for each element of the study. For example, element 3 of a given study may involve the application of a 40-pound force. Because of this use of force, an allowance of 9 percent would be used in the structure of the allowance computation for this element. It should be noted that this tabulation provides a basic 9 percent allowance to all effort elements, for personal delays and fatigue. To this basic 9 percent allowance is added applicable variable allowances as enumerated in the table.

There are two ways of applying the fatigue allowance. It can be handled as a percentage which is added to the normal time, as has been explained. In this method, the allowance is based on a percentage of the productive time only. As an alternative technique, fatigue allowance can be handled through the establishment of periodic rest periods.

The former way is preferred because it allows the physically stronger employee to participate in greater earnings. If compulsory rest periods are used, the strong employee not as subject to fatigue as the average employee will be restricted in his output.

It should be recognized that rest periods will definitely reduce fatigue. If 10-minute rest periods are introduced in a plant, as they frequently are, the fatigue allowance that formerly prevailed should be proportionally modified. For example, if a bench assembly operation earned a fatigue allowance of 8 percent and at some later date, through negotiation, a 10-minute rest period was provided in the morning and another

TABLE 16–3

1.	Constant Allowances:		
	a)	Personal allowance	5
	b)	Basic fatigue allowance	4
2.	Variable Allowances:		
	A.	Standing allowance	2
	B.	Abnormal position allowance—	
		a) Slightly awkward	0
		b) Awkward (bending)	2
		c) Very awkward (lying, stretching)	7

C. Use of force, or muscular energy (lifting, pulling, or pushing)—
Weight lifted, pounds

5	0
10	1
15	2
20	3
25	4
30	5
35	7
40	9
45	11
50	13
60	17
70	22

	D.	Bad light—	
		a) Slightly below recommended	0
		b) Well below	2
		c) Quite inadequate	5
	E.	Atmospheric conditions (heat and humidity)—	
		Variable	0–10
	F.	Close attention—	
		a) Fairly fine work	0
		b) Fine or exacting	2
		c) Very fine or very exacting	5
	G.	Noise level—	
		a) Continuous	0
		b) Intermittent—Loud	2
		c) Intermittent—Very loud	5
		d) High-pitched—Loud	5
	H.	Mental strain—	
		a) Fairly complex process	1
		b) Complex or wide span of attention	4
		c) Very complex	8
	I.	Monotony—	
		a) Low	0
		b) Medium	1
		c) High	4
	J.	Tediousness—	
		a) Rather tedious	0
		b) Tedious	2
		c) Very tedious	5

10-minute rest period in the afternoon, the fatigue allowance on this class of work would be diminished

$$\frac{20}{\text{Normal productive time}} = -\text{ percent}$$

The normal daily productive time on this class of work may be 400 minutes. The fatigue allowance accounted for by the 20-minute rest period would then be 20/400 or 5 percent. Thus future standards in this area will carry a fatigue allowance of 8 percent minus 5 percent, or 3 percent.

Unavoidable delays

This class of delays applies to effort elements and includes such items as interruptions from the foreman, dispatcher, time study analyst, and others; material irregularities; difficulty in maintaining tolerances and specifications; and interference delays where multiple machine assignments are made.

As can be expected, every operator will have numerous interruptions during the course of the working day. These can be due to a wide range of reasons. The foreman or group leader may interrupt the operator to give him instructions or to clarify certain written information. Then the inspector may interrupt him to point out the reasons for some defective work that passed through the operator's work station. Interruptions frequently occur from planners, expediters, fellow workers, production men, time study men, dispatchers, and others.

Unavoidable delays are frequently a result of material irregularities. For example, the material may be in the wrong location or it may be running slightly too soft or too hard. Again, it may be too short or too long, or may have excessive stock on it, as in forgings when the dies begin to wash out, or on castings due to incomplete removal of risers. When material deviates substantially from standard specifications, it may be necessary to restudy the job and establish allowed time for the extra elements introduced by the irregular material, as the customary unavoidable delay allowance may prove inadequate.

Machine interference

When more than one facility is assigned to an operator, there are times during the working day when one facility or more must wait until the operator completes his work on one of the other facilities he is servicing. As more facilities are assigned to the operator, the "interference" time delay is increased. In practice, machine interference has been found to "occur predominantly from 10 to 30 percent of the total working time, with extremes of from 0 to 50 percent."[3] The amount of machine interference is a function of the number of facilities assigned, the randomness of required servicing time, the proportion of service time to running time, the length of running time and the mean length of service time.

Although there have been many expressions, tables, and charts developed to determine the magnitude of machine interference, the expresssion developed by Wright (*Mechanical Engineering*, Vol. LVIII) is relatively simple and has proved to be satisfactory when the number of machines assigned is six or more. When the facilities assigned are two, three, four, five or six, Wright recommends using empirical curves as illustrated in Figure 16–4. For six or more facilities Wright developed:

$$I = 50[\sqrt{[(1 + X - N)^2 + 2N]} - (1 + X - N)]$$

where

I = Interference expressed as a percentage of the mean attention time
X = Ratio of mean machine running time to mean machine attention time
N = Number of machine units assigned to one operator

FIGURE 16–4

Interference in percentage of attention time when number of facilities assigned to one operator is six or less

---

[3] H. B. Maynard, *Industrial Engineering Handbook* (New York: McGraw-Hill Book Co., 1956), pp. 3–78.

Wright's formula for interference was developed from the solution of a problem in a congestion of telephone lines made by Thornton C. Fry of the Bell Telephone Laboratories.[4] The conditions applying to Dr. Fry's work included:

1. A telephone call requiring the use of a given trunk line will be delayed in the event the trunk line is currently in use from a call on a different line. The second call will continue to be delayed until the first call is completed.
2. All telephone calls are of equal duration.
3. Calls are assigned individually to groups of channels and collectively at random.

It can be seen easily that assumptions 2 and 3 do not always apply in multiple machine activity. However, as the number of machines increases, the random nature of servicing becomes more pronounced. Wright found his equation applicable in four entirely different industries, where the number of machines assigned was greater than six.

For example, in the development of a standard for quilling production, an operator has been assigned 60 spindles. The mean running minutes per package (unit of output) determined by stopwatch study is 150 minutes. The standard mean attention time per package developed by time study is 3 minutes.

The computation of the machine interference expressed as a percentage of the mean operator attention time would be:

$$I = 50[\sqrt{[(1 + X - N)^2 + 2N]} - (1 + X - N)]$$

$$I = 50\left[\sqrt{\left(1 + \frac{150}{3.00} - 60\right)^2 + 120} - \left(1 + \frac{150}{3.00} - 60\right)\right]$$

$$I = 50[\sqrt{(1 + 50 - 60)^2 + 120} - (1 + 50 - 60)]$$

$$I = 1160 \text{ percent}$$

Thus in this example we would have:

Machine running time.............................. 150   min.
Attention time including personal, fatigue, and unavoid-
    able delay allowance............................ 3.00 min.
Interference time (11.6) (3.00)...................... 34.80 min.
Standard time for 60 packages....................... 187.80 min.
Standard time per package $\dfrac{187.80}{60}$ = 3.13 minutes.

The reader should recognize that the amount of interference that takes place is related to the performance of the operator. Thus the operator demonstrating a low level of effort will experience more machine interference than when the time spent in attending the stopped machine is reduced through higher effort. The analyst endeavors to determine the

---

[4] Thornton C. Fry, *Probability and Its Engineering Uses* (Princeton, N.J.: D. Van Nostrand Co., Inc., 1928).

normal interference time which, when added to (1) the machine running time required to produce one unit and (2) the normal time spent by the operator in servicing the stopped machine, will equal the cycle time. The cycle time divided into the running time of each machine multiplied by the number of machines assigned to the operator will give the average machine running hours per hour. Thus we have the expression:

$$O = \frac{NT_1}{C}$$

where

O = Machine running hours per hour
N = Number of machines assigned to the operator
T_1 = Running time (hours) to produce one piece
C = Cycle time to produce one piece

and

$$C = T_1 + T_2 + T_3$$

where

T_2 = Time (hours) spent by normal operator attending the stopped facility
T_3 = Time lost by normal operator working at normal pace because of interference

Using waiting line theory, analysts have developed tables where the interval between service times is exponential and where the service time is either constant or exponential. Table A3–14, Appendix 3, tabularizes these values for various "k" which is the ratio of service time to facility running time $k = \dfrac{T_2}{T_1}$.

With reference to the previous example

$$k = \frac{3.00}{150.00} = 0.02$$
$$N = 60$$

From Table A3–14, Appendix 3, with exponential service time and $k = 0.02$ and $N = 60$, we have a waiting time (interference delay) of 16.8 percent of the cycle time. Denoting the interference time by T_3 we have $T_3 = 0.168C$ where C is the cycle time to produce one unit per spindle. Then:

$$150 + 3.00 + 0.168C = C$$
$$0.832C = 153$$
$$C = 184 \text{ minutes}$$

and

$$T_3 = 0.168C = 30.9 \text{ minutes}$$

The reader can note the close agreement between the interference time computed by Wright's equation and that developed by the queueing model. However, as N (the number of machines assigned) becomes small, there is a greater proportion difference between the two techniques.

Avoidable delays

It is not customary to provide any allowance for avoidable delays which include visits with other operators for social reasons, uncalled-for work stoppages, and idleness other than rest to overcome fatigue. Of course, these delays may be taken by the operator at the expense of his output, but no allowance is provided for these cessations of work in the development of the standard.

Extra allowances

In typical metal trade and related operations, the percentage allowance for personal, unavoidable, and fatigue delays usually approximates 15 percent. However, in certain cases, it may be necessary to provide an extra allowance to arrive at a fair standard. Thus, due to a substandard lot of raw material, it may be necessary to provide an extra allowance to take care of an unduly high generation of rejects caused by the poor material. Again, an operation may develop where, because of breakage of a jib crane, the operator is obliged to place a 50-pound casting in the chuck of his machine. Therefore, an extra allowance must be provided to take care of the additional fatigue brought on by the manual handling of the work.

Whenever practical, allowed time should be established for the additional work of any operation by breaking it down into elements and then including these times in the specific operation. If this is not practical, then an extra allowance must be provided.

A form of extra allowance frequently used, especially in the steel industry, is a percentage added to a portion or all of the cycle time when the operator must observe the process to maintain efficient progress of the operation. This allowance is frequently referred to as "attention time" allowance, and is applied on such operations as:

1. The inspector in the electrolytic tinning operation while observing the tin plate coming off the line.
2. The first helper in an open hearth while observing the condition of the performance or molten bath.
3. The first helper in an open hearth while reporting to or receiving instructions from the melter.

4. The craneman in a shipping department while receiving directions or signals from the crane hooker.
5. The hi-mill roller in the seamless hot mill while required, during the rolling process, to watch for any change in the length of pipe to signal the operator to return the pipe if too short and adjust the rolls as required.[5]

The amount of allowance added to the actual required time for required attention by the United States Steel Company is 35 percent. Thus an operator can earn 35 percent premium on a process paced operation if he is able to keep the process efficiently running during the entire working day.

Using an extra allowance on operations where a large portion of the cycle time is based on the machine or process cycle is quite popular in plants where incentive wage payment is practiced. The allowance is added so the operator may make earnings equivalent to those operators assigned to operations not machine-paced. Typical practice is to allow 30 percent extra allowance on that portion of the cycle time machine-controlled. This extra allowance provides the incentive for the operator to keep his facility productively employed during the entire working period.

Without this extra allowance, the operator would find it impossible to make the same earnings as his fellow employees. For example, if the machine-controlled portion of a cycle is two minutes and the operator controlled portion is one normal minute, the operator would have to work at a pace 25 percent above normal in order to realize a 7 percent increase in productivity.

$$1.07 = \frac{\dfrac{3 \text{ minutes (normal cycle time)}}{\dfrac{1 \text{ minute (normal effort time)}}{1.25 \text{ (operator performance during effort time)}}}}{\pm 2 \text{ minutes (machine-controlled time)}}$$

$1.07 - 1.00 = 0.07$ increase in productivity when operator is working at 25 percent above normal during the effort part of the cycle

Now, if an extra allowance of 25 percent were added to the machine-controlled portion of the cycle, the operator would be able to achieve 25 percent incentive earnings if he worked at a pace 25 percent above normal and did not utilize more allowance than what was provided for personal delays, unavoidable delays, and fatigue.

Clean work station and oil machine

The time required to clean and lubricate the operator's machine may be classified as an unavoidable delay. However, this time, when per-

---

[5] From United States Steel Time Study Manual.

TABLE 16–4

Clean machine allowance chart

	Percent per machine		
Item	large	medium	small
1. Clean machine when lubricant is used............	1	¾	½
2. Clean machine when lubricant is not used........	¾	½	¼
3. Clean and put away large amount of tools or equipment................................	½	½	½
4. Clean and put away small amounts of tools or equipment................................	¼	¼	¼
5. Shut machine down for cleaning (this percentage for machines equipped with chip pans, which are stopped at intervals to permit sweeper to clean away large chips).................	1	¾	½

Machine classification

Large machine	*Medium machine*
1. Turret lathe (20″ ck or over)	1. Turret lathe (10″ to 20″ ck)
2. Boring mill (60″ and over)	2. Boring mill (under 60″)
3. Punch press (100T and over)	3. Punch press (40T to 100T)
4. Planer (over 48″)	

Oil machine allowance chart

	Percent per machine		
Item	large	medium	small
1. Machine oiled or greased by hand..............	1½	1	½
2. Machine oiled automatically...................	½	½	½

formed by the operator, is usually included as a total cycle time allowance. The type and size of equipment, and the material being fabricated will have considerable effect on the time required to clean the work station and lubricate the equipment. When these elements are included as part of the responsibilities of the operator, applicable allowance must be provided. One concern has established the accompanying table of allowances to cover these items.

Frequently, the elements of "clean work station" and "oil machine" are handled by giving the operator 10 or 15 minutes at the end of the day in which to perform this work. When this is done, the standards established of course would not include any allowance for cleaning and oiling the machine.

Power feed machine time allowance

The allowance required for power feed elements frequently will differ from that required for effort elements. Two factors are usually considered in applying allowances for power feed: these are power variance and tool maintenance.

Allowances are made for variance in power for reduced speeds brought on by belt slippage and for shutdowns because of minor repairs. In case a major repair to the facility is needed, then an extra allowance would of necessity be provided. This extra allowance would not be applied within the standard but would be an independent standard covering the machine repair.

Tool maintenance allowance provides time for the operator to maintain his tools after the original setup. In the setup time the operator is expected to provide first-class tools properly ground. Generally, little tool maintenance takes place during the course of the average production run. Of course, in long runs, tools will have to be periodically sharpened. The percentage allowance for tool maintenance will vary directly with the number of perishable tools in the setup. For example, one manufacturer's tool maintenance allowance table is as follows:

Allowance for tool maintenance

		Percent
1.	One or more tools ground in tool crib	1
2.	One tool sharpened by operator	3
3.	Two or more tools cutting at one time sharpened by the operator	6

Application of allowances

The fundamental purpose of allowances is to add enough time to the normal production time to enable the average worker to meet the standard when performing at a normal pace. It is customary to express the allowance as a multiplier so the normal time, consisting of productive work elements, can be adjusted readily to the time allowed. Thus, if a 15 percent allowance were to be provided on a given operation, the multiplier would be 1.15.

Care must be exercised when including the allowance with the time study standard. It must be remembered that allowance is based on a percentage of the daily production time and not on the overall workday. For example, if a study revealed that in an eight-hour working day 50 minutes of delay time are to be allowed during 400 minutes of normal production time, then the percentage allowance applicable would be 50/400 or 12.5 percent.

Allowance is based on the normal production time, since it is this value that the percentage will be applied to on subsequent studies.

Typical allowance values

In an industrial survey comprising 42 different plants, the smallest average total allowance found to be in use was 10 percent. This was used

TABLE 16–5

Time study allowances for standard operations

Symbol	Facility or operation	Method	Total applied to effort time	Total applied to machine time	Personal	Clean work station	Oil machine	Power variance or shutdown	Tool maintenance	Unavoidable delays and fatigue
21	Anneal	Oven	10	...	5	½	...	...	...	4½
22	Blacksmith	Drop forge	21	...	7	1	...	...	...	13
23	Braze	Electric	14	...	5	½	½	½	...	8
24	Drill, sensitive, single, spindle	Hand feed	14	...	5	½	½	½	2	5½
25	Drill, sensitive, single, sensitive	Power feed	14	12	5	½	½	m-2 / e-1½	m-4 / e-2	e-5½
26	Engrave	Pantograph	18	...	5	½	½	½	7½	4
27	English Lathe	Over 36″	13	15	5	2	1	m-2	m-5	e-5
28	Mold	Machine (cores used)	18	...	6	2	...	...	...	10
29	Punch press	Up to 100 tons	13	...	5	½	1	½	...	6
30	Saw, circular	Hand feed	14	...	5	½	½	½	...	7½

in a plant producing household electrical appliances. The greatest average allowance found to be in effect was 35 percent being used in two different steel plants. The average allowance of all plants from which replies were received was 17.7 percent.

Typical allowances established in a certain plant for standard operations appear in Table 16–5. These values may or may not apply in other plants.

Summary

In establishing time study allowance values, the same care that prevails in taking individual studies should be exercised throughout. It would be folly to divide a job carefully into elements, precisely measure the duration of each element in one hundredths of a minute, accurately evaluate the performance of the operator, and then arbitrarily assign an allowance picked at random. Practices of this nature will lead to inaccurate standards. If the allowances are too high, obviously manufacturing costs will be unduly inflated, and if the allowances are too low, tight standards will result, which will cause poor labor relations and eventual failure of the system.

TEXT QUESTIONS

1. Compare the interference delay allowance using the queueing model and Wright's equation when $N = 20$, mean facility running time is 120 minutes and attention time is 3 minutes.
2. What three broad areas are allowances intended to cover?
3. To what three categories of the time study are allowances provided? Give several examples of each.
4. What are the two methods used in developing allowance standard data? Briefly explain the application of each technique.
5. Give several examples of personal delays. What percentage allowance seems adequate for personal delays under typical shop conditions?
6. What are some of the major factors that affect fatigue?
7. Under what groups have the tests of fatigue been classified?
8. What operator interruptions would be covered by the unavoidable delay allowance?
9. What percentage allowance is usually provided for avoidable delays?
10. When are "extra allowances" provided?
11. What fatigue allowance should be given to a job if it developed that it took 1.542 minutes to perform the operation at the end of continuous work and but 1.480 minutes at the beginning of continuous work?
12. Why are allowances based on a percentage of the productive time?
13. What is meant by "occupational physiology"?

14. Define "attention time." Why is it necessary to apply an allowance to attention time?

15. Based upon the International Labour Office's tabulation, what would be the allowance factor on a work element involving a 42-pound pulling force when there was inadequate light and exacting work was required?

16. Explain what relation, if any, there is between financial incentives and the effect of fatigue.

17. What are the advantages of having operators oil and clean their own machines?

GENERAL QUESTIONS

1. Do you feel that the operation or the operator determines the extent to which personal delay time is utilized? Why?

2. Why is fatigue allowance frequently applied only to the effort areas of the work cycle?

3. Should fatigue allowances vary with the different shifts for a given class of work? Why?

4. What are the objections to determining fatigue allowances by measuring the decline of production not attributed to method changes or personal or unavoidable delays?

5. Give several reasons for not applying an "extra" allowance to operations when the major part of the cycle is machine controlled and the internal time is small compared to the cycle time.

6. With the extension of automation and the tendency of many companies to go to the three-day week, do you feel that personal allowances should be increased? Why?

CHAPTER 17

The standard time

The standard time for a given operation is the time required for an average operator, fully qualified and trained and working at a normal pace, to perform the operation. It is determined by summarizing the allowed time for all of the individual elements comprising the time study.

Elemental allowed times are determined by multiplying the mean elapsed elemental time by a conversion factor. Thus, we have the expression:

$$T_a = (M_t)(C)$$

where:

T_a = The allowed elemental time
M_t = Mean elapsed elemental time
C = Conversion factor found by multiplying performance rating factor by one plus the applicable allowance

For example, if the mean elemental time of element number one of a given time study was 0.14 minute and the performance factor was 0.90 and an allowance of 18 percent was applicable, the allowed elemental time would be:

$$T_a = (0.14)(0.90)(1.18) = (0.14)(1.06) = 0.148$$

Allowed elemental times are rounded off to three places to the right of the decimal point. Thus, in the preceding example 0.1483 minute is recorded as 0.148 minute. If the result was 0.1485 minute, then the recording would be 0.149 minute allowed time.

377

Expressing the standard time

The sum of the elemental allowed times will give the standard in minutes per piece or hours per piece, depending on whether a decimal minute or decimal hour watch was in use. The majority of industrial operations have relatively short cycles (less than five minutes); consequently, it is usually more convenient to express standards in terms of hours per hundred pieces. For example, the standard on a press operation might be 0.085 hour per hundred pieces. This is a more satisfactory method of expressing the standard than 0.00085 hour per piece or 0.051 minute per piece. Thus, if the operator produced 10,000 pieces during the working day, he would have earned 8.5 hours of production, and would have performed at an efficiency of 106 percent. This is expressed as:

$$E = \left(\frac{He}{Hc}\right)(100)$$

where:

E = Percent efficiency
He = Standard hours earned
Hc = Clock hours on the job

In another instance, the standard time may have resulted in 11.46 minutes per piece. This would be converted into decimal hours per hundred pieces as follows:

$$S_h = 1.667 S_m$$

where:

S_h = Standard expressed in hours per hundred pieces
S_m = Standard expressed in minutes per piece
1.667 = Constant developed by converting minutes to decimal hours and multiplying by 100

thus:

$$S_h = (1.667)(11.46)$$
$$= 19.104 \text{ hrs.}/C$$

If an operator produced 53 pieces in a given working day, the standard hours produced would be:

$$H_e = (0.01)(P_a)(S_h)$$

where:

H_e = Standard hours earned
P_a = Actual production in pieces
S_h = Standard expressed in hours per hundred

or in this example:

$$H_e = (0.53)(19.104) = 10.125 \text{ hours}$$

Once the allowed time has been computed, the standard is released to the operator in the form of an operation card. The card can be run off

FIGURE 17–1

Typical production operation card

PRODUCTION OPERATION CARD

DESCRIPTION_____Shower head face_____DWG. NO.____JB-1102_____PART NO. J-1102-1____
MADE FROM_____2 1/2" diam. 70-30 extruded brass rod

Routing 9-11-12--14-12-18 _____ DATE___9-15

OP. NO.	OPERATION	DEPT.	MACHINE AND SPECIAL TOOLS	SET-UP MINUTES	EACH PC. MINUTES
1	Saw slug	9	J. & L. Air Saw	15 min	.077
2	Forge	11	150 Ton Maxi F-1102	70 min	.234
3	Blank	12	Bliss 72 F-1103	30 min	.061
4	Pickle	14	HCL. Tank	5 min	.007
5	Pierce 6 holes	12	Bliss 74 F-1104	30 min	.075
6	Rough ream and chamfer	12	Delta 17" D.P. F-1105	15 min	.334
7	Drill 13/64" holes	12	Avey D.P. F-1106	15 min	.152
8	Machine stem and face	12	#3 W.&S.	45 min	.648
9	Broach 6 holes	12	Bliss 74 1/2	30 min	.167
10	Inspect	18	F-1109, F-1110, F-1112	Daywork	

on a ditto machine, or some other duplicating process can be used. It will serve as the basis for routing, scheduling, instruction, payroll, operator performance, cost, budgeting, and other necessary controls for the effective operation of a business. Figure 17–1 illustrates a typical production operation card.

Temporary standards

It is common knowledge that time is required to become proficient in any operation that is new or somewhat different.

Frequently, the time study man will be required to establish a standard on an operation that is relatively new and on which there is insufficient volume for the operator to reach his top efficiency. If the analyst bases his grading of the operator upon the usual conception of output, the resulting standard will seem unduly tight, and the operator will in all probability be unable to make any incentive earnings. On the other hand, if he takes into consideration the fact that the job is new and that the volume is low, and establishes a liberal standard, he may find himself in trouble in the event of an increase in the size of the order, or if a new order for the same part is received.

Perhaps, the most satisfactory method of handling situations like this is through the issuance of temporary standards. By doing this the time study analyst will establish the standard giving consideration to the difficulty of the work assignment and the number of pieces to be produced. Then by using a learning curve for the type of work being studied and existing standard data, he can arrive at an equitable standard for the work at hand. The resulting standard will be considerably more liberal than if the job were being produced on a mass-production basis. The standard, when released to the production floor, will be clearly marked as a "temporary" standard and will show the maximum quantity for which it applies. It is good practice to issue temporary standards on vouchers of a different color than that of permanent standard vouchers, so as to indicate clearly to all affected parties that the rate is temporary and is subject to restudy in the event of additional orders or increase in the volume of the present order.

The analyst must be careful as to the number of temporary standards released, since too many such standards can result in a lowering of the approved conception of normal. Also, the operators may strongly object to the changing of temporary standards to permanent standards, since the tighter permanent standard appears to them as a rate or wage cutting procedure. Only new work that is definitely foreign to the operator and that involves limited quantities of production should be considered as suitable for issuance of temporary standards. When temporary standards are released, they should be in effect for the duration of the contract or for 60 days, whichever period is shorter. Upon their expiration, they should be replaced with permanent standards. Several union contracts specifically state that temporary standards lasting longer than 60 days must become permanent.

Setup standards

Those elements of work commonly included in setup standards involve all events that take place from the time the previous job was completed to the starting of the first piece of the present job. It is also customary to include in the setup standard, the "tear-down" or "put-away" elements: these include all items of work involved from the completion of the last piece to the setting up of the next job. Typical elements appearing in the setup standard would be:

1. Punching in on job
2. Getting tools from tool crib
3. Getting drawings from dispatcher
4. Setting up the machine
5. Punching out on the job
6. Removing tools from machine
7. Returning tools to crib

In establishing setup times, the analyst uses the identical procedure followed in establishing standards for production. First, he should be assured that the best setup methods are in effect and that a standardized procedure has been adopted. Then the work is carefully broken down into elements, accurately timed, performance rated, and subjected to the appropriate allowance. The importance of valid setup times cannot be overemphasized, especially in the case of job shops where setup time represents a high proportion of the overall time.

The analyst must be especially alert when timing setup elements because he will not have the opportunity to get a series of elemental values for determining the mean times. Also, he will not be able to observe the operator perform the elements in advance and, consequently, will be obliged to break the setup down into elements while the study is taking place. Of course, setup elements for the most part are long in duration, and the analyst will find that he has a reasonable amount of time to break the job down, record the time, and evaluate the performance as the operator proceeds from one work element to the next.

There are two ways of handling setup times: first they can be distributed over a specific manufacturing quantity such as 1,000 pieces or 10,000 pieces. This method is satisfactory only when the magnitude of the production order is standard. For example, industries that ship from stock and reorder on a basis of minimum-maximum inventories are able to control their production orders so as to conform to economical lot sizes. In cases like this, the setup time can equitably be prorated over the lot size. Suppose the economical lot size of a given item was 1,000 pieces and reordering was always done on the basis of 1,000 units. In the event the standard setup time in a given operation was 1.50 hours, then the allowed operation time could be increased by 0.15 hour per 100 pieces in order to take care of the makeready and put-away elements.

This method would not be at all practical, if the size of the order were not controlled. In a plant that requisitions on a job-order basis, that is, releases production orders specifying quantities in accordance with customer requirements, it would be impossible to standardize on the size of the work orders issued to the factory. Thus, this week an order may be issued for 100 pieces and next month an order for 5,000 units of the same part. In the example cited above, the operator would be allowed but 0.15 hour to set up his machine for the 100-unit order, which would be inadequate. On an order for 5,000 pieces, he would be given 7.50 hours, which would be considerably too much time.

It is more practical to establish setup standards as separate allowed times. Then, regardless of the quantity of parts to be produced, a fair standard prevails. In some concerns, the setup is performed by a person other than the operator to do the job. The advantages of having separate setup men are quite obvious. Lower skilled men can be utilized as operators when they do not have to set up their own facilities. Setups are more readily standardized and methods changes can be more easily introduced when the responsibility for setup rests with but one individual. Also, if sufficient facilities are available, continuous production performance can be achieved by having the next work assignment set up while the operator is working on his present job.

Partial setups

Frequently, it will not be necessary to set up completely a facility to perform a given operation, because some of the tools of the previous operation are required in the job that is being set up. For example, in hand screw machine or turret lathe setups, careful scheduling of similar work to the same machine will allow partial setups from one job to the next. Instead of having to change six tools in the hex turret, it may be necessary to change only two or three.

Since the sequence of work that is scheduled to a given machine seldom remains the same, it is difficult to establish partial setup times to cover all the possible variations. The standard setup for a given No. 4 Warner & Swasey turret lathe might be 0.80 hour. However, if this setup is performed after job X, it may take only 0.45 hour, and if it is performed after job Y, it would require 0.57 hour, while following job Z, 0.70 hour would be necessitated, and so on. The possible variations in partial setup time are so broad that the only practical way to establish their values is on the basis of standard data (see Chapter 18) for each job in question.

In plants where setup times are relatively short (less than one hour) and where production runs are reasonably long, it is common practice to allow the operator the full setup time for each job he performs. This is advantageous for several reasons: first, the operators will be considerably more satisfied because of higher earnings, and they will tend to plan their work to the best possible advantage. This will result in more production per unit of time and lower total costs. Also, considerable time and paper work is saved by avoiding the determination of a standard for the partial setup operations and its application in all pertinent cases. In fact, this saving tends to approach the extra amount paid to the operator resulting from the difference in time required to make the complete setup and the partial setup.

Maintenance of standard times

Considerable emphasis has been given to the necessity of establishing time standards that are fair. This means both fair to the worker and fair to the management. Once fair standards have been introduced, it is equally important that they be maintained.

The standard time is directly dependent upon the method used during the course of the time study. Method, in the broad sense, refers not only to the tools and facilities being used, but also to such details as operator motion pattern, work station layout, material conditions, and working conditions. Since method controls the time standard, it is essential, if equitable standards are to be maintained, that method changes and alterations be controlled. If method changes are not controlled, it will only be a short time until inequities develop in standards established and much of the work spent on development of consistent time standards will be undone.

Just as the financial records of a company are periodically subject to audit, so should all established time standards be checked at regular intervals to see if they are in line according to the method being used. The audit of time standards principally involves the investigation of the method currently being used by the operator. Frequently, minor changes will have been made by the operator, the foreman, or even the methods department, and no record of this change will have been given to the time study analyst. It is not uncommon for workers to conceal method changes for which they are responsible, so that they can increase their earnings or diminish their effort while achieving the same production. Of course, changes in method may develop which will increase the amount of time required to perform the task. These changes may be initiated by the foreman or inspector and may be of insufficient consequence, in his opinion, to adjust the standard.

As has been pointed out throughout this text, it is important that the operation being time-studied be analyzed for possible method improvements prior to the establishment of the standard. Operation analysis, work simplification, motion study, and standardization of the method and conditions always precede work measurement. A standard does not get out of line if the method that was time-studied is maintained by the operator. If methods study has developed the ideal method, and if this method is standardized and followed by the operator, then there is less need for maintenance of time standards.

Frequently, however, method changes will be introduced—both favorable and unfavorable. If these changes are extensive, they will be brought to the attention of management. Tight standards will be brought to management's attention by the operator. Standards that become very loose will be brought to management's attention through the payroll department where excessive earnings on the part of a given workman will be reported. However, it is the minor accruing method changes that frequently take place unnoticed and weaken the entire standard structure. In order to maintain standards properly, the time study department should periodically verify the method being used with the method that was studied when the standard was taken. This can readily be done by referring to the original time study where a complete description of the method employed was recorded. If this investigation reveals that the method has been changed adversely, then the reasons for the change should be investigated so that the better method can be employed. If the method has been improved, then the investigation should determine who was responsible for the innovation. If the operator developed the improvement, he should be justly rewarded through a "suggestion plan" or other means. Regardless of where the methods change came from, those elements affected should be restudied and the current standard introduced.

So as to first verify standards that may be out of line, the time study department will enlist the cooperation of the foreman. The foreman, being close to the operators coming under his jurisdiction, will at an early stage be aware of standards that may be either loose or tight. He will be able to advise the time study analyst as to the sequence in the audit of existing standards.

The audit frequency should be determined at the time the standard is developed. This is based on an estimate of the number of hours of application of the standard in one year. For example, one large company uses the following data to determine the frequency of the audit of methods and standards:[1]

Hours of application per standard per year	*Frequency of audit*
0–10	Once per 3 years
10–50	Once per 2 years
50–600	Once per year
Over 600	Twice per year

The auditing of methods and standards, when properly done, takes time and, consequently, is expensive. However, it is important that this maintenance is carried out to help assure the success of the program. The

---

[1] By H. B. Brandt, Associate Director, Industrial Engineering Division, Procter & Gamble Company.

audit should be carried out by a representative of the industrial engineering staff. Only completely qualified analysts should be used for auditing work. The auditor will observe the operation as performed to determine the correctness of the description, sequences, frequencies, conditions, and standard time allowances. It is usually satisfactory to check the accuracy of the standard time by measuring several cycles of the overall time, performance rating the data, and adding an appropriate allowance.

Conclusion

It is common practice to issue standards for setup operations independent of "piece" standards and to specify the allowed time in decimal hours or decimal minutes. Piece standards are expressed in hours per hundred pieces for ease in payroll computation, scheduling, and control. On extremely short-cycle operations, such as punch press work, diecasting, or forging, it may be more desirable to express standards in terms of hours per thousand pieces, since during the course of an eight-hour shift, several thousand pieces can be produced.

Work should be scheduled when feasible to take advantage of partial setups in order to improve delivery dates, decrease total cost, and allow greater remuneration for the operator. Where short setup times prevail and where an extensive variety of small-volume orders are handled daily, no attempt should be made to evaluate partial setup times, but credit for full setup should be given the operators. Where setup times are relatively long, such as setting up a six-spindle automatic screw machine, and where production runs are substantial, then consideration should be given for evaluation of partial setup times. Credit for this time should be given to the operator rather than credit for the complete setup time.

Time standards must be maintained in order to assure a satisfactory rate structure. This calls for a continuing analysis of methods. All standards should be periodically checked to verify that methods being employed are identical with those that were in use at the time the standard was established.

TEXT QUESTIONS

1. Define the term "standard time."
2. How is the conversion factor determined?
3. Why is it usually more convenient to express standards in terms of time per hundred pieces than time per piece?
4. For what reason are temporary standards established?
5. Express the standard of 5.761 minutes in terms of hours per hundred pieces. What would be the operator efficiency if 92 pieces were completed during a working day? What would be his efficiency if he set up

his machine (standard for setup = 0.45 hours) and produced 80 pieces during the eight-hour workday?

6. What elements of work are included in the setup standard?

7. What is the preferred method of handling setup time standards?

8. How is the operator compensated on partial setups on hand screw machines?

9. Determine the conversion factor and the allowed time for a job whose average time was 5.24 minutes and carried a performance factor of 1.15 and an allowance of 12 percent.

10. Explain why it is necessary that time standards be properly maintained.

11. Explain how you would use learning curves in the establishment of temporary standards.

GENERAL QUESTIONS

1. For what reasons might it be advantageous to express allowed times in minutes per piece?

2. How can excessive use of temporary standards cause poor labor relations?

3. How does a company effectively maintain standards and avoid the reputation of being a "rate-cutter"?

4. If an audit of a standard revealed that the standard as originally established was 20 percent loose, explain in detail the methodology to be followed to rectify the rate.

CHAPTER 18

Standard data

Standard time data for the most part are elemental time standards taken from time studies that have been proved to be satisfactory. These elemental standards are classified and filed so that they can readily be abstracted when needed. Just as the housewife refers to her cookbook to determine how many minutes to cream butter and sugar, how long to beat the mixture, and thus how much time is required to bake the cake, so can the analyst refer to standard data and determine how long it should take the normal operator to pick up a small casting and place it in a jig, close the jig and lock the part with a quick-acting clamp, advance the spindle of the drill press, and perform the remainder of the elements required to produce the part.

The application of standard time data is fundamentally an extension of the same kind of process as that used to arrive at allowed times through the medium of stopwatch time study. The principle of standard data application certainly is not new; many years ago Frederick W. Taylor proposed that each established elemental time be properly indexed so that it could easily be found and used in the establishment of time standards for future work. When we speak of standard data today, we refer to all the tabulated elemental standards, curves, alignment charts, and tables that are compiled to allow the measurement of a specific job without the necessity of a timing device, such as the stopwatch.

Work standards calculated from standard data will be relatively consistent in that the tabulated elements comprising the data are a result of many proven stopwatch time studies. Since the values are tabulated and it is only necessary to accumulate the required elements in establishing a standard, the various time study men within a given company will arrive at identical standards of performance for a given method. There-fore, consistency is assured for standards established by the different analysts within a plant as well as for the various standards computed by a given time study observer.

Standards on new work can usually be computed more rapidly through standard data than by means of stopwatch time study. The rapidity with which standards are established by means of standard data allows the establishment of standards on indirect labor operations which usually is impractical if done by stopwatch methods. Typically one work measurement analyst will establish 5 rates per day using stopwatch methods, while he will establish 25 rates a day with the standard data

TABLE 18–1

Operation	Number of time studies taken for development of standard data	Number of standards set in one year from standard data developed	Percent of standards set that would be covered by stopwatch studies
Coremaking.....................	60	7,500	0.8
Snag grinding..................	40	656	6.1
Visual inspection...............	53	422	12.6
Turret lathe operation...........	100	600	16.7

SOURCE: Phil Carroll, Jr., "Notes on Standard Elemental Data," *Modern Machine Shop*, April, 1950, p. 176.

technique. The use of standard data permits establishment of time stan-dards over a wide range of work. Table 18–1 illustrates the coverage that is possible when standard data elements are determined.

Development of standard time data

In the development of standard time data, it is necessary to distin-guish constant elements from variable elements. A constant element is one for which the allowed time will remain approximately the same for any part within a specific range. A variable element is one for which the allowed time will vary within a specified range of work. Thus, the ele-ment "start machine" would be a constant and the element "drill ⅜-inch diameter hole" would vary with the depth of the hole and the feed and speed of the drill press.

As standard data is developed, it should be indexed and filed. Setup elements should be kept separate from those elements incorporated in the each piece time, and constant elements should of course be kept separate from the variable elements. Typical standard data would be tabulated as follows:

1. Machine or operation
   A. Setup
      1. Constants
      2. Variables
   B. Each piece
      1. Constants
      2. Variables

Standard data are compiled from the different elements that have occurred on the time studies that have been taken on a given process over a period of time. Only those studies that have proven to be valid through use are employed. The analyst should be careful in the tabulation of standard data to define clearly end points. Otherwise, there may be an overlapping of time in the recorded data. For example, in the element "out stock to stop" done on a bar feed No. 3 Warner & Swasey turret lathe, the element could include reaching for the feed lever, grasping the lever, feeding of the bar stock through the collet to a stock stop located in the hex turret, closing the collet, and reaching for the turret handle. Then, again, this element may involve only the feeding of bar stock through the collet to a stock stop. Since standard data elements are compiled from a great number of studies taken by different time study men, care must be exercised in defining limits or end points of each element. Figure 18–1 illustrates a form used to summarize data taken from an individual time study for the purpose of developing standard data on die-casting machines.

In order to fill a specific need in a standard data tabulation, the analyst may resort to work measurement of the particular element in question. This is handled quite accurately by using the "fast" watch (see Chapter 13) which records elapsed times in 0.001 of a minute. In this type of analysis, the snapback method is used in recording the elapsed elemental time, as usually we are interested in determining allowed time for only a few of the elements comprising the study. Upon completion of the observations, the elemental elapsed times are summarized and the mean determined, as in the case of a typical time study. The average values are then performance rated and an allowance is added so as to arrive at fair allowed times.

Sometimes, because of the brevity of individual elements, it is impossible to measure their duration separately. It is possible to determine their individual values by timing groups collectively and using simultaneous equations to solve for the individual elements.

For example, element a might be "pick up small casting," element

FIGURE 18–1

DIE-CASTING MACHINE

MACH. NO.
PART NO._____& TYPE _____OPERATOR_____ DATE_____
              NO. OF PARTS   METHOD OF PLACING   TOTAL WT. OF FLSH,
OF_____IN TOTE PAN_____ PARTS IN TOTE PAN_____ PARTS, GATE & SPRUE____
        NO. OF PARTS   LIQUID METAL_____
_____PER SHOT_____ PLASTIC METAL _____CHILL____SKIM____DRAIN____
CAPACITY IN LBS.   DESCRIBE
HOLDING POT_____ GREASING_____

DESCRIBE
LOOSENING OF PART_____

DESCRIBE
LOCATION_____

ELEMENTS	TIME	END POINTS
Get metal in holding pot	_____	All waiting time while metal is being poured in pot
Chill metal	_____	From time operator starts adding cold metal to liquid metal pot until operator stops adding cold metal to liquid metal in pot.
Skim metal	_____	From time operator starts skimming until all scum has been removed.
Get ladleful of metal	_____	From time ladle starts to dip down into metal until ladleful of metal reaches edge of mach. or until ladle starts to tip for draining.
Drain metal	_____	From time ladle starts to tip for draining until ladleful reaches edge of machine.
Pour ladle of metal in machine	_____	From time ladleful of metal reaches edge of mach. until foot starts to trip press.
Trip press	_____	From time foot starts moving toward pedal until press starts downward.
Press time	_____	Complete turnover of press.
Hold plunger down	_____	From time plunger stops downward motion until plunger starts moving upward.
Press button and raise slug	_____	From time plunger stops moving until slug is raised out of cavity.
Remove slug--drop slug--lift	_____	From time slug is raised out of cavity until slug is pushed into tote pan or pot.
Trip pedal to open dies	_____	From time foot starts moving to pedal until dies start to open.
Wait for dies to open	_____	From time dies start to open until die stops moving.
Remove part from die	_____	From time die stops moving until part is free of die cavity.
Place part in tote pan	_____	From time part is free of die cavity until part is placed in tote pan.

b might be "place in leaf jig," *c* might be "close cover of jig," *d* would be "position jig," *e* "advance spindle," and so on. These elements could be timed in groups as follows:

$$a + b + c \text{ equals Element No. 1 equals 0.070 min.} = A \quad (1)$$
$$b + c + d \text{ equals Element No. 3 equals 0.067 min.} = B \quad (2)$$
$$c + d + e \text{ equals Element No. 5 equals 0.073 min.} = C \quad (3)$$
$$d + e + a \text{ equals Element No. 2 equals 0.061 min.} = D \quad (4)$$
$$e + a + b \text{ equals Element No. 4 equals 0.068 min.} = E \quad (5)$$

By adding these five equations:

$$3a + 3b + 3c + 3d + 3e = A + B + C + D + E$$

Then let

$$A + B + C + D + E = T$$
$$3a + 3b + 3c + 3d + 3e = T = 0.339 \text{ min.}$$

and

$$a + b + c + d + e = \frac{0.339}{3} = 0.113 \text{ min.}$$

therefore:

$$A + d + e = 0.113 \text{ min.}$$

and then:

$$d + e = 0.113 \text{ min.} - 0.07 \text{ min.} = 0.043 \text{ min.}$$

since

$$c + d + e = 0.073 \text{ min.}$$
$$c = 0.073 \text{ min.} - 0.043 = 0.03 \text{ min.}$$

Likewise:

$$d + e + a = 0.061$$

and

$$a = 0.061 - 0.043 = 0.018 \text{ min.}$$

Substituting in equation (1)

$$b = 0.070 - (0.03 + 0.018) = 0.022$$

Substituting in equation (2)

$$d = 0.067 - (0.022 + 0.03) = 0.015 \text{ min.}$$

Substituting in equation (3)

$$e = 0.073 - (0.015 + 0.03) = 0.028 \text{ min.}$$

In the determination of standard data elements by using simultaneous equations, extreme care must be exercised to be consistent when reading the watch at the terminal points of the established elements. Inconsistency in establishing terminal points will result in erroneous standard data elements.

Calculation of cutting times

Through knowledge of feeds and speeds for different types of material, it is a relatively easy matter for the analyst to calculate and tabulate the cutting times for different machining operations. Table 18–2 tabularizes recommended speeds and feeds for high-speed drills used on various kinds of material. This type of information is available in the various technical handbooks and can readily be obtained from the cutting tool manufacturers.

TABLE 18–2

A. Recommended drilling speeds for various materials with high-speed steel drills

Material	Recommended speed surface feet per minute
Aluminum and its alloys	200–300
Bakelite	100–150
Brass and bronze, soft	200–300
Bronze, high tensile	70–100
Cast iron, soft	100–150
Cast iron, hard	70–100
Magnesium and its alloys	250–400
Malleable iron	80–90
Nickel and monel metal	40–60
Slate, marble, and stone	15–25
Steel, forgings	50–60
Steel, manganese (15% Mn)	15–25
Steel, soft	80–110
Steel, stainless	30–40
Steel, tool	50–60
Wrought iron	50–60
Wood	300–400

NOTE: Carbon steel drills should be run at speeds approximately 40 to 50 percent of those recommended for high-speed steel.

B. Recommended feeds for various diameter drills

Diameter of drill—inches	Feed inches per revolution
Under ⅛	.001 to .002
⅛ to ¼	.002 to .004
¼ to ½	.004 to .007
½ to 1	.007 to .015
1 in. and over	.015 to .025

NOTE: It is best to start with a moderate speed and feed, increasing either one, or both, after observing the action and condition of the drill.
SOURCE: National Twist Drill & Tool Co.

Drill press work

A drill, according to the *Tool Engineers Handbook,* is "a fluted end-cutting tool used to originate or enlarge a hole in solid material." In drilling operations on a flat surface, the axis of drill is at 90° to the surface being drilled. When a hole is drilled completely through a part, the lead of the drill must be added to the length of the hole in order to determine the entire distance the drill must travel to make the hole. When a blind hole is drilled, the analyst does not add the lead of the drill

FIGURE 18–2

Distance *L* indicates distance drill must travel when drilling through (illustration at left) and when drilling blind holes (illustration at right) (lead of drill is shown by distance 1)

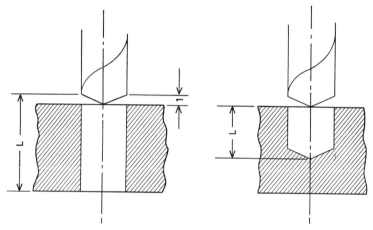

to the hole depth, because the distance from the surface being drilled to the farthest penetration of the drill is the distance that the drill must travel in order to make the required depth of hole (see Figure 18–2).

Since the commercial standard for the included angle of drill points is 118°, the lead of the drill may readily be found through the expression:

$$l = \frac{r}{\tan A}$$

where

l = Lead of drill
r = Radius of drill
$\tan A$ = Tangent of ½ the included angle of the drill

To illustrate, let us calculate the lead of a general purpose drill 1 inch in diameter:

$$l = \frac{0.5}{\tan 59°}$$

$$l = \frac{0.5}{1.6643}$$

$$l = 0.3 \text{ inches lead}$$

Once the total length that the drill must move has been determined, then the feed of the drill in inches per minute is divided into this distance for the purpose of determining the drill cutting time in minutes.

Drill speed is usually expressed in terms of feet per minute, and feed is expressed in thousandths of an inch per revolution. In order to change the feed into inches per minute when the feed per revolution and the speed in feet per minute are known, the student should substitute in the following equation:

$$F_m = \frac{3.82 \ (f)(Sf)}{d}$$

where

F_m = Feed in inches per minute
f = Feed in inches per revolution
Sf = Surface feet per minute
d = Diameter of drill in inches

For example, to determine the feed in inches per minute of a 1-inch diameter drill running at a surface speed of 100 feet per minute and a feed of 0.013 inch per revolution, we should figure

$$F_m = \frac{(3.82)(0.013)(100)}{1} = 4.97 \text{ inches per minute}$$

If we wished to determine how long it would take for this 1-inch drill running at the above-mentioned speed and feed to drill through 2 inches of a malleable iron casting, we should substitute in the equation:

$$T = \frac{L}{F_m}$$

where

T = Cutting time in minutes
L = Total length drill must move
F_m = Feed in inches per minute

and we should have

$$T = \frac{2 \text{ (thickness of casting)} + 0.3 \text{ (lead of drill)}}{4.97}$$

$$= 0.464 \text{ minutes cutting time}$$

The cutting time so calculated does not include any allowance, which of course must be added to determine the allowed time. The allowance will include time for variations in material thickness and tolerance in the setting of stops, both of which affect the cycle cutting time to some extent. Also personal and unavoidable delay allowance must be added in order to arrive at an equitable allowed elemental time.

It must be remembered that all speeds are not available on the machine being used. For example, the recommended spindle speed for a given job might be 1,550 rpm; however, the fastest speed that the machine is capable of running may be 1,200 rpm. In this case 1,200 rpm would be used and would be the basis of computing allowed times.

Lathe work

There are many variations of machine tools that can be classified in the lathe group. These would include the engine lathe, turret lathe, automatic lathe (automatic screw machine), and others. In all of these cases, the machine is used primarily with stationary tools or tools that translate over the surface to remove material from the revolving work, which may be in the form of forgings, castings, or bar stock. In some cases, the tool is revolved while the work is held stationary as on certain stations of automatic screw machine work. Thus, a slot in a machine screw head can be machined on the automatic screw machine in the slotting attachment.

Speeds and feeds are altered by many factors, such as condition and design of the machine tool, type of material being cut, condition and design of the cutting tool, coolant used for cutting, method of holding the work, and method of mounting the cutting tool. Table 18-3 outlines the approximate cuts, feeds, and speeds for certain metallic and nonmetallic turning.

As in drill press work, feeds are usually expressed in terms of thousandths of an inch per revolution and speeds in terms of surface feet per minute.

In order to determine the cutting time for L inches of cut, it is merely necessary to divide the length of cut in inches by the feed in inches per minute or expressed algebraically:

$$T = \frac{L}{F_m}$$

where

T = Cutting time in minutes
L = Total length of cut
F_m = Feed in inches per minute

TABLE 18-3

APPROXIMATE CUTS, FEEDS, AND SPEEDS FOR METAL AND NONMETALLIC TURNING

(Basic engine lathe practice. Tabular values are in fpm)

Class	Material, SAE No.	Cutting tool material	Cut, 0.005 to 0.015; feed, 0.002 to 0.005	Cut, 0.015 to 0.094; feed, 0.005 to 0.015	Cut, 0.094 to 0.187; feed, 0.015 to 0.030	Cut, 0.187 to 0.375; feed, 0.030 to 0.050	Cut, 0.375 to 0.750; feed, 0.030 to 0.090
Free-cutting steels	1112, X-1112 1120 1315, etc.	18-4-1 HSS	....	250- 350	175-250	80-150	55- 75
		Cast alloys	....	425- 550	315-400	215-300	100-210
		Sintered carbides	750-1,500	600- 750	450-600	350-450	175-350
Carbon and low-alloy steels	1010	18-4-1 HSS	....	225- 300	150-200	75-125	45- 65
		Cast alloys	....	375- 500	275-350	180-250	100-175
	1025	Sintered carbides	700-1,200	550- 700	400-550	300-400	150-300
Medium-alloy steels	1030	18-4-1 HSS	....	200- 275	125-175	70-120	40- 60
		Cast alloys	....	325- 400	230-300	160-225	80-150
	1050	Sintered carbides	600-1,000	450- 600	350-450	250-350	125-250
High-alloy steels	1060 1095 1350	18-4-1 HSS	....	175- 250	125-175	65-100	35- 55
		Cast alloys	....	250- 350	200-250	150-200	65-150
		Sintered carbides	500- 750	400- 500	300-400	200-300	100-300
Nickel steels	2330	18-4-1 HSS	....	200- 275	130-180	70-110	45- 60
		Cast alloys	....	300- 375	225-300	145-200	85-140
	2350	Sintered carbides	550- 800	425- 550	325-425	225-325	125-225
Chromium nickel-chrome steels	3120, 3450 5140, 52100	18-4-1 HSS	....	150- 200	100-125	50- 75	30- 50
		Cast alloys	....	230- 315	165-225	110-130	55-110
		Sintered carbides	425- 550	325- 425	250-325	175-250	75-175
Molybdenum steels	4130 4615	18-4-1 HSS	....	160- 210	110-140	60- 80	35- 55
		Cast alloys	....	250- 325	160-225	120-150	65-100
		Sintered carbides	475- 650	350- 475	275-350	200-275	100-200
Chrome, vanadium, and stainless steels	6120 6150 18 Cr-8Ni 6195	18-4-1 HSS	....	100- 150	80-100	50- 75	30- 50
		Cast alloys	....	210- 250	170-200	110-165	55-100
		Sintered carbides	375- 500	300- 375	250-300	175-250	75-175
Tungsten steels	7260, 18-4-1 annealed	18-4-1 HSS	....	120- 150	75-120	40- 75	25- 40
		Cast alloys	....	130- 175	110-130	80-100	35- 80
		Sintered carbides	325- 400	250- 325	200-250	150-200	50-150
Special steels	12-14 % Mn	18-4-1 HSS					
		Cast alloys	200- 250	125- 200	75-125	50- 75	
		Sintered carbides					
	Si elect. sheet ingot iron, etc.	18-4-1 HSS		300- 400	200-300	150-200	
		Cast alloys	400- 500	500- 600	350-450	250-300	
		Sintered carbides	1,000-1,200	800-1,000	600-800	500-600	

APPROXIMATE CUTS, FEEDS, AND SPEEDS FOR METAL AND NONMETALLIC TURNING.—(Continued)

Class	Material, SAE No.	Cutting tool material	Cut, 0.005 to 0.015; feed, 0.002 to 0.005	Cut, 0.015 to 0.094; feed, 0.005 to 0.015	Cut, 0.094 to 0.187; feed, 0.015 to 0.030	Cut, 0.187 to 0.375; feed, 0.030 to 0.050	Cut, 0.375 to 0.750; feed, 0.030 to 0.090
Cast iron	Soft Gray	18-4-1 HSS	....	120- 150	90- 120	75- 90	35- 75
		Cast alloys	....	225- 300	160- 220	125- 160	70- 125
		Sintered carbides	450- 600	350- 450	250- 350	200- 250	100- 200
	Medium and malleable	18-4-1 HSS	....	120- 150	90- 120	60- 90	30- 60
		Cast alloys	....	190- 225	150- 190	120- 150	60- 120
		Sintered carbides	350- 450	250- 350	200- 250	150- 200	75- 150
	Hard alloy	18-4-1 HSS	....	90- 125	60- 90	40- 60	20- 40
		Cast alloys	....	120- 170	80- 120	55- 80	35- 55
		Sintered carbides	250- 300	150- 250	100- 150	75- 100	50- 75
	Chilled	18-4-1 HSS	10- 15	10- 30			
		Cast alloys	....				
		Sintered carbides	30- 50	30			
Copper-base alloys	Leaded, free-cutting, soft brass, and bronze	18-4-1 HSS	....	300- 400	225- 300	150- 255	100- 150
		Cast alloys	....	500- 600	400- 500	325- 400	200- 325
		Sintered carbides	1,000-1,250	800-1,000	650- 800	500- 650	300- 500
	Normal brass, bronze low alloy	18-4-1 HSS	....	275- 350	225- 275	150- 225	75- 150
		Cast alloys	....	375- 425	325- 375	250- 325	175- 250
		Sintered carbides	700- 800	600- 700	500- 600	400- 500	200- 400
	Tough copper, high tin, manganese, and aluminum bronzes, gilding metal	18-4-1 HSS	....	100- 150	75- 100	50- 75	35- 50
		Cast alloys	....	225- 300	180- 225	125- 180	75- 125
		Sintered carbides	500- 600	400- 500	300- 400	200- 300	100- 200
Light alloys	Magnesium	18-4-1 HSS	500- 750	350- 500	275- 350	200- 275	125- 200
		Cast alloys	700-1,000	500- 700	400- 500	300- 400	200- 300
		Sintered carbides	1,250-2,000	800-1,250	600- 800	500- 600	300- 500
	Aluminum	18-4-1 HSS	350- 500	225- 350	150- 225	100- 150	50- 100
		Cast alloys	450- 650	300- 450	225- 300	150- 225	75- 150
		Sintered carbides	700-1,000	450- 700	300- 450	200- 300	100- 200
Plastics	Thermoplastic, thermosetting	18-4-1 HSS Cast alloys Sintered carbides	650-1,000	400- 650	250- 400	150- 250	
Abrasives	Glass, hard rubber, green ceramics, marble, slate	18-4-1 HSS Cast alloys Sintered carbides	150- 250	75- 150			

Source: Firth Sterling, Inc., Pittsburgh, Pa., and *Tool Engineers Handbook* (New York: McGraw-Hill Book Co.)

and

$$F_m = \frac{3.82(S_f)(f)}{d}$$

where

$$f = \text{Feed in inches per revolution}$$
$$S_f = \text{Speed in surface feet per minute}$$
$$d = \text{Diameter of work in inches}$$

Milling machine work

Milling refers to the removal of material with a rotating multiple-toothed cutter. While the cutter rotates, the work is fed past the cutter; thus, the milling machine differs from the drill press where the work usually is stationary. In addition to machining plane and irregular surfaces, the milling machine is adapted for cutting threads, slotting, and cutting gears.

In milling work, as in drill press and lathe work, the speed of the cutter is expressed in surface feet per minute. Feeds or table travel are usually represented in terms of thousandths of inch per tooth.

In order to determine the cutter speed in revolutions per minute from surface feet per minute and the diameter of the cutter, the following expression may be used:

$$N_r = \frac{3.82S_f}{d}$$

where

$$N_r = \text{Cutter speed in revolutions per minute}$$
$$S_f = \text{Cutter speed in feet per minute}$$
$$d = \text{Outside diameter of cutter in inches}$$

To determine the feed of the work in inches per minute into the cutter, use the expression

$$F_m = fn_tN_r$$

where

$$F_m = \text{Feed of the work in inches per minute into the cutter}$$
$$f = \text{Feed in inches per tooth of cutter}$$
$$n_t = \text{Number of cutter teeth}$$
$$N_r = \text{Cutter speed in revolutions per minute}$$

The number of cutter teeth suitable for a particular application may be expressed as:

$$n_t = \frac{F_m}{F_t \times N_r}$$

where

$$F_t = \text{Chip thickness}$$

Table 18-4 gives suggested feeds and speeds for milling under average conditions.

In computing cutting time on milling operations, the analyst must take into consideration the lead of the milling cutter when determining the

TABLE 18-4

Feeds and speeds for milling (average conditions)

			WIDTH OF CUT IN INCHES															
			¼	½	¾	1	1¼	1½	2	2½	3	4	5	6	7	8	10	12
	¼	Feed	4.5	4.5	4	4	4	3.5	3.5	3.5	3	3	3	2.5	2.5	2.5	2.25	2.25
		Speed	110	110	105	105	100	100	100	95	95	95	90	90	90	85	85	85
	½	Feed	4.5	4	4	4	3.5	3.5	3.5	3	3	3	2.5	2.5	2.25	2.25	2	2
		Speed	105	105	100	100	95	95	95	90	90	90	85	85	85	80	80	80
	¾	Feed	4	4	3.5	3.5	3.5	3	3	3	2.5	2.5	2.25	2.25	2	2	1.75	1.75
		Speed	100	100	95	95	90	90	90	85	85	85	80	80	80	75	75	75
DEPTH OF CUT IN INCHES	1	Feed	4	3.5	3.5	3.5	3	3	3	2.5	2.5	2.25	2.25	2	2	1.75	1.5	
		Speed	95	95	90	90	85	85	85	80	80	80	75	75	75	70	70	
	1¼	Feed	3.5	3.5	3.5	3	3	3	2.5	2.5	2.25	2	1.75	1.5	1.5	1.25		
		Speed	90	90	85	85	80	80	80	75	75	75	70	70	70	65		
	1½	Feed	3.5	3.5	3	3	3	2.5	2.5	2.25	2	1.75	1.5	1.25	1			
		Speed	85	85	80	80	75	75	75	70	70	70	65	65	65			
	2	Feed	3.5	3	3	3	2.5	2.5	2.25	2	1.75	1.5	1.25	1				
		Speed	80	80	75	75	70	70	70	65	65	65	60	60				
	2½	Feed	3	3	2.5	2.5	2.25	2	1.75	1.5	1.25	1						
		Speed	80	75	75	70	70	65	65	65	60	60						
	3	Feed	2.5	2.5	2.25	2	1.75	1.5	1.25	1								
		Speed	75	75	70	70	65	65	60	60								
	4	Feed	2.5	2	1.75	1.5	1.25	1										
		Speed	75	70	70	65	65	60										
	5	Feed	2	1.5	1.25	1												
		Speed	70	70	65	65												
	6	Feed	1.75	1.5	1													
		Speed	70	65	65													

Correction Factors

S.A.E. 1020	= 1.00
S.A.E. 1035—Annld.	= .80
Tool Steel—Annld.	= .60
Alloy Steels:	
Free Machining	= .80
Medium	= .65
Tough	= .50
Cast Steel	= .40
Cast Irons:	
Hard	= .70
Medium	= .95
Soft	= 1.20
Malleable Iron	= .80
Brass and Bronze:	
Free Machining	= 2.50
Medium	= 1.60
Hard	= .80
Monel Metal	= .70
Magnesium Alloys	= 5.00
Aluminum	= 2.00

Feeds are given in Inches per Minute.
Speeds are given in Surface Feet per Minute.

To obtain the proper Feed and Speed for a given material, multiply both Feed and Speed figures given in table by the correction factor for that material.

Source: National Twist Drill & Tool Co.

total length of cut under power feed. This can be determined by triangulation as illustrated in the example of slab-milling a pad shown in Figure 18–3.

In this case, the lead *BC* must be added to the length of the work (8 inches) in order to arrive at the total length that must be fed past the cutter. Clearance for removal of the work after the machining cut will, of course, be handled as a separate element because greater feed under

FIGURE 18–3

Slab-milling a casting 8 inches in length

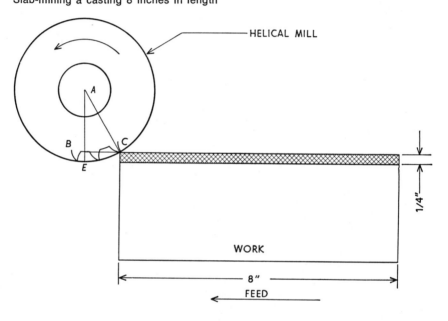

rapid table traverse will be used. By knowing the diameter of the cutter, the analyst determines *AC* as being the cutter radius, and calculates the height of the right triangle *ABC* by subtracting the depth of cut *BE* from the cutter radius *AE:*

$$BC = \sqrt{AC^2 - AB^2}$$

Let us assume, in the example above, that the cutter diameter is 4 inches, and that it has 22 teeth. The feed per tooth is 0.008 inch and cutting speed is 60 feet per minute. The cutting time is computed by using the equation

$$T = \frac{L}{F_m}$$

where

$$T = \text{Cutting time in minutes}$$
$$L = \text{Total length of cut under power feed}$$
$$F_m = \text{Feed in inches per minute}$$

then L would be equal to 8 inches $+ BC$ and

$$BC = \sqrt{4 - 3.06} = 0.975$$

therefore:

$$L = 8.975$$
$$F_m = fn_tN_r$$
$$F_m = (0.008)(22)N_r$$

or

$$N_r = \frac{3.82S_f}{d} = \frac{(3.82)(60)}{4} = 57.3 \text{ revolutions per minute}$$

then

$$F_m = (0.008)(22)(57.3) = 10.1 \text{ inches per minute}$$

and

$$T = \frac{8.975}{10.1} = 0.888 \text{ minutes cutting time}$$

Through a knowledge of feeds and speeds, the time study analyst can determine the required cutting or processing time for various types of work that will be performed in his plant. The illustrations cited in drill press, lathe, and milling work are representative of the techniques used in establishing raw cutting times. To these values must be added the necessary applicable allowances so that fair elemental allowed values can be determined.

Determining horsepower requirements

When developing standard data times for machine elements, it is advisable to tabulate horsepower requirements for the various materials in relationship to depths of cut, cutting speeds, and feeds. The analyst will frequently use standard data for the planning of new work. So that he does not overload existing equipment, it is important that he have information as to the work load being assigned to each machine for the conditions under which the material is being removed. For example, in the machining of high alloy steel forgings on a lathe capable of a developed horsepower of 10, it would not be feasible to take a ⅜-inch depth of cut while operating at a feed of 0.011 inch per revolution and a speed of 200 surface feet per minute. Table 18–5 indicates a horsepower

TABLE 18-5

Horsepower requirements for turning high-alloy steel forgings for ⅜" and ½" depth of cuts of varying speeds and feeds

Surface feet	⅜" depth cut Feeds, in./rev.						½" depth cut Feeds, in./rev.					
	0.009	0.011	0.015	0.018	0.020	0.022	0.009	0.011	0.015	0.018	0.020	0.022
150	6.5	8.0	10.9	13.0	14.5	16.0	8.7	10.6	14.5	17.3	19.3	21.3
175	8.0	9.3	12.7	15.2	16.9	18.6	10.1	12.4	16.9	20.2	22.5	24.8
200	8.7	10.6	14.5	17.4	19.3	21.3	11.6	14.1	19.3	23.1	25.7	28.4
225	9.8	11.9	16.3	19.6	21.7	23.9	13.0	15.9	21.7	26.1	28.9	31.8
250	10.9	13.2	18.1	21.8	24.1	26.6	14.5	17.7	24.1	29.0	32.1	35.4
275	12.0	14.6	19.9	23.9	26.5	29.3	15.9	19.4	26.5	31.8	35.3	39.0
300	13.0	16.0	21.8	26.1	29.0	31.9	17.4	21.2	29.0	34.7	38.6	42.5
400	17.4	21.4	29.1	34.8	38.7	42.5	23.2	28.2	38.7	46.3	51.5	56.7

requirement of 10.6 for these conditions. Consequently, the work would need to be planned for a feed of 0.009 inch at a speed of 200 surface feet, since in this case the required horsepower would be but 8.7. (See Table A3–12, Appendix 3, for horsepower requirements.)

Plotting curves

Because of space limitations, it is not always convenient to tabularize values for variable elements. By plotting a curve or system of curves in the form of an alignment chart, the analyst can express considerable standard data graphically on one page.

Figure 18–4 illustrates a nomogram used for determining turning and facing time. For example, if the problem is to determine the production in pieces per hour to turn 5 inches of a 4-inch diameter shaft of medium carbon steel on a machine utilizing a 0.015-inch feed per revolution and having a cutting time of 55 percent of the cycle time, the answer could be readily determined graphically. By connecting the recommended cutting speed of 150 feet per minute for medium carbon steel shown on scale 1 to the 4-inch diameter of the work shown on scale 2, a speed of 143 rpm is shown on scale 3. The 143-rpm point is connected with the 0.015-inch feed per revolution that is shown on scale 4. This line extended to scale 5 shows a feed of 2.15 inches per minute being used. This feed point connected with the length of cut shown on scale 6 (5 inches) gives the required cutting time on scale 7. This cutting time of 2.35 minutes when connected with the percentage of cutting time shown on scale 8 (in this case, 55 percent) gives the production in pieces per hour on scale 9 (in this case, 16).

There are, however, some distinct disadvantages to using curves. First, it is easy to introduce an error in reading from the curve because of a certain amount of interpolation that is usually required. Then, there is always the chance of outright error through incorrect reading or misalignment of intersections on the various scales.

When we refer to the plotting of curves to show the relationship between time and those variables that affect time, our solution may take the form of a single straight line, a curved line, a system of straight lines as in the ray chart, or a special arrangement of lines characteristic of an alignment chart or nomogram. In the plotting of simple, one-line curves, the analyst should observe certain standard procedures. First, it is standard practice to plot time on the ordinate axis of the charting paper and the independent variable on the abscissa. If practical, all scales should begin at zero so that their true proportions can be seen. Lastly, the scale selected for the independent variable should have a sufficient range to utilize fully the paper on which the curve is being plotted. Figure 18–5 illustrates a chart expressing "forming" time in hours per

FIGURE 18–4

Nomogram for determining facing and turning time

Crobalt, Inc.

FIGURE 18–5

hundred pieces for a certain gage of stock over a range of sizes expressed in square inches.

Each point in this chart represents a separate time study. Thus, 12 time studies were used in compiling data for this curve. Inspection of the plotted points revealed a straight-line relationship between the various studies. The equation for a straight line is:

$$Y = mx + b$$

(Equation of straight-line frequently expressed as: $Y = a + bx$)

where

$Y = $ Ordinate (hours per hundred pieces)
$x = $ Abscissa (area of piece in square inches)
$m = $ Slope of the straight line, or the proportional change of time on Y axis for each unit change on the X axis
$b = $ Intercept of the straight line with the Y axis when $x = 0$

The curve drawn by inspection shows an intercept value of 0.088 on the Y (ordinate) axis and the slope can be calculated by the equation:

$$m = \frac{y_1 - y_2}{x_1 - x_2} \text{ where } x_1y_1 \text{ and } x_2y_2 \text{ are specific points on the curve}$$

$$= \frac{0.182 - 0.144}{250 - 150} = 0.00038$$

The least squares method

It is also possible to solve for m and b using the method of least squares. In this technique, the resulting slope and y axis intercept will give a straight line whose sum of squares of vertical deviations of observations from this line is smaller than the corresponding sum of squares of deviations from any other line. The two equations that are solved simultaneously are:[1]

$$\Sigma y = Nb + m\Sigma x \qquad (1)$$
$$\Sigma xy = b\Sigma x + m\Sigma x^2 \qquad (2)$$

The derivations of these equations are available in most mathematical texts.

In the example cited, we can solve for m and b using the least squares method as shown in Table 18–6.

TABLE 18–6

Study	x or area	y or time	xy	x^2
1...........	25	0.104	2.60	625
2...........	65	0.109	7.09	4,225
3...........	77	0.126	9.70	5,929
4...........	112	0.134	15.01	12,544
5...........	135	0.138	18.63	18,225
6...........	147	0.150	22.05	21,609
7...........	185	0.153	28.31	34,225
8...........	220	0.174	38.28	48,400
9...........	245	0.176	43.12	60,025
10...........	275	0.182	50.05	75,625
11...........	287	0.186	53.38	82,369
12...........	300	0.202	60.60	90,000
	2,073	1.834	348.82	453,801

Substituting in equation (1) and (2):

$$12b = 1.834 - 2073m \qquad (1)$$
$$2{,}073b = 348.82 - 453{,}801m \qquad (2)$$

multiplying equation (1) by 2,073 and equation (2) by 12:

$$24{,}876b = 3{,}801.882 - 4{,}297{,}329m$$
$$\underline{24{,}876b = 4{,}185.840 - 5{,}445{,}612m}$$
$$0 = -383.958 + 1{,}148{,}283m$$

or

$$m = \frac{383.958}{1{,}148{,}283} = 0.000334$$

---

[1] These equations are frequently expressed: $\Sigma y = na + b\Sigma x$ and $\Sigma xy = a\Sigma x + b\Sigma x^2$.

and substituting in equation (1):

$$12b = 1.834 - 0.692$$
$$b = \frac{1.142}{12} = 0.095$$

Solving by regression line equations

As shown, the least squares method calls for solving simultaneous equations. These equations can get unwieldy. By solving these equations for the slope m and the y intercept b, direct substitution can be employed. Identical totals, as in the least squares solutions are used which include:

$$\Sigma x, \ \Sigma x^2, \ \Sigma y, \ \Sigma xy$$

and N, the number of data. The regression line equation to solve for the constant b is:

$$b = \frac{(\Sigma x^2)(\Sigma y) - (\Sigma x)(\Sigma xy)}{(N)(\Sigma x^2) - (\Sigma x)^2}$$

and the slope m is computed as follows:

$$m = \frac{(N)(\Sigma xy) - (\Sigma x)(\Sigma y)}{(N)(\Sigma x^2) - (\Sigma x)^2}$$

Solving for b and m in the foregoing example we get:

$$b = \frac{(453,801)(1.834) - (2,073)(348.82)}{(12)(453,801) - (2,073)^2}$$
$$= \frac{109,168}{1,148,283} = 0.095$$

and

$$m = \frac{(12)(348.82) - (2,073)(1.834)}{(12)(453,801) - (2,073)^2}$$
$$= \frac{383.96}{1,148,283} = 0.000334$$

Using standard data

Constant standard data elements are tabularized and filed under machine or process, for ease of reference. Variable data can be tabularized or may be expressed in terms of a curve or an equation, and are also filed under the facility or operation class.

Where standard data are broken down so as to cover a given machine and class of operation, it may be possible to combine constants with

FIGURE 18–6

CLASSIFICATION

KIND_____Fillet_____

TYPE_____Flat Position_____

ELECTRODE____E-6020 D.H._____

WELDING PROCEDURE GENERAL

PROCESS OF WELDING_____Shielded Metallic Arc_____POSITION____Flat_____

MATERIAL____Mild Steel to Mild Steel_____P.D.S.___1550, 1555____S.A.E.____1010_____

ELECTRODE____E-6020_____D.H._____Convex_____Heavy_____

A.W.S. CLASS   TYPE   SHAPE OF WELD   COATING

POWER SOURCE (A.C. OR D.C. – AND POLARITY IF D.C.)_____D.C. Straight_____

BACKING____None_____PEENING_____None_____CHIPPING_____None_____

PREHEAT_____None_____

STRESS RELIEVING_____None_____

WELDING PROCEDURE–DETAILS

SIZE OF WELD	SIZE OF ELECTRODE	THICKNESS OF PLATE	NUMBER OF PASSES	WELDING CURRENT (AMPERES)	WELDING VOLTAGE (@ ARC)	*MAN HOURS PER INCH WELD	*WELDING SPEED FT./HR.
1/8	1/8	1/8	1	160-190	26-28	.0025	33.3
3/16	5/32	3/16	1	160-190	26-28	.0028	29.8
1/4	3/16	1/4	1	180-230	32-36	.0033	25.3
3/8	1/4	3/4	1	280-330	32-36	.0050	16.7
1/2	1/4	3/4	2	280-330	32-36	.0078	10.7
5/8	1/4	1"	2	280-330	32-36	.0123	6.8
3/4	1/4	1 1/2	4	280-330	32-36	.0196	4.3
1	1/4	1 1/2	6	280-330	32-36	.0318	2.6

*NOTE: INCLUDES CHANGE ELECTRODE TIME, ARC TIME, WELD CLEANING TIME AND WELDING TIME.

variables and tabularize the summary, thus allowing quick reference data that will express the allowed time to perform a given operation completely. Figure 18–6 illustrates welding data in which the constants "change electrode" and "arc" have been combined with the variables "weld cleaning" and "welding," and the result has been expressed in man-hours required to weld 1 inch for various sizes of welds.

Table 18–7 illustrates standard data for a given facility and operation class where again, elements have been combined so that it is necessary only to identify the job in question as to distance that the strip of sheet stock is moved per piece, in order to determine the allowed time for the complete operation.

Setup elements also can frequently be combined or tabularized in combinations so as to diminish the time required for summarizing a series of elements. Table 18–8 illustrates standard setup data for No. 5 Warner & Swasey turret lathes applicable to a specific plant. In order to determine the setup time with this data, it is only necessary to visualize the tooling in the square and hex turret and refer to the table. For example, if a certain job required a chamfering tool, turning tool, and facing tool in the square turret, and needed two boring tools, one reamer, and a collapsible tap in the hex turret, the setup standard time would be determined as 69.70 minutes plus 25.89 minutes or 95.59 minutes. The value is established by finding the relevant tooling under the "square

TABLE 18–7

Standard data for blanking and piercing strip stock hand feed with piece automatically removed on Toledo 76 punch press

L (distance in inches)	T (time in hours per hundred hits)
1	0.075
2	0.082
3	0.088
4	0.095
5	0.103
6	0.110
7	0.117
8	0.123
9	0.130
10	0.137

turret" column (line 8) and the most time-consuming applicable tooling in the "hex turret" section, in this case, tapping. This gives a value of 69.7 minutes. Since three additional tools are located in the hex turret (1st bore, 2nd bore, and ream), we multiply 8.63 by 3 and get 25.89 minutes. The adding of the 25.89 minutes and the 69.70 minutes gives us the required setup time.

More frequently, standard data are not combined but left in their elemental form, thus giving greater flexibility in the development of time standards. Representative standard data applicable to a given plant would appear as shown in Table 18–9.

The data shown include the applicable personal delay and fatigue allowance. Let us see how this standard time data would be used to establish allowed setup and piece times to drill the two hold-down bolt holes in the gray iron housing casting illustrated in Figure 18–7.

The allowed setup time would equal

$$B + C + D + F + G + H + I = 8.70 \text{ minutes}$$

TABLE 18–8

Standard setup data for No. 5 turret lathes

				Basic tooling				
					Hex turret			
No.	*Square turret*	*Partial*	*Chamfer*	*Bore or turn*	*Drill*	*S. Tap or ream*	*C. Tap*	*C Die*
1.	Partial............. 31.5		39.6	44.5	48.0	47.6	50.5	58.5
2.	Chamfer........... 38.2		39.6	46.8	49.5	50.5	53.0	61.2
3.	Face or cut off....... 36.0		44.2	48.6	51.3	52.2	55.0	63.0
4.	Tn bo grv rad........ 40.5		49.5	50.5	53.0	54.0	55.8	63.9
5.	Face and chf......... 37.8		45.9	51.3	54.0	54.5	56.6	64.8
6.	Fa & Cut off......... 39.6		48.6	53.0	55.0	56.0	58.5	66.6
7.	Fa & tn or tn and cut off................ 45.0		53.1	55.0	56.7	57.6	60.5	68.4
8.	Fa, tn, and chf....... 47.7		55.7	57.6	59.5	60.5	69.7	78.4
9.	Fa, tn, and cut off..... 48.6		57.6	58.5	60.0	62.2	71.5	80.1
10.	Fa, tn, and grv....... 49.5		58.0	59.5	61.5	64.0	73.5	81.6

11.	Circled basic tooling from above................................		_____
12.	Each additional tool in square............. 4.20x_____	=	_____
13.	Each additional tool in hex.............. 8.63x_____	=	_____
14.	Remove and setup 3 jaws................ 5.9		_____
15.	Set up subassembly or fixture............ 18.7		_____
16.	Set up between centers.................. 11.0		_____
17.	Change lead screw..................... 6.6		_____

Total Setup_____Min.

Element *A* is not included in the setup time because of the simplicity of the job. The drawing is not issued to the operator because the operation card provides him with necessary information relative to drill jig number, drill size, plug gage number, feed and spindle speed to be used. Element *E* is not included in the setup since first-piece inspection is not in this case performed by the inspector. According to the operation card issued, the operator will periodically inspect his own work with the Go-No-Go gage provided. It is recommended that he check every 10th piece.

Since the casting in question would weigh less than 4 pounds, and

TABLE 18–9

Standard data

Application: Allen 17-inch Vertical Single Spindle Drill
Work Size: Small work—up to four pounds in weight and such that two or more parts
can be handled in each hand

Setup elements:		*Minutes*
A.	Study drawing	1.25
B.	Get material and tools and return and place ready for work	3.75
C.	Adjust height of table	1.31
D.	Start and stop machine	.09
E.	First-piece inspection (includes normal wait time for inspector)	5.25
F.	Tally production and post on voucher	1.50
G.	Clean off table and jig	1.75
H.	Insert drill in spindle	.16
I.	Remove drill from spindle	.14

Each piece elements:		
1.	Grind drill (prorate)	.78
2.	Insert drill in spindle	.16
3.	Insert drill in spindle (quick-change chuck)	.05
4.	Set spindle	.42
5.	Change spindle speed	.72
6.	Remove tool from spindle	.14
7.	Remove tool from spindle (quick-change chuck)	.035
8.	Pick up part and place in jig	
	a) Quick-acting clamp	.070
	b) Thumbscrew	.080
9.	Remove part from jig	
	a) Quick-acting clamp	.050
	b) Thumbscrew	.060
10.	Position part and advance drill	.042
11.	Advance drill	.035
12.	Clear drill	.023
13.	Clear drill, reposition part, and advance drill (same spindle)	.048
14.	Clear drill, reposition part, and advance drill adjacent spindle	.090
15.	Insert drill bushing	.046
16.	Remove drill bushing	.035
17.	Lay part aside	.022
18.	Blow out jig and part and lay part aside	.081
19.	Plug gage part	.12 per hole

two parts can easily be handled in one hand, the data outlined would be applicable.

After the analyst investigates the design of the drill jig to be used and makes an analytical motion study of the job in order to determine the elements required to perform the operation, he will make his elemental summary. This would appear as shown in Table 18–10.

To this 0.278-minute time must be added the actual drilling time to drill the two holes. This can readily be determined as previously outlined. For a ½-inch diameter drill used for drilling cast iron, we should

FIGURE 18–7

Cast-iron housing

use a surface speed of 100 feet per minute and a feed of 0.008 inch per revolution.

One hundred surface feet per minute would equal 764 revolutions per minute.

$$\text{rpm} = \frac{12S_f}{\pi d}$$

TABLE 18–10

Element number	Element	Allowed time (minutes)
8......	Pk. pt. pl. jig (quick-acting clamp)	0.070
9......	Rem. pt. jig (quick-acting clamp)	0.050
10......	Pos. pt. & adv. dr.	0.042
13......	Cl. dr. rep. pt. & adv. dr.	0.048
12......	Cl. dr.	0.023
17......	Lay pt. aside	0.022
19......	Plug gage pt. (10%)	0.012
1......	Gr. dr. (once per 100 pcs.)	0.008
2......	Insert dr. in sp. (once per 100 pcs.)	0.002
6......	Rem. tool from sp. (once per 100 pcs.)	0.001
		0.278 Minute

where

$$S_f = \text{Surface feet per minute}$$
$$\pi = 3.14$$
$$d = \text{Diameter of drill in inches}$$

However, investigation of the drill press for which this work has been routed reveals that 600 rpm or 900 rpm are the closest speeds that are available to the recommended 764 rpm. The analyst proposes to use the slower speed in view of his knowledge of the condition of the machine, and determines the drilling time as follows:

$$T = \frac{L}{F_m} \times 2$$
$$L = 0.437 + \frac{0.25}{\tan 59°} = 0.588 \text{ inches}$$
$$F_m = (600)(0.008)$$
$$= 4.8 \text{ inches per minute}$$
$$T = \left(\frac{0.588}{4.8}\right) 2 = 0.244 \text{ minute}$$

To this 0.244 minute cutting time must be added an appropriate allowance. If 10 percent allowance on the actual machining time is used, we should have a cutting time of 0.268 minute and a handling time of 0.278 minute or a total time of 0.546 minute to drill complete one casting on the single-spindle press available. This standard, supplemented with the setup time of 8.70 minutes, would be released as:

Setup.................. 0.145 hours
Each piece............ 0.91 hours per hundred

Thus if an operator set up this job, and ran 1,000 pieces in an eight-hour working day, he would be performing at an efficiency of 116 percent:

$$\frac{(0.91)(10) + 0.145}{8} = 116 \text{ percent}$$

Conclusion

Standard data, when properly applied, permit the establishment of accurate time standards in advance of the time that the job is to be performed. This feature makes its use especially attractive when estimating the cost of new work for quotation purposes and for subcontracting work.

Time standards can be achieved much more rapidly by using standard data, and the consistency of the standards established can be assured. Thus, this technique allows the economic development of indirect labor standards. For example the following standard data elements (Table

TABLE 18–11

Punch and verify standard elements (punch and verify section of tabulating department)

Code	Normal Min./Occ.	Description
P1001	0.377	*Get Material from Work Table.* Operator gets up from workplace, walks (4 feet to 22 feet) to obtain material, returns to workplace.
P1002	0.356	*Put Program Card on Machine.* Operator selects proper program card from small card file (4 × 7½ inch) at normal arms length on worktable at left. Operator removes program cylinder from machine, attaches program card, and locks cylinder in machine. (Includes remove previous program card.)
P1003	0.016	*Remove Cards from Machine; Stamp Copy.* Operator removes cards from machine receptacle at left, stamps copy (invoices, order IBM list, etc.), with operator identification stamp.
P1004	0.071	*Tube Code Reference.* Operator refers to reference board to obtain tube type tabulating code (6 digits). Reference board is indexed by RTMA tube type descriptions.
P1005	0.065	*Place Cards and Copy in Work Bin.* Operator places copy and cards in slots beneath worktable on left. Normal arm's reach.
P1006	0.377	*Give Cards and Copy to Verifier.* Operator gets up, walks (4 to 22 feet), and places cards and copy on worktable of verifier.
P1007	0.300	*Punch Group Card.* Operator punches group card containing information common to the group of work (see individual description).
P1008	0.300	*Punch Work Card.* Operator punches work card containing information common to the particular unit (order, invoice, bill, etc.) (see individual description).
P1009	0.300	*Punch Total Card.* Operator punches card containing common or total information (see individual description).
P1010	Chart	*Punch Detail Card.* Operator punches detail card containing information partially duplicated from group. Work on total card and punches information relevant to the individual item (example: a particular tube type as an item on an order).
P1011	Chart	*Punch Delivery Date Card.* Operator punches card bearing delivery dates of individual items.

18–11) allow the rapid development of standards in the tabulating department of one company. Standards developed from standard data tend to be completely fair to both the worker and management in that they are the result of already proven standards. It can be pointed out that the elemental values used in arriving at the standards have proven satisfactory as components of established and acceptable standards in use throughout the plant.

The use of standard data simplifies many managerial and administrative problems in plants having a union which operates as a bargaining agent. Union contracts contain many clauses pertaining to such matters as the type of study to be taken (continuous or snapback), the number of cycles to be studied, who shall be studied, and who shall observe the study. These restrictions frequently make it difficult for the analyst to arrive at a standard that is equitable to both the company and the operator. By using the standard data technique, the analyst may avoid restrictive details. Thus, not only is the determination of a standard simplified, but the sources of tension between labor and management are alleviated.

In general, the more refined the elemental times, the greater the coverage possible for the data. Consequently, in job shop practice, it is practicable to have individual elemental values as well as grouped or combined values, so that the data for a given facility will have the flexibility that will allow the setting of rates for all types of work scheduled to the machine.

The use of fundamental motion data for establishing standards, in particular on short-cycle jobs, is becoming more widespread. This data, by nature, is so basic that it allows the predetermination of standards on practically any class or type of manual elements. Of course, the "objective" or "do" basic divisions, such as "use," must be handled as variables, and tabularized data, curves, or algebraic expressions established. In Chapter 19 we will become acquainted with the principal fundamental motion data techniques.

From the illustrative examples cited, it is evident that the application of standard data is an exacting technique. Careful and thorough training in methods and shop practice is fundamental before an analyst can accurately establish standards using standard data. It is essential that the analyst know and recognize the need for each element in the class of work for which he is setting rates. Supplementing this background, it is necessary that the man working with standard data be analytic, accurate, thorough, conscientious, and completely dependable.

TEXT QUESTIONS

1. What do we mean by "standard data"?
2. What is the approximate ratio in time for setting standards by stopwatch methods and by standard data methods?
3. What advantages are there to establishing time standards through the medium of standard data rather than by taking individual studies?
4. What would the time for the element "mill slot" depend upon?
5. Of what use is the "fast" watch in the compilation of standard data?
6. Compute the times for elements a, b, c, d, and e when elements $a + b + c$ were timed as 0.057 minute and $b + c + d$ were found to equal 0.078 minute, $c + d + e = 0.097$ minute, $d + e + a = 0.095$ minute, and $e + a + b = 0.069$ minute.
7. What would be the lead of a ¾-inch diameter drill with an included angle of 118°?

8. What would be the feed in inches per minute of a ¾-inch drill running at a surface speed of 80 feet per minute and a feed of 0.008 inch per revolution?

9. How long would it take the above drill to drill through a casting 2¼ inches thick?

10. How are feeds usually expressed in lathe work?

11. How long would it take to turn 6 inches of 1-inch bar stock on a No. 3 W. & S. turret lathe running at 120 feet per minute and feeding at the rate of 0.005 inch per revolution?

12. A plain milling cutter 3 inches in diameter with a width of face of 2 inches is being used to mill a piece of cold-rolled steel 1½ inches wide and 4 inches long. Depth of cut is 3/16 inch. How long would it take to make the cut if the feed per tooth is 0.010 inch and a 16-tooth cutter running at a surface speed of 80 feet per minute is in use?

13. What are some of the disadvantages of using curves to tabulate standard data?

14. What standard procedures should be followed in the plotting of simple curves?

15. What would be the horsepower requirements of turning a mild steel shaft 3 inches in diameter if a cut of ¼ inch with a feed of 0.022 inch per revolution at a spindle speed of 250 rpm were established?

GENERAL QUESTIONS

1. What do you think is the attitude of labor toward establishing standards through the use of standard data?

2. Using the drill press standard data shown in the text, preprice a drilling job with which you are familiar. How does this standard compare with the present rate on the job? (Be sure that identical methods are compared.)

3. Does complete standard data supplant the stopwatch? Explain.

4. If you were president of your local union, would you advocate that standards be established by standard data? Why?

CHAPTER 19

Synthetic basic motion times

Since the time of Taylor, management has realized the desirability of having standard times assigned to the various basic divisions of accomplishment.

One of the earliest men to investigate this area was W. G. Holmes. He tabulated values based on the measurement of the various body members, including the finger, hand, foot, and arm, in a Time of Movements Chart.[1] Representative times established by Holmes are:

1. Hand with hinge movement at the wrist .0022 minute when moved 0 to 2 inches.
2. Arm with angular movement at the shoulder .0060 minute when moved 30 degrees.
3. Nerve reaction, eye to brain or reverse .0003 minute.

Actually, Holmes has taken his analysis to such a point that it is difficult and cumbersome to handle. He has provided times for nerve reactions from the eye to the brain, the knee to the brain, and the foot to the brain; also, times for mental process and mind decision such as time to hear or smell, or realize contact.

R. M. Barnes has advocated a technique similar to Holmes's in the development of basic motion data. Barnes states: "There is a trend toward the use of standard time values for therbligs or combination of

---

[1] W. G. Holmes, *Applied Time and Motion Study* (New York: Ronald Press Co., 1938), p. 244.

therbligs and under certain conditions such time values may be more useful than the time values for longer elements obtained from stopwatch
time studies."[2]

A related development was made by Harold Engstrom at the General
Electric Company in Bridgeport, Connecticut. Engstrom described his
technique as follows:

1. Analyze certain classes of work such as light bench assembly work or
    machine operation. The standards developed must be confined to par-
    ticular classes of work and no attempt made to embrace the entire gamut
    of industrial operations.
2. The jobs are then time studied to determine the basic elements of which
    they are comprised.
3. These time studied jobs are then photographed by means of a measure-
    ment camera for the purpose of micromotion analysis.
4. The evaluations of the effort of the worker are then made.
5. From the motion pictures previously taken, make combinations of ther-
    bligs into two major classifications, such as Get, which consists of Trans-
    port Empty and Grasp; Place, which consists of Transport Loaded, Pre-
    position, Position, and Release Load. Dispose should be treated as
    Place.
6. These data are then tabulated.[3]

Mr. A. B. Segur developed time equations in 1924 as a result of analyzing micromotion films taken of highly efficient operators during World
War I.

The films were taken originally in an effort to develop motion patterns
to train handicapped workers. These early studies revealed that if the
same motion was performed by various operators using the same motion
pattern, the time involved in performing the motion was relatively constant.

It has never been a question of need but a question of how can the
job of determining time values for the various basic divisions be done
practically. In recent years, considerable progress has been made in the
assignment of time values to basic elements of work. These time values
are referred to as synthetic basic motion times.

Definition of synthetic basic motion times

Synthetic basic motion times are a collection of valid time standards
assigned to fundamental motions and groups of motions that cannot be
precisely evaluated with ordinary stopwatch time study procedure. They
are the result of studying a large sample of diversified operations with a

---

[2] Ralph M. Barnes, *Motion and Time Study* (3d ed.; New York: John Wiley &
Sons, Inc., 1949), p. 439.

[3] *Proceedings, National Time and Motion Study Clinic, 1940*, pp. 45–46.

timing device such as the motion-picture camera that is capable of measuring very short elements. The time values are synthetic in that they are often the result of logical combinations of therbligs. For example, a series of time values may be established for different categories of grasp. Within the grasp time may be included the therbligs search, select, and grasp. The time values are basic in that further refinement is not only difficult but impractical. Thus, we have the term *synthetic basic motion times.*

Necessity of synthetic basic motion times

Since 1945 there has been a growing interest in the use of synthetic basic motion times as a modern method of establishing rates quickly and often accurately without using the stopwatch or other time recording device. In view of this, it is recommended that the student reread Chapters 7 and 8 after completing Chapter 18 on Standard Data. A by-product of synthesized time standards that probably has been as useful, if not more so, than the time standard itself, is a development of method consciousness to a refined degree in all parties associated with the establishment of standards using synthetic values. For this reason, the author believes that the entire subject of synthetic basic motion times should be meshed or integrated with the motion and micromotion techniques, even though it is also very closely allied to the work measurement phase.

Even with the laws of motion economy and basic division of accomplishment concept clearly established, the methods analyst without reliable time values of the basic divisions has only a portion of the facts necessary to engineer a method prior to beginning actual production. If he did not have time values of the basic divisions, how could he be sure that his proposed method was the best? With reliable motion times, he would be able to evaluate his proposed methods in terms of the average or normal worker, who would eventually be the recipient of his ideas. It is apparent that the method used determines time to do a task, and it follows that if time values for all forms of activity were available, then the most favorable methods could be determined in advance.

Today, the practicing methods analyst has several sources of established synthetic values from which he can obtain information that may be helpful in his work.

Work-Factor[4]

The Work-Factor Company, Inc. is one of the pioneer concerns in establishing standards synthetically with motion-time values. Work-

---

[4] "Work-Factor" is the service mark (trademark) of the Work-Factor Company, Inc., identifying their services as consultants to industry and their system of predetermined fundamental motion-time standards for the motion times themselves and the techniques used to apply them to methods determination and work measurement.

Factor data were made available in 1938, after four years of gathering values by the micromotion technique, stopwatch procedures, and the use of a "specially constructed photoelectric time machine."

Flexibility of the Work-Factor system has been achieved by developing four different procedures of application depending on the objectives of the analysis and accuracy required. The procedures are known respectively as the detailed, simplified, abbreviated, and ready techniques.

Detailed Work-Factor is designed to provide precise time standards for either daywork measurement or incentive pay plans. It also provides a precise tool for methods analyses. It is primarily used for short-cycle operations and for repetitive work. It is also commonly used for developing standard data.

Simplified Work-Factor is used when operations do not require as precise an analysis as is obtainable with detailed. It is generally used for medium quantity production. Simplified time standards can be obtained in about half the time as with detailed, and loss in accuracy normally does not exceed plus 5 percent.

Abbreviated Work-Factor is fast to apply. It is extremely useful for the short-order shop. Abbreviated varies from detailed about plus 10 to 12 percent.

Ready Work-Factor was developed to satisfy the need for a simple tool of evaluating manual work that can be taught readily to persons in functions other than time study such as product design, estimating, manufacturing methods, and production and office supervision. When correctly applied, ready Work-Factor times may be expected to average within 0 to plus 5 percent of detailed Work-Factor.

Detailed Work-Factor system

Work-Factor recognizes the following variables that influence the time required to perform a task:

1. The body member making the motion, such as arm, forearm, finger-hand, foot.
2. The distance moved (measured in inches).
3. The weight carried (measured in pounds, converted into work factors).
4. The manual control required (care, directional control or steering to a target, changing direction, stopping at a definite location; measured in work factors).

Through analysis of films, Work-Factor concluded, as the Gilbreths did many years earlier, that finger motions can be performed more rapidly than arm motions, and arm motions are made in shorter time than body motions. Work-Factor motion times have been compiled for the various body members. These include:

1. Finger-hand. Includes the movements of the fingers and thumb and movement of the hand about the wrist joint.
2. Arm. Includes movements of the lower arm around the elbow when used as hinge joint and all movements of the whole arm hinged at the shoulder except for swivels. Movement of the hand, fingers, and lower arm may occur simultaneously.
3. Forearm swivel. Here the lower arm rotates about the axis of the forearm such as when turning a screw driver, or the full arm rotates about the entire axis and the swivel takes place at the shoulders.
4. Trunk. A forward, backward, sidewise, or swiveling motion of the trunk of the body.
5. Foot. Here is included those motions of the foot when hinged at the ankle and the upper and lower leg remain in a fixed location.

All proponents of fundamental motion data techniques have recognized the element of distance in making reaches and moves and, in fact, all motions. The longer the distance the more time is required, of course. Work-Factor has tabularized values for finger and hand movements from 1 inch up to 4 inches, and for arm movements from 1 inch to 40 inches. Distances are measured as a straight line between the starting and stopping points of the motion arc. The actual motion path is measured only when a change in direction is involved.

Following is a list of the points at which distance should be measured for the various body members:

Body member	*Point of measurement*
Finger or hand	Fingertip
Arm	Knuckles (knuckle having greatest travel should be used)
Forearm swivel	Knuckles
Trunk	Shoulder
Foot	Toe
Leg	Ankle
Head turn	Nose

Weight or resistance will influence time according to the magnitude of the part being moved, the body member used, and the sex of the operator. It is measured in pounds for all body members except for "forearm swivel" motions where pound-inches of torque represent the unit of measurement.

Manual control is the most difficult variable to quantify. However, the Work-Factor system concluded that in the vast majority of instances work motions can be identified as involving one or more of the following four types of control:

1. Definite Stop Work-Factor. Here some manual control is required to stop a motion within a fixed interval. Definite stop does not exist when the motion is terminated by some physical barrier. The motion must be terminated by the muscular co-ordination of the operator.

2. Directional Control or Steer Work-Factor. Here manual control is necessary to bring or guide a part to a specific location or make a motion through
an area with limited clearance.

3. Care or Precaution Work-Factor. Here manual control is exercised to
prevent spilling or damage, such as moving a full vessel of acid or handling a
thin piece of glass.

4. Change of Direction Work-Factor. Here manual control is exercised
when the motion involves a direction change to reach a remote location,
or to get around some obstacle. For example, to move a nut in back of a
panel would require a change in direction once the moving hand reached the
front of the panel.

A work factor has been defined as the index of additional time required
over and above the basic time. It is a unit for identifying the effect of
the variables, manual control and weight. The other two variables that
affect the time to perform manual motions—body member used and distance—do not employ work-factors as a measure of magnitude. Here
member used and inches represent the quantitative yardstick. The simplest or basic motions of a body member involve no work factors. As complexities are introduced to a manual motion through the addition of
weight or control, work factors are added. And of course, each work factor
that is added represents an additional increment of time.

Table 19–1 illustrates the Work-Factor motion-time table including
all Work-Factor motion-time values. Note that there is a separate table
for each body member and that each table contains values for distances.
In the forearm swivel, motion distance is indicated in degrees while all
other motions are shown in inches. At the bottom of each table is tabularized weight data giving weight or resistance limits for men and women.
The forearm swivel motion resistance section is given in pounds-inches
of torque while all others are listed in pounds. The table gives the maximum resistance encountered that can be considered basic and also the
top values for a specific number of work-factors.

The Work-Factor System divides all tasks into eight "Standard Elements of Work." These are:

1. Transport (reach and move)
2. Grasp
3. Pre-position
4. Assemble
5. Use
6. Disassemble
7. Mental process (inspect, react, and so on)
8. Release

1. *Transport.* The element transport is the connecting link between
the other standard elements. It is broken into two classifications:

TABLE 19–1

Work-Factor motion-time table for detailed analysis time in Work-Factor* units

(A) Arm, measured at knuckles

Distance moved, inches	Basic	1	2	3	4
1	18	26	34	40	46
2	20	29	37	44	50
3	22	32	41	50	57
4	26	38	48	58	66
5	29	43	55	65	75
6	32	47	60	72	83
7	35	51	65	78	90
8	38	54	70	84	96
9	40	58	74	89	102
10	42	61	78	93	107
11	44	63	81	98	112
12	46	65	85	102	117
13	47	67	88	105	121
14	49	69	90	109	125
15	51	71	92	113	129
16	52	73	94	115	133
17	54	75	96	118	137
18	55	76	98	120	140
19	56	78	100	122	142
20	58	80	102	124	144
22	61	83	106	128	148
24	63	86	109	131	152
26	66	90	113	135	156
28	68	93	116	139	159
30	70	96	119	142	163
35	76	103	128	151	171
40	81	109	135	159	179
Weight, pounds:					
Male	2	7	13	20	Up
Female	1	3½	6½	10	Up

(L) Leg, measured at ankle

Distance moved, inches	Basic	1	2	3	4
1	21	30	39	46	53
2	23	33	42	51	58
3	26	37	48	57	65
4	30	43	55	66	76
5	34	49	63	75	86
6	37	54	69	83	95
7	40	59	75	90	103
8	43	63	80	96	110
9	46	66	85	102	117
10	48	70	89	107	123
11	50	72	94	112	129
12	52	75	97	117	134
13	54	77	101	121	139
14	56	80	103	125	144
15	58	82	106	130	149
16	60	84	108	133	153
17	62	86	111	135	158
18	63	88	113	137	161
19	65	90	115	140	164
20	67	92	117	142	166
22	70	96	121	147	171
24	73	99	126	151	175
26	75	103	130	155	179
28	78	107	134	159	183
30	81	110	137	163	187
35	87	118	147	173	197
40	93	126	155	182	206
Weight, pounds:					
Male	8	42	Up		
Female	4	21	Up		

(T) Trunk, measured at shoulder

Distance moved, inches	Basic	1	2	3	4
1	28	38	49	58	67
2	29	42	53	64	73
3	32	47	60	72	82
4	38	56	70	84	96
5	43	62	79	95	109
6	47	68	87	105	120
7	51	74	95	114	130
8	54	79	101	121	139
9	58	84	107	128	147
10	61	88	113	135	155
11	63	91	118	141	162
12	66	94	123	147	169
13	68	97	127	153	175
14	71	100	130	158	182
15	73	103	133	163	188
16	75	105	136	167	193
17	78	108	139	170	199
18	80	111	142	173	203
19	82	113	145	176	206
20	84	116	148	179	209
Weight, pounds:					
Male	11	58	Up		
Female	5½	29	Up		

(F, H) Finger-hand, measured at fingertip

Distance moved, inches	Basic	1	2	3	4
1	16	23	29	35	40
2	17	25	32	38	44
3	19	28	36	43	49
4	23	33	42	50	58
Weight, pounds:					
Male	⅔	2½	4	Up	
Female	⅓	1¼	2	Up	

(FT) Foot, measured at toe

Distance moved, inches	Basic	1	2	3	4
1	20	29	37	44	51
2	22	32	40	48	55
3	24	35	45	55	63
4	29	41	53	64	73
Weight, pounds:					
Male	5	22	Up		
Female	2½	11	Up		

(FS) Forearm swivel, measured at knuckles

	Basic	1	2	3	4
45 degrees	17	22	28	32	37
90 degrees	23	30	37	43	49
135 degrees	28	36	44	52	58
180 degrees	31	40	49	57	65
Torque, pound-inches:					
Male	3	13	Up		
Female	1½	6½	Up		

Work-Factor* symbols:

W = weight or resistance
S = directional control (steer)
P = care (precaution)
U = change direction
D = definite stop

Walking time

Type	30-inch paces		
	1	2	Over 2
General	As single	260	120 + 80 per pace
Restricted	steps	300	120 + 100 per pace

Add 100 for 120- to 180-degree turn at start

Up steps (8 inches rise, 10 inches flat).......126
Down steps...........................100

Visual inspection

Focus............20
Inspect..........30 per point
React............20

Head turn:
45 degrees...............40
90 degrees...............60

1 time unit = 0.0001 minute
= 0.006 second
= 0.00000167 hour

* Trademark.

By permission from H. B. Maynard, *Industrial Engineering Handbook* (New York: McGraw-Hill Book Co., 1956).

TABLE 19–2

Work-Factor® complex grasp table

COMPLEX GRASPS FROM RANDOM PILES

SIZE (Major dimension or length)		SOLIDS & BRACKETS [Thickness over 3/64" (.0469")]		THIN FLAT OBJECTS — THICKNESS				CYLINDERS AND REGULAR CROSS SECTIONED SOLIDS — DIAMETER							Add for Entangled, Nested or Slippery Objects *
				(less than 1/64") 0-.0156"		(1/64 to 3/64") .0156"-.0469"		0-.0625" (1/16)	.0626"-.125" (1/8)	.1251"-.1875" (3/16)	.1876"-.5000" (1/2)	.1876"-.5000" (1/2)	.5001" & up (over 1/2)	.5001" & up (over 1/2)	
inch	fraction	Blind —Simo	Visual —Simo	Blind —Simo	Visual —Simo	Blind —Simo	Visual —Simo	Blind, —Simo	Blind —Simo	Blind —Simo	Blind —Simo	Visual —Simo	Blind —Simo	Visual —Simo	—Simo
.0000"-.0625"	1/16" & less	120 172	B B	—	—	131 189	B B	S S	S S	S S	S S	S S	S S	S S	17 26
.0626"-.1250"	over 1/16" to 1/8"	79 111	B B	108 154	— B	85 120	B B	85 120	S S	S S	S S	S S	S S	S S	12 18
.1251"-.1875"	over 1/8" to 3/16"	64 88	B B	102 145	B B	74 103	B B	79 111	74 103	S S	S S	S S	S S	S S	12 18
.1876"-.2500"	over 3/16" to 1/4"	48 64	B B	72 100	B B	56 76	B B	79 111	68 94	64 88	S S	S S	S S	S S	8 12
.2501"-.5000"	over 1/4" to 1/2"	40 52	B B	64 88	B B	48 64	B B	62 85	56 76	56 76	44 58	B B	S S	S S	8 12
.5001"-1.0000"	over 1/2" to 1"	40 52	B 32	64 88	B 82	48 64	B 58	62 85	56 76	48 64	44 48	B 58	40 52	32 40	8 12
1.0001"-4.0000"	over 1" to 4"	37 48	20 22	53 72	36 46	45 60	28 34	56 76	48 64	40 52	40 52	36 46	37 48	20 22	8 12
4.0001" & up	over 4"	46 61	20 22	70 97	44 58	62 85	36 46	56 76	48 64	40 52	40 52	36 46	37 48	20 22	9 14

B = Use Blind column since visual grasp offers no advantage.   S = Use Solid Table.

* Add the indicated allowances when objects: (a) are entangled (not requiring two hands to separate); (b) are nested together because of shape or film; (c) are slippery (as from oil or polished surface). When objects both entangle and are slippery, or both nest and are slippery, use double the value in the table.

Note: Special grasp conditions should be analyzed in detail.

a) Reach: When a body member is relocated to go to a destination, location, or object.

b) Move: When a body member is relocated to transport an object.

2. Grasp. The element of grasp is the act of obtaining manual control of an object; it begins after the hand has moved directly to the object and ends when manual control has been obtained and a move can occur. The Work-Factor System recognized three types of grasps:

a) Simple Grasp: Used for isolated easy-to-grasp objects and requires not more than one single motion.

b) The Manipulative Grasp: The manipulative grasp includes all grasps of isolated or orderly stacked objects that require more than one motion of the fingers to gain control. There may also be arm motions, several finger motions or combinations of both.

c) The Complex Grasp: The complex grasp is defined as the grasp of an object from a random (jumbled) pile. The system provides a complete table for complex grasps. Complex grasps involve more than one motion and sometimes include arm movements.

Objects to be grasped are classified as:

a) Cylinders and Regular Cross-sectioned Solids: Defined as all objects having cylindrical or regular (all sides and angles equal) cross sections, such as square, hexagons, and so on.

b) Thin, Flat Objects: All flat objects with an effective dimension of $\frac{3}{64}$ inch or less in thickness.

c) Solids and Brackets: Defined as all objects over $\frac{3}{64}$ inch thick not otherwise classified as cylinders or thin flat objects.

3. Pre-position. Pre-position occurs whenever it is necessary to turn and orient an object so it will be in the correct position for a subsequent element. Pre-position frequently occurs on a percentage basis. Since sometimes the object will be in a usable position, other times it must be oriented. An example is a nail (0.100 in. $\times$ $\frac{3}{4}$ in.). In 50 percent of the cases it will be grasped in a usable position. In the remaining 50 percent of the cases it must be pre-positioned. Using the Work-Factor pre-position table (Table 19–3) the analysis would be: PP–0–50% = 24 units.

4. Assemble. Assemble occurs whenever two or more objects are joined together, usually through mating or nesting. The system provides a complete assemble table. Assemble time depends on:

a) Size of Target: The target is considered that part of an assembly that accepts the plug.

b) Plug Dimensions: A plug is considered as that part of an assembly that fits into the target.

c) Plug Target Ratio: Assembly difficulty and therefore assemble time is increased as the dimension of the plug approaches the dimension of the target. Therefore, assembly time is a function of the plug-target ratio.

$$\frac{\text{Plug dimension}}{\text{Target dimension}} = \text{Plug target ratio}$$

d) Type (Shape) of Target: There are two type targets in work-factor terminology—closed and open. Closed targets are those that are closed about the entire perimeter so align motions are required along two axes. Open targets are those that require align motions along one axis only.

When the above-listed facts are known it is a simple matter to determine assemble time from the table.

TABLE 19–3

Pre-position

			Type of Pre-position			
Number of points satisfactory for use	*Percent PP required*	*Optimum (⅜ in. or over) 3F1*	*Very small (under ⅜ in.) 3F1*	*Medium one hand (over 2 × 3 × ½ in.) 4F1*	*Medium two hands (over 3 × 3 × ½ in.) 2F1 + A4D*	*Large two hands (over 8 × 8 in.) 2F1W + A8D*
Two or more sides up:						
Four, three, or two opposite points.........	0	. . .	. . .	. . .	. . . .	. . .
Two adjacent points.....	25	12	20	16	18	25
One point only.........	50	24	40	32	35	50
One specific side up:						
Four, three, or two opposite points.........	50	24	40	32	35	50
Two adjacent points.....	62½	30	50	40	44	63
One point only.........	75	36	60	48	53	75
From stock, etc.:	100	48	80	64	70	100

1. PP of more than one finger motion or one forearm swivel cannot be done simo with a move.
2. End for end PP in fingers, 3F1—50 percent, 24 units.
3. Other PP must be analyzed. Table is a guide.

Allowances are added for increased difficulty due to distance between targets (two at a time), gripping distance (the distance from the hand to the end of the plug) and blind target (when the target is blind either before or during assembly).

5. Use. This element usually refers to machine time, special process time, and time that involves using tools. Use may involve manual motions, as in tightening a nut with a wrench or threading a pipe; in such cases the motions are to be analyzed and evaluated according to all rules and time values obtained from the motion-time tables.

6. *Disassemble.* As the name implies, disassemble is the opposite of assemble. Usually it is a single motion. Time values are taken from the motion-time table.

7. *Mental process.* This applies to all mental activity and process. It is the time interval for reaction and nerve impulses to take place.

Mental processes that can be measured are:

Eye motions	Inspections	Compute
Focus	Quality	Read
Shift	Quantity	Action
Reactions	Identity	Concept

8. *Release.* Release is the opposite of grasp and is the act of relinquishing control of objects. There are three types:

a) Contact: Contact release involves no motion, it is merely lifting the hand from an object.

b) Gravity: Gravity release occurs when objects drop from the Grasp as contact is broken and before the releasing finger motions are complete.

c) Unwrap: Unwrap release involves unwrapping the fingers from around the grasped object and is not complete until the unwrapping motions are complete.

All time values on the Work-Factor motion-time table are in 0.0001 minute. These values are in terms of select time, which has been defined as "that time required for the average, experienced operator, working with good skill and good effort (commensurate with good health and physical and mental well-being) to perform an operation on one unit or piece." To determine the standard time, the analyst must add an allowance to the Work-Factor values, since the select time includes no allowance for personal needs, fatigue, unavoidable delays, or incentive allowance. A typical breakdown study of a draw operation on a Bliss double-action 240-ton press is shown in Figure 19–1.

The symbols used in this analysis carry the following meaning:

W—Weight or resistance	A—Arm
S—Steering or directional control	L—Leg
P—Precaution or care	T—Trunk
U—Change direction	F—Finger
D—Definite stop	Ft—Foot
	FS—Forearm swivel
	H—Hand
	HT—Head turn

In making a Work-Factor study, the analyst first lists all motions made by both hands necessary to perform the task; then he identifies each motion in terms of the distance moved, body member used, and work factors involved. In recording distances, fractional inches are not used. Thus, motions of 1 inch or less are recorded as exactly 1 inch, and motions

TABLE 19-4

Work-Factor® assembly tables

AVERAGE NO. OF ALIGNMENTS (A1S Motions)

CLOSED TARGETS

TARGET DIAMETER	Ratio of Plug Dia. ÷ Target Dia.					
	To .224	.225 to .289	.290 to .414	.415 to .899	.900 to .934	.935 to 1.000
.875" & up	(D*) 18	(D*) 18	(D*) 18	(1/4) 25	(1/4**) 51	(1/4***) 59
.625" to .874"	(D*) 18	(D*) 18	(SD*) 18	(1/4) 25	(1/4**) 51	(1/4***) 59
.375" to .624"	(SD*) 18	(SD*) 18	(D*) 25	(1/2) 31	(1/2**) 57	(1/2***) 65
.225" to .374"	(1/2) 31	(1) 44	(1/4) 44	(1 1/2) 57	(1 1/2**) 83	(1 1/2***) 91
.175" to .224"	(1) 44	(1) 44	(1) 44	(1 1/2) 57	(1 1/2**) 83	(1 1/2***) 83
.125" to .174"	(1) 44	(1 1/4) 51	(1 1/2) 57	(1 1/2) 57	(1 1/2**) 83	(1 1/2***) 91
.075" to .124"	(2 1/2) 83	(2 1/2) 83	(2 1/2) 83	(2 1/2) 83	(2 1/2**) 109	(2 1/2***) 117
.025" to .074"	(3) 96	(3) 96	(3) 96	(3) 96	(3) 122	(3***) 130

OPEN TARGETS

TARGET DIAMETER	Ratio of Plug Dia. ÷ Target Dia.					
	To .224	.225 to .289	.290 to .414	.415 to .899	.900 to .934	.935 to 1.000
.875" & up	(D*) 18	(D*) 18	(D*) 18	(D*) 18	(1/4**) 51	(1/4***) 59
.625" to .874"	(D*) 18	(D*) 18	(SD*) 18	(SD*) 18	(1/4**) 51	(1/4***) 59
.375" to .624"	(SD*) 18	(SD*) 18	(SD*) 18	(1/2) 31	(1/2**) 57	(1/2***) 65
.225" to .374"	(1/4) 25	(1/2) 31	(1/2) 31	(3/4) 38	(3/4**) 64	(3/4***) 72
.175" to .224"	(1/2) 31	(1/2) 31	(1/2) 31	(3/4) 38	(3/4**) 64	(3/4***) 72
.125" to .174"	(3/4) 44	(1) 44	(1) 44	(1) 44	(1**) 70	(1***) 78
.075" to .124"	(1 1/2) 51	(1 1/4) 51	(1 1/4) 51	(1 1/4) 51	(1 1/4**) 77	(1 1/4***) 85
.025" to .074"	(1 1/2) 57	(1 1/2) 57	(1 1/2) 57	(1 1/2) 57	(1 1/2**) 83	(1 1/2***) 91

* Letters indicate Work Factors in move preceding Assembly.

** Requires A(X)S Upright for all ratios of .900 and greater. (Table value includes A1S Upright.)

*** Requires A(Y)S Upright and A(Z)P Insert for all ratios of .935 and greater. (Table value includes A1S Upright and A1P Insert.)

FIGURE 19–1

OPERATION NAME	Oldsmobile Case: 1st Draw Operation (2 Pin Die)						WORK FACTOR ANALYST H. B. Amster	
EQUIPMENT	Mach #1031; Bliss Double Action Draw Press 240 Tons 72.5 RPM							
MATERIAL	CR Steel: Tmk = .050 = .003" Dia = 19.25" Wt = 4.04 lbs.						SHEET 1 OF 1	

	LEFT HAND			Cumu-			RIGHT HAND		Mach.
NO.	Elemental Description	Motion Analysis	Elem. Time	lative Time	Elem. Time	Motion Analysis		Elemental Description	
1	Reach for blank	A20D	0080	0080	0080	0080	A20D	Reach for blank	
2	Grasp blank	F1W	0023	0103	0103	0023	F1W	Grasp blank	
3	Carry blank to die	A40WSD	0159	0262	0262	0159	A40WSD	Carry blank to die	
4	Release & clear fingers	F3W	0028	0290	0290	0028	F3W	Release & clear fingers	
5	Place fingers on blank	F3D	0028	0318	0399	0109	A40D	Reach for trip lever	
6	Push blank against pins	A2P	0029	0347	0415	0016	F1	Grasp lever (No W Req'd)	
7	Withdraw hand (A10) & wait		0146	0493	0493	0078	A10WW	Pull lever to trip press (10 lbs.)	
8	Move hand to hold blank (turn Simo)	A30D	0096	0589	0589	0096	A30D	Reach for oil rag (turn 90°-Simo)	
9	Press down to hold blank	A1W	0026	0615	0606	0017	F2	Grasp rag	
10	Hold Blank at center	---	----	0691	0691	0085	A12UD	Carry rag & dip in oil pan	
11	" " " "	---	----	0723	0723	0032	A6	Raise from oil pan	
12	" " " "	---	----	0749	0749	0026	A4	Shake (squeeze Simo)	
13	" " " "	---	----	0804	0804	0055	A18	Carry rag to stack of blanks	
14	" " " "	---	----	0913	0913	0109	A40U	Apply oil (circular motion)	
15	Release blank	A1W	0026	0939	0955	0042	A10	Raise rag from blank	
16	Withdraw hand from blank	A16	0052	0991	0997	0042	A10	Strike to dislodge blank	
17	Approach blank	A3D	0032	1023	1048	0051	A15	Withdraw rag to side	
18	Grasp blank	F1W	0023	1046		----	---	Hold rag	
19	Turn blank over (release Simo)	2A14W	0138	1184		----	---	" "	
20	Move hand to blank center	A13D	0067	1251		----	---	" "	
21	Press down to hold blank	A1W	0026	1277	1277	0055	A18	Carry rag to blank	
22	Hold blank at center	---	----	1386	1386	0109	A40U	Apply oil (circular motion)	
23	Release blank	A1W	0026	1412	1437	0051	A15	Toss rag near pan	
24	Hand idle (turn 90° Simo)	---	----	1517	1517	0080	A20D	Reach for trip lever (turn Simo)	
25	" "	---	----	1533	1533	0016	F1	Grasp handle (No W req'd)	
26	" "	---	----	1781	1781	0248		Wait (.0493 + .1380 - .1533 - .0092 = .0248)	
27	Move hand to piece on punch	A20D	0080	1873	1873	0092	A15WW	Push lever to stop press (10 lbs.)	
28	Catch piece on palm	React	0020	1893	1896	0023	F1W	Release handle	
29	Carry piece to chute (balance)	A40WPD	0159	2052		----	---	Hand idle	
30	Toss to chute or stack	A5W	0043	2095		----	---	" "	
31	Turn to worktable	120°	0100	2195	2195	0100	120°	Turn to worktable	

greater than 1 inch in length are recorded as the nearest integral number. He then selects from the table of values the appropriate figure for each of the basic motions and summarizes these to obtain the total time required by the normal operator to perform the task.

To this total time percentage allowances for personal delays, fatigue, and unavoidable delays must be added to determine the allowed time.

Simplified Work-Factor system

Simplified Work-Factor is designed to measure work where cycle times are 15 minutes or greater and when great precision is not required. Instead of recording individual motions and times as in detailed analysis, simplified analysis employs larger units of time. This provides a tool with a considerable speed advantage in application for long-cycle jobs.

This system affords a predetermined elemental time technique for nonrepetitive work and job shop-type of operations.

Times in the simplified tables are selected averages and can be traced to the detailed tables. Simplified time values will generally be about 0–5 percent higher than detailed.

Essentially the detailed rules apply to simplified with a few minor exceptions. The Simplified Work-Factor table includes the following:

1. A table for transport motions, applied to all body members. Time values are classified in ranges and the allowances for 2–3 and 4 work factors are averaged into single values.
2. Grasp table lists Work-Factor units for six grasp types with variations for visual, simo, entangled, nested, and slippery conditions. These values cover the many values for simple, manipulative, and complex grasps in detailed Work-Factor. Three of the six values apply to complex grasps classed as medium, difficult, and very difficult, according to type and size of the object being grasped. A parts classification table is provided as an objective guide of classifying grasps and pickups.
3. A pickup table provides simplified time values which combine the standard elements, transport and grasp, into values for picking up objects (that is, the motion sequence, reach to object, grasp object, and move object to new location.) The table is also used for place aside (that is, the motion sequence, move object to new location, release object, and reach to next point in operation).
4. A pre-position table similar to the detailed table.
5. An assemble table in condensed form.
6. A visual inspection table.
7. A release table with values for six different release situations.
8. Simplified values are provided for *walk and turn* and *apply pressure*.

Abbreviated Work-Factor system

Abbreviated Work-Factor is a rapidly applied technique for determining the approximate time required to perform the manual portion of any job. It is equally applicable to jobs done in the home, field, office, or factory. It is partially advantageous for estimating labor cost in advance of actual production on all types of work. It can be used for establishing incentive rates on small quantity nonrepetitive or long-cycle operation.

Abbreviated Work-Factor is convenient for studying operations of many minutes or hours in length. In some circumstances the motion descriptions and time values are applied as rapidly as the operator performs his task. Hence, when one cycle of the operation is completed, the time standard will be essentially completed. The speed with which abbreviated applications are made depends on the required accuracy, the analyst's skill, and the nature of the work studied.

Abbreviated values are so compiled that if in some situations accuracy is sacrificed, time is overallowed rather than underallowed. For this reason, abbreviated standards allow greater overall time than those established by detailed or simplified Work-Factor. They average about 12 percent more time than detailed analyses.

Ready Work-Factor

Although the ready technique is less precise than detailed Work-Factor, experience to date indicates that the deviations from detailed are not large and that the resulting time values are suitable for a wide range of applications.

The ready technique employs the ready unit, 0.0010 minutes (10 Work-Factor units) as its unit of time.

All ready units in the Ready Work-Factor Time Tables are simple numbers arranged in easily remembered sequences such as 1, 2, 3, and 4, or 3, 5, 7, 9, and 11.

Only a few simple rules of application are employed. These are explained in a ready Work-Factor manual.

Simple illustrations of correct analyses of each standard element are established as guideposts. Objects familiar and available to all, such as a pencil, a brick, and a washer are used. These examples form a framework of reference for correct application. It is relatively easy for an analyst to decide that the specific element he is evaluating is easier than one guidepost and more difficult than another.

Through simpler, more graphic terminology and a minimum number of time values, ready Work-Factor creates a work time relationship in the minds of its users. Time values become handy thoughts, easily applied mentally and conversationally. The practical person who uses ready Work-Factor learns to visualize time with the same ease as he does tools and materials.

Methods-Time Measurement (M.T.M.–1)

In 1948 the text *Methods-Time Measurement* was published, giving time values for the fundamental motions of reach, move, turn, grasp, position, disengage, and release.[5] The authors have defined M.T.M. as "a procedure which analyzes any manual operation or method into the basic motions required to perform it, and assigns to each motion a pre-determined time standard which is determined by the nature of the motion and the conditions under which it is made."[6]

The M.T.M. data, as in Work-Factor, are the result of frame-by-frame analysis of motion-picture films involving a diversified area of work. The data taken from the various films were "leveled" (adjusted to the time required by the normal operator) by the Westinghouse technique. This method of performance rating is described in Chapter 15 of this text. The

---

[5] H. B. Maynard, G. J. Stegemerten, and J. L. Schwab, *Methods-Time Measurement* (New York: McGraw-Hill Book Co., 1948).

[6] *Ibid.*

data were then tabulated and analyzed to determine the degree of difficulty caused by variable characteristics. For example, it was found that not only distance but also the type of reach affected reach time. Further analysis seemed to indicate that there were five distinct cases of reach, each requiring different time allotments to perform for a given distance. These are:

1.   Reach to object in fixed location, or to object in other hand, or on which other hand rests.
2.   Reach to single object in location which may vary slightly from cycle to cycle.
3.   Reach to object jumbled with other objects so that search and select occur.
4.   Reach to a very small object or where accurate grasp is required.
5.   Reach to indefinite location to get hand in position for body balance, or next motion, or out of way.[7]

Also, move time was influenced not only by distance and weight of the object being moved, but by the specific type of move. Three cases of move were found. These are:

1.   Move object to other hand or against stop.
2.   Move object to approximate or indefinite location.
3.   Move object to exact location.[8]

Table 19–5 summarizes M.T.M. values that have been developed to date. It will be noted that the time values of the therblig grasp vary from 2.0 TMU's to 12.9 TMU's (1 TMU equals 0.00001 hour) depending on the classification of the grasp. Likewise, there are 2 cases of release and 18 cases of position which influence time.

The steps followed in applying M.T.M. technique are similar to those for Work-Factor. First, the analyst summarizes all motions required to perform the job properly for both the left hand and the right hand. Then he determines from the methods-time data tables the leveled time in TMU's for each motion. The nonlimiting motion values should be circled or deleted, as only the limiting motions will be summarized, providing it is "easy" to perform the two motions simultaneously (see section X of Table 19–5), to determine the time required for a normal performance of the task. For example, if the right hand reached 20 inches to pick up a nut, the classification would be R20C and the time value would be 19.8 TMU's. If, at the same time, the left hand reached 10 inches to pick up a cap screw, a designation of R10C with a TMU value of 12.9 would be in effect. The right hand would be limiting, and the 12.9 value of the left hand would not be used in calculating the normal time.

The tabulated values presented do not carry any allowance for personal delays, fatigue, or unavoidable delays, and when used for estab-

---

[7] *Ibid.*

[8] *Ibid.*

TABLE 19–5

TABLE I—REACH—R

Distance Moved Inches	Time TMU A	Time TMU B	Time TMU C or D	Time TMU E	Hand In Motion A	Hand In Motion B	CASE AND DESCRIPTION
¾ or less	2.0	2.0	2.0	2.0	1.6	1.6	**A** Reach to object in fixed location, or to object in other hand or on which other hand rests.
1	2.5	2.5	3.6	2.4	2.3	2.3	
2	4.0	4.0	5.9	3.8	3.5	2.7	
3	5.3	5.3	7.3	5.3	4.5	3.6	**B** Reach to single object in location which may vary slightly from cycle to cycle.
4	6.1	6.4	8.4	6.8	4.9	4.3	
5	6.5	7.8	9.4	7.4	5.3	5.0	
6	7.0	8.6	10.1	8.0	5.7	5.7	
7	7.4	9.3	10.8	8.7	6.1	6.5	
8	7.9	10.1	11.5	9.3	6.5	7.2	**C** Reach to object jumbled with other objects in a group so that search and select occur.
9	8.3	10.8	12.2	9.9	6.9	7.9	
10	8.7	11.5	12.9	10.5	7.3	8.6	
12	9.6	12.9	14.2	11.8	8.1	10.1	
14	10.5	14.4	15.6	13.0	8.9	11.5	**D** Reach to a very small object or where accurate grasp is required.
16	11.4	15.8	17.0	14.2	9.7	12.9	
18	12.3	17.2	18.4	15.5	10.5	14.4	
20	13.1	18.6	19.8	16.7	11.3	15.8	
22	14.0	20.1	21.2	18.0	12.1	17.3	**E** Reach to indefinite location to get hand in position for body balance or next motion or out of way.
24	14.9	21.5	22.5	19.2	12.9	18.8	
26	15.8	22.9	23.9	20.4	13.7	20.2	
28	16.7	24.4	25.3	21.7	14.5	21.7	
30	17.5	25.8	26.7	22.9	15.3	23.2	

TABLE II—MOVE—M

Distance Moved Inches	Time TMU A	Time TMU B	Time TMU C	Hand In Motion B	Wt. (lb.) Up to	Factor	Constant TMU	CASE AND DESCRIPTION
¾ or less	2.0	2.0	2.0	1.7	2.5	0	0	
1	2.5	2.9	3.4	2.3				**A** Move object to other hand or against stop.
2	3.6	4.6	5.2	2.9	7.5	1.06	2.2	
3	4.9	5.7	6.7	3.6				
4	6.1	6.9	8.0	4.3				
5	7.3	8.0	9.2	5.0	12.5	1.11	3.9	
6	8.1	8.9	10.3	5.7				
7	8.9	9.7	11.1	6.5	17.5	1.17	5.6	
8	9.7	10.6	11.8	7.2				
9	10.5	11.5	12.7	7.9	22.5	1.22	7.4	
10	11.3	12.2	13.5	8.6				**B** Move object to approximate or indefinite location.
12	12.9	13.4	15.2	10.0	27.5	1.28	9.1	
14	14.4	14.6	16.9	11.4				
16	16.0	15.8	18.7	12.8	32.5	1.33	10.8	
18	17.6	17.0	20.4	14.2				
20	19.2	18.2	22.1	15.6				
22	20.8	19.4	23.8	17.0	37.5	1.39	12.5	
24	22.4	20.6	25.5	18.4				**C** Move object to exact location.
26	24.0	21.8	27.3	19.8	42.5	1.44	14.3	
28	25.5	23.1	29.0	21.2				
30	27.1	24.3	30.7	22.7	47.5	1.50	16.0	

TABLE III—TURN AND APPLY PRESSURE—T AND AP

Weight	30°	45°	60°	75°	90°	105°	120°	135°	150°	165°	180°
Small— 0 to 2 Pounds	2.8	3.5	4.1	4.8	5.4	6.1	6.8	7.4	8.1	8.7	9.4
Medium—2.1 to 10 Pounds	4.4	5.5	6.5	7.5	8.5	9.6	10.6	11.6	12.7	13.7	14.8
Large— 10.1 to 35 Pounds	8.4	10.5	12.3	14.4	16.2	18.3	20.4	22.2	24.3	26.1	28.2

APPLY PRESSURE CASE 1—16.2 TMU.   APPLY PRESSURE CASE 2—10.6 TMU

M.T.M. Association

TABLE 19–5 (Continued)

TABLE IV—GRASP—G

Case	Time TMU	DESCRIPTION
1A	2.0	**Pick Up Grasp**—Small, medium or large object by itself, easily grasped.
1B	3.5	Very small object or object lying close against a flat surface.
1C1	7.3	Interference with grasp on bottom and one side of nearly cylindrical object. Diameter larger than ½″.
1C2	8.7	Interference with grasp on bottom and one side of nearly cylindrical object. Diameter ¼″ to ½″.
1C3	10.8	Interference with grasp on bottom and one side of nearly cylindrical object. Diameter less than ¼″.
2	5.6	**Regrasp.**
3	5.6	**Transfer Grasp.**
4A	7.3	Object jumbled with other objects so search and select occur. Larger than 1″ x 1″ x 1″.
4B	9.1	Object jumbled with other objects so search and select occur. ¼″ x ¼″ x ⅛″ to 1″ x 1″ x 1″.
4C	12.9	Object jumbled with other objects so search and select occur. Smaller than ¼″ x ¼″ x ⅛″.
5	0	Contact, sliding or hook grasp.

TABLE V—POSITION*—P

CLASS OF FIT		Symmetry	Easy To Handle	Difficult To Handle
1—Loose	No pressure required	S	5.6	11.2
		SS	9.1	14.7
		NS	10.4	16.0
2—Close	Light pressure required	S	16.2	21.8
		SS	19.7	25.3
		NS	21.0	26.6
3—Exact	Heavy pressure required.	S	43.0	48.6
		SS	46.5	52.1
		NS	47.8	53.4

*Distance moved to engage—1″ or less.

TABLE VI—RELEASE—RL

Case	Time TMU	DESCRIPTION
1	2.0	Normal release performed by opening fingers as independent motion.
2	0	Contact Release.

TABLE VII—DISENGAGE—D

CLASS OF FIT	Easy to Handle	Difficult to Handle
1—Loose—Very slight effort, blends with subsequent move.	4.0	5.7
2—Close — Normal effort, slight recoil.	7.5	11.8
3—Tight — Considerable effort, hand recoils markedly.	22.9	34.7

TABLE VIII—EYE TRAVEL TIME AND EYE FOCUS—ET AND EF

Eye Travel Time $= 15.2 \times \dfrac{T}{D}$ TMU, with a maximum value of 20 TMU.

where T = the distance between points from and to which the eye travels.
D = the perpendicular distance from the eye to the line of travel T.

Eye Focus Time $= 7.3$ TMU.

TABLE 19–5 (Concluded)

TABLE IX—BODY, LEG, AND FOOT MOTIONS

DESCRIPTION	SYMBOL	DISTANCE	TIME TMU
Foot Motion—Hinged at Ankle.	FM	Up to 4″	8.5
With heavy pressure.	FMP		19.1
Leg or Foreleg Motion.	LM —	Up to 6″	7.1
		Each add'l. inch	1.2
Sidestep—Case 1—Complete when leading leg contacts floor.	SS-C1	Less than 12″	Use REACH or MOVE Time
		12″	17.0
		Each add'l. inch	.6
Case 2—Lagging leg must contact floor before next motion can be made.	SS-C2	12″	34.1
		Each add'l. inch	1.1
Bend, Stoop, or Kneel on One Knee.	B,S,KOK		29.0
Arise.	AB,AS,AKOK		31.9
Kneel on Floor—Both Knees.	KBK		69.4
Arise.	AKBK		76.7
Sit.	SIT		34.7
Stand from Sitting Position.	STD		43.4
Turn Body 45 to 90 degrees—			
Case 1—Complete when leading leg contacts floor.	TBC1		18.6
Case 2—Lagging leg must contact floor before next motion can be made.	TBC2		37.2
Walk.	W-FT.	Per Foot	5.3
Walk.	W-P	Per Pace	15.0

TABLE X—SIMULTANEOUS MOTIONS

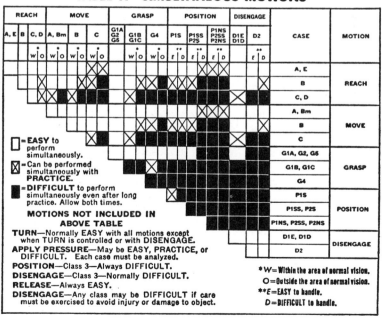

=EASY to perform simultaneously.

⊠=Can be performed simultaneously with **PRACTICE.**

■=DIFFICULT to perform simultaneously even after long practice. Allow both times.

MOTIONS NOT INCLUDED IN ABOVE TABLE

TURN—Normally EASY with all motions except when TURN is controlled or with DISENGAGE.
APPLY PRESSURE—May be EASY, PRACTICE, or DIFFICULT. Each case must be analyzed.
POSITION—Class 3—Always DIFFICULT.
DISENGAGE—Class 3—Normally DIFFICULT.
RELEASE—Always EASY.
DISENGAGE—Any class may be DIFFICULT if care must be exercised to avoid injury or damage to object.

*W=Within the area of normal vision.
O=Outside the area of normal vision.
**E=EASY to handle.
D=DIFFICULT to handle.

lishing time standards, an appropriate allowance must be added to the summary of the synthetic basic motion times.

M.T.M.—General Purpose Data

M.T.M.—G.P.D. has been defined by the M.T.M. Association as a "dynamic system of universally applicable motion patterns built with M.T.M. which is used in place of the more detailed M.T.M. procedures in building standard data for specific work applications wherever motion patterns are used."

M.T.M.—General Purpose Data is sponsored by the M.T.M. Association and is available to anyone who wishes to use it. The data are leased by the association.

The General Purpose Data system involves two levels of data. The first level (basic) provides data for the combination of the more common sequences of the detailed M.T.M. motions. The second level, known as multipurpose data, is a combination of the more common sequences of the first level. For example, in the first level "GET" table are codes that represent the time for a "reach," a "grasp," and a "release." The first-level "PLACE" table includes codes that represent the time for both a "move" and a "position." A typical second-level code would be the combination of the first-level "get" and the first-level "place" into one code called "multi-get." Thus, this multi-get would represent the time for a reach, a grasp, a move, a position, and a release of a part.

The coding used for the identification of M.T.M.—General Purpose Data is "alphamnemonic." The code is 7 digits, the first five being letters and the last two, numbers. For example, the code BGT-EV-06 would identify the data as being:

B	denotes basic (first) level
GT	signifies get category
E	implies an easy get
V	indicates that the object is in a variable location
06	denotes that the code contains a 6-inch reach

The first-level or basic data cover 13 categories with 353 codes. The six most used categories within this basic data are:

GET
PLACE
ELEMENTAL
BODY MOTIONS
READ
WRITE

The remaining seven categories of the data are:

ACTUATE
THREADED FASTENER
LUBRICATE
DIP
CLEAN
TOOL USE
INSPECT & TEST

The second-level or multipurpose data were published in 1964 and contain approximately 200 codes involving the five categories:

GET
PLACE
BODY MOTIONS
VISING
CLAMPING

Additional categories currently being reviewed for inclusion as supplements to the second-level listings include:

FASTEN—THREADED AND NONTHREADED
OBJECT HANDLING
PACKAGING
TOOL USE
ACTUATE

The M.T.M. Association has established the following requirements for obtaining M.T.M.—G.P.D.:

1. The company must be a member in good standing with the Association.
2. At least one of the employees of the company must be a qualified applicator of M.T.M., having taken the prescribed 105-hour training course and passed the Association's test for certification.
3. The company must certify employment of or access to qualified guidance in the use of M.T.M. and M.T.M.—G.P.D. This guidance can be obtained in one of two ways:
   a) Have one of their M.T.M. applicators certified by the Association Testing as an in-plant instructor.
   b) Employ the services of a licensed instructor from one of the 17 management council members of the association.

The M.T.M. Association has stated that M.T.M.—General Purpose Data will give an accuracy within 15 percent (when compared with M.T.M.) for cycle times over 0.120 minutes in 95 percent of the cycles analyzed. As the cycle time increases, the accuracy of the General Purpose Data will improve.

M.T.M.–2

In an effort to further the application of M.T.M. to work areas where the detail of M.T.M.–1 would economically preclude its use, the International Directorate of the M.T.M. Association initiated a research project to develop less refined data suitable for the majority of motion sequences. The result of this effort was M.T.M.–2 which has been defined by the M.T.M. Association of the United Kingdom as

a system of synthesized M.T.M. data and is the second general level of M.T.M. data. It is based exclusively on M.T.M. and consists of:
1. Single basic M.T.M. motions
2. Combinations of basic M.T.M. motions

The data is adapted to the operator and is independent of the work place or equipment used. It is not possible to replace any element in M.T.M.-2 by means of other elements in M.T.M.-2.

In general M.T.M.–2 should find application in those work assignments where:

1. The effort portion of the work cycle is more than one minute in length.
2. The cycle is not highly repetitive.
3. The manual portion of the work cycle does not involve a large number of either complex or simultaneous hand motions.

It has been observed that the variability between M.T.M.–1 (M.T.M.) and M.T.M.–2 is dependent to a large extent on the length of the cycle. This is reflected in Figure 19–2 where the range of percentage deviation of M.T.M.–2 with M.T.M. is shown. This range of "error" is considered to be the expected range 95 percent of the time.

FIGURE 19–2

Percentage variation of M.T.M.–1 when compared with M.T.M.–2 at increasing cycle lengths

M.T.M.–2 recognizes 10 classes of actions which are referred to as "categories." These 10 categories and their symbols are:

GET	G
PUT	P
GET WEIGHT	GW
PUT WEIGHT	PW
REGRASP	R
APPLY PRESSURE	A
EYE ACTION	E
FOOT ACTION	F
STEP	S
BEND & ARISE	B
CRANK	C

In using M.T.M.–2 distances are estimated by classes and affect the times of both the GET and PUT categories. As in M.T.M.–1 the distance moved is based on the length of the path traveled by the knuckle at the base of the index finger in the case of hand motions and where only the fingers move the distance is measured at the fingertips.

The codes for the five tabulated distance classes are:

Inches	*Code*
0–2	5
over 2–6	15
over 6–12	30
over 12–18	45
over 18	80

The categories GET and PUT are usually considered simultaneously. Three variables affect the time required to perform both of these variables. These variables are the case involved, the distance traveled, and the weight handled. The reader should recognize that GET can be considered a composite of reach and grasp while PUT is a combination of the therbligs move, position, and release.

Three cases of GET have been identified as A, B, and C. Case A implies a simple contact grasp such as when the fingers push an ashtray across the desk. If an object such as a pencil is picked up by simply enclosing the fingers with a single movement, a case B grasp is employed. If the type of grasp is not indicative of either an A or a B, then a case C GET is being employed.

The analyst can resort to the decision diagram (Figure 19–3) to assist in the determination of the correct case of GET.

Tabular values in TMU's of the three cases of GET applied to each of the five coded distances are shown in Table 19–6.

Just as three cases of GET have been established, so are there three cases of PUT.

FIGURE 19–3

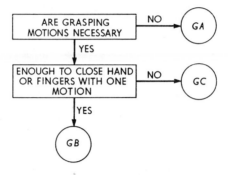

The decision diagram (Figure 19–4) may be utilized to determine which case of PUT is applicable.

Explanation of the three cases of PUT, as well as tabular values for each class applied to the five coded distances are shown in Table 19–7.

PUT is accomplished in one of two ways: insertion and alignment. An

TABLE 19–6

Tabular values for GET

		Distance code				
Case	*Description*	*5*	*15*	*30*	*45*	*80*
GA.........No grasp necessary		3	6	9	13	17
GB.........Simple closing of fingers or hand		7	10	14	18	23
GC.........Any other grasp		14	19	23	27	32

insertion involves placing one object into another such as a shaft into a sleeve while an alignment involves orienting a part on a surface such as bringing a rule up to a line.

Tolerance limits have been established to provide guidelines as to the most appropriate case of PUT. When one part is inserted into another

FIGURE 19–4

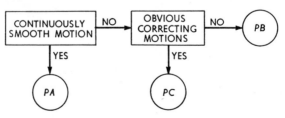

and more than 0.4-inch clearance exists, the parts can usually be brought together utilizing a smooth, continuous motion and consequently a case PA would be involved. If the clearance were reduced to less than 0.4-inch so that some irregularity in motion pattern occurs, yet no pressure is required to mate the objects the case would be PB. And if a close fit were involved where slight pressure was required to mate the objects or if a loose fit and difficult to handle part were encountered thus necessitating corrective mating, the case would be cataloged as PC.

For alignment type PUTS the following dimensional relations can be used as guidelines. If an object is placed adjacent to a line to a tolerance of less than $\frac{1}{16}$ inch the case is PC. However, if the tolerance is more than $\frac{1}{16}$ inch but less than $\frac{1}{4}$ inch it is classified as PB and if it is more than $\frac{1}{4}$ inch it is classified as PA.

TABLE 19–7

Tabular values for PUT

Case	Description	Distance Code				
		5	15	30	45	80
PA........	Smooth continuous motion	3	6	11	15	20
PB........	Some irregularity in motion pattern	10	15	19	24	30
PC........	Correcting motions obvious	21	26	30	36	41

Weight is considered in M.T.M.–2 in a fashion similar to M.T.M.–1.

The time value addition for "Get Weight" (GW) has been estimated as 1 TMU per effective kilogram. Thus if a load of 6 kilograms is handled by both hands the time addition due to weight would be 3 TMU's since the effective weight per hand was 3 kilograms.

For "Put Weight" (PW) additions have been estimated at 1 TMU per 5 kilograms of effective weight up to a maximum of 20 kilograms.

The category of regrasp (R) has been defined as under M.T.M.–1. Here, however, a time of 6 TMU's has been assigned. The authors of M.T.M.–2 point out that for a regrasp to be in effect, control must be retained by the hand.

Apply pressure has been assigned a time of 14 TMU's. The authors point out that this category can be applied by any member of the body and that the maximum permissible movement in order for an apply pressure to exist is $\frac{1}{4}$ inch.

Eye action (E) is allowed under either of the following cases:

a) When it is necessary for the eye to move in order to see the various aspects of the operation involving more than one specific section of the work area.

b) When the eye must concentrate on an object so as to recognize a distinguishable characteristic.

The estimated value of (E) is 7 TMU's. It is only allowed when it must be performed independently of other hand or body motions.

Crank (C) occurs when the hands or fingers are used to move an object in a circular path of more than ½ revolution. A PUT is indicated in those cranks of less than ½ revolution. Only two variables are associated with the category crank under M.T.M.–2. These are the number of revolutions and the weight or resistance involved. A time of 15 TMU's is allotted for each complete revolution. Where weight or resistance is significant, PW is applied to each revolution.

FIGURE 19–5

Foot movements are allowed 9 TMU's and step movements 18 TMU's. Time for the step movement is based upon a 34-inch pace. The decision diagram (Figure 19–5) can be helpful in ascertaining whether a given movement should be classified as a step or a foot movement.

The category BEND & ARISE (B) occurs when the body changes its vertical position. Typical movements characteristic of B are sitting down, standing up, kneeling, etc. A time value of 61 TMU's has been assigned

TABLE 19–8

A summary of M.T.M.–2 data (all time values are in TMU's)

Code	GA	GB	GC	PA	PB	PC
− 5.........	3	7	14	3	10	21
−15.........	6	10	19	6	15	26
−30.........	9	14	23	11	19	30
−45.........	13	18	27	15	24	36
−80.........	17	23	32	20	30	41

GW − 1/KG   PW − 1/5 KG

A	R	E	C	S	F	B
14	6	7	15	18	9	61

for B. The authors indicate that when an operator kneels on both knees the movement should be classed as 2 B.

A summary of M.T.M.–2 values are shown in Table 19–8. The reader should recognize, as in the case of M.T.M.–1, not all motions can be performed simultaneously with both hands in the same time as when performed by one hand only. Figure 19–6 reflects those motion patterns where the time required for simultaneous motions is the same as when the motion is performed by one hand. In these instances an X appears. When additional time is required to perform the simultaneous motion the magnitude of this extra amount is given with the appropriate coding.

As in all fundamental motion data systems, the novice should not try to apply the data until he has been properly trained in its use and application.

FIGURE 19–6

M.T.M.–2 simultaneous hand
motion allowances

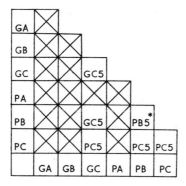

* If PB ___ is performed simultaneously with PB ___ an addition of PB5 is made only if the actions are outside the normal area of vision.

Basic Motion Timestudy

The Basic Motion Timestudy (B.M.T.) procedure developed in the period 1945 to 1951 by Ralph Presgrave and his associates in J. B. Woods & Gordon Limited of Toronto was a result of a research program endeavoring to measure accurately the effect of the various physical factors influencing the time of hand motions.

According to B.M.T., a basic motion is one in which a body member at rest moves and again comes to rest. For example, in reaching for a pencil lying on the table a basic motion would occur. The beginning of the motion would be the pause or point of rest just prior to the reach, and the termination of the basic motion would be the pause that occurs immediately after the fingers have grasped the pencil. B.M.T. was developed through laboratory study and experiment rather than analysis of uncontrolled factory operations. B.M.T. values have been established in ten thousandths of a minute, as shown in Table 19–9.

TABLE 19–9

BASIC MOTION TIMESTUDY VALUES
(Expressed in Ten Thousandths of a Minute)

REACH OR MOVE

Inches	½	1	2	3	4	5	6	7	8	9	10	12	14	16	18	20	22	24	26	28	30
A	27	30	36	39	42	45	47	50	52	54	56	60	64	68	72	76	80	84	88	92	96
B	32	36	42	46	49	52	55	58	60	62	64	68	72	76	80	84	88	92	96	100	104
BV	36	42	48	53	57	60	63	66	68	70	73	77	81	85	89	93	97	101	105	109	113
C	41	48	55	60	64	68	71	74	77	79	81	86	90	94	98	102	107	111	115	119	123
CV	45	54	62	67	72	76	79	82	85	87	90	95	99	104	108	112	116	120	124	128	132

PRECISION

Inches	1	2	3	4	5	6	7	8	9	10	12	14	16	18	20	22	24	26	28	30
1/2″ tol.	3	4	6	7	8	9	10	11	12	13	14	16	17	18	19	20	21	22	23	24
1/4″ tol.	13	16	18	21	23	25	27	29	31	32	36	39	42	45	48	51	53	55	57	59
1/8″ tol.	33	37	41	45	48	52	55	58	60	62	67	72	76	80	83	87	91	94	98	101
1/16″ tol.	60	65	69	73	76	80	83	87	90	93	98	103	107	112	115	119	123	127	131	135
1/32″ tol.	90	97	102	106	110	114	117	120	123	126	131	135	139	143	147	150	153	157	161	165

SIMULTANEOUS MOTIONS

Separation Distance	0	2	4	6	8	10	12	14	16	18	20	22	24
1/4″ tolerance and over	0	10	18	27	34	41	47	54	59	65	69	74	78
1/8″ ....″......″.....	0	12	21	30	37	44	51	57	63	68	73	78	82
1/16″....″ ....″.....	0	15	27	37	45	53	61	68	75	80	86	91	96
1/32″....″......″.....	0	19	34	47	58	68	77	84	90	97	103	107	111

FORCE

Apply Pressure, Start or Stop

Inches	6	12	24
2 pounds	2	3	3
4	6	6	7
6	8	9	10
8	10	11	13
10	13	14	16
15	18	20	22
20	23	26	28
30	31	35	38
40	38	43	47
50	45	50	55

TURN

Degrees	30	45	60	75	90	120	150	180
A	26	29	32	34	37	43	49	54
B	33	36	40	43	47	54	60	67
BV	40	44	48	52	56	65	72	80
C	56	60	64	68	72	81	88	96
CV	73	77	81	85	89	98	105	113

EYE TIME

80

BODY MOTIONS

LM (1′-6″) 50	Leg Motion	TB₁ 110	Turn Body
Add per inch .. 2		TB₂ 220	Turn Body
		B 180	Bend
FM 55	Foot Motion	S 180	Stoop
W 100	Walk One Pace	K₁ 180	Kneel on one Knee
SS₁ (1′-6″) 60	Side Step	AB etc. 200	Arise
Add per inch.. 2		K₂ 440	Kneel on Knees
		AK₂ 480	Arise from Knees
SS₂ (1′-6″) 120	Side Step	SIT 220	Sit
Add per inch.. 4		STAND 270	Stand

Note: subscripts in Body Motions read as TB_1, TB_2, K_1, K_2, AK_2, SS_1, SS_2.

The basic motions identified for purposes of B.M.T. are as follows:

Arm, Hand, and Finger Motions:
1. Reach
2. Move
3. Turn

Body Motions:

1. Foot motion	7. Arise
2. Leg motion	8. Sit
3. Sidestep	9. Stand
4. Bend	10. Turn body
5. Stoop	11. Walk
6. Kneel	12. Eye motions

Finger, hand, and arm motions are identified in terms of the muscular and visual controls that the operator must use to complete them according to the above specifications. The variable factors that affect these motions are described verbally and numerically.

The time data provide a bonus opportunity of some 25 to 30 percent for the average operator on incentive. They do not include provision for rest and personal requirements of the operator. These must be added to suit the individual jobs.

Basic motions

B.M.T. recognizes three distinct classes of arm motions. Class A motions are stopped by impact with a solid object. All muscular effort is used to move the arm in the direction of the motion and none is required to slow down or stop the action. Examples include the downstroke in hammering and the motion to push a flat sheet of metal against a stop in metal shearing.

Class B motions are motions stopped entirely by muscular control. Examples include the upstroke in hammering, the motion to toss an object aside, the motion to move the hands aside after placing a part in a foot-operated punch press, and the back-and-forth motions in using a rubber eraser.

Class C motions are motions that are stopped by using muscular control to slow the arm before coming to a stop in a grasping or placing action. Examples include reach to a machine lever and grasp, reach to pencil in other hand and grasp, and carry pencil to desk and place down.

The time to perform B and C class motions (motions requiring muscular control in the stopping action) is influenced by the type of visual control required to complete the motion. Whenever the eyes are needed to direct a motion to its destination, but cannot be focused on the end point before the motion begins, the time for the motion will be increased. Motions that are delayed by this form of eye activity are referred to as visually directed motions and are recognized in the B.M.T. time data by the introduction of two additional motion classifications BV and CV. This arrangement provides for five classes of motion, each requiring a different set of time data as shown in Table 19–9.

B.M.T. makes no distinction between the times to perform basic reaches (transport empty) and basic moves (transport loaded). The effect of the weight of an object being carried is provided for, when necessary, in the form of an allowance to the basic time as described later. For purposes of analysis, reaches and moves are identified by the code letters R and M respectively. A class C reach is coded R–C while a class C move is coded M–C.

Variable factors

The time to perform each of these basic motions is influenced by one or more variable factors.

One factor that affects all classes of motion is the distance covered by the motion. A direct relationship exists between the distance through which the motion is performed and the time to perform it. The amount of the variable present is expressed in inches. The complete coding for a class C reach 12 inches long is R12C.

Another factor that influences all classes of motion is defined as "force." The amount of the force factor to be allowed for handling a given weight depends upon the method of handling the weight and the distance through which it is handled. For example, the force allowance for tossing aside a 10-pound object that is already held in the hand, using a 24-inch arm motion, will require the basic allowance of 16, which is shown in the force time table. If the weight had to be picked up from a bench before being tossed aside, the allowance would be twice basic or 32. If the weight were picked up, carried 24 inches and again placed down, the allowance would be three times basic or 48.

These allowances are in the form of additions to the time for a basic motion. The complete code and standard time for the three examples used will be as follows:

1. Toss aside weight already held using a 24-inch motion

   M24B.............. 92
   1F10............. 16
   108 or 0.0108 min.

2. Pick up weight and toss aside

   M24B.............. 92
   2F10............. 32
   124 or 0.124 min.

3. Pick up weight, carry and place down

   M24C.............. 111
   3F10............. 48
   159 or 0.0159 min.

A third variable factor is referred to in B.M.T. as "precision." It is described as the extra care required when motions that use muscular control in the stopping action are completed within close limits.

Precision becomes a factor whenever the limits within which the finger tips can move to complete the action are reduced to ½ inch or less.

The allowance for precision is also in the form of additions to the time for a basic motion. The amount of the allowance depends upon the degree of precision and the length of the motion with which it is associated. The time data recognize five degrees of precision from ½ inch to ⅟₃₂ inch for motion distances up to 30 inches. The standard time for a motion that ends in grasping an object, where the limits within which the fingers can complete the action is no more than ¼ inch, is developed as follows:

$$
\begin{array}{lr}
\text{R12C} \dotfill & 86 \\
\text{P¼} \dotfill & \underline{36} \\
& 122 \text{ or } 0.0122 \text{ min.}
\end{array}
$$

Turns

Arm motions performed by turning or rotating the hand and forearm around the long axis of the forearm are treated as a typical type of arm motion and are called "turns." Separate time data are shown for the five classes of basic arm turns.

The influence of distance is expressed in degrees rather than inches and the code for a 90° C class turn is shown as T90C.

Simultaneous arm motion

B.M.T. provides an allowance for arm motions performed separately but simultaneously if each arm requires visual direction. The allowance is to compensate for the delay caused by one arm having to slow down or come to a complete stop at some point short of the destination while the eyes direct the other arm to its destination.

The amount of allowance depends upon the degree of precision in the ending actions and the distance separating the two end points. This allowance is also in the form of an addition to the time for a basic motion. The complete code and standard time for simultaneous arm motion are recorded in two stages. The first stage establishes the details for a one-handed operation. The second stage provides the allowance to cover the delay when simultaneous motions performed. The procedure is illustrated by showing the separate stages for simultaneous arm motion 12 inches long to place objects within limits of ⅛ inch, where the end points are 12 inches apart.

$$
\begin{array}{lll}
\text{1st stage:} & \text{M12CV} \dotfill & 95 \\
\text{1st stage:} & \text{P⅛} \dotfill & \underline{67} \\
& & 162 \\
\text{2nd stage:} & \text{Simo 12 inch} \dotfill & \underline{51} \\
& & 213 \text{ or } 0.0213 \text{ min.}
\end{array}
$$

Application technique

The B.M.T. procedures outline methods to be used for developing standards for other types of arm motions such as those that follow curved or circular paths. They also include time data for body motions such as steps, body bending, and turning actions, and describe procedures for developing standards that involve combinations of arm and body motion.

FIGURE 19–7

Basic element breakdown of assembling cap to fountain pen

BASIC ELEMENT STUDY					SHEET 1 OF 1	
DEPT.			DATE		SHEET OF	
OPERATION Assemble Cap to Fountain Pen			OPERATOR		OBSERVER	
DATA						
MAJOR ELEMENT	L.H. BASIC ELEMENT	SYMBOL	TIME	SYMBOL	R.H. BASIC ELEMENT	
	Reach to cap on table	R			Hold barrel	
	Move cap to pen point	M			"	
	Move cap along barrel	M			"	
	Hold cap			T	Rotate barrel half turn	
	"			T	Regrasp barrel	
	"			T	Rotate barrel final half turn	
	"			M	Place pen on desk	

Figure 19–7 illustrates the technique used in identifying the basic motions employed in a given method for assembling a cap to a fountain pen.

Motion-Time Analysis

Motion-Time Analysis was developed by A. B. Segur in the middle 1920's as a method of establishing time standards. Today, this fundamental motion procedure system, similar to the others discussed in this text, is finding its greatest use as a tool of the methods analyst for improving existing operations, and correctly planning and controlling future operations.

It is similar to the others mentioned in this chapter in that the analyst first makes a listing of the motions being performed by both hands. For each motion, an appropriate time value is assigned. If the motion is classified as being ineffective (of doubtful value in the job), the figures for its time are entered in red pencil. If the motion is classified as being effective (motion should be generally allowed), its value is posted in black. The number and extent of the red figures are an indication of the method improvement possibilities.

The basic concept of motion time analysis is that the time required to perform basic motions tends to be constant for different individuals. Consequently, time is a function of method. In other words, if the correct method is followed by any operator, he will achieve the standard that was established by that method.

Dimensional Motion Times

Dimensional Motion Times, referred to as DMT, is a procedure developed by the General Electric Company for measuring the work content by predetermined time values. This system has developed the following tables of values:

1. Grasp—jumbled parts in trays, rod—type parts
2. Grasp—jumbled parts in trays, block—type parts
3. Grasp—scattered parts on bench
4. Grasp—isolated parts on surface
5. Grasp—pre-positioned tools
6. Grasp—parts from confined area
7. Position hole to pin or pin to hole
8. Position parts to various nest
9. Position and start nut to screw, one hand
10. Position and start nut to screw, simo
11. Restricted area position
12. Rotate
13. Release
14. Transport
15. Time to turn crank
16. Directional turn
17. Weight factors applicable to move, grasp, position, and release
18. Miscellaneous motion times

DMT has emphasized "dimension" as the principal criteria affecting time to perform a motion. As in other fundamental motion data systems, this technique has its greatest application in the study and the improvement of methods and establishment of standards on manual, bench-type, high-volume work.

Master Standard Data

Master Standard Data is a simplified technique of applying fundamental motion data based on M.T.M. It was introduced by the Serge A. Birn Company in 1962.[9] The authors of MSD emphasize the effect of control on the time required to perform the fundamental motions and the ability to perform them simultaneously. The classification of control with typical examples of the most common motions are given in Table 19–10.

TABLE 19–10

MSD classification of control

Class of control	Motion				
	Reach	*Grasp*	*Move*	*Release*	*Align*
Little....... (A)	To an object in a fixed location or an object in the other hand	Simple pick-up grasp made by a closing of the fingers. Object is by itself and is easily grasped	An object against a positive stop	Control is relinquished by simple opening of the fingers	
Mental..... (B)	To an object in a location that may vary from cycle to cycle		An object to an approximate location. Tolerance of location is close		
Mental.... or Visual (C)	To an object jumbled with other objects or to a very small object	An object that cannot be controlled by a single closing of the fingers	An object to an exact location		Carefully one object with another object

As more control is required, so more time is needed to perform the basic motions. And, as would be expected, the greater the control, the less the probability of the typical operator being able to perform the motion simultaneously. Table 19–11 provides information as to the class of control and whether or not the operator should be expected to perform fundamental motions simultaneously.

The complete MSD data are shown in Table 19–12. The units of

---

[9] Richard M. Crossan and Harold W. Nance, *Master Standard Data* (New York: McGraw-Hill Book Co., 1962).

time are one-hundred-thousandth of an hour as in M.T.M. data. MSD recognizes only four distances for the application of the "obtain" and "place" motions. These are 2, 6, 12 and 18 inches. When assigning a time for performing an "obtain," in addition to distance, the degree of control needs to be considered. Only two considerations are dealt with: either some control must be exercised by the operator to bring the object under his control, or else high control is required. Some control is defined as taking place "when the object can be secured satisfactorily by a simple contact or closing of the fingers," and high control as taking place "if the object cannot be obtained with some control."

Finally, the number of obtains to be made must be taken into consideration. Thus, two "obtains" take place when we obtain a single thing

TABLE 19–11

Ability to perform various classes of control simultaneously

Class	A (Little)	B (Mental)	C (Mental or visual)
A. (Little)	Yes	Yes	No
B. (Mental)	Yes	Yes	No
C.	No	No	No

with both hands, and when two separate things are obtained, one with each hand. Other "obtains" are one in number for a particular movement.

As was the case in "obtain," "place" is characterized by varying degrees of control. Five parameters must be considered when analyzing a place element: distance, destination, number of alignments, accuracy of final placement, and weight of the object placed. Only three destinations are recognized by MSD: in the other hand, in a general location, and in an exact location. Exact location is differentiated from general location as being required in those instances where visual control is necessary in order to locate the part.

MSD allows 1 TMU (0.00001 hr.) extra for every 2 pounds of weight "placed" over 5 pounds. Thus, if a 13-pound object is moved, the allowed weight over 5 pounds per hand $= \dfrac{13 - 5}{2} = 4$ TMU.

It is apparent that the "OBTAIN" table tabularizes data for the combined basic motions of reach and grasp; and the "PLACE" table gives data for the combined motions move, position, and release. The authors of MSD state that probably 99 percent of hand and arm work is done by

TABLE 19–12

OBTAIN—O				
DISTANCE IN INCHES	DEGREE OF CONTROL			
	Some—S		High—H	
	1	2	1	2
2	8	8	17	30
6	13	13	21	34
12	17	17	25	38
18	21	21	30	42

PLACE—P					
DISTANCE IN INCHES	LOCATION				
	Other Hand	General	Exact		
			Loose—L		*Close—C*	
	0	6	1	2	1	2
2	7	5	11	26	21	47
6	11	9	16	31	27	52
12	15	13	21	36	31	57
18	19	17	26	41	37	62

Rotate			*Use*		*Finger*		*Body Motions*		
R			*U*		*Shift*		*B*		
H	F	9	V	4	FS	6	A	Arise-sit	108
	W	15	L	8			F	Foot	9
C	S	17	M	13			V	Vertical	61
	L	19	H	17	EF	11	W	Walk	17

"obtaining" and "placing" and, consequently, utilizes the data in these two tables. Of course, at times, special situations occur which require the use of the other tables.

The "finger shift" and "exert force" data are analogous to the "regrasp" and "apply pressure" values identified by the M.T.M. system. Finger shift has been defined as "a series of minor movements of the fingers performed for the purpose of pre-positioning an object prior to performing the basic element 'place.'" The element "finger shift" is performed for pre-positioning objects and is allowable only when visual control is required.

"Exert force" has been defined by the authors as "an instantaneous application of more than normal force applied for the purpose of overcoming initial resistance or forcing one object against or into another."

"Rotate" takes place when an object is turned on an axis that is parallel to the operator's forearm. It may be performed by grasping the work with the fingers and then rotating (an RH motion) or by a cranking motion (an RC motion). The RH motion may be made with the fingers (RHF) where the TMU value is 9, or with the wrist (RHW) having a TMU value of 15. In rotating by cranking, two possibilities may occur. A short path or crank diameter is identified with those cranking motions up to 6 inches and carries a TMU value of 17. Path or crank diameters more than 6 inches are classified as being long and a tabular value of 19 TMU's has been assigned.

"Use" is identified as those "back-and-forth movements of the fingers, hand, or hand and arm" that take place when work is being accomplished. Typical examples would be hammering a nail, sanding a table, erasing a paper, and so forth. In "use," only one variable is recognized— the displacement of the body member or members making it. Four degrees of displacement have been tabulated: very light (V), light (L), medium (M), and heavy (H). Very light "use" is performed only by the fingers or hand, and involves a displacement of less than 1 inch. Light "use" takes place when the displacement is about 2 inches and the motion is performed by the wrist alone. Medium "use" is based on a displacement of 4 inches, and heavy "use" involves a displacement of approximately 6 inches.

Master Standard Data identifies four body motions: arise-sit, foot, vertical, and walk. Body arise-sit begins the instant the operator is in front of his chair or bench and terminates when he has returned to this position after having sat down and arisen.

Foot body motions involve a movement of the foot hinged at the ankle. It is frequently used for depressing foot pedals on a wide variety of production equipment.

Vertical body motions represent those combinations of motions performed in order to get the hands to or near the floor and then return them to the waist level.

Walk body motions involve all horizontal body shifts resulting from moving the feet. Thus, foot shifts backward, forward, and sideward, or plain walking are examples of this body motion.

All body motions can be simultaneously performed with other motions. However, according to the authors, experience has established the rule that "when a body motion is followed immediately by an Obtain or Place, an 02 or P2 appropriate to the method is always allowed."

Master Standard Data unquestionably represents a significant contribution in the area of synthetic basic motion times. The authors have simplified the procedure for utilizing the tool of synthetic motion times so that the technique is more acceptable to methods and standards analysts, and to management. According to the authors, little, if any, accuracy is sacrificed in the utilization of MSD when compared with either leveled time study, standard data, or detailed M.T.M. They state "in literally thousands of instances it has proved 'accurate' well within the accepted work measurement consistency limits of plus or minus 5 percent."

Applying synthetic basic motion times

As a means of improving methods, a general knowledge of the fundamentals of synthetic motion-time standards will prove invaluable. For example, if the methods analyst has a grounding in M.T.M., he will design work stations to utilize the "G1A" grasps requiring but 2 TMU's rather than the more difficult grasps which require as much as 12.9 (G4C) TMU's. Likewise, he will endeavor to design for utilizing contact releases rather than normal releases and for symmetrical positioning rather than semisymmetrical or nonsymmetrical positioning. One of the important uses for any of the synthetic basic motion-time techniques lies in the area of methods. Once an analyst has an appreciation of this tool, he will find himself looking more critically at each and every work station, thinking how improvement may be made. Reaches and moves of 20 inches will appear unduly long to him, and he will immediately consider the savings possible through shortened motion patterns. Positioning elements that involve heavy pressure are automatically a sign of need for improvement. Operations that require eye travel and eye focus time can usually be improved.

Of course, standards of performance may be established through synthetic basic motion times. If the data are to be used for this purpose, a much greater knowledge of the techniques of application is required. In no case should an analyst endeavor to establish time standards to be used for rate purposes until he has had thorough training and has demonstrated his ability to use the tool precisely. Thus, the analyst must know if the distance moved is the linear distance taken by the hand or the circumferential distance taken by the arc that the hand makes. He must know if the distance is measured from the center of the hand, the knuckles, or the fingertips. He must know when application of pressure prevails and when it does not. He must clearly understand the elements of alignment and orientation as they affect positioning time. These and many other considerations must be mastered before an analyst can expect to establish consistent and accurate time standards with this tool.

Mr. A. B. Segur has not made the derivations and use of his Motion-Time Analysis values available to the public. He defends his position as follows:

Now I have heard in the last few years a great deal of criticism because the motion values that have gone with Motion-Time Analysis have not been generally published. As a matter of fact, these motions values have been very freely given to anyone who is sufficiently trained in the art of fundamental motion study to be able to use them correctly. But, as a matter of course, we know what would happen in a large plant if someone who is not sufficiently trained undertook to equate the working conditions, the exact motions and the correct times. The principle of fundamental motions could not be used, and the result would be disastrous. That is to say that those who are going to use this principle should be trained. By insisting upon that training, we get away from having our work discredited.[10]

It is only after thorough training that a group of analysts will arrive at consistent time standards using any of the synthetic motion-time techniques. In no case should any analyst endeavor to establish time standards with only a superficial knowledge of this tool.

Development of standard data

Today one of the broadest uses of predetermined times is in the development of standard data elements. With standard data, operations can be prepriced much faster than by the laborious procedure of summarizing long columns of fundamental motion times. In addition to saving time, clerical errors in applying standard data are reduced, since less arithmetic is involved.

With sound standard data, it is economically feasible to establish standards on maintenance work, material handling, clerical and office work, inspection work and other indirect and expense operations. Thus, elements involving long cycles and consisting of many short duration elements may be prepriced economically with standard data. For example, one company developed standard data applicable to radial drill operations in its toolroom. Standard data were developed for the elements required to move the tool from one hole to the next and to present and back off the drill. These standard data elements were then combined in one multivariable chart so they could be summarized rapidly. See Table 19–13.

---

[10] *Proceedings, National Time and Motion Study Clinic, 1940,* Industrial Management Society.

TABLE 19–13

Multivariable chart with two points of entry and with reference included for element: up spindle, swing and traverse head, and down spindle (Western Radial Drill)

NORMAL MINUTES

Depth‑of‑previous‑hole portion of the chart:

Reference Line	Depth of Previous Hole in Inches						
	0–1	2	3	4	5	6	7
	.010	.013	.015	.017	.019	.022	.024
.038	.048	.051	.053	.055	.057	.060	.062
.040	.050	.053	.055	.057	.059	.062	.064
.042	.052	.055	.057	.059	.061	.064	.066
.044	.054	.057	.059	.061	.063	.066	.068
.046	.056	.059	.061	.063	.065	.068	.070
.048	.058	.061	.063	.065	.067	.070	.072
.050	.060	.063	.065	.067	.069	.072	.074
.052	.062	.065	.067	.069	.071	.074	.076
.055	.065	.068	.070	.072	.074	.077	.079
.058	.068	.071	.073	.075	.077	.080	.082
.060	.070	.073	.075	.077	.079	.082	.084
.063	.073	.076	.078	.080	.082	.085	.087
.066	.076	.079	.081	.083	.085	.088	.090
.069	.079	.082	.084	.086	.088	.091	.093
.072	.082	.085	.087	.089	.091	.094	.096
.076	.086	.089	.091	.093	.095	.098	.100
.079	.089	.092	.094	.096	.098	.101	.103
.083	.093	.096	.098	.100	.102	.105	.107
.088	.098	.101	.103	.105	.107	.110	.112

Entry matrix — Traverse of Head in Inches (column headers) and Maximum Swing of Head in Inches (cell values):

Traverse of Head in Inches	0–1	2	3	4	5	6	7	8	9	10
Maximum Swing of Head in Inches (cell entries)	0–1; 0–1; 2; 3, 4, 6; 8, 10	0–1	0–1; 2, 3, 6; 8, 10	0–1, 2, 3; 4, 6, 10	0–1; 2, 3, 6; 10	0–2, 3; 4, 8, 10	0–1; 2, 4, 6; 10	0–1, 2, 3; 6, 10	0–1; 3, 6, 10	0–1, 3, 6, 10

FIGURE 19–8

Standard data for prepricing press operations

1. Length of blank_____	4. No. of cuts_____	7. _____
2. Width of blank_____	5. Machine_____	8. _____
3. Weight of blank_____	6. _____	9. _____

A. P/U Blank-Asy. To Stop-Day.--Piece Aside

Weight	Toss Pc. Aside	Place Pc. Aside	Stack Piece		
4 lbs.	.054	.062	.064	X____occ.= ____
4-14 lbs.	.071	.081	.084	X____occ.= ____
14-26 lbs.	.098	.109	.113	X____occ.= ____
26-40 lbs.	.103	.115	.119	X____occ.= ____
40 lbs.	.108	.121	.126	X____occ.= ____

B. Invert Part 180°

Weight	5"-9.9"	Major Dimension Inverted 10"-19.9"	20"-29.9"	30"-39.9"		
4 lbs.	simo	simo	.030	.034	X____occ.= ____
4-14 lbs.	simo	.031	.037	.041	X____occ.= ____
14-26 lbs.	.028	.035	.042	.046	X____occ.= ____
26-40 lbs.	-	.039	.047	.052	X____occ.= ____
40 lbs.	-	-	.050	.057	X____occ.= ____

C. Dsy. Pc.-Rotate 90°-Piece

Weight	5"-9.9"	Major Dimension Rotated 10"-19.9"	20"-29.9"	30"-39.9"
4 lbs.	.030	.036	.040	.043
4-14 lbs.	.038	.043	.050	.053
14-26 lbs.	-	.056	.062	.065
26-40 lbs.	-	.063	.070	.073
40 lbs.	-	.070	.077	.081

Dsy. Pc.-Rotate 180°Asy. Piece

Weight	5"-9.9"	Major Dimension Rotated 10"-19.9"	20"-29.9"	30"-39.9"
4 lbs.	.044	.053	.062	.068
4-14 lbs.	.055	.066	.075	.084
14-26 lbs.	-	.080	.090	.101
26-40 lbs.	-	.089	.100	.113
40 lbs.	-	.098	.110	.125

D. Trip Machine

1. When foot has to reach to pedal .009 X____occ. per blank=____(includes trip)
2. When foot stays on pedal .003 X____occ. per blank=____(includes trip)
3. Look for pedal .011 X____occ. per blank=____(does not include 1 & 2)

E. Machine Times

Machine	Value
Small Niagara	.008 X____occ. per blank=____
All Others	.010 X____occ. per blank=____

F. Material Handling

1. Push material truck to work area at beginning of operation ____no value
   (this value is usually included in the preceding operations)
2. Load pieces - fr.table or skid to machine bed .076 ÷ ____no. of pcs. = ____
                 fr.mach. bed to table or skid .076 ÷ ____no. of pcs. = ____
3. Exchange tote pans .327 ÷ ____no. of pcs. in pan= ____
4. Walk to rear of machine and return.
   (1). Small Niagara - .038÷ ____pcs. per sheet = ____value per blank.
   (2). All others   - .069÷ ____pcs. per sheet = ____value per blank.
5. Remove scrap at rear of machine.
   (1). Empty tote pan of scrap .327÷ ____no. of blanks cut per pan = ____.
   (2). Remove scrap by hand .078÷ ____no. of blanks cut per 20 lbs. load = ____.
6. Cover finished blank with separator - .023÷ ____no. of pcs. covered = ____

                                                    Total Select Time____

Figure 19–8 illustrates another application of synthetic basic motion times in the development of standard data. The work sheet shown gives all the standard elements for trimming blanks on punch presses. It is a matter of only minutes to predetermine a standard for trimming blanks with weights up to 40 pounds.

Another example illustrating the flexibility of synthetic basic motion times is the development of a formula for prepricing a clerical operation. The formula was for sorting time slips and included the following elements:

1. Pick up pack of departmental time slips and remove rubber band.
2. Sort time slips into direct labor (incentive), indirect labor, and day-work.
3. Record the total number of time slips.
4. Get pile of time slips, put rubber band around pack and put aside.
5. Get pile of time slips and bunch.
6. Sort "incentive" time slips into "parts" time slips.
7. Count piles of incentive "parts" time slips.
8. Record the number of "parts" of time slips and the number of incentive time slips.
9. Sort "parts" time slips into numerical sequence.
10. Bunch piles of numerical time slips and place in one pile on desk.

Each element was analyzed from the fundamental motion concept; synthetic values were assigned and variables determined. Resulting from this procedure was an algebraic equation allowing the rapid prepricing of the clerical operation.

Frequently, the stopwatch can be a helpful complement in developing standard data elements. Portions of an element may be more readily determined by synthetic basic motion times and other portions may be better adapted to measurement by using the stopwatch.

It is wise to verify standard data elements with a decimal minute (0.001) watch as an added check to their validity. When predetermined times are converted to standard data elements that have been verified, they will establish fair standards more consistent than those established through stopwatch procedure.

Summary

Basic Motion Timestudy, Work-Factor, Methods-Time Measurement, Dimensional Motion Times, Motion-Time Analysis, as well as several leading industries have made substantial contributions to a fund of knowledge available for analysis of fundamental motions. Frederick Taylor, many years ago, visualized the development of standards for basic divisions of work similar to what is currently being accomplished. In his paper on "Scientific Management" he brought out that the time would come when a sufficient volume of basic standards would be developed so as to make further stopwatch studies unnecessary.

As has been pointed out, the data that have been developed to date are comparatively new, and since the various tables of motion differ, there is some question of their accuracy. In applying various published data, broad differences in time values are realized on certain motion patterns. All values cannot be correct, but once valid values have been conclusively proven, they should be made available to practitioners of the science. For example, one study developed the fact that 79 percent more time was required to move a 15-pound weight a given distance than was necessary to move a 1-pound weight of the same size the same distance.[11] Other studies show considerably less influence of weight on time.

Inevitably, synthetic basic motion-time values are becoming more accurate as additional studies are being made. There is still a need for further research, testing, and refinement in this area. For example, there is a question of the validity of adding basic motion times for the purpose of determining elemental times in that therblig times may vary once the sequence is changed. Thus, the time for the basic element "reach 20 inches" may be affected by the preceding and succeeding elements and is not dependent entirely on class of reach and distance.

In general, it might be said that all work measurement techniques that have proved successful have made an effort to take care of the additivity of the elements of the motion in one way or another. Methods-Time Measurement, for instance, has provided three types of motion for the consideration of the movement of the hand, and several cases according to the nature of a move or reach. Work-Factor recognizes five elements of difficulty. Similar observations might be made about other fundamental motion techniques.

What has been done already has proved applicable in most instances; however, there are still some gaps to be filled. For example, more research needs to be undertaken in the development of data for combined motions. Reaches that involve a move during the first part of the motion are typical illustrations of where more basic study needs to be given. Likewise, moves that involve palming a component while enroute are typical of combination motions that require more research.

In the analysis of motion patterns with existing data, it is important that the analyst consider not only the main purpose of the motion, but also its complexity and characteristics. For example, if the hand is empty while moving toward an object, the motion will be classified as a reach; but if the hand holds an object while moving toward another object, not only the main purpose of the motion but also what the hand does with the object during the motion should be considered. If the hand is palming an object while reaching for something else, the motion cannot be classified as a basic reach. The time necessary to perform the combined motion depends on factors other than distance. The physical charac-

---

[11] B. W. Niebel and G. L. Thuering, "Let's Have More Accurate Time Standards for Basic Motions," *Factory Management and Maintenance*, September, 1951, p. 101.

teristics of the motion should not be neglected. When an object is being palmed while the hand is moving, in addition to the move, a simultaneous operation takes place. It is likely that the result might be a reduction in the average speed. This would allow the hand to establish control of the object during the distance moved. The longer the distance, the more time the hand has to palm the object in that particular motion. Thus, the longer the combined motion, the more the motion approaches the time required for a simple reach of the same distance.

On such combined motions, we have the problem of additivity and can obtain erroneous results if individual times for the elements of the combined motion are added. Such combined motions require additional research and study. More research in this area could result in basic times that would be modified by means of factors under prevailing conditions.

Further study will probably allow the tabulation of the majority of variables influencing time so it should be only a matter of a few years until completely reliable values will be available to practicing methods analysts and time study engineers. This will be a useful tool to supplement the stopwatch and moving-picture camera.

One of the paramount uses of basic motion times is that the analyst who endeavors to apply the synthetic procedure must carefully examine all factors affecting the motion pattern of a job. This minute scrutiny inevitably reveals opportunities for refinement of work methods.

In one company, $40,000 was allocated in an effort to provide advanced tooling to increase the rate of production on a brazing operation. Prior to retooling, a work measurement study of the existing method was made, and it developed that by providing a simple fixture and rearranging the loading and unloading area, production could be increased from 750 to 1,000 pieces per hour. The total cost of the synthetic basic motion-time study was $40, and as a result of its application it was not necessary to embark on the retooling program of $40,000.

Another manager of one of our leading electrical appliance companies has emphasized that basic motion times permit predetermining whether or not expenditures for new facilities and tools are warranted, and can accurately forecast the cost of reductions that may be achieved. This same manager states:

> We can recommend improvements in tool design for motion economy and better methods. We can accurately predetermine our labor costs for production. We can advise our product-design engineers so that parts can be designed for more efficient manufacture. We can establish consistent incentive-standard data.[12]

The above examples are representative of the methods improvement possibilities that can be gained with this tool which the methods analyst is rapidly realizing is essential in his kit of knowledge.

---

[12] "Short Cuts to Productivity," *Modern Industry*, May 15, 1950, p. 42.

The combining of synthetic basic motion times, in the form of standard data, permits application of basic motion times to a wide variety of work. Standard data thus developed is finding application on indirect and expense operations as well as on direct work. It is in this form that synthetic basic motion times has its broadest application.

It can be concluded that predetermined time systems have a definite place in the field of methods and work measurement and that they are no better than the people using them, that is, they should not be installed without professional help or a complete understanding of their application.

TEXT QUESTIONS

1. About when did synthetic time values begin to be used in industrial work?
2. What are the advantages of using synthetic basic motion times?
3. What variables are considered by the Work-Factor technique?
4. How did Work-Factor develop its values?
5. What is the time value of one TMU?
6. Who pioneered the M.T.M. system?
7. How was the development of the Basic Motion Timestudy values different from both M.T.M. and Work-Factor?
8. What variables are considered in the B.M.T. technique?
9. Who was originally responsible for thinking in terms of developing standards for basic work divisions? How did he contribute?
10. Calculate the equivalent in TMU's of 0.0075 hours per piece, of 0.248 minutes per piece, of 0.0622 hours per hundred, of 0.421 seconds per piece, of 10 pieces per minute.
11. How is M.T.M. related to the analysis of method?
12. For what reasons was M.T.M.–2 developed? Where does M.T.M.–2 have special application?
13. What classes of action are recognized by M.T.M.–2?
14. Why has Mr. A. B. Segur been reluctant to make his fundamental motion data available to the public?
15. Explain the relationship of fundamental motion times to standard data.
16. If you have finished drilling a hole 3 inches deep on a Western Radial Drill, how long would it take to present the drill and drill a second hole in a steel forging ½ inch in diameter and 3 inches deep? Traverse 6 inches, swing of head 8 inches, 0.007-inch feed, 50 feet per minute surface speed.
17. How has Work-Factor endeavored to take care of the additivity of the elements of a motion pattern?

GENERAL QUESTIONS

1. What does the future hold for synthetic basic time values?
2. Which of the three techniques outlined is the easiest to apply?

3. Which in your opinion will give the most reliable results? Why?

4. Describe as vividly as you can how you would explain to a workman in your forge shop who knows nothing about M.T.M. what it is and how it is applied.

5. Give several objections which you might receive from a workman in the application of M.T.M. and explain how you would overcome them.

6. Some companies have been experiencing a tendency for their time study men to become more liberal in their performance rating over a period of years. How does fundamental motion data offset this tendency toward creeping loose standards?

7. Is there consistency between M.T.M.–1 and M.T.M.–2 in the handling of simultaneous motions?

CHAPTER 20

Formula construction

Formula construction as applied to time study involves the design of an algebraic expression or system of curves that allow the establishment of a time standard in advance of the beginning of production by substituting known values peculiar to the job for the variable elements. A time study formula represents a simplification of standard data and has particular application in the nonrepetitive type of work where it is impractical to establish standards on the basis of an individual time study for each job.

Application of formulas

Time formulas are applicable to practically all types of work. They have been successfully used in office operations such as typing, in foundry work, maintenance work, painting, machine work of all types, forging, coil winding, grass cutting, window washing, floor sweeping, welding, and many others. If sufficient time studies are collected to give a reliable sample of data, it is possible to design a formula for a given range of work no matter what type of job is in question.

It is important to recognize that the formula should be applied only to those jobs that fall within the limits of the data used in developing the formula expression. If the boundaries of the formula are extended without supporting proof of individual time studies, erroneous standards, with all the resulting dangers brought about through inequitable rates, may result.

Once a formula has been built to cover a given operation, it should be immediately applied to all pertinent jobs within the range for which it was designed that do not already carry time standards.

Advantages and disadvantages of formulas

The advantages of using formulas rather than individual time studies for setting standards parallel those of using standard data. They may be summarized as follows:

1. More consistent time standards are established.
2. The duplication of time study effort on similar operations is eliminated.
3. Standards may be established much more rapidly.
4. A less experienced, less trained man may be used for establishing time standards.
5. Accurate, rapid estimates for labor costs in advance of beginning actual production may be made.

Probably the most significant advantage of the formula over the standard data method is that a less valuable man is needed to work with formulas than with standard data. Any high school graduate who is proficient in algebra will be able to work out a time study formula and solve for the allowed time required to perform the task. Then, too, standards are established more rapidly by formula than by accumulating standard data elements. Since columns of figures must be added in the standard data method, there is a greater chance for omission or arithmetic error in setting a standard than when using a formula.

In the development of formulas, caution must be exercised in the treatment of constants. There is a natural tendency to treat more elements as constants than should be. Thus, errors can creep into the formula design. It is true that a formula will give consistent results, and so it is also true that if it is not accurate, it will give standards that are consistently wrong.

Another disadvantage of the formula lies in its application. Sometimes, in the interests of arriving at a standard at the earliest possible time, industry will use formulas in instances where the variables are beyond the range of the data used in developing the formula. Thus, the formula may be used where it has no application and the resulting value will be far from valid.

Characteristics of the usable formula

A time study formula first must be completely reliable, and secondly, must be practical if it is to be used with confidence. For the expression to be reliable, it must always give accurate results. If the developed formula is accurate, it should verify the individual standards used in its development within plus or minus 5 percent. The greater the number of studies that can be used in the development of the formula, the better the chance for ending up with a reliable formula. At least 10 independent studies should be available for a given class of work before design of a formula is attempted. If tabularized standard data are available, these standards can be used for derivation of the formula. Frequently, when a formula is built, prevailing standard data, existing individual time studies, and new individual time studies will comprise the basic data used in its construction. Of course, it is understood that all mathematical calculation must be free from error before complete confidence can be vested in a formula.

The formula will give as accurate results as the data that entered into its derivation. The studies being used and the elements comprising them must show consistency in their end points and also in the method used, if the formula is to give constantly valid results.

For a formula to be practical, it should be clear, concise, and as simple as possible. The formulas best understood and most easily applied are the simplest expressions. Cumbersome expressions involving the taking of terms to powers should be avoided. Symbols of unknowns should not be repeated throughout the formula but should appear only in one place with their applicable suffixes, prefixes, or coefficients. Each symbol should be specifically identified as to the area of work it represents. Liberal substantiating data should be included in the formula report so that any qualified, interested party can clearly identify the derivation of the formula. It is important that the limitations of the formula be noted by describing in detail its applicable range. Formulas so constructed will allow their users to apply them rapidly and accurately with little difficulty in obtaining the required information.

Steps to follow in formula construction

The first step in formula construction is to determine what class of work is involved and what range of work is to be measured. For example, a formula may be developed for the curing of bonded rubber parts between 2 and 8 ounces in weight. The class of work covered by the formula would be "curing of molded parts," and the range of work involved would be 2 to 8 ounces. After this general overall analysis has been made and a clear understanding of what is required has been determined, the next step will be the collecting of the formula data. This step involves gathering former studies and standard data elements that have proven to be satisfactory and the taking of new studies in order to obtain a sufficiently large sample to cover the range of work for which the formula is needed. It is important that like elements in the different studies are consistent in their end points. This is essential in determining the variables that influence time, as well as in determining an accurate value for constant elements.

The elemental time study data are then posted on a work sheet for analysis of the constants and variables. The constants are combined and the variables are analyzed so that the factors influencing time can be expressed either algebraically or graphically.

Once the constant values have been selected and the variable elements equated, then the expression is simplified by combining constants and unknowns where possible. The next procedure is to develop the synthesis in which the derivation of the formula is fully explained, so that the person using it, and any other interested party, will be fully cognizant of its application and development.

Before the formula is put into use, it should be thoroughly checked for accuracy, consistency, and ease of application. Once this is done and the formula report has been completely written up, describing the method used, working conditions, limitations of its application, and so forth, then the formula is ready for installation.

In collecting the individual time studies to be used for constructing the formula, it is perfectly satisfactory for the observer to use existing time studies if they have been proven to be satisfactory, if the constant and variable elements in the studies have been properly separated, and if the studies were taken under prevailing conditions and methods.

FIGURE 20–1

		S-1	S-2	S-3	S-4
SHEET NO. 1					MASTER TABLE
OF 1 SHEETS					
FORMULA 73	STUDY				
DATE June 10,	OPERATOR	Petrecca	Winters	Ekey	Kumpf
	Performance Factor	110	110	90	110
	Diameter of Core	1 7/8	2 1/4	1 7/8	2 3/
	Length of Core	7 7/8	6 1/2	9 1/4	4 1
PART Cylindrical Core	Number of Clamps	1	1	2	1
OPERATION Made core from oil sand mix	L/D Ratio	4.2	2.89	4.93	1.5
PERFORMED ON Bench	Area	2.76	3.97	2.78	5.9
	Volume	21.7	25.8	25.6	25.
	C1 + D1 + F1	1.242	1.244	1.499	.89
COMPILED BY J. Bodesky					

SYMBOL	OPERATION DESCRIPTION	NORMAL TIME MINUTES	REFERENCE	Operation Class				
A-1	Close core box	.046	Average	C	.049	.041	.050	.053
B-1	Clamp core box (C- clamps)	.112 N	Time vs.No.Cl.	V	.110	.111	.243	.120
C-1	Fill partly full of sand	Y x CT	Time v.L/D v.Vol.	V	.085	.094	.093	.119
D-1	Ram	Y x CT	Time v.L/D v.Vol.	V	.225	.255	.242	.248
E-1	Place rod and wire	.0153L+.03	Time vs.Length	V	.150	.103	.168	.088
F-1	Fill and ram	Y x CT	Time v.L/D v.Vol.	V	.35	.668	.900	.280
G-1	Strike off with slick	.0157A+.07	Time vs. Area	V	.115	.135	.129	.152
H-1	Remove vent wire	.047	Average	C	.048	.050	.048	.056
J-1	Rap box	.043	Average	C	.039	.042	.045	.050
K-1	Remove clamps	.061N	Time vs.No.Cl.	V	.057	.062	.116	.048
M-1	Open box	.046	Average	C	.046	.040	.038	.052
N-1	Roll out core	.0057L+.045	Time vs.Length	V	.098	.082	.102	.075
P-1	Clean box	$\sqrt{.0067+.000016V^2}$	Time vs.Volume	V	.107	.112	.120	.110

JOB CHARACTERISTICS

When taking new studies for formula work, the analyst should use the same exacting care, principles, and procedures as when taking a study for an individual standard. However, when taking studies for a time formula, the observer should break the various studies into like elements, with end points terminating at identical places in the work cycle. Also, studies should be made of different operators to get as large a cross section as possible, and those jobs selected should cover the entire range of the proposed formula.

The number of studies that are needed to construct a formula will be influenced by the range of work for which the formula is to be used; the relative consistency of like constant elements in the various studies; and the number of factors that influence the time required to perform the variable elements.

As has been stated, at least 10 studies should be available before a formula is constructed. If less than 10 are used, the accuracy of the formula may be impaired through incorrect curve construction and data that are not representative of typical performance. Of course, the more studies that are used, the more data will be available and the more the normal conditions that prevail will be reflected.

DETAIL TIME STUDIES

-5	S-6	S-7	S-8	S-9	S-10	S-11	S-12	S-13	S-14	S-15	S-16	S-17
ısan	Markley	Noyes	Kinachan	Winters	Kumpf	Petrecca	Judd	Judd	Geiger	Plasan	Ekey	Noyes
5	105	105	98	120	100	108	95	102	117	85	.95	100
3/4	2	1 7/8	1 1/8	1	1 3/4	1 1/4	1 1/4	1 1/4	7/8	1 1/8	2	1 7/8
1/2	8	4 1/4	10	13 1/8	5 1/8	6 3/4	7 5/8	4 1/8	8 1/4	6 1/4	10	12 5/8
	1'	1	2	1	1	1	1	1	1	1	2	2
43	4	2.27	8.89	13.13	2.73	5.40	6.10	3.30	9.43	5.56	5.0	6.31
40	3.14	2.78	.99	.78	2.40	1.23	1.23	1.23	.60	.99	3.14	2.78
.8	25.1	11.8	9.90	10.3	12.3	8.27	9.33	5.05	4.96	6.19	31.4	35.1
557	1.316	.733	1.489	2.138	.804	1.159	1.181	.797	1.277	1.032	1.740	2.299
45	.042	.047	.050	.041	.043	.042	.047	.048	.049	.046	.043	.048
50	109	.087	.232	.218	.098	.114	.097	.128	.091	.099	.229	.240
21	.141	.082	.129	.206	.073	.102	.079	.062	.133	.100	.107	.195
72	.245	.160	.344	.436	.194	.281	.252	.090	.342	.162	.285	.480
71	.142	.093	.180	.222	.110	.125	.140	.090	.142	.120	.182	.210
32	.725	.258	.889	1.290	.392	.665	.850	.432	.802	.626	1.089	1.390
09	.120	.104	.078	.077	.198	.089	.084	.086	.074	.085	.119	.106
7	.042	.041	.052	.051	.043	.042	.042	.044	.040	.051	.052	.045
5	.041	.045	.057	.048	.040	.039	.042	.041	.050	.038	.047	.041
0	.039	.062	.116	.120	.071	.059	.056	.070	.058	.058	.140	.145
8	.041	.045	.054	.046	.066	.038	.065	.045	.040	.035	.038	.052
9	.091	.068	.108	.120	.080	.082	.090	.065	.090	.071	.110	.118
5	.118	.090	.089	.088	.090	.087	.085	.085	.085	.088	.138	.150

Analyzing the elements

After a sufficient number of time studies has been gathered, it is helpful to summarize the data for analysis purposes on one work sheet. Figure 20–1 illustrates a "Master Table of Detail Time Studies" form which has been designed for this purpose. In addition to the information called for on the form, any specific information, such as surface area, volume, length, diameter, hardness, radius, and weight, that has an effect on the variable elements should be posted under its corresponding study number in the "Job Characteristics" section of the form.

Here the name of the operator studied, his rating factor, and the part number of the job are also shown. A separate column has been assigned for each time study for the recording of all this pertinent information.

In the column, on the left-hand side of the work sheet, headed "Symbol," an identifying term is placed for each element. The letters of the alphabet followed by a suffix number are frequently used. Thus, we should have the symbols A-1, B-1, C-1, and so on on. When more than 26 elements are involved, then the alphabet is repeated, only this time the suffix 2 is used. These symbols are employed for identification and reference from the Master Table to elements grouped in the synthesis.

Under the "Operation Description," every element that has occurred on the individual time studies is recorded. The element description should be expressed clearly, so that any interested person in the future will be able to visualize exactly the work content of the element. After each element description in the column headed "Operation Class" indicate with a "C" or a "V" whether the element is a constant or a variable.

Next, the normal elemental times from the individual studies are transposed to the work sheet and are recorded in the appropriate spaces. After these data have been posted, the elemental time values for each element are compared and the reasons for variance are determined. As can be expected, a certain amount of variation will prevail, even in the constant elements, because of inconsistency in performance rating. In general, the constant elements should not deviate substantially, and the allowed time for each constant may be determined by averaging the values of the different studies. This average time should then be posted under the column "Normal Time," and under the column "Reference" should be shown the word "average."

The variable elements will show a tendency to vary in proportion to some characteristic or characteristics of the work, such as size, shape, or hardness. These elements will have to be studied carefully to determine which factors influence the time, and to what extent. By plotting a curve of time versus the independent variable, it is frequently possible for the analyst to deduce an algebraic expression in terms of time representing the element. This procedure is explained in a later section of this chapter. If an equation can be computed then it should be shown in the

"Normal Time" column and the curve or curves used in its deduction should be referred to in the adjacent "Reference" column.

Compute expressions for variables

If the analysis of the elemental data reveals that one variable characteristic governs the elemental time, then the analyst should construct a graphic relationship following the procedure outlined in Chapter 18 (See Figure 18–4). Thus, time in the plotting is the dependent variable since it is the value we want to predict. In those cases where time is to be estimated in terms of a single independent variable, y will be referred to as the random variable, time, whose distribution depends on the independent variable x. In most relations that we are estimating, x is not random, it is fixed for all practicality and we are concerned with the mean of the corresponding distribution of time y (the successive elements observed through stopwatch analysis) for given x. (See Figure 20–6.)

Plotted data may take several forms. These are straight line, parabola, hyperbola, ellipse, exponential, or no regular geometrical form whatsoever. Graphical procedures for obtaining predicting equations may be quite useful.

If the data plots as a straight line on uniform graph paper, then we can equate time as a function of the slope times the variable v and the y intercept as discussed on page 405.

Another linear relationship that frequently occurs that the reader should be cognizant of is the reciprocal function expressed by the equation:

$$y = \frac{1}{b + mv}$$

It can be seen that the reciprocal function involves a linear relationship for values of $\frac{1}{y}$ and v since by taking the reciprocal of both sides of the equation we get:

$$\frac{1}{y} = b + mv$$

The hyperbolic curve takes the form illustrated in Figure 20–2 and is expressed by the equation:

$$\frac{y^2}{a^2} - \frac{x^2}{k^2} = 1$$

If the plotted data take the form of a segment of the hyperbola, k may be computed graphically by drawing a tangent to the curve through the origin and using the resulting line as the diagonal of the rectangle

FIGURE 20–2

Segment of hyperbolic curve

whose height is *a*, the distance from the origin to the *y* intercept. Substituting time and the variable characteristic for *x* and *y* would give:

$$T = \sqrt{a^2 + \frac{(v^2)(a^2)}{k^2}}$$

The ellipse segment shown in Figure 20–3 is expressed by the equation:

$$\frac{x^2}{a^2} + \frac{y^2}{b^2} = 1$$

FIGURE 20–3

Segment of ellipse

When the plotted time values take the form of the ellipse, a and b may be computed graphically and their values substituted in the expression:

$$T = \sqrt{b^2 - \frac{b^2 v^2}{a^2}}$$

In other instances, the data may take the form of the parabola as illustrated in Figure 20–4. This curve is expressed by the equation:

$$x^2 = \frac{a^2 y}{b}$$

and after substituting graphic solutions for a and b, we have the equation:

$$T = \frac{b v^2}{a^2}$$

As in previous illustrations, T is equal to time and v is equal to the variable characteristic governing the elemental time.

FIGURE 20–4

Segment of parabola

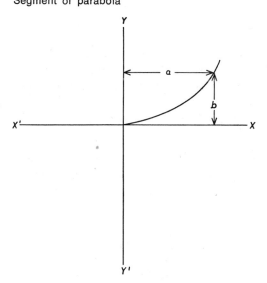

One additional relationship that has much application in formula development is the power function. This is of the form:

$$y = bm^v$$

When the data does not follow a straight line, parabola, hyperbola, or circle when plotted on uniform graph paper, the analyst should try using semilogarithmic so as to determine if the points will fall close to a straight line using a transformed scale. If the paired data gives a straight line when plotted on semilog paper, then the curve of *y* on *x* is exponential. By this we mean that for any given *x*, the mean of the distribution of the *y*'s (times in our work) is given by bm^x.

To illustrate, in the element "strike arc and weld" the following data were obtained from 10 detailed studies:

Study no.	Size of weld	Minutes per inch of weld
1	$\frac{1}{8}$	0.12
2	$\frac{3}{16}$	0.13
3	$\frac{1}{4}$	0.15
4	$\frac{3}{8}$	0.24
5	$\frac{1}{2}$	0.37
6	$\frac{5}{8}$	0.59
7	$1\frac{1}{16}$	0.80
8	$\frac{3}{4}$	0.93
9	$\frac{7}{8}$	1.14
10	1	1.52

When the data were plotted on rectangular coordinate paper, a smooth curve resulted (see Figure 20–5). The data were then plotted on semilogarithmic paper and the straight line as shown in Figure 20–6 was obtained.

This plotting can now be stated in equation form by the following derivation:

Select any two points on the straight line:

$$\text{Point 1} \quad X = 1, \qquad Y = \log 1.52$$
$$\text{Point 2} \quad X = \tfrac{3}{8}, \qquad Y = \log 0.24$$

Solving for the slope *m*:

$$m = \frac{Y_1 = Y_2}{X_1 - X_2}$$
$$= \frac{\log 1.52 - \log 0.24}{1 - \tfrac{3}{8}}$$
$$= 1.28$$

To determine the equation of the line from the equation $Y - Y_1 = m(X - X_1)$, we get:

$$\log Y - \log 1.52 = 1.28(X - 1)$$
$$\log Y - 0.18184 = 1.28X - 1.28$$
$$\log Y = 1.28X - 1.10$$

FIGURE 20–5

Plotted curve on regular coordinate paper takes exponential form

From the exponential form

$$Y = AB^x$$
$$\log Y = \log A + X \log B$$

and

$$\log A = -1.10$$
$$A = 0.07944$$
$$\log B = 1.28$$
$$B = 19.05$$

and

$$Y = (0.07944)(19.05)^x$$

rounding off:

$$Y = (0.08)(19)^x$$

This equation would then be a component of the formula expression and would be less cumbersome than referring to the curve shown in Figure 20–6. It can be checked as follows:

With ½-inch weld:

$$\text{Time} = (0.08)(19)^{.5}$$
$$= 0.35 \text{ minutes}$$

This checks quite closely with the time study value of 0.37 minutes.

FIGURE 20–6

Data plotted on semilogarithmic paper takes the form of a straight line with equation $Y = AB^X$

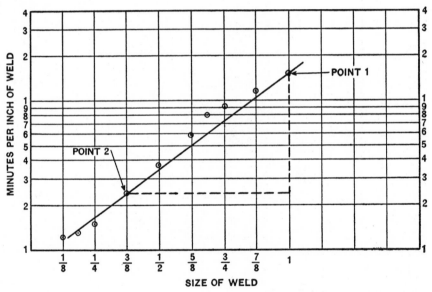

Sometimes the data when plotted on logarithmic paper will result in a straight line. For example, the equation $Y = AX^m$ written in logarithmic form becomes:

$$\log Y = \log A + m \log X$$

It is evident here that $\log Y$ is linear with $\log X$ and when plotted on logarithmic paper a straight line will be obtained.

Graphic solutions for more than one variable

When more than one variable affects time, it is often practical to use graphic techniques even if the relationships are nonlinear.

For example, it is possible to solve for time when we have two or more variables of which one or more are nonlinear by constructing a chart for each variable. The first chart will plot the relationship between time and one of the variables in selected studies in which the values of the other variables tend to remain constant. The second chart will show the relationship between the second variable and time that has been adjusted so as to remove the influence of the first variable. The procedure is extended with a third chart if there is an additional variable affecting the time to perform the element.

Let us look at an example to illustrate the application of this procedure. It is decided to construct a formula for rolling various width and length of 0.072-inch thick, cold-rolled sheet metal on a bench roll. Element 1 shown on the master table of detail time studies, is "pk. up pc. & pos." and element 3 is "lay aside pc. & pos." Since both of these elements involve handling time of the same amount of stock, their values are combined so as to simplify the final algebraic expression. The values shown in Table 20–1 were obtained.

TABLE 20–1

Study no.	Width	Length	Element 1 + Element 3
1............	2	16	0.18
2............	3	18	0.13
3............	8	1	0.09
4............	10½	32	0.14
5............	7	84	0.55
6............	8½	69	0.38
7............	20	30	0.22
8............	11	55	0.26
9............	10	75	0.68
10............	20½	41	0.66
11............	10½	90	1.80
12............	16	64	1.44

First inspection seemed to suggest that the time for element 1 plus element 3 would vary with the area of the part handled. However, upon plotting, it was apparent that something else was influencing the time required to perform these elements. Further analysis revealed that the long and narrow pieces required considerably more time than the nearly square parts, even though their respective areas were about the same. It was decided that two variables were affecting time: these were the area of the part and the increased difficulty of handling the relatively longer pieces. The latter may be expressed as a ratio of length to width.

Of the 12 studies appearing on the master work sheet, it was noted that four (studies 5, 6, 7, and 8) were taken on stock having areas of about 600 square inches. It was also apparent that these four studies had a relatively wide spread of "length divided by width" ratio which was apparently responsible for the range in allowed elemental times.

Since these four studies had areas relatively the same, the effect of L/W could be shown by plotting a simple curve. This was done as shown in Figure 20–7. Now, in order to see what the effect of area is on the elemental time, it will be necessary to adjust all the tabularized time study values by the relative amount of time brought about by the influence of the variable L/W. To get a factor that can be used to divide the time study values so as to arrive at an adjusted time that varies with area, we construct a scale parallel to the Y axis and call it "Factor A" (adjust-

FIGURE 20–7

Time plotted against the ratio of length to width for constant areas of about 600 square inches

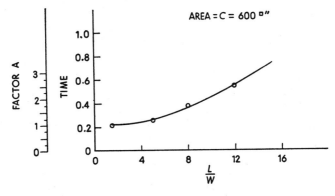

ment factor). By extending the lowest point on our L/W curve horizontally to the adjustment axis, we get a distance from the origin that can be evaluated as unity on the adjustment axis. Proportional values can then be constructed so as to get a scale on the adjustment axis.

Now by taking the L/W value of all the studies appearing on the master table, we can determine adjustment factors graphically for each study by moving horizontally to the Factor A axis from the specific point on the L/W versus Time curve. Once the adjustment values have been determined for each study, then the adjusted time can be computed by dividing the allowed elemental time study values by the adjustment factor. The resulting adjusted times can then be plotted against area (see Figure 20–8).

The system of curves so developed represents the graphic solution and can be used for establishing standards within their range in the following manner. First, the area and the length over width ratio of the sheet is calculated. Using the L/W ratio, we can refer to the first curve to obtain an adjustment factor. Referring to the second curve we can determine

FIGURE 20–8

Adjusted time plotted against area

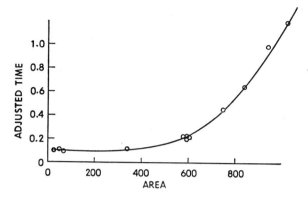

an adjusted time. The product of the adjusted time and the adjustment factor will give the allowed time to perform elements 1 and 3.

By extending this procedure, it is possible for the analyst to solve graphically elemental time values when more than two variable characteristics govern the elemental time.

Sometimes variables will remain relatively constant within a specific group. However, once the limits of the specific group are extended, the variable will tend to show a pronounced change in value. For example, the handling of boards of 1-inch white pine to a planer may be classified:

Group	Allowed time
Small (up to 300 square inches).............	0.070 min.
Medium (300 to 750 square inches).........	0.095 min.
Large (750 to 1,800 square inches)..........	0.144 min.

This method of grouping will tend to give erroneous values at the extremities of each group. Thus, in the above example, a board of 295 square inches would be allowed 0.070 minute handling time while one 305 square inches would be given 0.095 minute. The chances are that in the first case, 0.070 minute would represent a tight standard and in the latter case, 0.095 minute would be somewhat loose.

When elements are grouped in the manner shown, it is important that the grouping be clearly and specifically defined so that there will be no questions as to which category an element belongs.

Least squares and regression techniques

Although graphical procedures may be quite useful in establishing a predicting equation for one dependent variable as a function of one independent variable, one may want to resort to more sophistic methods of curve fitting such as least squares and regression techniques. This is indeed even more true when one dependent variable y is viewed as a function of more than one independent variable. However, least squares and regression techniques can often be employed by the novice dangerously with resultant blunders.

As has already been pointed out we are interested in determining the mean of the distribution of times for a given variable x. The reader should

FIGURE 20–9

Four distributions of time for four values of α and the resulting true curve passing through the means of these distributions

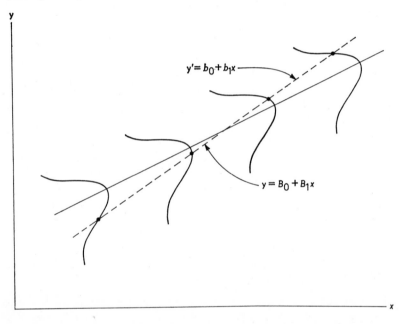

recognize that there is a distribution of the random variable time for a given value of the independent variable x. Figure 20–9 illustrates such a relationship with the true straight line of the equation $y = B_0 + B_1 X$ passing through the mean of each of the four distributions of y. This relationship is referred to as the regression curve of y on x.

When the analyst is gathering his data he is only able to approximate the mean of the time distributions. Any observed time may differ from the true mean by some finite amount. In order to determine the value of the estimates b_0 and b_1 of the parameters B_1 and B_0 for a given set of data (n paired observations x_iy_i), where it is assumed that the regression of

y on x is linear, we want to determine the equation of the line that best fits the data. By best fit, we mean the equation of the line $y' = b_0 + b_1x$ where the sum of the squared vertical distances $(y - y')$ for the points comprising the data is a minimum.

The normal equations involving the parameters b_1 and b_0 whose values for the line of best fit of the data are:

$$\sum_{i=1}^{n} y_i = b_0 n + b_1 \sum_{i=1}^{n} x_i \tag{1}$$

$$\sum_{i=1}^{n} x_i y_i = b_0 \sum_{i=1}^{n} x_i + b_1 \sum_{i=1}^{n} x_i^2 \tag{2}$$

These can readily be solved simultaneously to provide the numerical values of the slope "b_1" and the y intercept b_0. For example, referring to page 406, we can solve for b_1 and b_0 using the above equations as follows:

TABLE 20–2

Study	x or area	y or time	xy	x^2
1.............	25	0.104	2.60	625
2.............	65	0.109	7.09	4,225
3.............	77	0.126	9.70	5,929
4.............	112	0.134	15.01	12,544
5.............	135	0.138	18.63	18,225
6.............	147	0.150	22.05	21,609
7.............	185	0.153	28.31	34,225
8.............	220	0.174	38.28	48,400
9.............	245	0.176	43.12	60,025
10.............	275	0.182	50.05	75,625
11.............	287	0.186	53.38	82,369
12.............	300	0.202	60.60	90,000
	2,073	1.834	348.82	453,801

Substituting in equation (1) and (2):

$$12b_0 = 1.834 - 2,073b_1 \tag{1}$$
$$2,073b_0 = 348.82 - 453,801b_1 \tag{2}$$

multiplying equation (1) by 2,073 and equation (2) by 12:

$$24,876b_0 = 3,801.882 - 4,297,329b_1$$
$$24,876b_0 = 4,185.840 - 5,445,612b_1$$
$$\overline{0 = -383.958 + 1,148,283b_1}$$

or

$$b_1 = \frac{383.958}{1,148,283} = 0.000334$$

and substituting in equation (1):

$$12b_0 = 1.834 - 0.692$$
$$b_0 = \frac{1.142}{12} = 0.095$$

The above equations can be transformed so that we can solve directly for the slope b_1 and the y intercept b_0 by substituting in the following relationships:

$$b_0 = \frac{(\Sigma x^2)(\Sigma y) - (\Sigma x)(\Sigma xy)}{(n)(\Sigma x^2) - (\Sigma x)^2}$$

$$b_1 = \frac{(n)(\Sigma xy) - (\Sigma x)(\Sigma y)}{(n)(\Sigma x^2) - (\Sigma x)^2}$$

The least squares technique is also applicable in fitting of curves and exponential relationships plotting as straight lines on semilog and log-log paper.

For example, in the case of the exponential relationship involving semilog paper where

$$\log y = \log b_0 + x \log b_1$$

we can solve for the y intercept b_0 from the equation:

$$\log b_0 = \frac{(\Sigma x^2)(\Sigma \log y) - (\Sigma x)(\Sigma x \log y)}{(n)(\Sigma x^2) - (\Sigma x)^2}$$

and for the slope b_1 from the equation:

$$\log b_1 = \frac{(n)(\Sigma x \log y) - (\Sigma x)(\Sigma \log y)}{(n)(\Sigma x^2) - (\Sigma x)^2}$$

In those cases where the dependent variable y is a nonlinear function of one independent variable x and a simple graphic procedure is not indicated, we may endeavor to fit our data by the polynomial equation:

$$y' = b_0 + b_1 x + b_2 x^2 + b_3 x^3 \ldots, b_q x^q$$

For example, let us assume that we have a set of n points of data $(y_i x_i)$. In order to estimate the coefficients $b_0, b_1, b_2, b_3 \ldots, b_q$ we minimize:

$$\sum_{i=1}^{n} \left[y_i - (b_0 + b_1 x_i + b_2 x_i^2 + b_3 x_i^3 \ldots, b_q x_i^q) \right]^2$$

Here we are merely applying the least squares technique by minimizing the sum of squares of the vertical distances from the points to the curve. By differentiating partially with respect to $b_0, b_1, b_2 \ldots, b_q$, equating these partial derivatives to zero and rearranging some of the terms we obtain $q + 1$ normal equations. These are:

$$\Sigma y = nb_0 + b_1\Sigma x + \ldots, b_q\Sigma x^q$$
$$\Sigma xy = b_0\Sigma x + b_1\Sigma x^2 + \ldots, b_q\Sigma x^{q+1}$$
$$\Sigma x^q y = b_0\Sigma x^q + b_1\Sigma x^{q+1} \ldots, b_q\Sigma x^{q+q}$$

Multiple regression

At times the analyst will recognize that more than one independent variable is influencing the dependent variable (time). If two independent variables are involved in a linear relationship then we are fitting a plane to a set of "n" points so as to minimize the sum of squares of the vertical distances from the points to the plane. Thus, we are minimizing

$$\sum_{i=1}^{n}\left[y_i - (b_0 + b_1x_i + c_1z_i) \right]^2$$

(See Figure 20–10.)

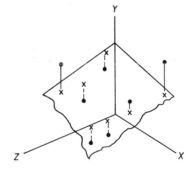

FIGURE 20–10

Two independent variables characterize the best fit of a plane in a geometrical cube

The resulting normal equations are:

$$\Sigma y = nb_0 + b_1\Sigma x + c_1\Sigma z$$
$$\Sigma xy = b_0\Sigma x_1 + b_1\Sigma x^2 + c_1\Sigma xz$$
$$\Sigma zy = b_0\Sigma z + b_1\Sigma xz + c_1\Sigma z^2$$

Let us look at an example utilizing the multiple regression technique. The analyst decides to construct a formula for bagging hardware in various size burlap bags. He finds that time is not only dependent upon the number of components placed in each bag but also upon the total weight of the components placed in each bag. From a master table of detailed time studies (see page 466) the information shown in Table 20–3 was gathered for the second element which is "place hardware components in bag."

TABLE 20–3

Study No.	y Time	x Total Weight of Components	z Number of Components
1	0.264	6.62	11
2	0.130	1.15	6
3	0.202	5.61	8
4	0.126	4.01	4
5	0.220	6.14	9
6	0.332	7.25	14
7	0.222	7.02	6
8	0.155	1.75	8
9	0.345	5.45	17
10	0.256	6.91	10
	2.252	51.91	93

Substituting

$$\Sigma x = 51.91, \; \Sigma z = 93, \; \Sigma x^2 = 312.75$$
$$\Sigma xz = 515.27, \; \Sigma z^2 = 1{,}003, \; \Sigma y = 2.252$$
$$\Sigma xy = 12.772, \; \Sigma zy = 23.429$$

into the normal equations gives us:

$$2.252 = 10b_0 + 51.91b_1 + 93c_1$$
$$12.772 = 51.91b_0 + 312.75b_1 + 515.27c_1$$
$$23.429 = 93b_0 + 515.27b_1 + 1{,}003c_1$$

The solution of this system of equations provides the following results: $b_0 = 0.016$, $b_1 = 0.0139$, $c_1 = 0.0147$. It is now possible to estimate the time (y) to bag parts having a total weight (x) and number of components (z) by direct substitution in the equation:

$$y^1 = 0.016 + 0.0139x + 0.0147z$$

Multiple regression techniques are also applicable for nonlinear cases. The interested reader can explore these areas in several of the texts on regression analysis.

Some precautions

As previously stated, regression methods may present difficulties of interpretation and analysis to the uniformed. These difficulties are primarily concerned with the statistical and engineering analyses used in the selection of the number of independent variables and the significance that each variable plays in the predicting equation. The form of the equation selected (i.e., linear or nonlinear) and the inclusion of cross products of the variables in the equation when interaction effects are present may additionally further complicate the analysis. It may be advantageous to consult with an analyst competent in regression techniques under these circumstances. However, in the interest of ease of application, it is a good general practice to make predicting equations as simple as possible. From a statistical point of view, it is also true that complicated predicting equations may result in time estimates little if any more reliable than equations of a simpler form.

Develop synthesis

The purpose of the synthesis in the formula report is to give complete explanation of the derivation of the various components entering into the formula so as to facilitate its use. Furthermore, a clearly developed synthesis will help in explaining and selling the formula in the event questions come up at some later date as to its suitability.

In order that the final expression may be in its simplest form, all constants and symbols should be combined wherever possible, with due respect to accuracy and the flexibility of the formula. Elemental operations may be classified under specific headings as preparation, handling by hand, handling by jib crane, and operation. Constant values will appear under each elemental class. These values can be combined to simplify the final expression of the specific formulas. Details of the combinations are explained in the synthesis. A typical illustration of a synthesis for a constant element would be:

$$A1 + C1 + \text{constant from equation } 4 + H1 = 0.11 + 0.17 + 0.09 + 0.05$$
$$= 0.42 \text{ minute}$$

In the treatment of variable elements, a more detailed explanation is usually required due to the added complexities associated with this class of elements. For example, we may wish to combine elements $B1$ and $D1$, in that they have been influenced by the ratio of L/D. The two equations may be:

$$B1 = 0.1 \frac{L}{D} + 0.08$$

$$D1 = 0.05 \frac{L}{D}$$

and the combination of these would give

$$B1 + D1 = 0.15 \frac{L}{D} + 0.08$$

Thus, the synthesis would clearly show where the 0.15 L/D came from.

Compute expression

The final expression may not be entirely in algebraic form. It may have been more convenient to express some of the variables in terms of systems of curves, nomographs, or single curves. Then, too, some of the variable data may have been made up into tables, and these will be referred to by a single symbol in the formula. A typical example of a formula would be:

$$\text{Normal time} = 0.07 + \text{Chart 1} + \text{Curve 1} + \frac{0.555N}{C}$$

where

$$N = \text{Number of cavities per mold}$$
$$C = \text{Cure time in minutes}$$

In applying this formula, the analyst would refer to Chart 1 in order to pick out the applicable tabularized value. He would also refer to Curve 1 to obtain the numerical value of another variable entering into the formula. Knowing the number of cavities in the mold and the cure time in minutes, he would substitute in the latter part of the expression and summarize the values of the three variables with the constant time of 0.07 minute to get the resulting normal time.

Check for accuracy

Upon completion of the formula, the analyst should verify it before releasing for use. The easiest and most rapid way to check the formula is to use it to check existing time studies. This can best be done by tabularizing the results under the following heads: *Part Number, Time Study Value, New Formula Value, Difference,* and *Percentage Difference.*

Any marked differences between the formula value and the time study value should be investigated and the cause determined. It would be expected that the formula show an average percentage difference of less than 5 percent from the time study values of those studies used in deriving the formula. If at this point, the formula does not appear to have the expected validity, then the analyst should accumulate additional data by taking more stopwatch studies. Once the formula has been satisfactorily tested over a range of work, it will be acceptable to those who are affected directly and indirectly by its application. At this point, it would be time well spent for the analyst to go over the formula with the foreman of the department where it will be used. After the foreman understands its derivation and application and has verified its reliability, the analyst can be assured of his backing on standards resulting from its use.

Write formula report

All data, calculations, derivations, and applications of the formula should be consolidated in the form of a complete report prior to putting the formula into use. Then all the facts relative to process employed, operating conditions, and scope of formula will be available for future reference.

The Westinghouse Electric Corporation includes 14 separate sections in its formula reports. These are:

1.	Formula number, division, data, and sheet number	8.	Procedure
2.	Part	9.	Time studies
3.	Operation	10.	Table of detail elements
4.	Work station	11.	Synthesis
5.	Normal time	12.	Inspection
6.	Application	13.	Wage payment
7.	Analysis	14.	Signature of constructor and approver

Formula number

For ease of reference, all paper work entering into the development of the formula should be identified by the assignment of a number to the formula. The formula number is made up of a prefix which identifies the department or division wherein the formula will be used and a number which gives the chronological arrangement of the formula with reference to other formulas being used in the department. Thus, the formula 11N–56 would infer that it was the 56th formula designed for use in department 11N. The date that the formula was put into use is also included, so as to connect working conditions in effect at the time the formula was designed with standards established through its application.

Part

The part number or numbers together with drawing numbers should be given, with a concise description of the work, so that the products for which the formula has application are clearly defined. For example: "Parts J–1101, J–1146, J–1172, J–1496, side plates ranging from 12×24 inches to 48×96 inches" would identify the parts for which the formula may be used.

Operation and work station

The operation covered by the formula should be clearly stated, such as "roll radius" or "fabricate inner and outer members" or "broach key-ways" or "assemble farm tank." In addition, the work station should be completely described with information as to equipment, jigs, fixtures, gages, and their size, condition, and serial number. A photograph will often help to define the method in effect at the time of compilation of the formula.

Normal time

When expressing the formula for the normal time, use separate equations for the "setup" time and the "each piece" time. Immediately following the formula should be a key which outlines the meaning of the symbols used in each equation. All tables, nomograms, and system of curves should be included at this point, as well as a sample solution, so that the person using the formula clearly understands it.

Application

After the expressions for the allowed time have been concisely stated, then a clear explanation of the application of the formula should be given. This should give in detail the nature of the work on which the formula may be used and specifically state the limits within which it may be applied. For example, the application of a formula for curing bonded rubber parts may be written as follows: "This formula applies to all curing operations done in 24 × 28-inch platen presses when the number of cavities range between 8 and 100 and the cubic inches of rubber per cavity range between 0.25 inch and 3 inches."

Analysis

Under the analysis is given a detailed account of the entire method employed, which will include the tools, fixtures, jigs, and gages and their application; workplace layout; methods of material handling; method of obtaining supply materials; and nature of setup with details as to how the operator is assigned the job, distance to the tool crib, and other pertinent data.

In the analysis section of the report is included information as to the breakdown of the allowances used in the formula. The reason for any special or extra allowance should be clearly stated. The allowance for personal time, fatigue, and unavoidable delays should be shown independently so that if any question comes up in the future as to the inclusion of an allowance in the formula, it can be clearly shown what allowances were included and why.

Procedure

After the analysis of the job has been established, the procedure used by the operator in performing the work should be written up in detail. The best way of doing this is to include all the elements appearing on the master work sheet in their correct chronological arrangement. While abbreviations were liberally used on the time studies and on the master table, care should be exercised to avoid their use in writing up the operator's procedure. Individual elements should be written in exact detail. Then all parties will have no doubt as to the work elements included in the scope of the formula.

Time studies

It is not necessary to include the actual time studies used in compilation of the formula in the formula report, as they are usually available in their own independent files. However, reference should be made to the time studies used. This can be done in tabular form as follows:

Time study no.	Part	Drawing	Plant	Date taken	Taken by
S–112	J–1102	JB–1102	A	9–15–	J. B. Smith
S–147	J–1476	JA–1476	B	10–24–	A. B. Jones
S–92	J–1105	JB–1105	B	6–11–	J. B. Smith

Table of detail elements

This table is used as a reference source for information as to the normal element time and its derivation. The information for composing this table is taken from the master table of detailed elements and is recorded in chart form as follows:

Symbol	Element description	Normal time	Reference
Al	Close core box	0.046 min.	Average
Cl	Fill partly full of sand	A × C.T.	All Studies
Jl	Rap box	0.043 min.	Average

Synthesis

After recording the table of detail elements, the analyst includes the synthesis of the report. The synthesis, as previously explained, tells the manner in which the allowed time was derived.

Inspection, payment, and signatures

Upon completion of the synthesis the constructor records the following information in order: the inspection requirements appearing on the drawings of the jobs covered by the formula; the type of wage payment plans where the formula will be used, such as daywork, piecework, and group incentive; and finally his signature and that of his supervisor.

Representative formula

The following formula report will illustrate and help clarify the procedures discussed in this chapter:

FORMULA No.: M–11–No. 15
DATE: September 15, 19–
SHEET: 1 of 15

PART: Cylindrical oil sand mix cores ⅞″ in diameter to 2¾″ diameter and 4″ long to 13″ long.
OPERATION: Make core complete in wood core box.
WORK STATION: 30″ × 52″ Bench 36″ high.
NORMAL TIME: Piece time in decimal minutes equals:

$$0.173N + 0.0210L + \sqrt{0.0067 + 0.000016V^2} + Y \times C.T. + 0.0157A + 0.327$$

Where

$$
\begin{aligned}
N &= \text{Number of ``C'' clamps} \\
L &= \text{Length of core in inches} \\
V &= \text{Volume of core in cubic inches} \\
Y &= \text{Adjustment factor (Curve 1)} \\
CT &= \text{Adjusted time (Curve 2)} \\
A &= \text{Cross-sectional area of core}
\end{aligned}
$$

EXAMPLE:

Calculate normal time to make a green sand core 2″ in diameter and 8″ long. Volume would be 25.1 cubic inches and with 8″ length, only one clamp would be required. L/D would be equal to 8/2 or 4.

THEN:

$$
\begin{aligned}
\text{Normal time} &= (0.173)(1) + (0.0210)(8) + \sqrt{0.0067 + (0.000016)(25.1^2)} \\
&\quad + (1.5)(.76) + (0.0157)(3.14) + 0.327 = 1.987 \text{ minutes}.
\end{aligned}
$$

APPLICATION

This formula applies to all cylindrical cores made of oil sand mix between diameters ranging from ⅞ inch to 2¾ inches and lengths ranging from 4 inches to 13 inches. This work is performed manually in wooden split core boxes.

ANALYSIS

The following hand tools are provided the operator for making cores covered by this formula: C-clamps, slick, and rammer. The work is done at a bench with the operator standing. Oil sand mix for producing the cores is piled on the floor by the move man approximately 4 feet from the operator. Periodically, the operator replenishes a supply of sand on his bench from the inventory on the floor, through the use of a short-handled shovel. Rods and reinforcing wires are requisitioned from the storeroom by the operator. He usually acquires a full day's supply with each requisition.

The work voucher placed above the operator's work station by the departmental foreman indicates the sequence of jobs to be performed and is the authority for the operator to begin a specific job. Operation cards and drawings must be obtained by the operator from the tool crib.

The standard allowance which must be added when applying this formula is 17 percent. This involves 5 percent for personal delays, 6 percent for unavoidable delays, and 6 percent for fatigue.

PROCEDURE

The working procedure followed in making oil sand mix cores covered by this formula includes 14 elements exclusive of setup and put-away elements. These are:

1. Pick up two sections of core box and close together.
2. Clamp core box shut using one clamp for cores 9 inches or less and two clamps for cores greater than 9 inches in length.
3. Fill core box partly full of sand (about one third depending on core).
4. Ram the sand solid in the core box.
5. Place the vent rod and reinforcing wire.
6. Fill the remainder of the core box with sand and ram solid.
7. With slick, strike off sand on both ends of core box so sand core is flush with box.
8. Remove the vent wire from the core and lay aside.
9. Rap box lightly.
10. Remove clamps and lay aside.
11. Open core box.
12. Roll out core on rack beside work station.
13. Clean core box with kerosene rag.

TIME STUDIES

The following summary includes the time studies used in developing this formula:

Time study no.	Part number		Plant	Date taken	Taken by
S–13	P–1472	PB–1472	A	6–15	Black
S–111	P–1106	PB–1106	A	12–11	Black
S–45	P–1901	PB–1901	A	7–13	Hirsch
S–46	P–1907	PB–1907	B	7–14	Black
S–47	P–1908	PA–1908	B	7–14	Black
S–32	P–1219	PA–1219	A	8–10	Black
S–76	P–1711	PA–1711	A	11–12	Obe
S–70	P–1701	PB–1701	B	11–9	Obe
S–17	P–1311	PB–1311	B	6–16	Black
S–18	P–1312	PB–1312	B	6–16	Black
S–59	P–1506	PB–1506	A	7–26	Hirsch
S–60	P–1507	PB–1507	A	7–26	Hirsch
S–50	P–1497	PB–1497	B	7–19	Obe
S–51	P–1498	PA–1498	B	7–20	Obe
S–52	P–1499	PA–1499	B	7–21	Obe
S–53	P–1500	PA–1500	B	7–21	Obe
S–54	P–1501	PA–1501	B	7–22	Obe

Table of Detail Elements

Symbol	Element description	Decimal minute normal time	Reference
A–1	Close core box	0.046	Average
B–1	Clamp core box	$0.112N$	Time vs. no. clamps
C–1	Fill partly full of sand	$Y \times CT$	Time vs. L/D & vol. Time vs. vol.
D–1	Ram	$Y \times CT$	Time vs. L/D & vol. Time vs. vol.
E–1	Place rod and wire	$0.0153L + 0.03$	Time vs. length
F–1	Fill and ram	$Y \times CT$	Time vs. L/D & vol. Vs. vol.
G–1	Strike off	$0.0157A + 0.07$	Time vs. area
H–1	Remove vent wire	0.047	Average
J–1	Rap box	0.043	Average
K–1	Remove clamps	$0.061N$	Time vs. no. clamps
M–1	Open box	0.046	Average
N–1	Roll out core	$0.0057L + 0.045$	Time vs. length
P–1	Clean box	$\sqrt{0.0067 + 0.000016V^2}$	Time vs. volume

Synthesis

Standard time = Sum of allowed elemental time

$$= \text{A–1} + \text{B–1} + \text{C–1} + \text{D–1} + \text{E–1} + \text{F–1} + \text{G–1}$$
$$+ \text{H–1} + \text{J–1} + \text{K–1} + \text{M–1} + \text{N–1} + \text{P–1}$$

Since Elements C–1, D–1, and F–1 are all dependent on the variables volume and length/diameter, their values may be combined before plotting on co-ordinate paper. The combined values for these three elements for the 17 time studies are:

Study No.	C–1 + D–1 + F–1
S–13	1.045
S–111	1.017
S–45	1.235
S–46	0.647
S–47	1.325
S–32	1.110
S–76	0.500
S–70	1.362
S–17	1.932
S–18	0.659
S–59	0.988
S–60	1.181
S–50	0.584
S–51	1.277
S–52	0.888
S–53	1.481
S–54	2.065

For reference purposes, the combination of C–1 + D–1 + F–1 will be designated R–1 [see Figures 20–11 and 20–12]. Curves 1 and 2 are used to solve for the allowed time for these three elements by first getting adjustment factor from curve 1 and then getting the adjusted time from curve 2. The product of these two values will give the allowed time for C–1 + D–1 + F–1.

The time for elemental E–1 (place rod and wire) has been plotted on curve 3 [see Figure 20–13], where its relationship to core length is shown. This curve can be expressed algebraically by the equation:

$$T = fv + C$$

or

$$\text{Time} = (\text{Slope})(\text{length}) + y \text{ intercept}$$

Solving graphically:

$$f = \frac{0.210 - 0.100}{12 - 4.8} = \frac{0.110}{7.20}$$
$$= 0.0153$$
$$C = 0.03 \text{ (from graph)}$$

Thus:

$$\text{Time} = 0.0153L + 0.03$$

Element G–1 (strike off) has also been solved as a straight-line relationship. Here a cross-sectional area of the core has been plotted against time (see curve 4) [Figure 20–14]. In this case

$$\text{Time} = (f)(\text{area}) + 0.07$$

and

$$f = \frac{0.132 - 0.08}{4 - 0.7} = \frac{0.052}{3.3}$$
$$f = 0.0157$$

FIGURE 20–11

Then:

$$\text{Time} = 0.0157A + 0.07$$

Element N–1 (Roll out core) is shown on curve 5 [see Figure 20–15]. Here

$$\text{Time} = f(\text{length}) + 0.045$$

and

$$f = \frac{0.125 - 0.068}{14 - 4}$$
$$= 0.0057$$

Then:

$$\text{Time} = 0.0057L + 0.045$$

FIGURE 20–12

The time for element P–1 (clean box) when plotted against volume of core, gives a hyperbolic relationship as shown in curve 6 [Figure 20–16]. This relationship with time can be expressed algebraically as follows:

$$\text{Time} = \sqrt{a^2 + \frac{v^2 a^2}{k^2}}$$

$$= \sqrt{\frac{1}{0.082^2} + \frac{(v^2)(0.082)^2}{400}}$$

$$= \sqrt{0.0067 + 0.000016 v^2}$$

Elements, A–1, H–1, J–1, M–1 were classified as constants with the following respective allowed times determined by taking their average values: 0.046, 0.047, 0.043, 0.046. When these constants are added to the sum of the y intercept values of equations (3), (4), and (5), a total constant time of 0.327 minute is determined:

FIGURE 20–13

A–1.. 0.046
Curve 3 intercept.............................. 0.030
H–1.. 0.047
Curve 4 intercept.............................. 0.070
J–1.. 0.043
M–1.. 0.046
Curve 5 intercept.............................. 0.045
$$C_T = 0.327 \text{ minute}$$

Both elements B–1 and K–1 are proportional to the number of clamps N. Thus, these two elements may be combined for simplicity as follows:

$$\begin{array}{l} B\text{–}1 = 0.112N \\ K\text{–}1 = 0.061N \\ \hline S\text{–}1 = 0.173N \end{array}$$

Since elements E–1 (place rod and wire), and N–1 (roll out core) are proportional to length of core, we may combine their equated relationships with length and designate the combined total by the Symbol T–1.

Thus:

$$\begin{array}{l} E\text{–}1 = 0.0153L \\ N\text{–}1 = 0.0057L \\ \hline T\text{–}1 = 0.0210L. \end{array}$$

FIGURE 20–14

Simplifying our initial equation:

$$\text{Normal time} = \text{S–1} + \text{T–1} + \text{P–1} + \text{R–1} + \text{G–1} + \text{C}_T$$
$$= 0.173N + 0.0210L + \sqrt{0.0067 + 0.000016V^2}$$
$$+ Y \times \text{CT} + 0.0157A + 0.327$$

INSPECTION

The only inspection requirement on the cores covered by this formula is visual inspection done by the operator at the time the core is rolled free from the core box.

PAYMENT

This formula is to be used in development of allowed times that will be applied to the individual standards in a one-for-one incentive wage payment plan.

APPROVED: *John Purdy*   *Scott Dickinson*
           Supervisor   Formula Constructor

FIGURE 20–15

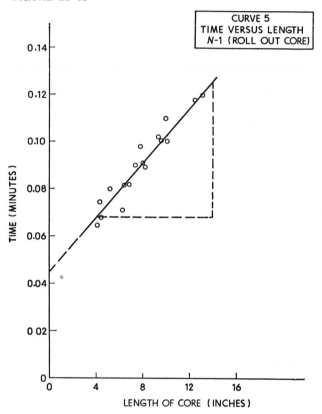

Use of the digital computer

Once a formula has been designed, it can be used for establishing standards on all work fitting the parameters of the formula. The resulting time standards can then be tabulated for rapid reference.

Rather than solve the formula innumerable times with a slide rule or desk calculator, the analyst should consider the electronic computer to compute in the least possible time *all* standards for which the formula is applicable.

An automatic digital computer is a mechanization not only of the arithmetic operations which can be executed using a desk calculator, but of the operator who determines the sequence in which these operations are performed.

Description of a modern digital computer

A modern digital computer consists of: (1) a control unit which roughly corresponds to the control portion of the keyboard of a desk

FIGURE 20–16

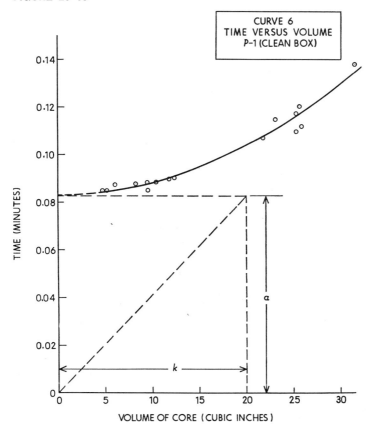

calculator; (2) the arithmetic unit which corresponds to the computing wheels of a desk calculator; (3) the input-output unit which corresponds to the numeric portion of the keyboard and the answer wheels on the carriage; and (4) the memory or storage units which, until the late 1960's, had no correspondent in the simple electromechanical desk calculator, unless it be off-line on paper or in the operator's head.

The memory units of a digital computer have become very fast in speed of operation, widespread in type, and extensive in capacity during the past two decades and it is expected that there will be substantial improvements in speed, type, and capacity between now and 1990. Memory units are divided into three functional types: (a) random access memories, generally typified by magnetic core memories, wherein each memory word can be accessed by its address from the arithmetic unit for storage or retrieval of the word—in whole or in part. It should be noted that each word is composed of a fixed number of binary (zeros and ones) bits. Basic collections of bits smaller than words are called bytes or fractional words. Several manufacturers have standardized eight bits to the byte and four bytes (32 bits) to the word. The choice of the eight-bit byte is reinforced by the 256 character American Standard Code for Information Exchange (ASCII) code which is represented in terms of eight one-zero bits. Henceforth, we use the terms byte to represent 8 bits and word to represent 32 bits; then 16 bits are 2 bytes or a half-word and 64 bits are a double word. Random access memory sizes of as low as 4,000 bytes or as high as 1,000,000 bytes are not uncommon. (*b*) Cyclical access memory units, as typified by rotating magnetic drums or disks, wherein bytes are stored in sequence and must be written or read in sequence. However the sequences are broken up much like pages in a book and one can start reading and writing on any page. These pages may be further subdivided into records of variable length analogous to sentences on a page. Thus, a page of 4,000 bytes might have 20 records of 200 bytes, for example, each record representing a simple job work order with reference information. (*c*) Sequential access memory, as typified by the magnetic tape unit, wherein bites are stored sequentially in records, each record separated from its neighbors by an inter-record gap. A magnetic tape might have 18,000,000 bytes strung in sequence on it. Given a typical byte density of 800 bytes per lineal inch of tape and an average density of 500 bytes per inch with inter-record gaps, the 18,000,000 bytes translate into a tape of length 3,000 feet. Assuming that the tape can be transported over the heads of the equipment at a speed of 10 feet a second, then it would require five minutes to go from one end of the tape to the other. Because of the time problem of search and finding a given record on tape, tapes are often restricted to uses where long sequences are natural or of little concern. For example, tapes find application in: daily operations records, history, payrolls, dead records, little used records. The cost of storing tape is small as compared with the cost of storing on disk or drum. These latter are used for current records or tables of frequent use. In any case, when a record is being used in computing, a copy is made from the disk, drum, or tape, and placed into the random access memory. It is the copy in random access memory that is utilized or amended through computation; when appropriate, an amended record is taken from random access memory and stored in place of the original record on disk, drum, or tape.

The input-output unit handles communication and information flow between the arithmetic unit and numerous devices (and sometimes between the devices themselves), including, (*a*) the cyclic and sequential memory storage units; (*b*) units that interface with private or public telecommunication links; (*c*) direct lines to other compatible computers; (*d*) analog-to-digital and digital-to-analog convertors, counters, and so forth that provide information from sensors and to servomechanisms; (*e*) devices primarily meant for direct human consumption such as printers, audio devices, lights, dials, digital numeric displays, plotters; and (*f*) means for human direction of computers such as reading and punching cards and paper tapes. Often distinct from the regular input-output unit described is (g) the memory access device which closely relates the arithmetic unit to the random access memory.

The arithmetic unit is basically a logical processor and accomplishes the actual computation with the aid of various kinds of registers: (a) data registers, (b) control registers, and (c) specialized memory registers or words. The modern digital computer operates on a programmed instruction basis. This means that part of the random access memory is filled with words that are interpretable as computational instructions if placed in the appropriate control register. Interpretation causes operations on one or more other data registers including getting (loading) and storing random access memory data words for or from the registers, respectively. The basic three-stage scheme of instruction cycle operation is:

1. The instruction is drawn from random access memory from the address location signified by the program counter (a control register) and transmitted to the control section.
2. The control section interprets the instruction and causes the appropriate action to take place, including memory access for data, possible modification program counter address, as well as operation of the arithmetic unit.
3. When the action is completed, the control section increments the address location stored in the program counter by one and the operation returns to stage 1.

If the basic cycle time of memory access is one microsecond (μs), then the average time of the three-stage instruction cycle is about three μs.

The control unit serves to control all operations: arithmetic operations, as can be seen from the above, and input-output operations. An appropriate function of the control section is the handling of interrupts and priorities. An interrupt is basically information sent to some hypothetical "control supervisor" resident in the computer indicating that some device or function is in need of service or has completed a job. For example, a printer might print a line of print in 50 milliseconds. In order for the printer to achieve its maximum print rate of 1,200 lines per minute, it sends an interrupt to the "control supervisor." This causes interruption of the current program, a laying it aside, and the operation of a supervisory program which determines the next line to be printed (if any), inserts it in the printer's buffer register, and instructs its printing; then the original program is taken up again. Against a basic 1μs memory cycle time, interrupt may require from 50 to 500 μs to answer. Often, several interrupts occur almost simultaneously and they are answered in order of their priority in importance, first, and their arrival, second. Interrupts can be classified by type; these are, following IBM's classification, (*a*) machine check caused by machine malfunction; (*b*) program caused by data processing or instruction anomalies; (*c*) supervisor call caused by a programmed call for assistance; (*d*) external caused by some outside device, timer, or console operator; and (*e*) input-output at the beginning and termination of input-output operations. Lastly, a computer is started in computation by the control section after pushbutton insertion of a start address in the program counter followed by a start (external) interrupt; it may often be restarted by data interrupt from a card reader, for example. It can be stopped by external interrupt or programmed halt or pause instructions.

Computers as logic processors

Information is stored and operated on in binary bits, each bit taking one of two possible states: true-false, one-zero, on-off, clockwise-counterclockwise, the interpretation assigned being that which the analyst or the computer designer chooses. Most primitively the computer needs the capability to set (make a 1) or reset (make a 0) a bit. Logical computation occurs when two distinct bits are operated on by the two fundamental logical operators: union and intersection; or as they are known computationally, OR and AND. The resultant bit formed from their operation is illustrated below along with exclusive OR or EXOR

	OR				*AND*				*EXOR*			
First bit.............	1	1	0	0	1	1	0	0	1	1	0	0
Second bit...........	0	1	0	1	0	1	0	1	0	1	0	1
Resultant bit.........	1	1	0	1	0	1	0	0	1	0	0	1

As pointed out previously, bits are grouped together into bytes and bytes into half-words, words, and so forth. In this form they can represent a set of logical true-false variables such as have just been described or they can be used to represent a number. For a 16-bit halfword the binary representation in integer or fixed point mode is

$$+ (a_{14}2^{14} + a_{13}2^{13} + \cdots + a_2 2^2 + a_1 2^1 + a_0 2^0)$$

where bits 1 through 15 take on the numeric values one and zero and are represented as a_{15-i} above while bit zero is the sign bit: a zero meaning plus, a one meaning minus. Because of the size limitations of the fixed point mode, half-words being restricted to ±32,767 and full words to ±2,147,483,647, a scientific or floating point method is also used wherein the number is represented by a binary mantissa or fraction of 24 bits (lead bit is usually 1) multiplied by 2 raised to a power called a characteristic (7 bit binary representation) and a sign bit. This allows for magnitudes from about 10^{20} to about 10^{-20} and mantissas accurate to seven decimal places. Double precision words are also possible. The numeric representations in register form are shown with the character or byte form (Figure 20–17).

FIGURE 20–17

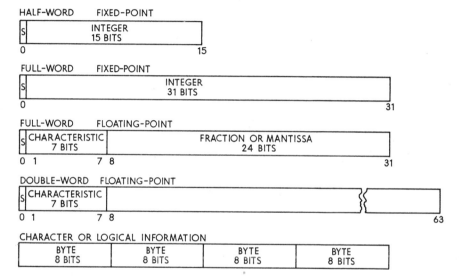

The operation on the contents of a pair of registers in an arithmetic manner is just a specialized logical operation, involving "carry bits." This is illustrated below for fixed point addition of two half-word numbers with the resultant number and hypothetical carry and next carry bits shown in register form. Addition proceeds from right to left with addition logic shown progressing downward.

Carry bits..................	0	0	0	0	0	0	0	1	1	1	1	0	0	0	
1st number..................	0	0	0	0	0	1	1	0	0	1	0	1	1	0	1	0
2nd number..................	0	0	0	0	0	0	0	0	0	1	1	1	0	0	1
Resultant no..................	0	0	0	0	0	1	1	0	1	0	0	1	0	0	1	1
Next carry..................		0	0	0	0	0	0	0	1	1	1	1	0	0	0

It should be noted that the hypothetical next carry and carry registers are displaced or shifted by one bit position and are presented for pedagogic reasons only.

One, two, and three half-words can also be grouped to represent computer instructions. When loaded into the appropriate control registers, instruction decoding matrices operate on the bits to set in motion the sequence of electronic events that constitute execution of the instructions. Interpretation of instructions is but another logical process such as the decoding of bytes as characters, numbers, or pure Venn-diagram logic. IBM in their System/360 have five logical instruction formats in three instruction length as follows.

Abbreviation	Format type	Length
RR...............	Register-Register	half-word
RS...............	Register-Storage	one word
RX...............	Register-Indexed	one word
SI...............	Storage-Immediate	one word
SS...............	Storage-Storage	three half-words

The first byte of each instruction is called the operation code and is used to distinguish both the instruction format and the particular operation to be performed. The remainder of the instruction deals mostly with addresses of registers, index registers, base registers, and storage locations. The detail of the particular machine language instructions are not of concern to the average user. However, the types of categories of machine language instructions may be of interest. The principal types are:

Arithmetic.................	Add, subtract, multiply, divide
Compare.................	Greater than, equal to, less than, sign
Branch...................	Branch to another location (program counter address), branch on condition or index, branch and save return address
Logic....................	AND, OR, EXOR
Load and Store............	Storage-storage and register-storage transfers
Shift.....................	Left, right; single or double registers; shift normalized
Change and Move.........	Character manipulations, decimals
Input-Output.............	Start I/O, test I/O, and halt I/O, for example, cover operations with cyclic and sequential memory, other devices, and computers

Operations with computers

Fortunately for the general user, computer facilities are most often organized and operated to provide services. Generally there are two ways to enter programs for computational services; the first and oldest of these is called batch processing; the newer way is called remote terminal entry. Batch processing features the bringing of the program deck of punched cards (or magnetic tape or other acceptable media) to the computer center where it is accepted and put in a queue for service. Then depending upon the job, the queueing policy, and the center's load; the completed computation is finished and is available at the center in minutes, hours, or days. Remote terminal entry is becoming increasingly associated with groups of time-shared computers. Entry is usually through a typewriterlike keyboard but maybe through punched cards or magnetic tape; often the program used is a standard one for the user and he is merely inputing data. Generally, the response time is a matter of seconds until the first line of print occurs and the delay is scarcely noticed by the user. However, typewriters are slow and many minutes may be required for total output.

In any case, the general user is not confronted with the problem of intimate knowledge of the computer. A number of general purpose tertiary languages such as FORTRAN, ALGOL, COBOL, and a growing group of specialized quaternary languages such as GPSS, APT, MPS, and APL are available. These languages have been devised with the user in mind. Their statements and concepts are analogous to mathematical formulas (FORTRAN), business practices (COBOL), or block diagrams (GPSS), to name a few. The user must only learn the computer language or dialect which best fits his line of work; the computer system operators have compilers which convert from the human work-oriented tertiary and quaternary languages to the primary language, machine language— possibly through the intermediate step of secondary or assembly language. Thus, the computer language of one's choice plus a few control cards or lines before and after constitute the way that the program is constructed by the general user.

The principal task that the general user faces is that of organizing himself to utilize the computer. This involves both a general education task on his part and a specific application task for each problem to be computerized. In general education, the task is threefold:

a) Contact the computation center or centers that you might use; discuss the broad range of problems that you might wish to run with members of the center's Applications Service. Determine whether it is worthwhile to utilize the computer and the costs, both direct and indirect, involved in its utilization.

b) Take the advice of the Application's programmers and learn the basics of the most suitable language for your jobs. While eventually you may employ a battery of programmers yourself, remember it's difficult to instruct them as to what you want without them understanding your problems.

c) Do a few trial problems on the computer to get the feel for good preparation and handling, debugging, and documentation procedures.

When you are ready for a specific application task, a threefold approach is advised.

a)   Determination of whether or not the problem is economic to solve on the computer.

b)   Numerical analysis and flow charting the problem; that is, developing formulas in forms that are efficiently handled by computers and sequencing the operations to be performed by the computer.

c)   Programming the problem in the computer language you choose from those available at the computation center.

Types of problems economic to solve on digital computer

The electronic digital computer can handle any record keeping or mathematical problem that can be reduced to a routine procedure or formula. There are four broad classes of problems which are frequently economical to solve on the computer. These are:

1.   Those problems that are quite simple but require many repetitive calculations. Typical problems falling under this class would be production schedules, sales analyses, inventories, bills, payrolls, cost reports, and budget estimates.

2.   Those problems that are quite long but can be solved by iterative processes. Problems falling under this class would be the solution of typical formulas as developed in this chapter, where computations of fractional and whole powers are required in addition to simple arithmetic operations.

3.   Experimental design requiring solutions under varying conditions. Under this class would be typical design problems. For example, the design of large standard-line core-form power transformers and large induction motors would be realistic examples. Transformers of this type are basically simple. Yet almost all are custom designed. With the known practical ranges of performance, size, and so on programmed into a computer plus production limitations and manufacturing codes, final working electrical design data can be obtained quite rapidly.

4.   Simulations such as plant layouts, queues, inventory, general Monte Carlo techniques—the types of problems which have no explicit computational method to reach an optimal solution. For these a carefully thought through simulation can reveal system problems and utilities when other methods are inapplicable.

Numerical analysis and flow charting

Plan to develop formulas suitable for computer computation. This often means that integrals are replaced by discrete summations, differentials by finite differences, that denominators are checked for being nonzero and so forth. The general principle of computing is the use of the replacement form of equations. For example, if it is desired to increment a value A by B then one writes $A = A + B$ in FORTRAN; it means that B is added to the original value of A and the resulting number is stored in the memory location assigned to A; henceforth, until it is again changed, any reference to A in a formula means reference to the new value. Often, the same formulas are used over and over again in a given program. If a formula is to be used a million times in a run, then it pays to make it efficient. For example, FORTRAN statement $A*X**2 + B*X + C$ requires three multiplications and two additions; on the other hand $(A*X + B)*X + C$ involves two multiplications and two additions, about 25 percent less computation time. Computers are so fast and the user's time so valuable, that the general user need not worry much about efficiency unless the expression is used about 10^5 or more times in a computation. There are many texts available that give formulas and flow charts for standard scientific types of computation. These should be consulted in preference to the general user's invention of his own programs. For example, Ralston and Wilf, *Mathematical Methods for Digital Computers* (1967) provide formulas involving elementary functions, matrices and linear equations, ordinary differential equations, partial differential equations, statistics and other methods. There is no need to reinvent the wheel except for pedagogic reasons.

Once one has numerically analyzed a problem, it often pays to flow chart it prior to programming to ensure completeness and accuracy. Some standardized symbols, adapted from Gray and London, "Documentation Standards," Brandon/Systems Press, 1969, are shown in Figure 20–18. These are consistent with U.S.A. Standard X3.5–1968.

A simple example of an equation to determine knurling times will suffice to illustrate both flow charting and programming. Let the equation for Knurling times be given by

$$T = 0.1A + 1.5$$

where

$T = $ Normal time
$A = $ Surface area of knurled shaft

Suppose it is desired to generate a table of times (T) for areas (A) where A varies from 3 to 80 square inches by increments of $\frac{1}{4}$ inch. The flow chart for this very simple example is given in Figure 20–19. The parenthetical numbers relate to program statement numbers as they appear in the program.

FIGURE 20–18

Program flow chart symbols

General Operation Symbol: Used for any operation which creates, alters, transfers or erases data, or any other operation for which no specific symbol has been defined in the Standard.

Subroutine (Predefined Process) Symbol: Used when a section of program is considered as a single operation for the purpose of this flowchart.

Generalized Input/Output Symbol: Used to represent the input/output (I/O) function of making information available.

Branch Symbol: Has one entry line and more than one exit. The symbol contains a description of the test on which the selection of an exit is based. The various possible results of this test are shown against the corresponding exits.

Offpage Connector Symbol: Used as a linkage between two blocks of logic that are to be found on separate pages of the flowchart. The symbol is only used on the "exit" page, on the "entry" page an onpage symbol is used.

Onpage Connector Symbol: Used as a linkage between two blocks on the same page, when it is not desirable to connect them using a linkage line. The label of the block to which the connection is being made is written inside the symbols.

Terminal Symbol: Used as the beginning or end of a flowline (e.g., start or end of a program).

Annotation Symbol: Used to add additional information to a symbol or block of program.

Flowlines (Linkage Lines): Used to show the flow between blocks of a flowchart. The normal flow is from top to bottom and left to right of the page. The programmer may dispense with the use of the direction arrows when the chart follows the normal flow. They must be used, however, for any portion of the diagram which does not follow the normal flow.

Programming

Let's continue with the Knurling times example which has been flow charted. It is easy to translate it into FORTRAN. For the achievement of repetitive formula computation the branching IF statement is used. Every READ and WRITE statement requires a FORMAT statement, the number of which given by the second of the couple in the parenthetic expression after each; the first number represents the device: six being the printer. The source program is as follows:

```
C       PRØGRAM TØ PRØDUCE TABLE ØF KNURLING TIMES
C       EQUATIØN—TX.1A+1.5
        WRITE (6,100)
        A=3.0
    1  T=.1*A+1.5
        WRITE (6,101) A,T
        A=A+.25
        IF (A.LT.80.0) GO TO 1
        STØP
  100  FØRMAT (1H1,10X,14HKNURLING TIMES/1H ,12X,9HT=
        .1A+1.5/1HO,8X,4HAREA1,10X,4HTIME/)
  101  FØRMAT (1H ,F12.2,F15.3)
        END
```

The job control language cards are not included in the source program as often these are unique to the computer installation. Generally, this requires less than 10 seconds compile and execute time on a System/360 model 50 or above. The result of this program is shown in Figure 20–20.

FIGURE 20–19

Knurling times flow chart

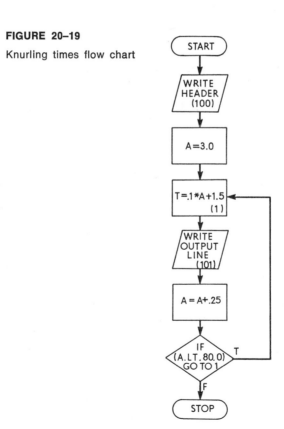

FIGURE 20–20

Conclusion

Through the design of a time study formula, it is possible to establish standards in a fraction of the time required by taking individual studies. However, before a formula is released for use, the mathematics used in its development should be carefully checked to assure that the expression is correct. Then, too, several test cases should be tried to be certain that the formula will establish true, consistent standards. The formula should be clearly identified as to its range of application, and in no case should standards be established with data that are beyond the scope of the formula.

In summary, the following steps represent the chronological procedure in time study formula design:

1. Collect data.
    a) Using time studies already available.
    b) Using standard data already available.
    c) Taking new time studies.
2. Compile master work sheet and identify formula.
3. Analyze and classify elements.
    a) Constants.
    b) Variables.
4. Develop synthesis.
5. Compute the final expression.
6. Check mathematics of developed formula.
7. Test formula.
8. Write formula report.
9. Use formula.

By systematically following these nine steps, the analyst will have little difficulty in designing reliable time study formulas.

KNURLING TIMES $T = .1A + 1.5$	
AREA	TIME
3.00	1.800
3.25	1.825
3.50	1.850
3.75	1.875
4.00	1.900
4.25	1.925
4.50	1.950
4.75	1.975
5.00	2.000
5.25	2.025
5.50	2.050
5.75	2.075
6.00	2.100
6.25	2.125
6.50	2.150
6.75	2.175
7.00	2.200
7.25	2.225
7.50	2.250
7.75	2.275
8.00	2.300
8.25	2.325
8.50	2.350
8.75	2.375
9.00	2.400
9.25	2.425
9.50	2.450
9.75	2.475
10.00	2.500
10.25	2.525
10.50	2.550
10.75	2.575
11.00	2.600
11.25	2.625
11.50	2.650
11.75	2.675
12.00	2.700
12.25	2.725
12.50	2.750
12.75	2.775
13.00	2.800
13.25	2.825

Once a formula has been designed, it can be programmed on the digital computer and solved for all possible variations within the scope of the formula. Thus tabulated standards can be made available for broad variations in the work assignment.

TEXT QUESTIONS

1. What advantages does the formula offer over standard data in establishing time standards?
2. Is the use of time study formulas restricted to machine shop operations where feeds and speeds influence allowed times? Explain.
3. What are the characteristics of a sound time study formula?
4. What is the danger of using too few studies in the derivation of a formula?
5. What is the function of the synthesis in the formula report?
6. Write the equation of the ellipse with its center at the origin and axes along the coordinate axes and passing through $(2, 3)$ and $(-1, 4)$.
7. Find the equation of the hyperbola with center at $(0, 0)$ and $a = 4$, $b = 5$, foci on the y axis.
8. What 14 sections make up the formula report?
9. What nine steps represent the chronological procedure in the design of time study formulas?
10. Explain in detail how it is possible to solve graphically for time when two variables are influential and they cannot be combined.
11. Develop an algebraic expression for the relationship between time and area from the following data:

Study no.	1	2	3	4	5
Time	4	7	11	15	21
Area	28.6	79.4	182	318	589

12. If the data shown in Figure 20–1 were plotted on logarithmic paper, would the plotting be a straight line? Why?
13. Describe the modern digital computer.
14. What is the purpose of the control unit?
15. What types of problems lend themselves to solution on the digital computer?
16. Explain the term "instruction word."
17. What is meant by "floating point numbers?"
18. Determine the numbers used in the addition logic example and check that the resultant number is correct.
19. Considering that each letter on a page including blanks, numbers, punctuation marks, etc., can be represented as an eight-bit byte, count the total number of bytes possible on a page of this text.

GENERAL QUESTIONS

1. Would the company union prefer standards to be set by formulas or standard data? Why?

2. Would it be necessary for the "chart and formula" designer to have a background in time study work? Why?

3. If an operator objected strongly to a rate established through a formula, explain in detail how you would endeavor to prove to him that the rate was fair.

4. Count the number of characters including blanks on a given line and the number of lines on a full page of text in this book. Multiply and determine the number of characters per page. How does this figure compare with 4,000 bytes to a computer page?

CHAPTER 21

Work sampling studies

Work sampling is a technique used to investigate the proportions of total time devoted to the various activities that comprise a job or work situation. The results of work sampling are effective for determining allowances applicable to the job, for the determining of machine utilization, and for establishing standards of production. This same information can be obtained by time study procedures. Work sampling is a method that frequently will provide the information faster and at considerably less cost than by stopwatch techniques.

In conducting a work sampling study, the analyst takes a comparatively large number of observations at random intervals. The ratio of the number of observations of a given state of activity to the total number of observations taken will approximate the percentage of time that the process is in that given state of activity. For example, if 10,000 observations at random intervals over a period of several weeks showed that a given automatic screw machine was turning out work in 7,000 instances, and in 3,000 instances, it was idle for miscellaneous reasons, then it would be reasonably certain that the downtime of the machine would be 30 percent of the working day, or 2.4 hours, and the effective output of the machine would be a matter of 5.6 hours per day. The application of work sampling was first made by L. H. C. Tippett in the British textile industry. Later under the name "ratio-delay" study,[1] it received considerable attention in this country. The accuracy of the data determined by work sampling depends upon the number of observations; unless the sample size is of sufficient quantity, inaccurate results will occur.

[1] R. L. Morrow, *Time Study and Motion Economy* (New York: Ronald Press Co., 1946).

The work sampling method has several advantages over that of acquiring data by the conventional time study procedure. These are:

1. It does not require continuous observation by an analyst over a long period of time.
2. Clerical time is diminished.
3. The total man-hours expended by the analyst are usually much fewer.[2]
4. Operator is not subjected to long-period stopwatch observations.
5. Crew operations can be readily studied by a single analyst.

The whole theory of work sampling is based on the fundamental laws of probability. If at a given instant an event can either be present or absent, statisticians have derived the following expression, which shows the probability of x occurrences of an event in n observations:

$$(p + q)^n = 1$$

$p =$ The probability of a single occurrence
$q = (1 - p)$ the probability of an absence of occurrence
$n =$ Number of observations

If the above expression, $(p + q)^n = 1$, is expanded according to the Binomial Theorem, the first term of the expansion will give the probability that $x = 0$, the second term $x = 1$, and so on. The distribution of these probabilities is known as the Binomial Distribution. Statisticians have also shown that the mean of this distribution is equal to np and the variance is equal to npq. The standard deviation is, of course, equal to the square root of the variance.

One may now logically ask, of what value is a distribution that allows only one event to either occur or not occur? For the answer to this, consider the possibility of taking one condition of the work sampling study at a time. All the other conditions can then be considered as nonoccurrences of this one event. Using this approach we can now proceed with the discussion of binomial theory.

Elementary statistics tell us that as n becomes large the Binomial Distribution approaches the Normal Distribution. Since work sampling studies involve quite large sample sizes the Normal Distribution is a satisfactory approximation of the Binomial Distribution. Rather than use the distribution of the number of occurrences a with mean np and variance npq, it is more convenient to use the distribution of a proportion with a mean of p, i.e., $\dfrac{np}{n}$ and a standard deviation of

$$\sqrt{\frac{pq}{n}} \left(\text{i.e., } \frac{\sqrt{npq}}{n} \right)$$

as the approximately normally distributed random variable.

---

[2] *Ibid.*, p. 334.

In work sampling studies, we take a sample of size n in an attempt to estimate p. We know according to elementary sampling theory that we cannot expect the $\hat{p}$ ($\hat{p}$ = the proportion based on a sample) of each sample to be the true value of p. We do however, expect the $\hat{p}$ of any sample to fall within the range of $p \pm 2$ sigma approximately 95 percent of the time. In other words, if p is the true percentage of a given condition, we can expect $\hat{p}$ of any sample to fall outside the limits $p \pm 2$ sigma only about 5 times in 100 due to chance alone. This theory will be used to derive the total sample size required to give a certain degree of accuracy. It will be used also for subsample sizes a little later.

Illustrative example

To clarify the fundamental theory of work sampling, it would be helpful to interpret the results of an experiment. Let us assume the following circumstances: we have observed one machine that has random breakdowns for a 100-day period. During this period, we have taken eight random observations per day.
Let:

n = The number of observations per day
N = The total number of random observations
x_i = The number of breakdown observations observed in n random observations on day i
$x = 0, 1, 2, 3, \ldots , n$
$i = 1, 2, 3, \ldots , k$
N_x = The number of days that the experiment showed x number of breakdowns in n random observations
$P(x)$ = Probability of x observations down in n observations by the binomial distribution

$$P(x) = \frac{n!}{x! \, (n - x)!} \, p^x q^{n-x}$$
$$p + q = 1$$

where

p = Probability of machine being down
q = Probability of machine running
$\tilde{P} = \dfrac{x_i}{n}$ = observed proportion of down time per day

$$\hat{P} = \frac{\sum\limits_{i=1}^{k} x_i}{N}$$

An all-day time study for several days revealed that $p = 0.5$. Table 21–1 shows the number of days in which x breakdowns were observed

$(x = 0, 1, 2, 3, \ldots, n)$ and the expected number of breakdowns given by our binomial model.

TABLE 21–1

x	Nx	$P(x)$	$100P(x)$
0........................	0	0.0039	0.39
1........................	4	0.0312	3.12
2........................	11	0.1050	10.5
3........................	23	0.2190	21.9
4........................	27	0.2730	27.3
5........................	22	0.2190	21.9
6........................	10	0.1050	10.5
7........................	3	0.0312	3.12
8........................	0	0.0039	0.39
	100	1.00*	100*

* Approximately.

The reader can observe the close agreement between the observed number of days that a specified number of breakdowns were encountered (Nx) and the expected number computed theoretically $100P(x)$ when $p = 0.5$. An hypothesis that the theoretical information shows close enough agreement to the observed information for the theoretical binomial to be accepted, may be tested by the chi-square (χ^2) distribution. The χ^2 distribution tests whether the observed frequencies in a distribution differ significantly from the expected frequencies.

In the example, where the observed frequency is N_x and the expected frequency is $100 P(x)$:

$$\chi^2 = \sum_{x=0}^{k} \frac{[N_x - 100P(x)]^2}{100P(x)}$$

That is, the quantity under the summation is distributed approximately as χ^2 for K degrees of freedom. In this example we have $\chi^2 = 0.206$.

The analyst must determine whether the calculated value of χ^2 is sufficiently large to refute a null hypothesis that the difference between the observed frequencies and computed frequencies are due to chance alone. This experimental value of χ^2 is so small that it could easily have occurred through chance causes alone. Therefore, we accept the hypothesis that the experimental data "fits" the theoretical binomial distribution.

In the typical industrial situation, p (which was known to have a value of 0.5) is unknown to the analyst. The best estimate of p is $\hat{p}$ which may be computed as $\frac{x}{n}$. As the number of observations taken at random per day (n) increases $\hat{p}$ will approach p. However, with a limited number of random observations the analyst is concerned with the accuracy of $\hat{p}$.

If a plot of $P(x)$ versus x were made from the above example, it would appear as follows:

FIGURE 21–1

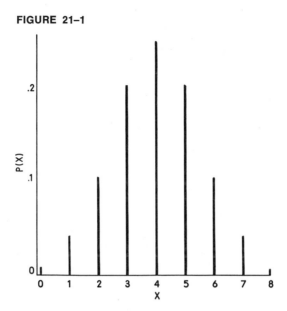

When n is sufficiently large, regardless of the actual value of p, the binomial distribution will very closely approximate the normal distribution. This tendency can be seen in the above example when p is approximately 0.5. When p is near 0.5, n may be small and the normal can be a good approximation to the binomial.

When using the normal approximation, we set

$$u = p$$

and

$$\sigma p = \sqrt{\frac{pq}{n}}$$

To approximate the binomial distribution the variable z used for entry in the normal distribution (see Table A3–2, Appendix 3) may take the following form:

$$z = \frac{\hat{p} - p}{\sqrt{\dfrac{pq}{n}}}$$

Although p is unknown in the practical case, we are able to estimate p from $\hat{p}$ and can determine the interval within which p lies using confidence limits. For example, we can imagine the interval defined

$$\hat{p} - 2\sqrt{\frac{\hat{p}\hat{q}}{n}}$$

and

$$\hat{p} + 2\sqrt{\frac{\hat{p}\hat{q}}{n}}$$

contains p 95 percent of the time.

Graphically this may be represented as:

We can derive the expression for finding a confidence interval for p as follows: let us suppose we want an interval which will contain p 95 percent of the time; that is, a 95 percent confidence interval. For n sufficiently large, the expression,

$$z = \frac{\hat{p} - p}{\sqrt{\frac{\hat{p}\hat{q}}{n}}}$$

is approximately a standard normal variable. Therefore, we can set the probability

$$P\left(z_{.025} < \frac{\hat{p} - p}{\sqrt{\frac{\hat{p}\hat{q}}{n}}} < z_{.975} \right) = 0.95$$

Rearranging the inequalities then gives:

$$P\left(\hat{p} - z_{.975}\sqrt{\frac{\hat{p}\hat{q}}{n}} < p < \hat{p} + z_{.975}\sqrt{\frac{\hat{p}\hat{q}}{n}} \right) = 0.95$$

remembering $-z_{.025} = z_{.975} = 1.96$ or approximately 2. The interval with approximately a 95 percent chance of containing p is then

$$\hat{p} - 2\sqrt{\frac{\hat{p}\hat{q}}{n}} < p < \hat{p} + 2\sqrt{\frac{\hat{p}\hat{q}}{n}}$$

These limits imply that the interval defined contains p with 95 percent confidence since z has been selected as having a value of 2.

The underlying assumptions of the binomial are that p, the probability of a success (the occurrence of downtime), is constant each random instant we observe the process. Therefore, it is necessary always to take random observations when taking a work sampling study.

Selling work sampling

Before beginning a program of work sampling, it is a good idea for the analyst to sell the use and the reliability of the tool to all members of the organization to be affected by the results. If it is to be used for establishing allowances, it should be sold to the union and the foreman, as well as company management. This can be done by having several short sessions with representatives of the various interested parties and explaining examples of the law of probability, thus illustrating why ratio delay procedures will work. Unions as well as workmen look with favor upon work sampling techniques, once the procedure is fully explained, since work sampling is completely impersonal, does not utilize the stopwatch, and is based on accepted mathematical and statistical methods.

In the initial session where work sampling is explained, the simple study in tossing unbiased coins may be used. All participants will, of course, readily recognize that a single coin toss stands a 50-50 chance of being heads. When asked how they would determine the probability of heads versus tails, they undoubtedly will propose tossing a coin a few times to find out. When asked if two times is adequate, they will respond "No." Ten times may be suggested and the response will be "that may not be adequate." When 100 times is suggested, the group will agree: "That should do it with some degree of assurance." This example will firmly plant the principal requisite of work sampling: adequate sample size to ensure statistical significance.

The instructor would next discuss the probable results of tossing four unbiased coins. It can be explained that there is only one arrangement in which the coins can fall showing no heads, only one arrangement that permits all heads. However, three heads can result from four possible arrangements and likewise one head can result from four possible arrangements. There are six possible arrangements that will give two heads.

With all 16 possibilities thus accounted for, the group will recognize that if four unbiased coins are tossed continually they will distribute themselves as shown in Figure 21–2.

After the above explanation and the demonstration of this distribution by making several tosses and recording the results, it will readily be accepted that 100 tosses could demonstrate a normal distribution. Furthermore, it will be understood that a thousand tosses would probably approach a normal distribution more closely and 100,000 would give a nearly perfect distribution, but not sufficiently more accurate than the 1,000 toss distribution to be economically worth the extra effort. Here the idea of approaching significant accuracy rapidly at first, and then at a diminishing rate, can be established.

Now it can be pointed out that a machine or operator could be in a heads or tails state. For example, a machine could be running (heads) or

FIGURE 21–2

Distribution of number of heads with infinite number of tosses using four unbiased coins

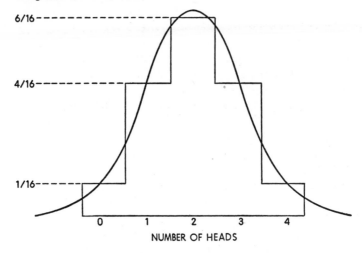

NUMBER OF HEADS

idle (tails). An example can be demonstrated where 360 observations are made on a turret lathe. These observations might give the data shown in Figure 21–3.

A cumulative plot of "running" would level off, giving an indication of when it would be safe to stop taking readings (see Figure 21–4). All those in attendance would understand that "idle" machine time could be broken down into the various types of interruptions and delays and could be accounted for and evaluated.

Once the validity of work sampling has been sold up and down the

FIGURE 21–3

OPERATION	OBSERVATION	TOTAL	PERCENT
RUNNING	ͲͰͰ ͲͰͰ ͲͰͰ ͲͰͰ ͲͰͰ ͲͰͰ ͲͰͰ ͲͰͰ ͲͰͰ ͲͰͰ II ͲͰͰ	252	70
IDLE	ͲͰͰ ͲͰͰ ͲͰͰ ͲͰͰ ͲͰͰ ͲͰͰ ͲͰͰ ͲͰͰ ͲͰͰ III ͲͰͰ ͲͰͰ ͲͰͰ ͲͰͰ ͲͰͰ ͲͰͰ ͲͰͰ ͲͰͰ ͲͰͰ ͲͰͰ ͲͰͰ ͲͰͰ	108	30
		TOTAL 360	100

FIGURE 21–4

Cumulative percentage of running time

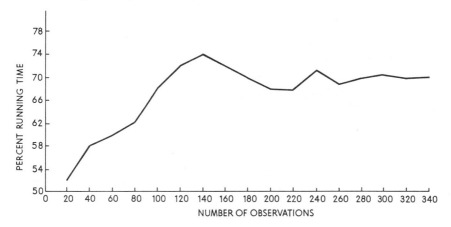

line, the analyst then should clearly define his problem. If he wishes to establish allowance data, he should make a summary of all elements customarily included in the various allowance categories. To do this, he would be wise to make a preliminary survey of the class of work for which the allowances are to be determined. It may be necessary to spend several hours on the production floor observing all types of delays encountered, so the element listing can be complete.

Planning the work sampling study

After the analyst has explained and obtained the approval of the supervisor involved, he is ready to perform the detailed planning that is essential before beginning actual observations.

His first step is to make a preliminary estimate of those activities on which he is seeking information. These would be the activities referred to earlier. This estimate may involve one or more than one activity. Frequently this estimate can be made from historical data. If the analyst does not feel he can make a reasonable estimate, he should work sample the area or areas involved for a short period (two or three days) and use the information obtained as the basis of his estimates (see Figure 21–3).

Once the preliminary estimates have been made, he should determine the accuracy that is desired of the results. This can best be expressed as a tolerance within a stated confidence level.

Having made a preliminary estimate of the percentage occurrences of the elements being studied and determining an accuracy desired at a given confidence level, the analyst will now make an estimate of the number of observations to be made.

Knowing how many observations that need to be taken and the time that is available to conduct the study, he can determine the frequency of observations.

His next step will be to design the work sampling form or card on which the data will be tabulated and the control charts that will be used in conjunction with the study.

Determining observations needed

To determine the number of observations needed, the analyst must know how accurate his results must be. The larger the number of observations, the more valid the final answer will be. Three thousand observations will give considerably more reliable results than 300. However, if the accuracy of the result is not the prime consideration, 300 observations may be ample.

In random sampling procedures, there is always the chance that the final result of the observations will be beyond the acceptable tolerance. These sampling errors will diminish as the size of the sample increases. The standard error σ_p of a sample proportion or percentage as shown in most textbooks on statistics may be expressed by the equation:

$$\sigma_p = \sqrt{\frac{pq}{n}} = \sqrt{\frac{p(1-p)}{n}}$$

where

σ_p = The standard deviation of a percentage

p = True percentage occurrence of the element being sought expressed as a decimal

n = Total number of random observations upon which p is based

By approximating the true percentage occurrence of the element being sought (which we can designate as $\hat{p}$) and knowing the allowable standard error permitted, it is possible to substitute back in the above expression and compute n.

$$n = \frac{\hat{p}(1-\hat{p})}{\sigma_p^2}$$

For example, it is desired to determine the number of observations required with 95 percent confidence so that the true proportion of personal and unavoidable delay time is within the interval 6–10 percent. It is expected that the unavoidable and personal delay time encountered in the section of the plant under study is 8 percent. These assumptions expressed graphically are shown in Figure 21–5.

In this case, p would equal 0.08 and $\sigma_{\hat{p}}$ would equal 1 percent or 0.01. Using these values, we can solve for n as follows:

$$n = \frac{0.08(1 - 0.08)}{(0.01)^2}$$
$$= 736 \text{ observations}$$

Frequently it is desirable to express the interval of the element being sought as a percentage element tolerance. In the example given, we use a ± 25 percent element tolerance $(0.02/0.08)$. To simplify the calculation of n for varying tolerances of the element being sought for a given confidence level, it is possible to construct an alignment chart. Figure 21–6 illustrates such an alignment chart for 95 percent confidence limits (± 2 standard deviations).

FIGURE 21–5

Tolerance range of percentage of unavoidable delay allowance required within a given section of a plant

.06	$\hat{P} = .08$	.10

After the initial estimate of the number of observations has been obtained, a more accurate estimation of p may be computed. By using the above equation,

$$n = \frac{\hat{p}(1 - \hat{p})}{\sigma_{\hat{p}}^2}$$

again the achieved accuracy is computed. If the achieved accuracy is as good or better than the desired accuracy, we accept this $\hat{p}$ as the true value of the population value p. If the desired accuracy has not been obtained, more observations are taken and the above process is repeated.

Determining the frequency of the observations

The frequency of the observations depends for the most part on the number of observations required and the time limit placed on the development of the data. For example, if 3,600 observations were needed and the study was to be completed in 30 calendar days, we should need to obtain approximately:

$$\frac{3,600 \text{ observations}}{20 \text{ working days}} = 180 \text{ observations per working day}$$

Of course, the number of analysts available and the nature of the work being studied will also influence the frequency of the observations. For example, if only one analyst is available and if he is accumulating allowance data on a limited battery of facilities, it may be impractical for him

FIGURE 21–6

Nomogram to determine number of random observations for various confidence levels

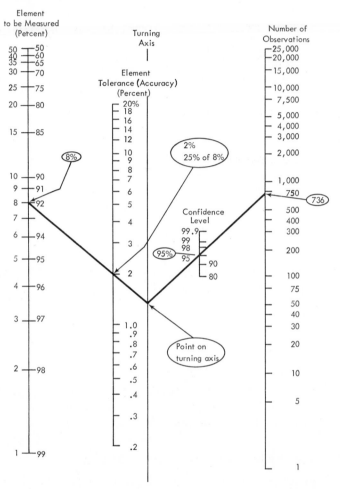

Arnold D. Moskowitz

to take 180 observations during one working day. Once the number of observations per day has been determined, then the actual time that the analyst records his observations must be selected. To obtain a representative sample, it is important that observations be taken at all times of the working day.

In the example cited, we may assume that one analyst is available and that he is studying a battery of 20 turret lathes to determine personal and unavoidable delay allowance. He has calculated that 180 observations per day will be required and since he has 20 machines to observe, he must make nine random trips to the machine floor every eight-hour working day for a period of 20 days. The time of day selected for these nine observations should be chosen at random daily. Thus no set pattern should be established from day to day for the appearance time of the analyst on the production floor.

One method that may be used is to select daily 9 numbers from a statistical table of random numbers, ranging from 1 to 48 (see Appendix 3, Table A3–4). Let each number carry a value in minutes equivalent to 10 times its size. The numbers selected can then set the time in minutes from the beginning of the working day to the time for taking the observations. For example, the random number 20 would mean that the analyst should make a series of observations 200 minutes after the beginning of the shift. If the working day began at 8:00 A.M., then at 20 minutes after 11:00 A.M. an inspection of the 20 turret lathe operators (in the example cited above) would be made.

Designing the work sampling form

The analyst will need to design an observation form to best record the data that will be gathered during the course of the work sampling study. No standard form should be used since each work sampling study is unique from the standpoint of the total number of observations needed, the random times that observations will be made, and the information being sought. The best form is the one that is tailored for the objectives of the study.

A work sampling study form is illustrated in Figure 21–7. This form was designed to determine the preparation of time being utilized for various productive and nonproductive states in a maintenance repair shop. It can be seen that this form was designed to accommodate 20 random observations during the working day.

Use of control charts

The control chart techniques, used so extensively in statistical quality control work, can be applied readily to work sampling studies. Since work sampling studies deal exclusively with percentages or proportions, the "p" chart is most used.

To understand how the "p" chart can be of value in a work sampling study, the reader should understand the theory behind control charting. While a complete discussion of control chart theory is impractical in a text of this nature, a brief discussion will now be presented to enable the reader to see the logic in using control charts.

The first problem encountered in setting up a control chart is the choice of limits. In general, a balance is sought between the cost of looking for

FIGURE 21-7

WORK SAMPLING STUDY

MAIN REPAIR SHOP _____

NUMBER WORKING THIS STUDY _____ DATE _____ BY _____

REMARKS _____
_____

OBS. NO.	RANDOM TIME	PRODUCTIVE OCCURENCES						NON-PRODUCTIVE OCCURENCES								TOTAL OBSERVATIONS	PERCENTAGE PRODUCTIVE	PERCENTAGE NON-PRODUCTIVE
		Mch	Weld	Pipe Fit	Gen. Labor	Elect.	Carpen.	Janitor	Get Tools	Grind Tools	Wait Job	Wait Crane	Confer Foreman	Personal	Idle			
1																		
2																		
3																		
4																		
5																		
6																		
7																		
8																		
9																		
10																		
11																		
12																		
13																		
14																		
15																		
16																		
17																		
18																		
19																		
20																		
TOTALS																		

an assignable cause when there is none present and not looking for an assignable cause when there is one present. As an arbitrary choice the 3 sigma limits will be used throughout the remaining discussion for establishing control limits on the "*p*" chart.

Suppose *p* for a given condition is 0.10 and samples of size 180 are taken each day. By substituting in the equation for *n* (page 520), control limits of ±0.07 are obtained. The nomogram (Figure 21–8) is designed

FIGURE 21–8

Nomogram: finding control limits on results of work sampling

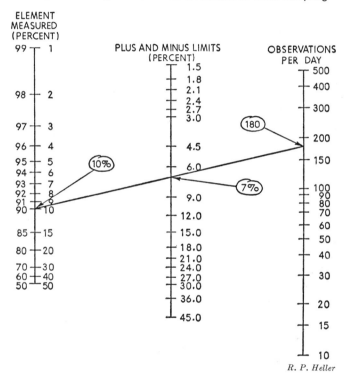

R. P. *Heller*

to give the correct 3 sigma limits for various sample sizes and various values of *p*. A control chart similar to Figure 21–9 could then be constructed. The *p'* values for each day would be plotted on the chart. (Note that $\frac{\Sigma p'}{N} = \hat{p}$ where *N* equals number of days work sampling study was made and approximately the same number of observations are made each day of the study.)

What does a control chart indicate? In quality control work we say that the control chart indicates whether or not the process is in control. In

FIGURE 21–9

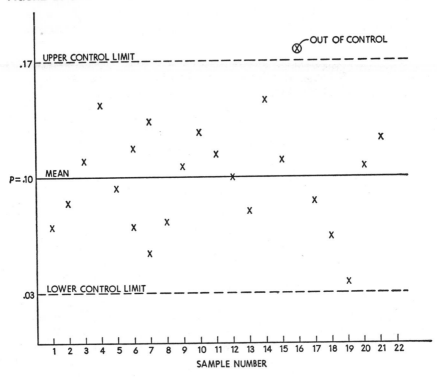

a similar manner, the analyst in work sampling considers points beyond 3 sigma limits of p out of control. Thus, a certain sample that yields a value of p' is assumed to have been drawn from a population with an expected value of p if p' falls within the plus or minus 3 sigma limits of p. Expressed another way, a sample with a value p' is assumed to be from some different population or the original population has been changed if p' falls outside the 3 sigma limits.

$$3\sigma_p = 3\sqrt{\frac{p(1-p)}{n}} \tag{1}$$

As in quality work, points other than those out of control may be of some statistical significance. For example, it is more likely that a point will fall outside the 3 sigma limits than that 2 successive points will fall between the 2 and 3 sigma limits. Hence, 2 successive points between the 2 and 3 sigma limits would indicate that the population had changed. Series of significant sets of points have been derived. This idea is discussed in most statistical quality control texts under the heading of "Theory of Runs."

A hypothetical example will show how control charts can facilitate a work sampling study. Company XYZ wishes to measure the percentage of machine downtime in the lathe department. An original estimate shows downtime to be approximately 0.20. The desired results are to be within ±5 percent of p with a level of significance of 0.95. The sample size is computed to be 6,400. It was decided to take the 6,400 readings over a period of 16 days at the rate of 400 readings per day. A p' value was com-

FIGURE 21–10

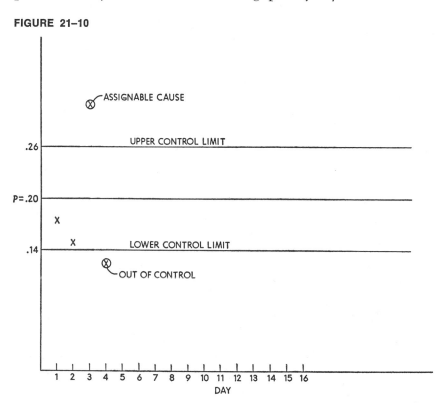

puted for each daily sample of 400. A p chart was set up for $p = 0.20$ and subsample size $N = 400$ (see Figure 21–10). Readings were taken and p' was plotted each day. On the third day the point for p' went above the upper control limit. An investigation revealed there had been an accident in the plant and several of the men had left their machines to assist the injured employee to the plant hospital. Since an assignable cause of error was discovered, this point was discarded from the study. If a control chart had not been used, these observations would have been included in the final estimate of p.

On the fourth day the point for p' fell below the lower control limit. No assignable cause could be found for this occurrence. The industrial engineer in charge of the project also noted that the p' values for the first two days were below the mean p. He decided to compute a new value for p using the values from days 1, 2, and 4. The new estimate of p turned out to be 0.15. To obtain the desired accuracy n is now only 8,830 observations. The control limits also change as shown in Figure 21–11. Observations were taken for 12 more days and the individual p' values were plotted on the new chart. As can be seen, all the points fell within the

FIGURE 21–11

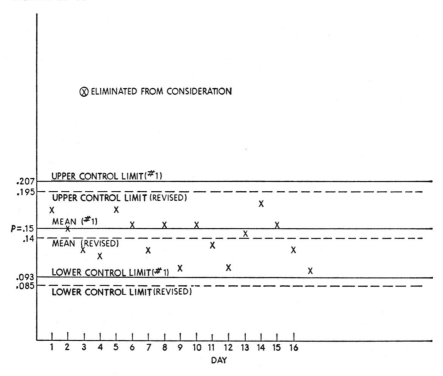

control limits. A more accurate value of p was then calculated using all 6,000 observations. The new estimate of p was determined to be 0.14. A recalculation of achieved accuracy showed it to be slightly better than the desired accuracy. As a final check, new control limits were computed using p equal to 0.14. The dashed lines superimposed on Figure 21–11 showed that all points were still in control using the new limits. If a point would have fallen out of control, it would have been eliminated and a new value of p would have been computed. This process would then be repeated until the desired accuracy is achieved and all p' values were in control.

One may ask, is there any reason to assume that since the percentage downtime today is 0.14 that it will be 0.14 a year from now? Improvement should be a continuing process and percentage downtime should diminish. One purpose of work sampling is to determine areas of work that might be improved. After discovering such areas, an attempt is made to improve the situation. Control charts can be used to show progressive improvement of work areas. This idea is especially important if work sampling studies are used to establish standard times, for such standards must be changed whenever conditions change if they are to remain realistic.

Observing and recording the data

A representative sample form for a shift study is shown in Figure 21–12. Here six random observations of each facility were made per shift. A digit designating the particular observation was indicated in the space provided for the state of each facility under study. Since 14 facilities were being studied, a total of 84 observations were made per shift.

As the analyst approaches the work area, he should not anticipate the recording he expects to make. He should walk to a point a given distance from the facility, make his observation, and record the facts. It might be helpful to make an actual mark on the floor on which the analyst must stand before making his observations. If the operator or machine being studied is idle, the analyst should determine the reason for idleness, confirming the reason with the line foreman before making the proper entry. The analyst should learn to take visual observations, making his written entries after leaving the scene of the work area. This will minimize a feeling of being watched on the part of the shopworkers and they will perform in their accustomed manner.

To help assure that the operators perform in their usual fashion, it is advisable to inform them of the purpose of the study. The fact that no watch is used tends to relieve the operators of a certain mental tension; little difficulty is experienced in getting their full cooperation.

Using random activity analysis camera

Even by observing the requisites of work sampling, the data will tend to be biased when the technique is used for studying people only. This is because the arrival of the observer at the work center will immediately influence the activity of the operator. The operator will have a tendency to become productively engaged as soon as he sees the analyst approaching the work center. Then, too, there is a natural tendency for the observer to record what just *has* happened or what *will* be happening rather than what *is* actually happening at the exact moment of the observation.

The use of a random activity analysis camera similar to that described in Chapter 9, will permit unbiased work sampling studies of problems in-

FIGURE 21-12

Observation form for recording events on 14 facilities during work sampling study

WORK SAMPLING OBSERVATION RECORD

STUDY NO. 46

PLANT DuBois

DATE 5/13 OBSERVER R. Guild

STUDY AREA Section C of Heavy Machine Shop

REMARKS Were Producing Three Cylinder Turbines

MACHINE	DWG.	CUTTING	SETUP	MACHINE IDLE	CRANE WAIT	WAIT-INSPECTION	AID INSPECTION	WAIT-TOOLS NOT AVAILABLE	WAIT-TOOL TROUBLE	CONFER WITH OTHER SHIFT	TOOL HANDLING	GET OR GRIND TOOLS	CONFER WITH FOREMAN, INSP.	WAIT FOR JOB	REMOVE CHIPS CLEAN TABLE	MISCELLANEOUS	NO OPERATOR
20' VBM	93J967	3 5	4						1	6		2					
16' VBM Ⓢ	98J469 / 90J384	2 5 / 2 6	1	3									4 6 1				
28' VBM	34E9	2 6	4	3 5													
12' VBM	96J961	2 5	4						1	3 6							
16' PLANER	98J184	3 4 5 6	1							2							
8' IMM	97J686	3 4 / 1 6										5					
16' VBM	96J939	1 2 3 4 5 6															
14' PLANER	92J518	1 2 3 4 5 6															
72" E.LATHE	97J43	2 4 5 6	1							3							
96" E.LATHE	E-1810 / 30F307	2 3 4	1 6							5							
96" E.LATHE	36F463	2 3 5 6	1 4														
160" E.LATHE	93J771	6				5			1	4							
11-1/2' PLNR Ⓢ	90J158 / 96J798	3	2 4 5 6							1							
32' VBM	96J739	1 2 3 4 5 6															
		40	13	10	1	2	1		3	9		2	3				= 84

volving people. In a work sampling study recently made by the author to determine the attentiveness of each worker, the value of the random activity analysis camera was significantly demonstrated. A work sampling study by conventional, manual means was made of the same activity under study with the random activity analysis camera. The results of the two studies were then compared. The work center was a data processing installation, where the workers involved were required to keypunch and verify various quantities of data processing machine cards. The study was concerned only with elements "working" and "not working." Working time included the elements of adjusting cards, removing cards, punching cards, and so on, while not working involved absence from work station and idleness.

The data collected with the random activity analysis camera revealed a 12.3 percent greater "not working" average than the personal observation study indicated. Table 21–2 summarizes the daily "Absent and Not Working" percentages for the two work sampling methods.

TABLE 21–2

Percentage of absent and not working time for women engaged in data processing activities

Day	1	2	3	4	5	6	7	8	9
Camera study	42.9	47.1	48.9	47.9	45.7	53.2	50.7	49.3	43.6
Personal observation study	36.8	40.7	37.1	32.1	32.1	31.9	35.2	34.5	42.0

Two thousand five hundred twenty (2,520) observations were made during a nine-day period with the random activity analysis camera, and 2,170 observations during the next nine-day period were made by manual observation means. The daily observations by the two techniques are shown in Table 21–3.

TABLE 21–3

Day	*Number observations with camera*	*Number personal observations*
1	280	280
2	280	140
3	280	294
4	280	280
5	280	280
6	280	210
7	280	210
8	280	252
9	280	224
Total	2,520	2,170

A "*t*" test was made comparing the data gathered by both techniques to determine if the difference in the data was significant. Accordingly, the null hypothesis was established, stating that personal observations work sampling results and those obtained by memomotion camera studies are the same.

Table 21–4 represents the difference in the percentage of "Absent and Not Working" times observed during the nine-day study by the two methods.

TABLE 21–4

Difference between camera study and personal observation study results in determining percentage of absent and not working times

Day	1	2	3	4	5	6	7	8	9
Difference	6.1	6.4	11.8	15.8	13.6	21.3	15.5	14.8	1.6

The mean difference is $\dfrac{\Sigma X}{n} = \dfrac{106.9}{9} = 11.9$

If there were no bias between the two methods, we should expect that the mean difference would not differ significantly from 0.

With the assumed value of the population mean discrepancy of 0, we can compute a "*t*" value from the expression:

$$t = \frac{(\bar{X} - \bar{x})\sqrt{n-1}}{s}$$

where

$$s = \text{The standard deviation of the differences}$$

$$s^2 = \frac{\Sigma d^2}{n} - \bar{d}^2$$

$$= 33.04$$

and

$$s = 5.75$$

thus

$$t = \frac{(11.9 - 0)\sqrt{8}}{5.75}$$

$$= 5.86$$

By comparing the computed value of "*t*" (5.86) with the tabularized value at the 0.001 probability level for eight degrees of freedom (see Appendix A3–3) 5.041, we can conclude that the difference in the data obtained from the two methods is highly significant.

Work sampling for the establishment of allowances

One of the most extensive uses of work sampling has been in establishing allowances to be used in conjunction with normal times to determine allowed times. However, the technique is also being used for establishing standards of production, determining machine utilization, allocating work assignments, and improving methods.

As explained in Chapter 16, the determination of time allowances must be correct if fair standards are to be realized. Prior to the introduction of work sampling, allowances for personal reasons and unavoidable delays were frequently determined by taking a series of all-day studies on several operations, and then averaging the results. Thus, the number of trips to the rest room, the number of trips to the drinking fountain, the number of interruptions, and so forth could be recorded, timed, and analyzed, and a fair allowance determined. Although this method gave the answer, it was a costly, time-consuming operation that was fatiguing to both the analyst and the operator. Through ratio delay study, a great number of observations (usually over 2,000) are taken at different times of the day, and of different operators. Then if the total number of legitimate occurrences other than work that involve the operators is divided by the total number of working observations, the result will tend to equal the percentage allowance that should be given the operator for the class of work being studied. The different elements that enter into personal delays and unavoidable delays can be kept separate, and an equitable allowance determined for each class or category. Figure 21–13 illustrates a summary of a ratio delay study for determining unavoidable delay allowances on bench, bench machine, machine, and spray operations. It will be noted that in 26 cases out of 2,895 observations made on bench operations, there were interferences. This indicated an unavoidable delay allowance of 0.95 percent on this class of work.

Work sampling for determination of machine utilization

Machine utilization is readily determined by the work sampling technique in the same manner that was explained in establishing allowances. To give the reader a clearer understanding of the steps involved, a case history will be related.

It was desired to gain information on machine utilization in a section of a heavy machine shop. Management had estimated that actual cutting time in this section should be 60 percent of the working day to comply with quotations being submitted. There were 14 facilities involved in this section of the shop, and it was estimated that approximately 3,000 observations should be taken to get the accuracy desired.

A work sampling form was then designed (see Figure 21–12) to accom-

FIGURE 21–13

Summary of interruptions on various classes of work taken from work sampling study for determining unavoidable delay allowance

	XYZ ELECTRIC PRODUCTS, INC.											
PLANT 26	SUMMARY SHEET (RATIO DELAY)									DATE 4/22/54		
DEPARTMENT 4												
	NUMBER OF OBSERVATIONS											
OPERATION	Engineer	Supply	Quality	Mechanic	Supervision	Turning of Light	Miscellaneous	Working		Number of Interferences	TOTAL OBSER.	PER CENT ALLOWANCE
Bench	1	11	1	0	12	1	119	2,750		26	2,895	.95
Bench Machine	0	2	0	0	5	0	69	984		7	1,060	.71
Machine	0	1	6	11	9	0	29	1,172		27	1,228	2.30
Spray	0	0	0	7	36	0	262	1,407		43	1,712	3.06

REMARKS: Summary Sheet for Interference Allowances. See observation sheet for details of Miscellaneous. Miscellaneous was included in working category because in all cases downtime was credited to the operators.

NOTE: ALL OBSERVATIONS ARE TO BE TAKEN AT RANDOM.

modate the 16 possible states that each of the facilities under study might be in at the time of an observation.

To assure random observations, a random pattern of visitation to the shop area was established. Six observations of the 14 facilities were made during each shift. To get the required total number of observations, 36 separate shifts were observed—12 studies on each of the 3 shifts.

Since there were 14 machines and 6 observations of each per shift, a quick check for 84 separate readings per sheet assured complete coverage of the shift (see Figure 21–12). Each trip took the analyst about 15 to 20 minutes, thus he was occupied on this work only about two hours per shift, leaving him free to perform his other work during the remaining six hours.

Since it was principally desired to learn the status of the actual cutting time in this section, a cumulative percentage machine cutting chart was kept (see Figure 21–14). At the beginning of each day's study, all previous cutting observations were taken cumulatively as a ratio to the total observations to date. By the end of the 10th day of study, the percentage of machine cutting time began to level off at 50.5 percent.

After 36 shifts had been studied, the sums of all observations in each category divided by the total number of observations resulted in per-

FIGURE 21–14

Cumulative percentage machine cutting

centages that represented the distribution of the cutting time, setup time, and the various delay times listed. Figure 21–15 illustrates the summary sheet of this study. It will be noted that cutting time amounted to 50.7 percent. The percentage of time required by the various delays indicated areas for method improvement that would help increase the cutting time.

Work sampling in establishing indirect and direct labor standards

Some companies[3] are finding this tool applicable for establishing incentive standards on indirect as well as direct labor operations. The technique is the same as for allowance determination. A large number of random observations are taken; then the percentage of the number of observations that the facility or operation is working will approximate the percentage time that it is truly in that state.

One company's technique for taking work sampling studies on clerical operations is to take observations on each operator at one-minute intervals. The various elements of work in which the operator may be engaged are assigned identifying numbers, and the analyst, at the time of the observation, merely checks the appropriate number in the space provided on his form. Every five minutes, the analyst rates the performance of the operator in the space provided. At the end of the study, a selective average rating factor is determined.

The normal minutes required for a given element of work may be expressed:

$$T_n = \frac{P \times N}{P_a}$$

---

[3] Aluminum Company of America and Douglas Aircraft Co.

FIGURE 21-15

Work sampling summary sheet

DATE __7-15__
OBSERVER __R. Guild__

MACHINE	DWG.	CUTTING	SETUP	MACHINE IDLE	CRANE WAIT	WAIT-INSPECTION	AID INSPECTION	WAIT-TOOLS NOT AVAILABLE	WAIT-TOOL TROUBLE	CONFER WITH OTHER SHIFT	TOOL HANDLING	GET OR GRIND TOOLS	CONFER WITH FOREMAN, INSP.	WAIT FOR JOB	REMOVE CHIPS CLEAN TABLE	MISCELLANEOUS	NO OPERATOR	
20' VBM		101	7	14	2	3	1			2	37	5	3			6	35	216
16' VBM		102	34	14	15	3	1			1	28	5	1	4	4			216
28' VBM		119	34	10	5	5	2				18	2	1			2	18	216
12' VBM		109	24	12	13	6	1		3		26	6	2	3	3	4	6	216
16' PLANER		127	17	6	9	2				2	22	2	2	15		12	12	216
8' IMM		64	18	17	16	3				2	30	7	3		1	28	28	216
16' VBM		147	19	10	14	3	1			2	15	2		1		3	3	216
14' PLANER		140	8	5	7	2			2	2	17	3			11	11	18	216
72" E.LATHE		99	13	12	7	3			1	2	32	8	2		3	3	36	216
96" E.LATHE		89	9	29	18	11		3	2		29	8	3		1	1	10	216
96" E.LATHE		109	14	12	8	10				2	32	9	8	2	1	4	5	216
160" E.LATHE		72	34	13	14	6	2		4	4	21	3	3	1	1	8	37	216
11-1/2' PLNR		106	35	11	10	4			1	1	11	4	5	3	2	8	16	216
32' VBM		151	23	8	7	1		3	1	1	10		1	5	2	5		216
		1535	289	173	145	62	8	6	3	19	328	64	34	45	13	76	224	3024 =
%		50.7	9.6	5.9	4.8	2.1	.3	.2	.1	.6	10.8	2.1	1.1	1.5	.4	2.5	7.4	100% =

where

$$T_n = \text{Normal minutes to perform the element}$$
$$P = \text{Selective average rating factor}$$
$$N = \text{Total observations for the given element}$$
$$P_a = \text{Total production for period studied}$$

For example, to determine the normal time for the element "write report heading on one BM report," the analyst may have prepared a work sampling study showing 84 observations during which the employee was actually engaged in performing this work element. During the study period, 12 reports were made and it was determined that the selective average rating factor was 110 percent. The normal time would then equal:

$$\frac{(110\%)(84)}{12 \text{ reports}} = 7.7 \text{ minutes normal time per report heading}$$

Figure 21–16 illustrates the study form developed for taking a 40-minute study. The columns I, P, and M are to accommodate idle, personal delays, and miscellaneous observations. Under the column headed "Lev." is recorded every five minutes the performance factor of the operator. The table of standard data shown on page 414 illustrates representative standard data developed by the technique just outlined.

A more generalized expression for determining the normal minutes to perform the element under study where observations are taken at intervals of fixed duration would be:

$$T_n = \frac{\dfrac{\Sigma \text{ Ratings}}{100} \times I}{P_a}$$

where:

$$I = \text{The established interval between observations}$$

For example, let us assume that 30 observations are made at 0.50 minute intervals on a work assignment involving three elements, and 12 units of product have been produced. The tabular data involved is shown in Table 21–5 and the normal minutes for the three elements would be as follows:

$$T_1 = \frac{8.60 \times 0.50}{12} = 0.358 \text{ minutes}$$
$$T_2 = \frac{7.05 \times 0.50}{12} = 0.293 \text{ minutes}$$
$$T_3 = \frac{11.80 \times 0.50}{12} = 0.490 \text{ minutes}$$

This company's technique can be criticized in that random observations have not been taken. Consequently, biased results could occur. For

FIGURE 21–16

Work sampling time study form for clerical operations

1. SIGHT—VERIFY REPORT TOTAL	11. OBTAIN INFORMATION (DISCUSS, PHONE, ETC.)
2. HEADINGS	12. OBTAIN SUPPLIES (PLUS TRIPS)
3. POSTING FROM REPORT	13. FILING
4. DELIVERY	14.
5. MANUAL REPORT PREPARATION	15.
6. EDITING—ASSIGN NO'S (RECAP NO'S ETC.)	16.
7. CORRECT ERROR CARDS	17.
8. ADDING	18. IDLE TIME
9. TYPING	19. PERSONAL TIME
10. TELEGRAMS—RECEIVING—SENDING	20. MISCELLANEOUS

TABULATING—CLERICAL

FROM __8:00__ TO __8:40__   DATE __1/12/__ *(handwritten)*

MI.	1	2	3	4	5	6	7	8	9	10	11	12	13	14	15	16	17	I	P	M	LEV.	REMARKS
1																				✓		NOT HERE
2																				✓		NOT HERE
3						✓																
4						✓																
5						✓															110	
6						✓																
7			✓																			
8			✓																			
9						✓																
10						✓															115	
11						✓																
12						✓																
13						✓																
14						✓																
15						✓															115	
16						✓																
17						✓																
18						✓																
19						✓																
20						✓															100	
21						✓																
22						✓																
23						✓																
24						✓																
25																				✓	105	SEARCH FOR STAMP
26																				✓		DATE STAMP
27							✓															
28							✓															
29							✓															
30																				✓	110	OBTAIN CLIPS
31							✓															
32							✓															
33							✓															
34							✓															
35							✓															110	
36							✓															
37							✓															
38							✓															
39							✓															
40							✓															115	
TOTAL			2			20	13													5		

example, some short-cyclic element may be completely omitted by observing at regular one-minute intervals. This would not happen if sufficient random observations were taken. The expression used by this company for establishing standards on office work can be modified to be applicable on work sampling studies involving random observations rather than regular ones a minute apart. This may be expressed:

$$T_n = \frac{(n)(T)(P)}{(P_a)(N)}$$

$$T_a = T_n + \text{Allowances}$$

TABLE 21–5

Tabular data of a three-element work sampling study

Observation number	Element 1 performance rating observed	Element 2 performance rating observed	Element 3 performance rating observed	Idle
1.......................	90			
2.......................				100
3.......................		110		
4.......................	95			
5.......................	100			
6.......................		100		
7.......................			105	
8.......................	90			
9.......................			110	
10......................	85			
11......................			95	
12......................		90		
13......................			100	
14......................			95	
15......................	80			
16......................			110	
17......................		105		
18......................			90	
19......................	100			
20......................			85	
21......................			90	
22......................			90	
23......................	110			
24......................			100	
25......................		95		
26......................				100
27......................		105		
28......................		100		
29......................			110	
30......................	110			
Σ Rating	860	705	1180	100
$\dfrac{\text{Σ Rating}}{100}$	8.60	7.05	11.80	1.00

where

T_n = Normal elemental time
T_a = Allowed elemental time
P = Performance rating factor
P_a = Total production for period studied
n = Total observations of element under study
N = Total observations of study
T = Total operator time represented by study

For example, assume that a standard was to be established on the maintenance operation of lubricating fractional horsepower motors. If a work sampling study of 120 hours revealed that, after 3,600 observations, lubrication of fractional horsepower motors on the facilities being studied was taking place in 392 cases and a total of 180 facilities using fractional horsepower motors were maintained and the average performance factor was 0.90, then the normal time for lubricating a fractional horsepower motor would be:

$$\frac{(392 \text{ observations}) \ (7,200 \text{ minutes}) \ (0.90 \text{ performance factor})}{(180 \text{ total production}) \ (3,600 \text{ total observations})} =$$

$$\frac{(392) \ (7,200) \ (0.90)}{(180) \ (3,600)} =$$

3.92 minutes to lubricate one fractional horsepower motor

This tool has many applications. Machine downtime can be determined, the relative amount of setup and put-away elements for all classes of work can be made known, and the relative amount of manual, mental, and delay times for clerical work, direct labor, and administrative work can be studied for establishing the ideal work assignments and methods procedures.

Conclusion

The work sampling method is another tool made available to the time and methods study analyst allowing him to get the facts in an easier, faster way. Every person who is in the field of methods, time study, and wage payment should become familiar with the advantages, limitations, uses, and application of this technique. In summary the following considerations should be kept in mind:

1. Explain and sell the work sampling method before using it.
2. Confine individual studies to similar groups of machines or operations.
3. Use as large a sample size as is practical.
4. Take individual observations at random times so observations will be recorded for all hours of the day.
5. Take the observations over a reasonably long period (two weeks or more).

TEXT QUESTIONS

1. Where was work sampling first used?
2. What advantages are claimed for the work sampling procedure?
3. In what areas does work sampling have application?

4. How many observations should be recorded in determining the allowance for personal delays in a forge shop if it is expected that a 5 percent personal allowance will suffice, and this value is to remain between 4 and 6 percent 95 percent of the time?

5. How is it possible to determine the time of day to make the various observations so biased results will not occur?

6. What considerations should be kept in mind on taking work sampling studies?

7. To get ±5 percent precision on work that is estimated to take 80 percent of the workers' time, how many random observations will be required at the 95 percent confidence level?

8. If the average handling activity during a 10-day study is 82 percent and the number of daily observations is 48, how much tolerance can be allowed on each day's percentage activity?

9. If it should develop that four seconds of time would be desirable at each random observation and a sample size of 2,000 was necessary, how often would the analyst need to service the random activity analysis camera?

10. Over how long a period is it desirable to continue to acquire sampling data?

11. How biased can we expect work sampling data to be? Will this bias vary with the work situation? Explain.

GENERAL QUESTIONS

1. Is there an application for work sampling studies in determining fatigue? Explain.

2. How can the validity of work sampling be sold to the employee not familiar with probability and statistical procedure?

3. What are the pros and cons for using work sampling to establish standards of performance?

CHAPTER 22

Establishing standards on indirect and expense work

Since 1900 the percentage increase of indirect and expense workers has more than doubled that of direct labor workers. Groups usually classified as indirect labor include shipping and receiving, trucking, stores, inspection, material handling, toolroom, janitorial, and maintenance. Expense personnel include all other positions not coming under direct or indirect—office clerical, accounting, sales, management personnel, engineering, and so on.

This rapid growth in the number of office workers, maintenance workers, and other indirect and expense employees is due to several reasons. First, the increased mechanization of industry and complete automation of many processes has decreased the need for craftsmen and even for operators. This trend toward mechanization has resulted in a greater demand for electricians, technicians, and other servicemen. Also, the design of complicated machines and controls has resulted in greater demand for engineers, designers, and draftsmen.

The tremendous increase in paper work brought on by federal, state, and local legislation is responsible, to a large extent, for the number of clerical employees utilized today.

Another reason for the rise in the number of indirect and expense employees is that office and maintenance work has not been subjected to methods study and technical advances that have been applied so effectively to industrial processes.

With a large share of most payrolls being earmarked for indirect and expense labor, progressive management is beginning to realize the opportunities for the application of methods and standards in this area.

Automation

The term automation may be defined as "increased mechanization." A completely automated manufacturing process is capable of operating for prolonged periods without human effort. Few industries or even processes within an industry are completely automated. However, there is a pronounced tendency toward semiautomation in American, Japanese, and European industry. With the increasing demand for greater production at lower costs, it is anticipated that as much as 20 percent of American industry will be automated or semiautomated within the next decade.

A program of automation begins with developing the fully automatic machine (such as the automatic screw machine) integrated with automatic transfer handling devices, so a series of operations may be performed automatically.

To determine the extent of automation justified, two factors should be considered: (1) the quantity requirements of the product, (2) the nature or design of the product itself.

If quantity requirements of the product are large, the design engineer will endeavor to design the product so it lends itself to automation. Frequently, by adding something to a part, such as a lug, fin, extension, or hole, it will be possible to provide means of mechanical handling to and from the work station. Such a redesign can accommodate indexing at a work station for successive production operations. For example, a holding fin was added to the die casting for producing a compressor piston. This permitted mechanical fingers to hold the work while processing, as well as to automatically transport the work between production stations (see Figure 22–1).

Complete automation is feasible for the continuous processing of chemical products, such as gasoline, oil, and detergents. Partial automation is now widespread in the making of many types of mass-produced items—food products (cookies, cereals, pretzels, etc.), light bulbs, radio tubes, automobile parts, cigarettes, and so forth.

Factors that encourage plant automation include:

1. Increasing cost of labor.
2. Increasing competition, especially from foreign manufacturers, that stimulates reduction in selling prices and lessening of profits.
3. Prospects of market expansion through cost and price reduction.

Among the principal factors that may discourage automation in a particular plant are:

1. The large capital investment necessary which must, subsequently, be absorbed in operating profit.
2. A market potential presently inadequate to absorb the increased output.
3. An existing technology unable to provide automation to produce a particular design.
4. Opposition by production workers, and the possibility of community relations affected for the worse by a reduction in the labor force.

FIGURE 22–1

Die casting with fin so work can be handled in automated type equipment

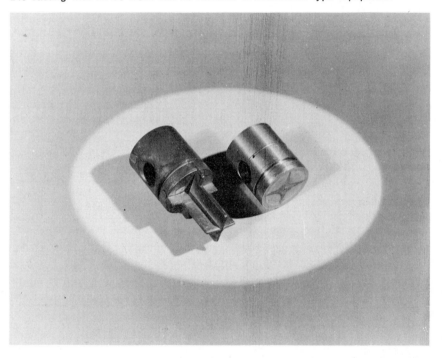

However, there is no doubt that the present trend toward automation will continue.

As automation equipment is developed, the need for effective preventative maintenance is apparent. A failure of a single minor component may cause the shutdown of a complete process or even the entire plant. This fact, together with the complexity of automated equipment through the use of pneumatic, hydraulic, and electronic controls, brings out the reasons for the growth of indirect workers not only in numbers but in diversification of occupation.

Methods improvements on indirect and expense work

The systematic approach to methods standards and wage payment outlined in Chapter 1 is just as applicable to indirect and expense areas as it is to direct labor. A program for establishing standards on indirect and expense labor should be preceded by careful fact finding, analysis, development of proposed method, presentation, installation, and development of job analysis. The method analysis procedure in itself will result in the introduction of economies.

Work sampling is a good technique to determine the severity of the problem and the potential savings in the indirect and expense area. It is not unusual to find that the work force is productively engaged only 40 to 50 percent of the time or even less. For example, in maintenance work, which represents a large share of the total indirect cost, the analyst may find the following reasons are responsible for much of the time lost during the working day.

1. *Lost time due to inadequate communications.* For example, it is quite common to find that incomplete and even incorrect job instructions are provided on the work order. This necessitates additional trips to the toolroom and supply room to obtain parts and tools that should have been available when the craftsman first started to work on the job. The work order that merely states "Repair leak in oil system" is indicative of poor planning and communications. The workman will need to know if a new valve is required, if a new pipe is needed, or if a new gasket will do the job or will the valve need repacking.

2. *Lost time due to unavailability of parts, tools, or equipment.* If the craftsman does not have the facilities and parts to do the job he will be obliged to improvise in such a manner that will usually be wasteful of time and frequently result in an inferior job. Proper planning will assure that the correct tools and equipment to perform the job are available and that suitable spares are supplied to the job site.

3. *Lost time due to interference of production employees.* With improper scheduling, maintenance employees may find they are unable to begin a repair, service, or overhaul operation in that the facility is still being used by production employees. This can result in the craftsman waiting idly by until the production department is ready to turn over the equipment.

4. *Lost time due to overmanning the maintenance job.* In the experience of the writer, this has been one of the principal causes of lost time in maintenance work. Too often a crew of three or four are supplied when two or three are really all that is needed.

5. *Lost time because the work is unsatisfactory and must be redone.*
Poor planning will frequently result in an attitude of "this will get by" on
the part of the mechanic. This will result in the repair work having to be
repeated.

6. *Lost time due to the craftsman having to wait for instructions to
begin the next job.* With improper planning, the "wait for work" idle
time can be significant. Good planning assures there is ample work ahead
of the maintenance man so that he seldom if ever will have to wait for
the next job.

After good methods have been developed, they must be standardized
and taught to the workers who will be using them. This seems apparent,
but is too often neglected by management.

By giving the same attention to operation improvement in indirect
work that has been exercised in direct labor operations, industry can get
good results.

Indirect labor standards

A time standard can be established on any operation or group of operations that can be quantified and measured. If the elements of work performed by the electrician, blacksmith, boilermaker, sheet metal worker,
painter, carpenter, millwright, welder, pipe fitter, material handler, toolmaker, and others performing indirect work, are broken down and studied, it usually will be possible to evolve an equitable standard by summarizing the direct, transportation, and indirect elements. The tools used
for establishing standards for indirect and expense work are identical with
those used in direct labor work: time study, predetermined motion time
standards, standard data, time formulas, and work sampling.

Thus, a standard can be established for such tasks as hanging a door,
rewinding a 1-horsepower motor, painting a centerless grinder, sweeping
the chips from a department, or delivering a skid of 200 forgings. Standard times for each of these operations can be established by measuring
the time required for the operator to perform the job, then performance
rating the study and applying an appropriate allowance.

Careful study and analysis will reveal more unavoidable delays in indirect work than on direct work because of crew balance and interference.
Crew balance is that delay time encountered by one member of a crew
while waiting for other members of the team to perform elements of the
job. Interference time is the time that a maintenance or other worker is
delayed in waiting for other production workers to do necessary work.
Both crew-balance delays and interference delays may be thought of as
unavoidable delays; however, they are usually characteristic of indirect
labor operations only, such as those performed by maintenance workers.
Queueing theory is a useful tool for the best estimate of the magnitude
of the waiting time.

Because of the high degree of variability characteristic of most maintenance and material handling operations, it will be necessary to conduct a sufficient number of independent time studies of each operation to assure completely that average conditions have been determined and that the resulting standard is representative of the time needed for the normal operator to do the job under these average conditions. For example, if a study indicates that 47 minutes are required to sweep a machine floor 60 feet wide by 80 feet long, it will be necessary to assure that average conditions prevailed when the study was taken. Obviously, the work of the sweeper would be considerably more time consuming if the shop was machining cast iron than if an alloy steel was being cut. Not only is the alloy steel much cleaner, but the chips are easier to handle and the fact that slower speeds and feed would be used would result in fewer chips. If the standard of 47 minutes was established when the shop was working with alloy steel, it would be inadequate when the department was producing cast iron parts. It would be necessary to take additional time studies to assure that average conditions had been determined and that the resulting standards were representative of those conditions.

In a similar manner, standards can be established for painting. Thus, a standard will be determined for overhead painting based on square footage. Likewise, vertical and floor painting can be measured, and time standards can be developed on a square-footage basis.

Just as the automotive industry has established time standards for common repair jobs such as grinding valves, replacing piston rings, and adjusting brakes, so can standards be determined for typical maintenance and repair operations performed on the machine tools within the plant. Thus, a set of time standards can be determined for rewinding fractional horsepower motors. A standard can be established for rewinding $\frac{1}{8}$ HP, $\frac{1}{4}$ HP, $\frac{1}{2}$ HP, $\frac{3}{4}$ HP, and so on.

Toolroom work is very similar to work done in job shops. The method by which such tools as a drill jig, milling fixture, form tool, or die will be made can be predetermined quite closely. Consequently, it is possible by time study and/or predetermined elemental times for the analyst to establish a sequence of elements and measure the normal time required for each element. Work sampling provides an adequate tool to determine the allowances that must be added for fatigue, personal, unavoidable, and special delays. The standard elemental times thus developed can be tabularized in the form of standard data or may be used to design time formulas for pricing future work.

Factors affecting indirect and expense standards

All work that can be classified as indirect and/or expense can be thought of as being a combination of four divisions: (1) direct work; (2) transportation; (3) indirect work; (4) unnecessary work and delays.

The direct work portion of indirect and/or expense labor is that segment of the operation that discernibly advances the progress of the work. For example, in the installation of a door, work elements may include: cut door to rough size, plane to finish size, locate and mark hinge areas, chisel out hinge areas, mark for screws, install screws, mark for lock, drill out for lock, install lock, and so on. Such direct work can be measured quite easily by using conventional techniques such as stopwatch time study, standard data, or fundamental motion data.

Transportation refers to work performed in movements during the course of the job or from job to job. Transportation may take place horizontally, vertically, or both horizontally and vertically. Typical transportation elements include: walk up and down stairs, ride elevator, walk, carry load, push truck, ride on motor truck, and so on. Transportation elements similiar to direct elements can easily be measured and standard data be established. For example, one company uses 0.50 minutes per 100-foot zone as standard for horizontal travel time and 0.30 minutes as standard time for 10 feet of vertical travel.

The indirect portion of indirect and/or expense labor as a general rule cannot be evaluated by physical evidence in the completed job or at any stage during the work except by deductive inference as implied by certain characteristic features of the job. Indirect work elements may be separated into three divisions: (a) tooling, (b) material, and (c) planning.

Elements of work that may be assigned to tooling are those having to do with acquiring, disposition, and maintenance of all the tools needed to perform the operation. Typical elements under this category would include: getting and checking tools and equipment; returning equipment at completion of job; cleaning tools; repairing, adjusting, and sharpening. The tooling work elements are easily measured by conventional means, and statistical records can provide data for frequency of occurrence. Waiting line or queueing theory can provide information on the expected waiting time at supply centers.

The elements associated with material are those having to do with acquiring material and disposing of scrap and checking the material used in the operation. Here work elements such as making minor repairs to materials, picking up and disposing of scrap, and getting and checking materials, are characteristic of those in this division. As with tooling elements, the elements associated with material may be measured readily and their frequency accurately determined through historical records. In acquiring material from storerooms, queueing theory provides the best estimate of waiting time.

Planning elements represent the most difficult area in which to establish standards. Here we have elements such as: consultation with the foreman; planning work procedures, inspection, checking and testing.

Work sampling techniques provide a basis for determining the time required to perform the planning elements. Planning elements may also be measured through stopwatch procedures, but the frequency of occurrence is difficult to determine; consequently, work sampling is the more practical tool to use for this class of elements.

The unnecessary work and delays represent that portion of the cycle that should be eliminated through planning and method improvement. It is not unusual to find that the unnecessary work and the delays represent as much as 40 percent of the indirect and expense payroll. Much of this wasted time is management oriented, and it is for this reason that the systematic procedure recommended in Chapter 1 should be carefully followed prior to establishing standards. In this work the analyst should get and analyze the facts, develop and install the method before endeavoring to establish the standard.

Much of the delay time encountered in indirect and expense work is because of the formation of queues. Thus, the workman is obliged to wait in line at the tool crib, at the storeroom, at the stock room, waiting for a fork-lift truck, a desk calculator, or other piece of office equipment. The analyst frequently is able to determine the optimum number of servicing units required for the circumstances involved through the application of queueing theory. Such studies should be made to optimize the delay time in indirect and expense work.

Basic queueing theory equations

Queueing system problems may occur when a flow of arriving traffic (people, facilities, and so on) establishes a random demand for service at facilities (men, machines, and so on) of limited service capacity. The time interval between arrival and service will obviously vary inversely with the level of service capacity. The greater the number of service stations and the faster the rate of servicing, the less the time interval between arrival and service.

The methods and work measurement analyst should endeavor to select an operating procedure that minimizes total cost of operation. There must be an economic balance between waiting times and service capacity.

The following four characteristics define queueing problems:

1. *The pattern of arrival rates.* The arrival rate (for example, a machine breaking down for repair) may be constant or random. If random, the pattern should be described in terms of a probability distribution of the various values of intervals between successive arrivals. A probability distribution of the random pattern may be definable or nondefinable.

2. *The pattern of the servicing rate.* Servicing time may also be constant or random. Where random, the analyst should endeavor to define the probability distribution that fits the service time random pattern.

3. The number of servicing units. In general, multiple servicing type queueing problems are more complex than single-service systems. However, most problems are of the multiple servicing type such as the number of mechanics to be employed to keep a battery of machines in operation.

4. The pattern of selection for service. Usually the service is on a "first-come, first-served" basis; however, in some cases, the selection may be completely random or according to priorities.

The methods of solution to queueing systems may be classified into two broad categories: analytical and simulation. The analytical category covers a wide range of problems where mathematical probability and analytical techniques have provided equations representing systems with various assumptions about the above characteristics. One of the most common assumptions about the arrival pattern or arrivals per unit time interval is that they follow the Poisson probability distribution:

$$p(k) = \frac{a^k e^{-a}}{k\,!}$$

where a is the mean arrival rate, and k is the number of arrivals per time interval. A helpful graphical presentation of the cumulative Poisson probabilities is shown in Figure 22–2.

A further consequence of a Poisson-type arrival pattern is that the random variable time between arrivals obeys an exponential distribution with the same parameter a. The exponential distribution being a continuous distribution has a density function $f(x) = ae^{-ax}$. The exponential distribution has a mean $\mu = \frac{1}{a}$ and variance $= \frac{1}{a^2}$. μ can be recognized as the mean interval between arrivals. In some queueing systems the number of services per unit time may follow the Poisson pattern and subsequently the service times follow the exponential distribution. Figure 22–3 illustrates the exponential curve $F(x) = e^{-x}$ which shows the probabilities of exceeding various multiples of any specified service time.

The basic equations governing the queue applicable to Poisson arrivals and service in arrival order may be classified into five categories. These are as follows:

1. Any service time distribution and single server.
2. Exponential service time and single server.
3. Exponential service time and finite servers.
4. Constant service time and single servers.
5. Constant service time and finite servers.

Equations have been developed for each of the above categories. These provide quantitative answers to problems such as mean delay time in the waiting line and mean number of arrivals in the waiting line, and so on.

Let us follow through on a typical example to see how queueing theory is applied. The analyst wishes to determine a standard for inspecting the hardness of large motor armatures. The time is composed of two distinct quantities: the time the inspector takes to make his Rockwell observations and the time the operator must wait until the next armature shaft is made available for inspection. The following assumptions will apply: (1) single server; (2) Poisson arrivals; (3) arbitrary servicing time; and (4) first-come, first-served discipline.

This is a situation which fits in the first category classified above. The equations which apply are:

$$a) \quad P > 0 = u$$

$$b) \quad w = \left[\frac{uh}{2(1-u)}\right]\left[1 + \left(\frac{\sigma}{h}\right)^2\right]$$

$$c) \quad m = \frac{w}{P > 0} = \frac{w}{u}$$

where

a = Average number of arrivals per unit of time

h = Mean servicing time

w = Mean waiting time of all arrivals

m = Mean waiting time of delayed arrivals

n = Number of arrivals present (both waiting and being served) at any given time.

s = Number of servers

u = Servers occupancy ratio = $\dfrac{ah}{s}$

σ = Standard deviation of servicing time

$P(n)$ = Probability of n arrivals being present at any random time

$P(\geqq n)$ = Probability of at least n arrivals present at any random time

t = Unit of time

$P > t/h$ = Probability of a delay greater than t/h multiples of mean holding time

$P(d > 0)$ = Probability of any delay (delay greater than 0)

L = Mean number of waiting individuals among all individuals

Through stopwatch time study, a normal time of 4.58 minutes per piece is established for the actual hardness testing. The standard deviation of the service time is 0.82 minutes and 75 tests are made for every eight-hour working day. From the above data, we have:

$s = 1$

$a = \dfrac{75}{480} = 0.156$

$h = 4.58$

$\sigma = 0.82$

$u = (0.156)(4.58) = 0.714$

$w = \left[\dfrac{(0.714)(4.58)}{2(1-0.714)}\right]\left[1 + \left(\dfrac{0.82}{4.58}\right)^2\right]$

$= 5.95$ mean waiting time of an arrival

FIGURE 22–2

Poisson distribution of arrivals

$$P(c, a) = \sum_{x=c}^{\infty} \frac{e^{-a}a^x}{x!}$$

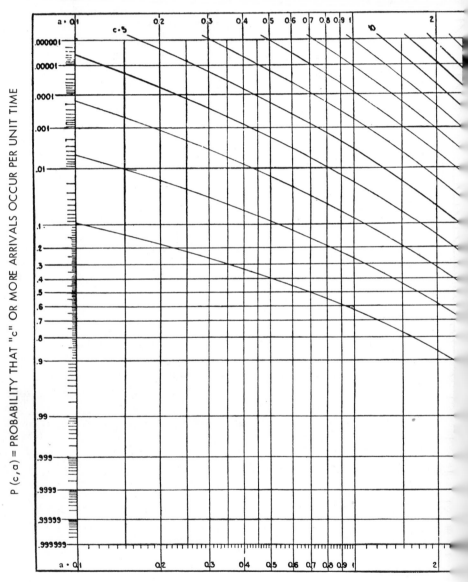

a = AVERAGE NUMBER OF ARRIVALS PER UNIT TIME

FIGURE 22-3

The exponential distribution

$$F(x) = e^{-x}$$

The Port of New York Authority

Thus, the analyst is able to determine a total time of 10.53 minutes per shaft.

Many industrial problems fit into the second category; that is exponential service and single server with Poisson arrivals. The equations that apply here are:

a) $P > 0 = u$

b) $P > (t/h) = ue^{(u-1)(t/h)}$

c) $P(n) = (1 - u)(u)^n$

d) $P(\geqq n) = u^n$

e) $w = \dfrac{h(P > 0)}{(1 - u)} = \dfrac{uh}{1 - u}$

f) $m = \dfrac{w}{(P > 0)} = \dfrac{h}{(1 - u)}$

g) $L = \dfrac{m}{h} = \dfrac{1}{(1 - u)}$

For example, arrivals at a tool crib are considered to be Poisson with an average time of seven minutes between one arrival and the next. The length of service time at the crib window is assumed to be distributed exponentially, with a mean of 2.52 minutes determined through stopwatch time study. The analyst wishes to determine the probability that a person arriving at the crib will have to wait and the average length of the queues that form from time to time so he can evaluate the practicality of opening a second tool dispensing window. This information can be determined from those equations summarized above.

a = 0.14 average number of arrivals per minute

h = 2.52 minutes mean service time

s = 1 server

$P > 0 = u$

$$u = \frac{ah}{s} = 0.35 \text{ probability of a person arriving at crib having to wait}$$

$$L = \frac{1}{(1 - u)} = 1.52 \text{ average length of the queue formed}$$

Monte Carlo simulation

The method of simulation for solution of queueing system problems does not employ formal mathematical models as the models may be too complex or the systems too unique in light of the mathematical models in existence. Here a model of a queueing system is created by a series of numerical statements. A sample set of input values drawn from specified arrival and service time distributions are introduced. This input data generates a sample output distribution of waiting line results for the period. This sampling procedure is referred to as "Monte Carlo."

The expected waiting time and service times can be estimated and an optimum solution developed through proper balance of service stations, servicing rates, and arrival rates. This technique is most helpful to analyze the waiting line problem involved in the centralization-decentralization storage location of tools, supplies and service facilities.

The Monte Carlo simulation technique can also be applied to problems with a Poisson arrival pattern. However, Monte Carlo is usually used for problems from which neither standard nor empirical formulas are obtainable.

For example, the analyst may wish to determine the number of operators to be used to set up machines in an automatic screw machine section to minimize total costs. An analysis of past records in the automatic department reveals the following probability distributions of the number of work stoppages per hour and the time required to service a machine.

Labor rate...........................	$ 3.00 per hour
Machine rate.........................	$12.00 per hour
Number of operators.................	3
Number of automatics................	15

Work stoppages per hour	Probability
0	0.108
1	0.193
2	0.361
3	0.186
4	0.082
5	0.040
6	0.018
7	0.009
8	0.003
	1.000

Hours to get machine in operation	Probability
0.100	0.111
0.200	0.254
0.300	0.009
0.400	0.007
0.500	0.005
0.600	0.008
0.700	0.105
0.800	0.122
0.900	0.170
1.000	0.131
1.100	0.075
1.200	0.003
	1.000

Note that the time to get a machine into operation results in a bimodal distribution and does not conform to any standard distribution.

The analyst now assigns blocks of three-digit numbers, in direct proportion to the probabilities associated with the data for both the arrival and service rates.

So 1,000 three-digit numbers have been assigned to both the arrival and service distributions. By using a table of random numbers, it is possible to simulate the behavior of what would be expected in the screw ma-

Work stoppages per hour	Probability	Numbers assigned
0	0.108	000–107
1	0.193	108–300
2	0.361	301–661
3	0.186	662–847
4	0.082	848–929
5	0.040	930–969
6	0.018	970–987
7	0.009	988–996
8	0.003	997–999

Hours to get machine in operation	Probability	Numbers assigned
0.100...................	0.111	000–110
0.200...................	0.254	111–364
0.300...................	0.009	365–373
0.400...................	0.007	374–380
0.500...................	0.005	381–385
0.600...................	0.008	386–393
0.700...................	0.105	394–498
0.800...................	0.122	499–620
0.900...................	0.170	621–790
1.000...................	0.131	791–921
1.100...................	0.075	922–996
1.200...................	0.003	997–999

chine section over a period. Let us take 80 random observations, to simulate the number of work stoppages occurring during two weeks of activity on the floor. These 80 random numbers applied to work stoppages give the following:

Hour	Random number	Work stoppages	Hour	Random number	Work stoppages
1.............	221	1	29.............	375	2
2.............	193	1	30.............	616	2
3.............	167	1	31.............	934	5
4.............	784	3	32.............	219	1
5.............	032	0	33.............	952	5
6.............	932	5	34.............	978	6
7.............	787	3	35.............	699	3
8.............	236	1	36.............	043	0
9.............	153	1	37.............	610	2
10.............	587	2	38.............	859	4
11.............	573	2	39.............	217	1
12.............	485	2	40.............	156	1
13.............	619	2	41.............	028	0
14.............	369	2	42.............	871	4
15.............	188	1	43.............	988	7
16.............	885	4	44.............	100	0
17.............	097	0	45.............	479	2
18.............	129	1	46.............	228	1
19.............	859	4	47.............	678	3
20.............	386	2	48.............	276	1
21.............	534	2	49.............	337	2
22.............	407	2	50.............	131	1
23.............	021	0	51.............	689	3
24.............	951	5	52.............	137	1
25.............	357	2	53.............	096	0
26.............	262	1	54.............	204	1
27.............	778	3	55.............	733	3
28.............	464	2	56.............	071	0

Hour	Random number	Work stoppages	Hour	Random number	Work stoppages
57.............	923	4	69.............	920	4
58.............	995	7	70.............	987	6
59.............	938	5	71.............	004	0
60.............	184	1	72.............	579	2
61.............	245	1	73.............	125	1
62.............	220	1	74.............	315	2
63.............	071	0	75.............	961	5
64.............	297	1	76.............	854	4
65.............	579	2	77.............	728	3
66.............	333	2	78.............	913	4
67.............	494	2	79.............	775	3
68.............	651	2	80.............	372	2

A different group of random numbers should be selected as input for each work stoppage to estimate the time required to get a machine into operation after it has stopped. These values indicate the following:

Hour	Random number	Hours to get machine in operation	Hour	Random number	Hours to get machine in operation
1.............	341	0.200	30.............	851	1.000
2.............	112	0.200	31.............	411	0.700
3.............	273	0.200	32.............	822	1.000
4.............	106	0.100	33.............	985	1.100
5.............	597	0.800	34.............	997	1.200
6.............	337	0.200	35.............	234	0.200
7.............	871	1.000	36.............	773	0.900
8.............	728	0.900	37.............	423	0.700
9.............	739	0.900	38.............	607	0.800
10.............	799	1.000	39.............	220	0.200
11.............	202	0.200	40.............	915	1.000
12.............	854	1.000	41.............	684	0.900
13.............	599	0.800	42.............	366	0.300
14.............	726	0.900	43.............	220	0.200
15.............	880	1.000	44.............	920	1.000
16.............	496	0.700	45.............	346	0.200
17.............	128	0.200	46.............	347	0.200
18.............	794	1.000	47.............	639	0.900
19.............	383	0.500	48.............	308	0.200
20.............	472	0.700	49.............	319	0.200
21.............	870	1.000	50.............	848	1.000
22.............	397	0.700	51.............	562	0.800
23.............	280	0.200	52.............	481	0.700
24.............	976	1.100	53.............	000	0.100
25.............	693	0.900	54.............	587	0.800
26....	870	1.000	55.............	275	0.200
27.............	520	0.800	56.............	267	0.200
28.............	527	0.800	57.............	430	0.700
29.............	153	0.200	58.............	160	0.200

Hour	Random number	Hours to get machine in operation	Hour	Random number	Hours to get machine in operation
59	096	0.100	70	322	0.200
60	653	0.900	71	610	0.800
61	876	1.000	72	855	1.000
62	086	0.100	73	167	0.200
63	085	0.100	74	463	0.700
64	898	1.000	75	886	1.000
65	422	0.700	76	081	0.100
66	164	0.200	77	826	1.000
67	255	0.200	78	566	0.800
68	145	0.200	79	228	0.200
69	144	0.200	80	491	0.700

In the light of the above-indicated outcomes for 80 hours of operation in our automatic screw machine department, we can look at the machine downtime predicted because of insufficient operators.

Hour	Random number	Work stoppages	Random number	Hours to get machine in operation	Operators available for next work stoppages	Downtime hours because of lack of operators for servicing
1	221	1	341	0.200	2	
2	193	1	112	0.200	2	
3	167	1	273	0.200	2	
4	784	3	106	0.100	2	
			597	0.800	1	
			337	0.200	0	
5	032	0	...	...	3	
6	932	5	871	1.000	2	
			728	0.900	1	
			739	0.900	0	
			799	1.000	0	0.9
			202	0.200	0	0.9
7	787	3	854	1.000	0	
			599	0.800	0	0.100
			726	0.900	0	0.900
8	236	1	880	1.000	1	
9	153	1	495	0.700	2	
10	587	2	128	0.200	2	
			794	1.000	1	
11	573	2	383	0.500	2	
			472	0.700	1	
12	485	2	870	1.000	2	
			397	0.700	1	
13	619	2	280	0.200	2	
			976	1.100	1	
14	369	2	693	0.900	1	
			870	1.000	0	
15	188	1	520	0.800	2	

Hour	Random number	Work stoppages	Random number	Hours to get machine in operation	Operators available for next work stoppages	Downtime hours because of lack of operators for servicing
16.......... 885		4	527	0.800	2	
			153	0.200	1	
			851	1.000	0	
			411	0.700	0	0.200
17.......... 097		0	...	...	3	
18.......... 129		1	985	1.100	2	
19.......... 859		4	997	1.200	1	
			234	0.200	0	
			773	0.900	0	0.100
			423	0.700	0	0.200
20.......... 386		2	607	0.800	1	
			220	0.200	0	
21.......... 534		2	915	1.000	2	
			684	0.900	1	
22.......... 407		2	366	0.300	2	
			220	0.200	1	
23.......... 021		0	...	...	3	
24.......... 951		5	346	0.200	2	
			347	0.200	1	
			639	0.900	0	
			308	0.200	1	0.200
			319	0.200	0	0.200
25.......... 357		2	898	1.000	2	
			562	0.800	1	
26.......... 262		1	481	0.700	2	
27.......... 778		3	000	0.100	2	
			587	0.800	1	
			275	0.200	0	
28.......... 464		2	267	0.200	2	
			430	0.700	1	
29.......... 375		2	160	0.200	2	
			096	0.100	1	
30.......... 616		2	653	0.900	2	
			876	1.000	1	
31.......... 934		5	086	0.100	2	
			085	0.100	1	
			898	1.000	0	
			422	0.700	0	0.100
			920	1.000	0	0.100
32.......... 219		1	164	0.200	1	
33.......... 952		5	255	0.200	2	
			145	0.200	1	
			144	0.200	0	
			322	0.200	0	0.200
			610	0.800	0	0.200
34.......... 978		6	855	1.000	2	
			167	0.200	1	
			463	0.700	0	
			886	1.000	0	0.200
			081	0.100	0	0.700
			826	1.000	0	0.800

Hour	Random number	Work stoppages	Random number	Hours to get machine in operation	Operators available for next work stoppages	Downtime hours because of lack of operators for servicing
35.......... 699		3	566	0.800	0	
			228	0.200	0	0.200
			491	0.700	0	0.400
36.......... 043		0	...	...	2	
37.......... 610		2	188	0.200	2	
			702	0.900	1	
38.......... 859		4	323	0.200	2	
			354	0.200	1	
			464	0.700	0	
			806	1.000	0	0.200
39.......... 217		1	494	0.700	1	
40.......... 156		1	050	0.100	2	
41.......... 028		0	...	...	3	
42.......... 871		4	441	0.700	2	
			390	0.600	1	
			543	0.800	0	
			077	0.100	0	0.600
43.......... 988		7	941	1.100	2	
			667	0.900	1	
			317	0.200	0	
			336	0.200	0	0.200
			650	0.900	0	0.400
			651	0.900	0	0.900
			370	0.300	0	1.100
44.......... 100		0	...	...	0	
45.......... 479		2	011	0.100	2	
			976	1.100	1	
46.......... 228		1	229	0.200	1	
47.......... 678		3	072	0.100	2	
			167	0.200	1	
			144	0.200	0	
48.......... 276		1	843	1.000	2	
49.......... 337		2	768	0.900	2	
			404	0.700	1	
50.......... 131		1	636	0.900	2	
51.......... 689		3	970	1.100	2	
			954	1.100	1	
			951	1.110	0	
52.......... 137		1	562	0.800	0	0.100
53.......... 096		0	...	...	3	
54.......... 204		1	866	1.000	2	
55.......... 733		3	348	0.200	2	
			327	0.200	1	
			995	1.100	0	
56.......... 071		0	...	...	2	
57.......... 923		4	539	0.800	2	
			616	0.800	1	
			181	0.200	0	
			647	0.900	0	0.200

Hour	Random number	Work stoppages	Random number	Hours to get machine in operation	Operators available for next work stoppages	Downtime hours because of lack of operators for servicing
58 995		7	273	0.200	1	
			683	0.900	0	
			623	0.900	0	0.100
			018	0.100	0	0.200
			748	0.900	0	0.300
			408	0.700	0	0.900
			688	0.900	0	1.000
59 938		5	297	0.200	0	0.200
			985	1.100	0	0.400
			777	0.900	0	0.600
			294	0.200	0	0.900
			417	0.700	0	1.100
60 184		1	509	0.800	0	0.500
61 245		1	571	0.800	1	
62 220		1	925	1.100	2	
63 071		0	. . .	. . .	2	
64 297		1	753	0.900	2	
65 579		2	448	0.700	2	
			060	0.100	1	
66 333		2	899	1.000	2	
			238	0.200	1	
67 494		2	872	1.000	2	
			051	0.100	1	
68 651		2	123	0.200	2	
			886	1.000	1	
69 920		4	001	0.100	2	
			914	1.000	1	
			049	0.100	0	
			150	0.200	0	0.100
70 987		6	128	0.200	2	
			229	0.200	1	
			356	0.200	0	
			507	0.800	0	0.200
			114	0.200	0	0.200
			342	0.200	0	0.200
71 004		0	. . .	. . .		
72 579		2	513	0.800	2	
			361	0.200	1	
73 125		1	711	0.900	2	
74 315		2	619	0.800	2	
			558	0.800	1	
75 961		5	630	0.900	2	
			694	0.900	1	
			482	0.700	0	
			059	0.100	0	0.700
			321	0.200	0	0.900
76 854		4	027	0.100	1	
			426	0.700	0	
			161	0.200	0	0.100
			524	0.800	0	0.100
77 728		3	572	0.800	2	
			780	0.900	1	
			298	0.200	0	

Hour	Random number	Work stoppages	Random number	Hours to get machine in operation	Operators available for next work stoppages	Downtime hours because of lack of operators for servicing
78 913		4	556	0.800	2	
			098	0.100	1	
			896	1.000	0	
			509	0.800	0	0.100
79 775		3	654	0.900	2	
			340	0.200	1	
			600	0.800	• 0	
80 372		2	996	1.100	2	
			651	0.900	1	
					Total	19.1

From the simulated model, we can expect to have 19.1 hours of machine downtime every two weeks because of the lack of an operator. At a machine rate of $12 per hour, this amounts to a weekly cost of $114.60. Since the cost of a fourth operator would result in an added weekly direct labor cost of $120 (40 × $3), the present set up of three men to service the 15 automatic screw machines appears to be the optimum solution.

Expense standards

More and more management is recognizing its responsibility to determine accurately the appropriate office forces for a given volume of work. To control office payrolls, management must develop time standards, since they are the only reliable "yardstick" for evaluating the size of any task.

As for other work, methods analysis should precede work measurement in all expense operations. The flow process chart is the ideal tool for presenting the facts of the present method. Once presented, the present method should be reviewed critically in all its detail. Such factors as purpose of operation, design of forms, office layout, elimination of delays resulting from poor planning and scheduling, and adequacy of existing equipment, should be considered; the primary approaches to operation analysis should be used.

After the completion of a thorough methods program, standards development can commence. Many office jobs are repetitive; consequently, it is not particularly difficult to set fair standards. Central typing pools, billing groups, file clerks, addressograph operators, punch card operators, and tabulating machine operators are representative groups that readily lend themselves to work measurement either by stopwatch or motion-picture techniques. In studying office work, the analyst should carefully identify element end points, so standard data may be established for pricing future work. For example, in typing production orders, the following elements of work normally occur on each page of each order typed:

1. Pick up production order from pile and position in typewriter.
2. Pick up sheet to be copied from, and place in Copy Right.
3. Read product order instructions.
4. Type heading on order.
   - *a*) Date
   - *b*) Number of pieces
   - *c*) Material
   - *d*) Department

Once standard data have been developed for most of the common elements used in the office, time standards can be achieved quite rapidly and economically. Of course, many clerical positions within an office are made up of a series of diversified activities that do not readily lend themselves to time study. Such work is not made up of a series of standard cycles that continually repeat themselves and, consequently, is more difficult to measure than direct labor operations. Because of this characteristic of some office routines, it is necessary to take many time studies, each of which may be but one cycle in duration. Then, by calculating all studies taken, the analyst develops a standard for typical or average conditions. Thus, a time standard may be calculated for copy typing based on the page. Granted, some pages of technical typing requiring the use of symbols, radicals, fractions, formulas, and other special characters or spacing will take considerably longer than typing the routine page. But if the technical typing is not representative of average conditions, it will not result in an unfair influence on the operator's performance over a period; simple typing and shorter than standard pages will tend to balance the extra time needed to type the complex letter.

It usually is not practical to establish standards on office positions that require creative thinking. Thus, jobs such as tool designing and product designing should be carefully considered before a decision is made to establish time standards on the work done by the men filling these positions. If standards are established on work of this nature, they should be used for such purposes as a basis for scheduling, control, or labor budgeting and should not be used for purposes of incentive wage payment. Work demanding creative thinking can be retarded if pressure is put on the employee. The result may lead to inferior designs that can be more costly to the business than the amount saved through greater productivity of the designer.

In setting standards for office workers, the analyst usually will find that, since the white-collar worker is not accustomed to having his work measured, he will not like the practice. Therefore, it is important that the same observance of good human relations practiced in the shop be adhered to in the office.

Supervisory standards

By establishing standards for supervisory work, it is possible to determine equitable supervisor loads and maintain a proper balance between supervision, facilities, clerical employees, and direct labor.

The work sampling technique is probably the most fruitful tool for the development of supervisory standards. The same information could also be attained through all-day stopwatch studies, but the cost usually would be prohibitive before reliable data could be obtained. Supervisory standards can be expressed in terms of "effective machine running hours" or some other bench mark.

For example, one study of a manufacturer of vacuum tubes revealed that 0.223 supervisory hours were required per machine running hour in a given department (Figure 22–4). The work sampling study showed that, out of 616 observations, the supervisor was working with the grid machines, inspecting grids, doing desk work, supplying material, walking, or engaged in activity classified as miscellaneous allowances a total of 519 times. This figure converted to prorated hours revealed that 518 indi-

FIGURE 22–4

				INDIRECT LABOR STANDARD				
JOB – SUPERVISION					DEPT. – GRID		DATE – 4-16-58	
Cost Center	Number of Observations	Per cent of Observations	Prorated Hours	Base Indirect Hours	Effective Machine Running Hours (EMRH)	Direct Labor Hours		Base Indirect Hours Per Machine Running Hour (Includes 6% Personal)
Grid Machines	129	21	130	130	2,461			.223
Inspect Grids	161	26	160	160				
Desk Work	54	9	56	56				
Supply Material	18	3	18	18				
Misc. Allow.	150	24	148	148				
Walking	7	1	6	6				
Out of Dept.	11	2	12					
Idle	86	14	86					
Total	616	100	616	518	2,461			.223

rect hours were required while 2,461 machine running hours took place. When a 6 percent personal allowance was added, a standard of 0.223 supervisory hours per machine running hour was computed.

$$\frac{518}{(2,461)\,(1.00 - 0.06)} = 0.223$$

Thus, if one supervisor handled a department of a given type of facility operating 192 machine running hours a week, his efficiency would be:

$$\frac{192 \times 0.223}{40\ (\text{hrs./week})} = 107 \text{ percent}$$

Standard data on indirect and expense labor

The development of standard data for establishing standards on indirect and expense labor operations is quite feasible. In fact, in view of the diversification of indirect labor operations, standard data is, if anything, more appropriate on office, maintenance, and other indirect work than it is on standardized production operations.

As individual time standards are calculated, it is wise to tabularize the elements and their respective allowed times for future reference. As the inventory of standard data is built up, the cost of taking new time studies will decline proportionally.

For example, tabularizing standard data for fork-lift truck operations is based on only six different elements: travel, brake, raise fork, lower fork, tilt fork, and the manual elements required to operate the truck. Once standard data have been accumulated for each of these elements (through the required range), the standard time to perform any fork truck operation may be determined by summarizing the applicable elements. In a similar manner standard data can readily be established on janitorial work elements such as sweep floor; wax and buff floors; dry mop; wet mop; vacuum rugs; clean, dust, and mop lounge.

The maintenance job of "inspecting seven fire doors in a plant and make minor adjustments" can readily be estimated from standard data. For example, this standard was developed in the Department of the Navy as follows:

Operation	Unit time (hours)	No. units	Total time (hours)
Inspection of fire door, roll-up type (manual chain, crankshaft, or electrically operated) fusible link. Includes minor adjustment....................	0.170	7	1.190
Walk 100 feet between each door, obstructed walking...........................	0.00009	600	0.054
			1.24

The standard data time of 0.00009 hours per foot of obstructed walking was established from fundamental motion data time and the inspection time of 0.170 hours per fire door from stopwatch time study.

Several manufacturers of material handling equipment have taken detailed studies of their product and make standard data, applicable to the equipment, available when the facility is purchased. This information will save the analyst many hours in developing material handling time standards.

Universal indirect standards

Where the number of maintenance and other indirect operations is great and diversified, the task of developing standard data and/or formulas to preprice all indirect operations may appear to be more costly than the expected savings brought about by introducing time standards. To reduce the number of different time standards for indirect operations, there has been an effort by some engineers to develop universal indirect standards.

The principle behind universal standards is assigning the major proportion of indirect operations (perhaps as much as 90 percent) to appropriate groups. Each group will have its own standard which will be the average time for all indirect operations assigned to the group. For example, group A may include the indirect operations of replacing defective union; repairing door (replace two hinges); replacing limit switch; replacing two sections (14 feet of 1-inch pipe). The standard time for any indirect operation performed in group A may be 20 minutes. This time will represent the mean ($\bar{x}$) of all jobs within the group and the dispersion of the jobs within the group for $\pm 2\sigma$ will be some predetermined percentage of $\bar{x}$ (perhaps ± 10 percent).

Standards may be established for each group by developing many (several hundred) time standards using standard data, formulas, and stopwatch procedure for typical indirect operations. These standards will be arranged in ascending sequence and then be bracketed in sufficient divisions so the range of any bracket does not exceed the desired accuracy of any operation included in the bracket. Similar operations, that have not been studied, but have had the method standardized, may be assigned to the bracket that is representative of the work elements of the operation.

This procedure may utilize as few as 100 standards to cover many thousands of different indirect operations. Since the majority of operations will cluster about the mean of their respective brackets, the total average error introduced by such standards will be slight. This will be especially true when indirect employees perform a broad variety of assignments, which is usually the case. For example, the following jobs have been given a standard of 4.4 hours by the Department of the Navy in conjunction with their engineered performance standards program. These jobs along with many others have been assigned to a specific category:

a) Fabricate eight anchor plates, 1 × 10 × 6 inches. Cut off eight pieces from milled steel stock with power hacksaw. Drill four 1-inch holes in corners using Cincinnati 21-inch vertical single-spindle drill press.

b) Fabricate one 8-inch flat belt pulley with 2-inch hole through center, ¼-inch keyway and four 1½-inch stress holes. Material used 9-inches diameter × 3 inches wide cast-iron blank. Machines used engine lathe, horizontal mill, and radial drill.

c) Fabricate one shaft to dimensions from 4½ inches O.D. × 25 inches milled steel. Turn four diameters, face, thread, mill keyway and drill center pin holes. Machines used power hacksaw, lathe, horizontal mill, and single-spindle vertical drill press.

When studying a new part to be made, the analyst will be able to fit the job to a category where similar jobs have been studied and standards established.

The application of universal indirect standards offers the opportunity to introduce standards on the majority of indirect operations at a moderate cost and also minimizes the cost of maintaining the indirect standard system.

Advantages of work standards on indirect work

Standards on indirect work offer distinct advantages to both the employer and the employee. Some of these advantages are:

1. Installation of standards will lead to many operating improvements.
2. The mere fact that standards are being established will result in better operation performance.
3. Indirect labor costs can be related to the work load regardless of fluctuation in the overall work load.
4. Budgeting of labor loads can be achieved.
5. Efficiency of various indirect labor departments can be determined.
6. Costs of such items as specific repairs, reports, and documents can be easily determined. This frequently results in elimination of needless reports and procedures.
7. System improvements can be evaluated prior to installation. Thus, it is possible to avoid costly mistakes by choosing the right procedure.
8. It is impossible to install incentive wage payment plans on these positions, thus allowing employees to increase their earnings.
9. All indirect labor work can be planned and scheduled more accurately, with the obvious resulting benefits of getting the job done on time.
10. Less supervision is required, as a program of work standards tends

to enforce itself. As long as each employee knows what is required of him, he will not arbitrarily waste or "kill" time.

Conclusion

The nonrepetitive task, characteristic of many indirect labor operations, is more difficult to study and determine representative standard times for than is the task performed over and over again. Since indirect labor operations are difficult to standardize and study, they have not been widely subjected to methods analysis. Consequently, this area usually offers a greater percentage potential for reducing costs and increasing profits through methods and time study than any other.

After good methods have been introduced and operator training has taken place, it is not only readily possible but it is practical to establish standards on indirect labor operations. The usual procedure is to take a sufficiently large sample of stopwatch time studies to assure the representation of average conditions, and then to tabularize the allowed elemental times in the form of standard data. Fundamental motion data also have a wide application for establishing standards on indirect work. Thus, allowed operation times may be established consistently, accurately, and economically.

Those indirect elements involving waiting time can be estimated accurately by using waiting line or queueing theory. It is important that the analyst has an understanding of elementary waiting line theory so he can establish the mathematical model that fits the parameters of the problem. Where the problem does not fit established waiting line equations, the analyst should consider Monte Carlo simulation as a tool for determining the extent of the waiting line problem in the work area being studied.

The reader should recognize that there is no automatic means for determining a standard job time for a maintenance or other type of indirect or expense job. The analyst must review each job request and determine both the labor and material requirements. He usually goes through the following steps:

1. He examines the work request in detail. He may council the initiator of the work request or even visit the job site in order to determine the exact requirements of the job.
2. He prepares a material estimate for the job.
3. He studies the job from the standpoint of the work elements to be performed.
4. From standard data tables or universal time standards, he selects the appropriate direct work or task times and the applicable tooling, material, and planning times.
5. If no specifically applicable times exist, he assigns an estimated time

from similar work shown on the master table of universal standard times or spread sheet.

6. After selection of the appropriate times, he adds standard times to cover the transportation times for the work order being analyzed. To this sum is added the necessary allowance to cover unavoidable delays, personal delays, and fatigue.

TEXT QUESTIONS

1. What would be the expected waiting time per shipment if it were established through stopwatch time study that the normal time to prepare a shipment was 15.6 minutes? Twenty-one shipments are made every shift (eight hours). The standard deviation of the service time has been estimated as 1.75 minutes. It is assumed that the arrivals are Poisson distributed and the servicing time is arbitrary.

2. Using Monte Carlo methods, what would be the expected downtime hours because of lack of operator for servicing if four operators were assigned to the work situation described in the text?

3. Differentiate between indirect labor and expense labor.

4. Explain what is meant by "queueing theory."

5. What four divisions constitute indirect and expense work?

6. How are standards established on the "unnecessary and delays" portion of indirect and expense work?

7. The arrivals at the company cafeteria are Poisson with an average time between arrivals of 1.75 minutes during the lunch period. The average time for a customer to obtain his lunch is 2.81 minutes and this service time is distributed exponentially. What is the probability that a person arriving at the cafeteria will have to wait and what will be the time that he can expect to wait?

8. Why has there been a marked increase in the number of indirect workers employed?

9. Why do more unavoidable delays occur in maintenance operations than on production work?

10. What is meant by crew balance? By interference time?

11. Explain how time standards would be established on janitorial operations.

12. What office operations are readily time studied?

13. Why are standard data especially applicable to indirect labor operations?

14. Summarize the advantages of standards established on indirect work.

15. Why is work sampling the best technique for establishing supervisory standards?

16. Explain the application of "slotting" under a universal standard system.

17. Why will a universal standard system involving as few as 20 bench mark standards work in a large maintenance department where thousands of different jobs are performed each year?

GENERAL QUESTIONS

1. Discuss the implications of establishing time standards for a tool designer, for a product engineer, and for a purchasing agent.

2. Explain how productivity should be reported in an office involving clerical work.

3. Would you recommend establishing standards for incentive purpose in a toolroom? In a maintenance department? Discuss.

CHAPTER 23

Follow-up method and uses of time standards

The last of the nine systematic steps in installing a methods improvement program is the step involving follow-up. Follow-up is as important as any of the other steps, yet it is the most frequently neglected. There is a natural tendency for the analyst to consider the methods improvement program complete after developing time standards. However, a methods installation should never be considered complete. The follow-up is made principally to be assured that the proposed method is being followed, that the established standards are being realized, and that the new method is being supported by labor, supervision, the union and management. Follow-up will usually result in additional benefits accruing from new ideas and new approaches that will eventually stimulate the desire to embark again on a method engineering program of the existing design or process. The procedure is to repeat the method improvement cycle shortly after it is completed, so each process and each design is being continually scrutinized for finding a better way.

Without follow-up, it is easy for proposed methods to revert to the original procedures. The writer has made innumerable method studies where the follow-up revealed that the method under study was slowly reverting to or had reverted to the original method. Humans are creatures of habit and a work force must develop the habit of the proposed method if it is to be preserved. Continual follow-up is the only way to be assured that the new method is maintained long enough to have all those associated with its details become completely familiar with its routines.

Making the follow-up

The initial follow-up should take place approximately one month after the development of time standards for production jobs. A second follow-up should be made 3 months after the development of standards, and a third follow-up 6 to 12 months after the development of standards. As brought out on page 384, the frequency of the audit should be based on the expected hours of application per year.

On each follow-up the analyst should review his original method report and the development of the standard to be certain that all aspects of the proposed method are being followed. At times he will find that portions of the proposed method are being neglected and that the workman has reverted to his old ways. When this has happened, the analyst should contact the foreman immediately and determine why the unauthorized change has taken place. If no satisfactory reasons can be given for going back to the old method, the analyst should insist that the correct procedure be followed. Tact coupled with firmness is essential, and the analyst will need to display salesmanship and technical competence.

Not only should the method be followed up, but a follow-up should also be made on the performance of the operator. A check should be made on his daily efficiency. It should be verified that he is continually operating at a performance greater than standard. His performance should be evaluated with typical learning curves for the class of work. If the operator is not making the progress anticipated, a careful study should be made, including a conference with the operator to discover what unforeseen difficulties he may have encountered.

A thorough and regular follow-up system will help assure the expected benefits from the proposed method.

Methods of establishing standards

We have found that time standards may be determined in several ways:

1. By estimate (see Chapter 12).
2. By performance records (see Chapter 11).
3. By stopwatch time study (see Chapter 14).
4. By standard data (see Chapter 18).
5. By time study formulas (see Chapter 20).
6. By work sampling studies (see Chapter 21).
7. By queueing theory (see Chapter 22).

Methods 3, 4, 5, 6, and 7 will give considerably more reliable results than either method 1 or 2. If standards are to be used for wage payment, it is essential that they be determined as accurately as possible. Consequently, standards determined by estimate and performance records will not suffice. Of course, standards developed through performance records and estimates are better than no standards at all and frequently can be used to exercise controls throughout an organization.

All of these methods have application under certain conditions and all have limitations on accuracy and cost of installation.

In the operation of any manufacturing enterprise or business, it is fundamental that we have time standards. Time is the one common denominator from which all elements of cost may be evolved. In fact, everyone uses time standards for practically everything he does or wants anyone else to do. A man rising in the morning will allow himself one hour to wash, shave, dress, eat breakfast, and get to work. This surely represents a time standard that has a bearing on the number of hours of sleep he gets. A football game involves but 60 minutes of playing time. This also represents a standard. The student reading this chapter will allow himself so many minutes to cover the assignment. This, too, is a standard that will effect the student's program for the remainder of the day.

We are particularly interested in the use of time standards as applied to the effective operation of a manufacturing enterprise or business. Several of the results of time study will be discussed.

Basis for wage incentive plans

Time standards are usually thought of in their relation to wage payment. As important as this is, there are many other uses of standards in the operation of an enterprise. However, the need for reliable and consistent standards is more pronounced in connection with wage payment than in any other area. Without equitable standards, no incentive plan that endeavors to compensate in proportion to output can possibly succeed. If we have no yardstick, how can we measure individual performance? With standardized methods and standard times, we have a yardstick that will form a basis for wage incentive application.

Common denominator in comparing various methods

Since time is a common measure for all jobs, time standards are a basis for comparing various methods of doing the same piece of work. If, for example, we thought it might be advantageous to install broaching on a close tolerance inside diameter rather than to ream the part to size as is currently being done, we could make a sound decision on the practicality of the change, if time standards were available. Without reliable standards, we would be groping in the dark.

Securing an efficient layout of available space

Time is the basis for determining the amount of each kind of equipment needed. By being able to know exact requirements for facilities, we can achieve the best possible utilization of space. If we know that we shall require 10 milling machines, 20 drill presses, 30 turret lathes, and 6 grinders in a particular machining department, then we can plan for the layout of this equipment to best advantage. Without time standards, we may have overprovided for one facility, and underprovided for another, inefficiently utilizing the space available.

Storage and inventory areas are determined from the length of time a part is in storage and the demand for the part. Again time standards are the basis for determining the size of those areas.

Means for determining plant capacity

Through the medium of time standards, not only machine capacity, but also department and plant capacity are determined. It is a matter of simple arithmetic to estimate product potential once we know the available facility hours and the time required to produce a unit of product. For example, if the bottleneck operation in the processing of a given product required 15 minutes per piece, and if 10 facilities for this operation existed, then the plant capacity based on a 40-hour per week operation on this product would be:

$$\frac{40 \text{ hours} \times 10}{0.25 \text{ hours}} = 1{,}600 \text{ pieces per week}$$

Figure 23–1 illustrates a weekly graphic analysis of the direct labor re-

FIGURE 23–1

Time standards allow determination of projected direct labor requirements

quirements for a specific industrial plant. Note how clearly this chart indicates when the plant will be in a position to produce new customer orders.

Basis for purchasing new equipment

Since time standards allow us to determine machine, department, and plant capacity, they also provide the necessary information for determining how many of what type of facilities need be provided for a given volume of production. Accurate comparative time standards also highlight the advantages of one facility over its competitors. For example, we may find it necessary to purchase three additional single-spindle, bench-type drill presses. By reviewing available standards, we shall be able to procure the style and design of drill press to give the most favorable output per unit of time.

Basis for balancing working force with available work

By having concrete information on required volume of production, as well as amount of time needed to produce a unit of that production, we are able to determine the required labor force. For example, if our production load for a given week is evaluated as 4,420 hours, then we should need 4,420/40 or 111 operators. This use of standards is especially important in a retrenching market where volume of production is going down. When overall volume diminishes, if there is no yardstick to determine the actual number of people needed to perform the reduced load, then there will be a tendency for the entire working force to slow down so the available work will last. Unless we balance our working force with available volume of work, unit costs will progressively rise. It will only be a matter of time, under these circumstances, until production operations will be performed at a substantial loss, thus necessitating increasing selling prices and facing further reductions in volume. The cycle will repeat until it becomes necessary to close the plant.

In an expanding market, it is equally important to be able to budget labor. As customer demands rise, necessitating greater volume of manpower, it is essential that the exact number and type of personnel to be added to the payroll is known so they can be recruited in sufficient time to meet customer schedules. If accurate time standards prevail, it is a matter of simple arithmetic to convert product requirements to departmental man-hours.

Figure 23–2 illustrates how overall plant capacity may be provided in an expanding market. Here the plant anticipates doubling its man-hour capacity in the period between January and November. This budget was based on projecting the scheduled contracts in terms of man-hours and allowing a reasonable cushion (crosshatched section) for receiving additional orders.

In addition to budgeting plant labor requirements, time standards serve in budgeting the labor needs of specific departments. Figure 23–3 illustrates the budgeting of spindle hours in the multiple winding department of one of the Owens-Corning Fiberglas plants. It will be noted that four product areas are served: "streamline," "serving," "straight-edge,"

Figure 23–2

Chart illustrating actual projected man-hour load and budgeted man-hour load

and "fishing rod." In view of present customer requirements, 75 spindles have been allotted for multiple winding of "streamline" products, 42 spindles for "serving," 14 for "straight-edge," and 15 for "fishing rod." Based on this budgeting of spindle and man-hours, the load for "streamline" extends to the end of the first week in November, "serving" to the middle of October, "straight-edge" to the middle of November, and "fishing rod" to the last week in October. Although customer requirements fluctuate, it will be possible through the use of time standards to adjust the labor budget of this department to best meet all customer requirements. The solid bar on this chart shows the material that has been allocated to the various product classes as of September 1.

With valid time standards, we are able to keep our working force in proportion to the volume of production required, thus controlling costs and maintaining operation in a competitive market.

FIGURE 23–3

Chart illustrating the budgeting of spindle hours of a specific department so as to best meet customer needs

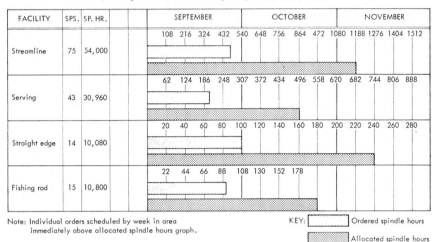

Load chart, Huntingdon Plant, Owens–Corning Fiberglas Corp. multiple winding department

Note: Individual orders scheduled by week in area immediately above allocated spindle hours graph.

KEY: [ ] Ordered spindle hours
[▒] Allocated spindle hours

Improving production control

Production control is that phase of operation that schedules, routes, expedites, and follows up production orders so operating economies are achieved and customer requirements are best satisfied. The whole function of controlling production is based upon determining where and when the work will be done. This obviously cannot be achieved unless we have a concrete idea of the "how long."

Scheduling, one of the major functions of production control, is usually handled in three degrees of refinement: (1) long-range or master scheduling, (2) firm order scheduling, and (3) detailed operation scheduling or machine loading.

Long-range scheduling is based on existing volume of production and anticipated volume of production. In this case, specific orders are not given any particular sequence, but are merely lumped together and scheduled in appropriate time periods. Firm order scheduling involves scheduling existing orders to meet customer demands and still operate in an economical fashion. Here degrees of priority are assigned to specific orders, and anticipated shipping promises are evolved from this schedule. Detailed operation scheduling, or machine loading, is assigning specific operations day-by-day to individual machines. This scheduling is planned to minimize setup time and machine downtime while meeting firm order schedules. Figure 23–4 illustrates the machine loading of a specific de-

FIGURE 23–4

Machine load of a machining department for one week (notice several schedules depend on receiving additional raw material)

DORBEN MANUFACTURING COMPANY

MACHINE LOAD - JULY 29,

partment for one week. Note that considerable capacity exists on milling machines, drill presses, and internal thread grinders.

No matter what the degree of refinement in the scheduling procedure, it would be utterly impossible without time standards. The success of any schedule is in direct relation to the accuracy of the time values used in determining the schedule. If time standards do not exist, schedules formulated only on the basis of judgment cannot be expected to be reliable.

Through the use of time standards, rate of flow of materials and work in progress may be predetermined, thus forming the basis for accurate scheduling.

Accurate control and determination of labor costs

With reliable time standards, a plant does not have to be on incentive wage payment to determine and control its labor costs. The ratio of departmental earned production hours to departmental clock hours provides information on the efficiency of the specific department. The reciprocal of the efficiency multiplied by the average hourly rate will give the hourly cost in terms of standard production. For example, the finishing department in a given plant using straight daywork may have had 812 clock hours of labor time, and in this period let us assume that it has earned 876 hours of production. The departmental efficiency would then be:

$$E = \frac{He}{Hc} = \frac{876}{812} = 108 \text{ percent}$$

If the average daywork hourly rate in the department was \$3.20, then the hourly direct labor cost based on standard production would be:

$$\frac{1}{1.08} \times \$3.20 = \$2.96$$

Let us look at another example. We might assume in another department that the clock hours were 2,840 and the hours of production earned for the period were only 2,760. In this case, the efficiency would be:

$$\frac{2,760}{2,840} = 97 \text{ percent}$$

and the hourly direct labor cost based on standard production with an average daywork rate of \$3.20 would equal:

$$\frac{1}{0.97} \times \$3.20 = \$3.30$$

In the latter case, management would realize that its labor costs were running \$0.10 per hour more than base rates and could take steps with supervision so total labor costs would be brought into line. In the first example, labor costs were running less than standard, which would allow a downward price revision, increasing the volume of production, or making some other adjustment suitable to both the management and labor. Figure 23–5 illustrates a direct labor variance report where departmental performance above and below standard is indicated.

Requisite for standard cost methods

Standard cost methods refer to the procedure of accurate cost determination in advance of production. The advantage of being able to predetermine cost is apparent. It is really necessary in many instances today to compute costs and contract work at the predetermined price. By having time standards on direct labor operations, it is possible to preprice those elements entering into the prime cost of the product. (Prime cost is usually thought of as the sum of the direct material and direct labor costs.)

As a basis for budgetary control

Budgeting is the establishment of a course of procedure: the majority of budgets are based on the allocation of money for a specific center or area of work. Thus we may establish a sales budget for a given period, a production budget, and so forth. Since money and time are definitely related, any budget is a result of standard times regardless of how the standards were determined.

As a basis for supervisory bonus

Wage incentives will be discussed at length in later chapters of this text. At this time, it will suffice to point out that any type of supervisory bonus keyed to workers' earnings will directly depend on having equitable time standards. And since workers receive more and better supervisory attention under a plan where the supervisory bonus is related to workers' pay, the majority of supervisory plans give consideration to worker productivity as the principal criterion for bonus. Other factors that are usually considered in the supervisory bonus are indirect labor costs, scrap cost, product quality, and method improvements.

Quality standards are enforced

The establishing of time standards forces the maintenance of quality requirements. Since production standards are based on the quantity of acceptable pieces produced in a unit of time, and since no credit is given for defective work turned out, there will be a constant intense effort by

FIGURE 23-5

Weekly report illustrating departmental performance in a specific manufacturing plant (Regular print indicates hours and percentage earned over standard. Italics indicate to what degree standard has not been achieved)

DIRECT LABOR VARIANCE HOURS
Week Ending June 3

No.	Name	Allowed direct labor	Efficiency Variance Week Ending 6/3	5/26	5/19	Weekly Average First Qtr.	Weekly Average Apr.	Percent Total Variance Over-Under Standards Week Ending 6/3	5/26	5/19	4 Weeks, April	First Qtr.*
11	Machine shop	892	204	29	110	33	3	22.9	2.5	9.2	0.2	2.2
12	Wire brush	178	…	…	…	…	…	…	…	…	…	…
19	Punch press	41	18	8	…	6	3	43.9	9.5	…	4.5	9.1
20	Rubber milling	21	101	43	124	21	51	481.0	18.1	172.2	37.4	13.8
31	Rubber fabricating	1,183	36	29	12	116	59	3.0	1.5	0.7	3.2	5.2
35	Pilot plant	53	…	…	…	…	…	…	…	…	…	…
39F	Finishing	339	60	107	27	42	50	17.7	18.5	5.8	10.0	6.6
39P	Paint	23	1	9	12	8	3	4.3	12.7	23.1	11.0	26.4
40	Assembly	13	1	15	15	14	4	7.7	28.3	25.9	6.0	19.9
50	Reclaim	20	…	…	…	…	…	…	…	…	…	…
65	Toolroom	…	…	…	…	…	…	…	…	…	…	…
	Total—This week	2,763	217	148	192	104	59	7.9%	3.7%	4.5%	1.2%	1.9%
	—Last week	4,462										

NOTE: The latest planning and method changes are reflected in all groups.
* First Quarter includes the 13 weeks beginning January 1, through March 31.

all workmen to produce only good parts. If an incentive wage payment plan is in effect, operators are compensated for good parts only, and to keep their earnings up they will keep their scrap down.

If some of the pieces produced are found to be defective through subsequent inspection, either the operator that produced the parts will be held responsible for their salvage or else his earnings will be diminished by the number of pieces of scrap produced.

Personnel standards are raised

Where standards are used, there will be a natural tendency to "put the right man on the right job," so the standards established will be either met or exceeded. Placing employees on work for which they are best suited goes a long way toward keeping them satisfied. Workers tend to be motivated when they know the goals that have been established and how these goals dovetail with organizational objectives.

Problems of management are simplified

With time standards go many control measures that it would be impossible to exercise unless time standards were available, such as scheduling, routing, material control, budgeting, forecasting, planning, and standard costs. With tight controls on practically every phase of an enterprise, including production engineering, sales, and cost, the problems of management are minimized. By exercising the "exception principle" where attention is given only to the items deviating from the planned course of events, managerial efforts need be devoted only to a small segment of the total activity of the enterprise.

Governmental operations have found time standards extremely helpful. Added emphasis was given to the need for a standards program in all governmental agencies when President Truman, by Executive Order 10072, in July of 1949, and the Eighty-First Congress, by Public Law 429, passed the same year, emphasized the need for continuous examination and review of governmental operations to ensure the achievement of planned programs in each department. Title X of Public Law 429 makes specific provisions for establishing an efficiency awards system in each government agency. Time standards provide means to evaluate the individual or groups of individuals submitting proposals, and also provide the basis for those submitting entries to examine the potential of their ideas.

Service to customers is bettered

With the use of time standards, up-to-date production control procedures can be introduced with the resulting advantage to the customer of getting his merchandise when he wants and needs it. Also, time standards tend to make any company more time and cost conscious; this usually results in lower selling prices to the customer. As has been explained, quality will be maintained under a work standards plan, thus assuring the customer of more parts made to required specifications.

Conclusion

Thorough and regular follow-up will help assure the expected benefits from the proposed method.

Several of the uses of time standards have been briefly summarized. There are, of course, many more applications in all areas of any enterprise. Probably the most significant result of time standards is mainte-

FIGURE 23–6

Relationship of labor cost to efficiency

Developed from data furnished by AC Spark Plug Division,
General Motors Corp.

nance of overall plant efficiency. If efficiency cannot be measured, it cannot be controlled, and without control it will markedly diminish.

Once efficiency goes down, labor costs rapidly rise and the result is eventual loss of competitive position in the market. Figure 23–6 illustrates the relationship of labor cost to efficiency in one leading manufacturer's business of automobile accessories. By establishing and maintaining effective standards, a business can standardize direct labor costs and control overall costs.

TEXT QUESTIONS

1. Explain the use of learning curves in the "follow-up" step of the systematic approach to motion and time study.
2. In what different ways may time standards be determined?
3. How can valid time standards help develop an ideal plant layout?
4. Explain the relationship between time standards and plant capacity.
5. In what way are time standards used for effective production control?
6. How do time standards allow the accurate determination of labor costs?
7. How does developing time standards help maintain the quality of product?
8. In what way is customer service bettered through valid time standards?
9. What is the relationship between labor cost and efficiency?
10. If a daywork shop was paying an average rate of $3.30 per hour and had 250 direct labor employees working, what would be the true direct labor cost per hour if during a normal month 40,000 hours of work were produced?
11. How are management problems simplified through the application of time standards?
12. In what way did President Truman provide emphasis for the use of time standards in governmental operations?
13. Explain how inventory and storage areas can be predicted accurately.

GENERAL QUESTIONS

1. What other uses of time standards not mentioned in this chapter can be realized?
2. What is the relationship between accuracy of time standards and production control? Does the law of diminishing returns apply?
3. How does work measurement improve selection and placement of personnel?
4. When is it no longer necessary to follow up the installed method?
5. Do you believe the typical worker today is motivated if the company goals and objectives are clearly presented to him? Discuss and give examples.

CHAPTER 24

Methods and standards automation

If data processing equipment is to be utilized in connection with methods and standards work, it is axiomatic that standard data are being tabularized from either, or both, stopwatch time studies and fundamental motion data. With these data available, the digital computer offers a means of storing and recovering detailed standard data as well as elemental standard data, for application on new jobs that are being performed for the first time, and for the development of proposals.

This chapter outlines the content of the basic files necessary for the implementation of an automated methods and work measurement system, and the flow charts and procedures that would be typically utilized when operating such a system.[1]

Data processing and the establishment of standards

The conventional procedure for the establishment of a new standard without data processing equipment, but utilizing standard data, is illustrated in Figure 24–1.

Here, the method analyst develops a work station layout and motion pattern based on his knowledge of motion economy and shop operations. From this proposed method, he makes an elemental breakdown, and looks up the appropriate standard data times. If fundamental motion

---

[1] The author is indebted to the IBM Company for assisting in the preparation of this chapter.

data is being used, the elemental breakdown is further subdivided so that basic motion times may be assigned. The time standard for the operation is developed by extending elemental time values by their frequency, totaling the times for each element, applying the correct allowance, and finally summarizing the allowed elemental times in order to determine the allowed operation time.

FIGURE 24–1

Development of time standards through the application of standard data

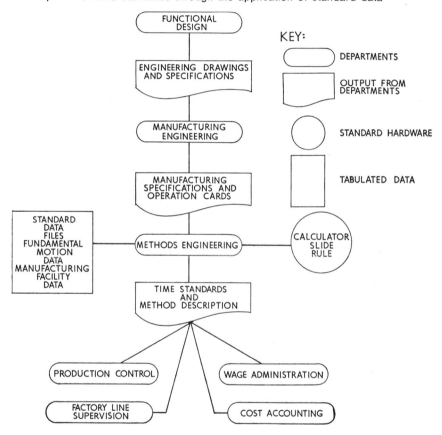

It is apparent that much of the above procedure represents burdensome clerical activities prone to human error. An automated methods and standards data processing system can minimize this clerical and computational work in the establishment of a time standard.

Such a data processing system would operate as follows:

1. Methods engineering develops a work station layout and motion pattern.

2. The proposed method is identified in detail by an elemental breakdown.
3. Through the utilization of data processing equipment, the description of each element is retrieved, the normal elemental times are identified, the elemental times are extended by frequencies, allowances are applied, and the allowed time for the operation is computed.
4. All associated reports are prepared by the system.
5. The operation time and description is entered into a permanent file for future use and maintenance.

The reader should understand that the only way the data processing system can accomplish step 3, as enumerated above, is by standard data coding. The coding can take any format a company may wish to use: numeric, alphabetic, or mnemonic. Generally, coding similar to what is used in the fundamental motion data systems (M.T.M., Work-Factor, BMT) is appropriate.

Advantages of methods and standards automation

The principal advantages of methods and standards automation include increased coverage, more accurate standards, and improved standard maintenance. Since standards may be developed much more rapidly through the use of data processing, it follows that from the standpoint of both time and money it becomes feasible to increase the plant coverage of measured work. The less the amount of unmeasured work, the greater the opportunity for effective control and efficient operation.

Standards that are developed through the medium of data processing are inevitably more error free, since manual arithmetic and look-up techniques are subject to human error.

Manual techniques prohibit accurate standard maintenance for no other reason than the avalanche of clerical work involved. For example, if basic research revealed that 2.2 TMU's was a more valid value for a GIA grasp than 2.0 TMU's, think of the clerical work involved to adjust every existing standard in the plant by increasing all GIA grasps by 10 percent! With a carefully installed data processing system, such a change could be economically effected within a short period of time.

Approach to automation through data processing

In order to use data processing equipment, it is necessary to develop files of all the existing standard data, which must be identified by an acceptable code. For example, a standard data element characteristic of this file might be:

Code	Element description	Standard time
PSP3A............	Pick up small piece, place in three-jaw air chuck and clamp	0.062

Here the code "PSP3A" represents the input to the system and the element description "pick up small piece, place in three-jaw air chuck and clamp," along with the standard time of 0.062, the output.

It is possible to program the computer so that greater amounts of detail can appear on a specific output document, such as a detailed instruction sheet. This is done by placing special symbols at appropriate locations within the element description.

For example, the lozenge (◊) symbol might be inserted between the words "piece" and "place" as follows: "pick up small piece ◊ place in three-jaw air chuck and clamp." One output document would show the element as stated and another could show additional detail such as: "pick up small piece, casting #437106, place in three-jaw air chuck and clamp."

The flow of information that takes place in the development of a detailed instruction sheet, operation card, and operation standard is illustrated in Figure 24–2. Process information—such as cutting feeds, cutting speeds, depth of cut, and so on, along with a listing of the codes of the elements required, with their frequencies—is keypunched and entered into the system. The element description and its standard time is retrieved from the standard data element file for each element involved in the operation. Those records involved in the development of the operation standard are stored in a temporary file until final review of the output has been completed by the analyst. Upon completion of the operation review, the operation records are transferred to a permanent operation file which may be either in tape or disk form.

The output may take many forms. Typically included in output is the operation standard, which lists the applicable elements and their standard times; an operation card, which gives a brief description of the operation and its standard in minutes per piece and pieces per hour (this can serve as a move card, pay voucher, and such); and an instruction sheet, which may be used by operating personnel.

With an automated data processing system, it is relatively easy to introduce a change that affects one or several operations. With details of operations stored in a file of magnetic tapes or disks, retrieval techniques allow changes to be made through "add" and/or "delete" instructions entered for those sections of the operation where the change should be applied. When the operation file is initially generated, each element of an operation is assigned a line number identification. Space signifying line numbers is provided for possible element additions. When a deletion of a part of an operation is required, reference is made to the line number. When an element is to be added, it is assigned a line number in the proper sequence that heretofore had been reserved for possible future additions of elements.

FIGURE 24–2

Automated work measurement systems for processing new operations, and changing existing operations (dotted line applies to change operations only and solid lines apply to both change and new operations)

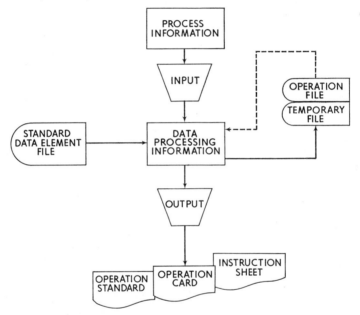

The work measurement system

The general flow of information through a typical work measurement system is illustrated in Figure 24–3.

By the application of motion study (either visual or micromotion), time study, and process information, a method study is made resulting in the development of a work station utilizing the basic principles of motion economy and operation analysis. The proposed method is then described in appropriate element coding on the input document. Subsequently, data cards are punched and verified for each line entry on the input document. The data cards are now processed and their information is transferred to disk storage. Simultaneously, the input records are edited

FIGURE 24-3

Flow of information in work measurement system

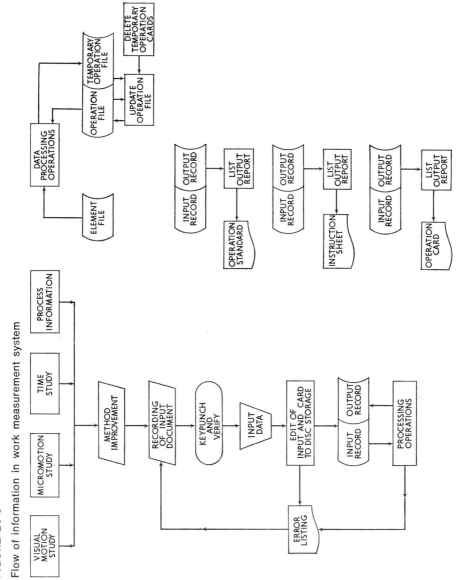

for any obvious errors. If errors have occurred, the recording of the corrected input document is made and corrected data cards are punched and verified.

Now, while input records are being processed, information is retrieved from the major input files, i.e., the element file and the operation file.

A temporary file is produced for all output records including operations, and any error conditions are listed.

The output records are processed and the various reports are printed.

After the analyst has reviewed the output reports, the operation file is updated using the temporary file.

In the installation of a work measurement system, two major input files are needed: the element file and the operation file. The element file is more basic than the operation file since it contains the element description and its normal time for all existing elements. This information is retrieved when a new operation is processed by the work measurement system. After the new operation has been processed, its records are stored in the operation file.

In order to create an operation record on an existing operation, an analysis input sheet is keypunched and entered into the system. The computer program then retrieves element record data from its element file, applies the data to each recorded element, performs the required frequency time multiplications and accumulations, applies the appropriate allowances, and stores the entire operation in a temporary storage tape or disk location. Upon approval of the operation standard, the temporary operation records are transferred to the operation file.

The operation record is normally composed of two sections: (1) heading information where the operation is described and its standard time is recorded, and (2) element information where the elements involved in the operation are described and assigned a time value. Each element in an operation is usually given a "line item" number automatically by the computer in order to provide for an easy method of updating a particular element.

It is apparent that both the element and operation files must be adequately maintained if the work measurement system is to be reliable. It is emphatic that all operations be processed by using the most recent elemental descriptions and time values.

A typical work measurement input document is illustrated in Figure 24–4. The computer program compares the element code with its element master file, retrieves, and computes the time standard based upon the element time value, its frequency, and the appropriate allowance.

Changes in element description and/or time may have an appreciable effect on existing standards and operating instructions. Under a manual system, it would not be feasible to review all existing standards in order to introduce every elemental change. However, an automated methods

FIGURE 24-4

Work measurement input document

000	STUDY NO.	PART NO.	E.C. NO.	M.E. NO.	MC. NO.	DEPT. & MGR.	PFO %	DESCRIPTION
H	01 MTMST12	0347550	0000000	00016	05144	0911	15	1 ASSEMBLY OF TRIGGERS

CODE	OPER.	PARA.	STEP		DESCRIPTION
CODE	ELEMENT CODE	FREQUENCY NUMER DENOM		START ELEMENT GRID CODE OR ELEMENT DESCRIPTION	ADJUSTMENT / HRS/C / REPEAT LINE NO.
1	0010			ASSEMBLE AND HOT UPSET 347551/1/231461/1 -THIS OPERATION TO BE RUN	
				ON MACHINE WITH CHILL AND TEMPER CONTROL ONLY	
	001	99		ASSEMBLE PN/PO347551 TRIGGER WITH PN/PO231461 USING TN/TO13 8739	
				ANVIL AND PLACE IN FIN. PARTS CONTR A70	
			01		
2	R6C			WITH RIGHT HAND AND	
	G4B			TRIGGER.	
	R1C			WITH LEFT HAND AND	
	G4B			STUD	
	M6C			AND	
	P2 SD			STUD IN ANVIL	
	G2			TO ORIENT,	
	M2C			AND	
	P2 SD			TRIGGER ON STUD.	
	AP2			TO HOLD SQUARE.	

IBM Corporation, Data Processing Division

and standards system can readily incorporate those element changes that would result in a significant alteration of the operation standard.

This can be handled by generating a special file to obtain the impact of standard data changes. Those operations that have a significant change can then be reprocessed and a new standard developed.

In addition to the rapid development and maintenance of time standards, an automated work meaesurement system is capable of rendering several helpful reports. For example, it is possible to develop a report that shows the old and new standard for the operation, the variance, and percentage of variance. Thus, the effect of change by area or department is readily available. Another helpful report is the "where-used index." This summary can identify where specific components, tools, and so on are used. For example, a particular drill jig may be used for the production of several components. The "where-used" index can show the study numbers, as well as the specific lines where the drill jig is employed.

It is possible to generate a workplace layout to be used by line supervision to help assure the prescribed method is being employed. Figures 24–5 and 24–6 represent typical input and output documents.

The automated system can be extremely helpful in the rapid development of time estimates and quotations. Many businesses today are experiencing substantial costs in the preparation of quotations, only a small fraction of which result in contracts. Let us review how the system would function in a small job shop automatic screw machine business that prepares approximately 100 quotations per week.

The request for the quotation along with a drawing of the part will be studied by a methods analyst, who will prepare a planning sheet including the following information:

1. Alloy of material required, size (diameter, etc.), material weight, cost per pound of material.
2. Length of material required per piece (length of part plus cutoff).
3. Recommended cutting speed in surface feet per minute.
4. Recommended feed in inches per revolution.
5. Money rate of the automatic to be employed.
6. Coding of setup elements.
7. Dollar rate of setup man.
8. Percent efficiency of production machine employed.
9. Any miscellaneous costs and one-time charges.

The planning sheet along with the request for quotation will then be routed to the computer operator who will prepare the quotation. The computer operator's responsibilities are to:

1. Place a magnetic ledger card into the magnetic ledger card reader which will read and print out on the primary printer the customer's name and address on the quotation as shown on the request for

FIGURE 24-5

Input document calling for workplace layout

N	GROUP	STUDY NO.	PART NO.	E.C. NO.	M.E. NO.	M.C. NO.	DEPT. & MOR.	PFD %	DESCRIPTION
N	01	MTMST02	0347550	0000000000	000016	05144	0911	15	11 ASSEMBLY ØF TRIGGERS

CODE	OPER	PARA	STEP			
CODE	ELEMENT CODE	FREQUENCY NUMBER / DENOM	START ELEMENT GRID CODE OR ELEMENT DESCRIPTION		ADJUSTMENT HRS./C	REPEAT LINE NO.

				DESCRIPTION	NEXT	
1	0010		ASSEMBLE AND HØT UPSET 347551/1/231461/1/-THIS ØPERATIØN		
			ØN MACHINE WITH CHILL AND TEMPER CØNTRØL ØNLY		
WP	WØRK ARE	M	A31	12 TO 138739 ANVIL/1/STD.ELECTRØDE/1/	0000Q	
WP	ØPER SEAT		B31	00 80 000123 ØPERATØR SEAT	0000Q	
WP	PART LØC		A21	18 PO 231461 STUDS	0500Q	
WP	PART LØC		A41	06 PO 347551 TRIGGERS	0100Q	
WP	PART LØC		A42	06 PO 347550 FIN. PARTS IN SMALL CØNTR.	0050Q	
WP	CNTR	405	A11	18 PO 231461 STUD SUPPLY	0500Q	
WP	CNTR	705	B11	18 PO 347551 TRIGGER SUPPLY	0500Q	
WP	CNTR	150	B41	12 PO 347550 FIN. PARTS IN CØNTR.A70	0200Q	
1	001		ASSEMBLE PN/PO347551 TRIGGER WITH PN/PO231461 USING TN/TO		
			ANVIL AND PLACE IN FIN PARTS CØNTR A70		
			01			
2	R6C			WITH RIGHT HAND AND		
	G4B			TRIGGER		
	R1C			WITH LEFT HAND AND		
	G4B			STUD		
	M6C			AND		
	P2SD			STUD IN ANVIL		
	G2			TØ ØRIENT.		
	M2C			AND		
	P2SD			TRIGGER ØN STUD.		
	AP2			TØ HØLD SQUARE.		

IBM Corporation, Data Processing Division

FIGURE 24–6

Output document showing workplace layout

GROUP 01   ASSEMBLY OF TRIGGERS   PART NUMBER 0347550
STUDY MTMST02   MAY 20, 19--
EC 00000000 ME 00016   OCN 05-20-4 DEPT 091-1

0010

```
XXXXXXXXXXXXXXXXXXXXXXXXXXXXXXXXXXXXXXXXXXXXXXXXXXXXXX
X                X            X            X                X
X   VENDORS      X   PART     X            X   PART LOC 2   X
X   CONTAINER    X            X   WORK     X                X
X   --------     X   LOCATION X            XXXXXXXXXXXXXXX
X                X            X   AREA     X                X
X   SEALED       X     1      X            X   PART LOC 1   X
X                X            X            X                X
XXXXX -A1- XXXXXXXXXX -A2- XXXXXXXXXX -A3- XXXXXXXXX -A4- XXXXX
XXXXXXXXXXXXXX                              XXXXXXXXXXXXXX
X                X                          X                X
X                X              XXXXXXX      X                X
X   705          X              X     X  X   X   PLASTIC      X
X   STACK        X              X  X     X   X   TOTE BOX     X
X   BIN          X                XXX        X   WITH PROT.   X
X                X              OPERATOR     X                X
X                X                           X                X
XXXXX -B1- XXXXX                    -B3-     XXXXX -B4- XXXXX
```

PARTS LOCATION TABLE

FROM LOC.	TO LOC.	PART/TOOL NUMBER	DIST	PART QTY.	PART/TOOL DESCRIPTION	REP. QTY.
A1-1		P0231461	18	0500	STUD SUPPLY	
A2-1		P0231461	18	0500	STUDS	
A3-1		T0138739	12	0000	ANVIL/1/STD. ELECTRODE/1/	
A4-1		P0347551	06	0100	TRIGGERS	
A4-2		P0000000	06	0050	FIN. PARTS IN SMALL CONTR.	
B1-1		P0347551	18	0500	TRIGGER SUPPLY	
B3-1			00			
B4-1			12	0200	FIN. PARTS IN CONTR. A70	

IBM Corporation, Data Processing Division

quotation. Other pertinent information, such as the part name, part number, or customer request number, can be printed out from the magnetic ledger card or else be typed manually on the quotation.

2. Key in as a column heading the quantities which are being quoted on, as read from the request for quotation.

3. Type in the size, shape, and kind of material required as shown on the planning sheet.

4. Key in part length, and cutoff length.

5. Key in the material weight (pounds per foot).

6. Key in the cost per hundredweight according to price as read from the planning sheet.

7. Key in the major diameter and recommended surface feet as read from the planning sheet.

8. Key in the throw and feed for each operation.

9. Key in the percent of efficiency.

The computer will calculate the amount of material needed per hundred pieces (or some other unit of production) and print this information on the quotation. Also, such information as pounds of material per hundred pieces, weight per quantity quoted on, cost per hundredweight, gross and net production, and spindle speed required for each operation will be automatically computed.

The computer operator will type in the description of the operation as read from the planning sheet, and key in the gross and net production, and the dollar rate of the facility. The computer will automatically calculate the dollar amount per hundred pieces and will print out this information on the quotation.

This procedure will be repeated for each line of charges on the quotation.

To total the quotation, the operator will depress a command key and the total price per 100 pieces will print out in the appropriate quantity breakdown column on the quotation.

Such information as miscellaneous or nonrecurring tooling charges, delivery schedule, and so on will now be typed in.

Upon completion of the quotation preparation, the computer will automatically tab to the quotation journal in the primary printer, and post a recap of the quotation for future reference purposes. This recap would contain such information as the customer name, customer request number, quotation number, prices per quantity quoted on, and delivery time. As this journal was printing, the printer inside the magnetic ledger card reader would post the same information to the customer account card so that it would provide a reference of quotations outstanding, by customer.

The procedure outlined would permit processing about 10 quotations per hour. Figure 24–7 illustrates the flow of information on this estimating and quotation writing procedure.

A computer program for indirect labor standards

In order to utilize data processing equipment for standard development through measurement, the time study analyst must record his data in a language acceptable to the computation equipment being utilized. Figure 24–8 illustrates a time study observation sheet designed for use with the IBM 360 system and for establishing standards on indirect labor work.[2] Pertinent information is transferred from this observation sheet to the IBM keypunched input card (see Figure 24–9) by the keypunch operator. It should be noted that one card is utilized for each line of information on the time study form and the information from the form

---

[2] This method and program developed by Kenneth Kopp of The Pennsylvania State University.

FIGURE 24–7

Estimating and quotation writing procedure

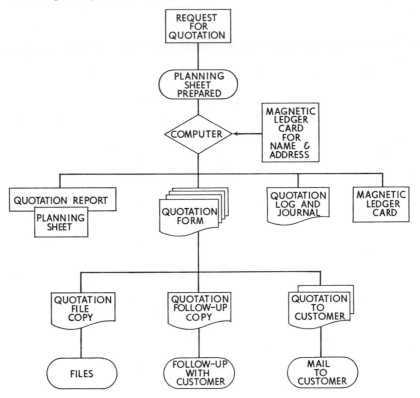

is transferred to the identical column on the keypunch card. The time study form as designed permits 25 elements or readings per page.

The following information has been included in this example:

Heading

The date, employee, job or operation description, the job location, and the name of the analyst are included. This information is compatible with that provided on most time study forms.

Date

Columns 01, 02, and 03 are reserved for the recording of the date the study was taken. A number is assigned to each calendar day of the year. Thus the number 41 would indicate February 10.

Study Number

Two columns, 04 and 05, are used to identify the study number. Thus space is provided for up to 99 studies per day. Each day, the first study taken is assigned the number 01.

FIGURE 24–8

Time study observation sheet for use with the IBM 360 system

Date/Year _____
Employee _____
Job Description _____
Job Location _____
Time Study by

THE PENNSYLVANIA STATE UNIVERSITY
DEPARTMENT OF MANAGEMENT ENGINEERING
TIME STUDY OBSERVATION SHEET

Page ____ of ____

Date	Study No.	Cost Center	Position or Location		Job Desig Code	Time	Worker					Foreign Elements or Delays							Pcs. Studied	Remarks
			Build or Zone	Area			Act Code	Pace Rate	PFD	Pcs.	Start Time	Stop Time	Act Code	Pace Rate	PFD	Quan	Need			

Cost Center

The columns 06, 07, and 08 are used to identify the specific cost center applicable to the study being taken.

Position or Location

Columns 09 through 18 are used to identify the building and room where the worker is engaged during the course of the study.

Job Description

A three-digit number is used to identify each job description. The three-digit number associated with the study being made is recorded in columns 19, 20, and 21.

Time

Five columns (23 through 27) are used to record the elapsed time for each element.

FIGURE 24–9

IBM keypunched input card

Code

Column 22 has been introduced for verification purposes. This column provides the means to ascertain that each keypunched card is in its proper location within the deck of cards before the run on the computer starts. Column 22 provides for as many as nine interruptions during the course of one study. The first is identified as 1, the second as 2, and so on. In order to put the keypunched cards in their proper location within the deck, a check on column 22 is made. If no entry is shown, the cards are placed in numerical sequence based on the time entries shown in columns 23 through 27. If a recording is shown in column 22, the sorter will put all the 0's together, 1's next, 2's next, and so on, before going to the time column.

Combine

When an element is interrupted by a foreign element prior to its completion, it is necessary to combine that portion of the elemental time prior to the interruption with that portion of time required to complete the element after the interruption. By placing like digits (0 through 9) in column 28 to the rear of the two stopwatch readings, the computer will add these two values to arrive at the total elemental elapsed time.

Activity Code

Columns 29, 30, and 31 are used to identify standard elemental descriptions through the use of a three-digit number. For example, the three-digit number 111 might signify "dry mop floor."

Pace Rate

The performance rating factor is shown in columns 32, 33, and 34.

P-F-D

The allowance for personal, fatigue, and delay time is shown in column 33. The number 1 indicates a 10 percent allowance, the number 2 a 15 percent allowance, the number 3 a 20 percent allowance, the number 4 a 25 percent allowance, and so on.

Pieces

The number of units completed during each element will be entered in columns 36, 37, and 38. This permits the computer to compute an average elemental time per piece. No entry in the piece columns is interpreted as one unit being processed.

Foreign Elements or Delays

Columns 39 through 64 are used for recording foreign elements or delays as they occur.

Combine

Column 39 is used to combine entries made under the foreign elements or delays section.

Start Time and Stop Time

Columns 40 through 49 provide space for the recording of the start and stop time for each foreign element or delay.

Activity Code, Pace Rate, P-F-D

Columns 50 through 56 are used in conjunction with foreign elements so as to identify their activity code, pace rating factor, and applicable allowance.

Quantity

Columns 57 through 60 are used to identify the quantity involved in conjunction with the foreign element taking place.

Need

The quantity of materials needed to complete the study is shown in columns 61 through 63. The fraction of the quantity processed (as shown in columns 57 through 60) in order to meet the need is shown in column 64.

Pieces Studied

The total number of units studied is entered in columns 65 through 68.

Remarks Column

This column is for the analyst's use as required.

Figure 24–10 illustrates a time study taken on the cleaning of an office and Figure 24–11 shows the print-out of the information supplied by the data processing department.

Here the stopwatch readings as they appear on the time study are reproduced. Also recorded is the elemental rating factor and the P-F-D allowance. The normal and allowed elemental times are computed and coded for identification purposes. Also the mean elemental rating factor and allowance are computed along with the operation standard.

FIGURE 24-10

Time study of office cleaning operation

Date/Year __9/20/--__
Employee __Jack Keller__
Job Description __Custodian__
Job Location __Willard Building__
Time Study by __K. Kopp__

THE PENNSYLVANIA STATE UNIVERSITY
DEPARTMENT OF MANAGEMENT ENGINEERING
TIME STUDY OBSERVATION SHEET

Remarks column entries (Pcs. Studied):

- Start Room 300
- 100 Walk
- 201 Instructions from Foreman
- 200 Get Supplies & Cart
- 101 Unlock Door Turn on Light
- 106 Empty Pencil Sharpener
- 110 Empty Waste Basket
- 107 Dust Desk Top
- 108 Dust Telephone
- 103 Dust Chairs
- 104 Dust Tops of Files
- 113 Dust Table Top
- 301 Talk
- 105 Wash Chalk Board (5' x 10')
- 206 Get Bucket of Water
- 207 Get Supplies (Erasers)
- 111 Dry Mop Floor
- 202 Change Mop Head
- 222 Miscellaneous (Close Window)
- 167 Adjust Shades
- 115 Turn off Lights, Lock Doors
- 12.32 Went For Lunch

FIGURE 24-10 (Continued)

THE PENNSYLVANIA STATE UNIVERSITY
DEPARTMENT OF MANAGEMENT ENGINEERING
TIME STUDY OBSERVATION SHEET

Date/Year 9/20/--
Employee Jack Keller
Job Description Custodian
Job Location Willard Building
Time Study by K. Kopp

FIGURE 24–11

Print-out of time study taken on office cleaning operation

CTR	LOCATN	AREA	DSC	TIME	ACT. TIME	RATING	EXTENSION	PFD	EXTENSION	CODE	DELAYS
				THE PENNSYLVANIA STATE UNIVERSITY					PAGE	1	
				MANAGEMENT ENGINEERING							
STUDY NUMBER 263–05				MOTION AND TIME STUDY							
				DEC 8, 19--							
290	184	300	293	00000							
			0303	00280	1.57	100	1.5700	115	1.8055	100	
				00187	1.23	100	1.2300	115	1.4145	201	
				00426	1.46	105	1.5330	115	1.7630	200	
			0315	00440	.14	100	.1400	115	.1610	100	
				00453	.13	105	.1365	115	.1570	101	
				00485	.32	105	.3360	115	.3864	106	
				00511	.26	105	.2730	115	.3140	106	
				00542	.31	105	.3255	115	.3743	110	
				00579	.37	105	.3885	115	.4468	110	
				00655	.76	105	.7980	115	.9177	107	
				00690	.35	105	.3675	115	.4226	108	
				00700	.10	105	.1050	115	.1208	107	
				00713	.13	105	.1365	115	.1570	103	
				00736	.23	105	.2415	115	.2777	103	
				00749	.13	105	.1365	115	.1570	103	
				00765	.16	105	.1680	115	.1932	103	
				00790	.25	105	.2625	115	.3019	104	
				00910	1.20	105	1.2600	115	1.4490	107	
				01232	.79	105	.8295	115	.9539	113	2.43
				00000							
				01050	8.70	100	8.7000	115	10.0050	105	
				00480	1.80	100	1.8000	115	2.0700	206	
				01130	.48	100	.4800	115	.5520	105	
				01102	.04	100	.0400	115	.0460	207	
				01345	.53	100	.5300	115	.6095	105	
				01300	1.62	100	1.6200	115	1.8630	206	
				01464	1.19	105	1.2495	115	1.4369	111	
				01576	1.12	100	1.1200	115	1.2880	202	
				01610	.34	105	.3570	115	.4106	111	
				01698	.70	105	.7350	115	.8453	167	
				01643	.03	100	.0300	115	.0345	222	
				01723	.25	105	.2625	115	.3019	115	
					26.69	1.03	27.1615	1.15	31.2360		
					UNITS	1		AVERAGE	31.24		

TEXT QUESTIONS

1. Explain in detail how an automated methods and standards data processing system can minimize standards clerical and computational work.
2. Outline how a change that affects several operations is introduced where an automated data system is employed.
3. What two major input files are needed in the installation of a work measurement system?
4. What helpful management reports can be readily generated if an automated work measurement system is being used?

GENERAL QUESTIONS

1. What disadvantages, if any, do you visualize can exist if an automated work measurement system is installed?
2. What percentage time do you feel the work measurement analyst would save using the computer technique illustrated in Figure 24–8? Will the keypunch operator make as many input errors as the time study man's arithmetic errors? Why?

CHAPTER 25

Significant wage payment plans

Experience has proven that workmen will not give extra or sustained effort unless some incentive, either direct or indirect, is in the offing. Incentives in one form or another have been used in industry for many years. Several of the incentive wage payment plans developed a generation or more ago are still in effect today with slight modifications. Before designing a wage payment plan for a specific plant, it is wise for the analyst to review the strength and weaknesses of past plans. For this reason the more important historical plans will be reviewed in this chapter.

In the broad sense, all incentive plans that tend to increase the employee's production will fall under one of the following three classes: (1) direct financial plans, (2) indirect financial plans, and (3) plans other than financial.

Direct financial plans

Direct financial plans include all plans in which the workman's compensation is commensurate with his output. In this category are included both individual incentive plans and group plans. In the individual type of plan, each employee's compensation is governed by his own performance for the period in question. Group plans are applicable to two or more persons who are working as a team on operations that tend to be dependent on each other. In these plans, each employee's compensation within the group is based upon his base rate and the performance of the group for the period in question.

The incentive for high or prolonged individual effort is not nearly as great in group plans as in individual plans. Hence, there has been a tendency for industry to favor individual incentive methods. In addition to lower overall productivity, group plans have other drawbacks: (1) personnel problems brought about by nonuniformity of production coupled with uniformity of pay, and (2) difficulties in justifying base rate differentials for the various opportunities within the group.

Of course, group plans do offer some decided advantages over individual incentive, noteworthy of which are: (1) ease of installation brought about through ease of measuring group rather than individual output, and (2) reduction of cost in administration of the plan through reduced amount of paper work, less verification of inventory in process, and less in-process inspection.

In general, higher rates of production and lower unit cost of the product can be expected under individual incentive plans. If practical to install, the individual incentive plan should be given preference over group systems. On the other hand, the group approach has more application where it is difficult to measure individual output and where individual work is variable and frequently performed in cooperation with another employee on a team basis. For example, where four men are jointly working together in the operation of an extrusion press for extruding brass rods, it would be virtually impossible to install an individual incentive system, but a group plan would be applicable.

Indirect financial plans

Those company policies that tend to stimulate employee morale and result in increased productivity, yet have not been designed to bring about a direct relation between amount of compensation and amount of production would fall in the indirect financial classification. Overall company policies such as fair and relatively high base rates, equitable promotion policies, sound suggestion systems, guaranteed annual wage, and relatively high fringe benefits will lead to building healthy employee attitudes which stimulate and increase productivity. Thus, they are classified as indirect financial plans.

All indirect incentive methods have the weakness of allowing too broad a gap between employee benefits and production. After a period of time, the employee takes for granted the benefits bestowed upon him and fails to realize that the means for their continuance must be a result entirely of his productivity. The theories, philosophies, and techniques of indirect incentives are beyond the scope of this text; for added information in this area, the student is referred to books on personnel administration.

Plans other than financial

Nonfinancial incentives include any rewards that have no relation to pay, and yet improve the spirit of the employee to such an extent that added effort will be evidenced. Under this category would come such company policies as periodic shop conferences, frequent talks between the supervisor and the employee, proper employee placement, job enrichment, job enlargement, nonfinancial suggestion plans, maintenance of ideal working conditions, posting of individual production records, and many other techniques utilized by effective supervisors and capable, conscientious managers.

Nonfinancial incentives represent an area that is thoroughly covered in texts on industrial relations and will not be further discussed in this book.

Classification of direct wage financial plans

Two classifications of direct wage financial plans may be made within which the majority of individual plans may be placed. These two divisions with representative specific plans are outlined as follows:

I.   Employee participates in all the gain above standard
   A.   Piecework
   B.   Standard hour plan
   C.   Taylor multiple piece rate
   D.   Merrick multiple piece rate
   E.   Measured daywork
II. Employee shares the gains with his employer above standard
   A.   Halsey plan
   B.   Bedaux system
   C.   Rowan plan
   D.   Emerson plan
   E.   Profit sharing

There are some plans where the relationship between output and earnings has been established empirically, and at different levels of performance, the plan may either allow the employee all the gains, or a share of the gains. For purposes of simplicity, plans with these characteristics have been included in the group of "gain sharing with the employer."

Piecework

Piecework implies that all standards are expressed in terms of money and the operator is rewarded in direct proportion to his output. Under piecework, the day rate is not guaranteed. Today, piecework is not used since federal law requires a minimum guaranteed hourly rate. Prior to

World War II, piecework was used more extensively than any other incentive plan. The reasons for the popularity of piecework is that it is easily understood by the worker, easily applied, and one of the oldest types of wage incentive plans.

Since World War II, the popularity of piecework has rapidly declined. There have been several reasons for this, first and foremost being that under piecework all standards are expressed in terms of money. Thus every adjustment in base rates involves a monumental amount of clerical work to change all standards to agree with the revised hourly base rates. From 1930 to 1940, base rates of pay remained relatively stable, and standards expressed in terms of dollars and cents were seldom changed. However, following World War II to the present writing, there has been practically an annual increase in base rates. Piece rates expressed in money have been exceedingly difficult to maintain, and for this reason many concerns have discontinued their use.

In piece rate plans, the worker is made aware of the close relationship between his earnings and the time study man. This situation makes it difficult for the time study analyst to convince the worker that the analyst's only interest is in establishing a fair rate of production, and that he is not concerned with restricting operator earnings. Then, too, the term "piece rate" was used extensively by the old "efficiency expert" who did so much to hinder the progress of the methods, standards, and wage payment function. Even today, the name "piece rate" leaves a sour taste with many of our older employees.

Figure 25–1 illustrates graphically the relationship between operator's earnings and unit direct labor costs under a piecework plan.

Standard hour plan

The fundamental difference between the standard hour plan and piecework plan is that under the former, standards are expressed in terms of time rather than money. The operator is rewarded throughout in direct proportion to his output.

Graphically, the relationship between operator earnings and unit direct labor cost, when plotted against production and money, would be identical to piecework.

For example, a standard may be expressed as 2.142 hours per 100 pieces. It is an easy operation to calculate either the money rate or the operator's earnings, once the base rate of the operator is known. If the operator had a base rate of $3, then the money rate of this job would be: $(3.00)(2.142) = \$6.42$ per hundred or $0.0642 per piece. Let us assume that an operator produced 412 pieces in an eight-hour working day; his earnings for the day would be: $(\$3.00)(2.142)(4.12) = \$26.48$ and his hourly earnings would be: $26.48/8$ or $3.310. The operator efficiency

FIGURE 25–1

Operator earnings and unit direct labor cost under piecework

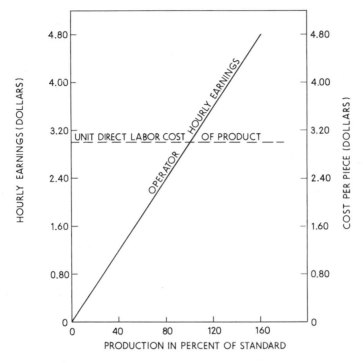

for the day, in this case, would then be: $(2.142)(4.12)/8$ or 110 percent.

The standard hour plan offers all the advantages of piecework and eliminates the major disadvantages. However, it is somewhat more difficult for the workman to compute his earnings than if standards were expressed in terms of money. The principal advantage is, of course, that standards are not changed when base rates are altered. Thus, clerical work is reduced over a period of time when compared to the piecework plan. Moreover, the term "standard hour" is more palatable to the worker than "piecework," and with standards expressed in time, the amount of money earned by the workman is not quite so closely linked with time study practice. For these reasons there has been a marked growth in the popularity of standard hour plans.

Taylor differential piece rate

The Taylor differential piece rate plan is not used in very many plants today. In this plan two piece rates were established and expressed in terms of money. The lower rate compensated in direct proportion to output until the operator's performance reached standard. Once standard performance was achieved or exceeded, the high piece rate went into effect. Thus the workman was encouraged not only to reach standard, but also, since he was paid in direct proportion to output beyond standard, he was encouraged to execute his maximum performance. Under the Taylor plan, standards were set "tight" enough so that only the pro-

FIGURE 25–2

Operator earnings and unit direct labor cost under the Taylor differential piece rate plan

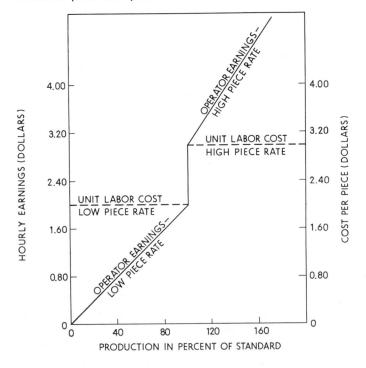

ficient employees could exceed it. On so doing they were generously compensated. It is also to be noted that the poor worker was penalized.

Under this plan, for example, the piece rates for machining a part may be $0.40 each up to a standard of seven pieces per hour. Daily production averaging seven or more pieces per hour may be paid $0.50 each. Thus, if an operator turned out 56 pieces during a day, his earnings would be $28. However, if he produced only 55 pieces he would be paid at the lower piece rate and would have earned $22 for the day. Figure 25–2 illustrates the unit cost and earnings' relationship of this plan.

Merrick multiple piece rate

Under the Merrick multiple piece rate plan, three graded piece rates were established rather than two as advocated by Taylor. There was a piece rate established for beginners, one for average employees, and one for the superior workmen. This plan endeavored to correct the low rate paid to operators performing below task and so overcome the defects of Taylor's plan, which had caused such severe criticism by employees. Merrick chose 83 percent of task as the point for his first step, which involved a piece rate with a 10 percent bonus. His high piece rate beginning at standard included an additional 10 percent bonus.

Measured daywork

During the early 1930's, shortly after the era of the "efficiency expert," there was an effort by organized labor to get away from time study practice and, in particular, piece rates. At this time, measured daywork was introduced as an incentive system that broadened the gap between the establishment of a standard and the worker's earnings. Many modifications of measured daywork installations are in operation today, and the majority of them follow a specific pattern. First, base rates are established by job evaluation for all opportunities falling under the plan. Then standards are determined for all operations by means of some form of work measurement. A progressive record of each employee's efficiency is maintained for a period of time, usually one to three months. This efficiency, multiplied by his base rate, forms the basis of his guaranteed base rate for the next period. For example, the base rate of a given operator may be $3.30 per hour. Let us assume that the governing performance period is one month or 173 working hours. If, during the month the operator earned 190 standard hours, his efficiency for the period would be 190/173 or 110 percent. Then, in view of the performance, the operator would receive a base rate of (1.10)(3.30) or $3.63 for every hour worked during the next period regardless of his performance. However, his achievement during this period would govern his base rate for the succeeding period.

In most measured daywork plans, the base rate is guaranteed; thus an operator falling below standard (100 percent) for any given period would receive his base rate for the following period.

The length of time used in determining performance usually runs three months so as to diminish the clerical work of calculating and installing new guaranteed base rates. Of course, the longer the period, the less incentive effort can be expected. When the spread between performance and realization is too great, the effect of incentive performance is diminished.

The principal advantage of measured daywork is that it takes the immediate pressure off the workman. He knows what his base rate is and realizes that, regardless of his performance, he will receive that amount for the period.

The limitations of measured daywork are apparent. First, because of the length of the performance period, the incentive feature is not particularly strong. Then, in order to be effective, it places a heavy responsibility on supervisors for the maintenance of production above standard. Otherwise, the employee's performance will drop, thus lowering his base rate for the following period and causing employee dissatisfaction. Clerical work is costly for the keeping of detailed rate records and the making of periodic adjustments in all base rates. In fact, as much clerical work is involved under measured daywork as under any straight incentive plan where the employee is rewarded according to his output.

Although we have classified measured daywork as a type of wage payment plan wherein the employee participates in all the gain above standard, it can be seen that this method of wage payment is really a hybrid of the other "one-for-one" plans. As the workman's seniority increases, his total earnings will approximate the amount he would have earned if he had been paid in direct proportion to his output. Therefore, the plan is, in effect, similar to other types discussed that fall under this category.

Halsey plan

About 1890, Frederick Halsey developed a wage incentive plan that was one of the first to deviate from piecework. In Mr. Halsey's method, standards were established from past records, as time study had not yet come into use. The resulting standards, as could be expected, were loose.

However, if the workman failed to meet the standard, he was paid his regular wages; thus this early proposal guaranteed the base rate, which is a requisite of an effective wage payment plan today. In Halsey's original plan, he compensated the operator for performance above standard so that the workman received one third of the time saved. The amount of premium in subsequent installations varied with individual plants but tended to be set at 50 percent. Using this percentage, it was easy to present the plan to the employees as an equitable arrangement in which both the employee and the company participated in one half the time saved.

Another characteristic of the Halsey method that has sound application today was that the standards were expressed in terms of time rather than money.

The Halsey plan was established as a curb to runaway piece rates that were characteristic of the time because scientific methods of work measurement had not as yet been developed and methods improvements were the prerogative of the employee. Since the employee was assured his base rate and was given up to half the share of the earnings above task, he was usually attracted to the plan. Figure 25–3 illustrates the curves depicting operator's earnings and unit direct labor cost for a modified Halsey system. Inspection of these curves will show that a varying unit labor cost is provided. This is one distinct disadvantage of the Halsey plan and all plans where the employee shares the gain with his employer. With variable unit labor costs, it is difficult to establish true

FIGURE 25–3

Operator earnings and unit direct labor cost under the Halsey plan

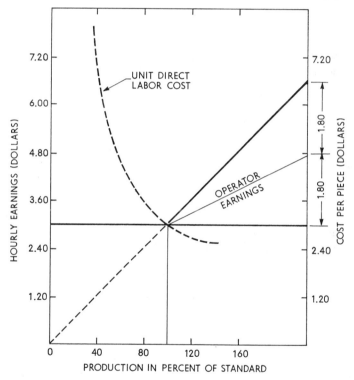

overall costs and budgets which are so necessary in the efficient operation of any business.

Since the Halsey plan does not reward the operator in direct proportion to his output, it is not readily accepted by labor today. Labor's attitude is that, if management is willing to pay a given amount per piece at the task point, it should be willing to pay the worker a like amount for production beyond task. Since total unit cost declines with increased productivity in view of being able to spread overhead over more pieces, management can afford to compensate the worker in direct proportion to his output.

Bedaux point system

The Bedaux point system, as introduced in 1916 by Charles E. Bedaux, is similar in many respects to the Halsey plan just discussed. The hourly rate is guaranteed up to task or standard, and beyond this point constant sharing of time saved takes place. Bedaux expressed his standards in terms of "B's," which was defined as one minute "composed of relative proportions of work and rest as indicated by the whole job." A normal operator was expected to perform 60 B's every hour he worked. The number of B's comprising any job was determined by time study practice. Under the original Bedaux plan, the worker participated in 75 percent of the B's earned above standard. The remaining 25 percent of B's earned above standard was used to compensate indirect labor and supervision.

For example, if an operator earned 520 B's during the working day, his efficiency would be: 520/480 or 108.3 percent.

Of the 40 B's above standard earned, the operator would be compensated for 75 percent, or 30. Let us assume an hourly rate of $1.80. Then each B would have a value of $0.03 and the incentive earned on the above job would be $0.90. Graphically, the operator earnings curve and unit cost curves for the Bedaux point system would be identical to those for the Halsey plan except for the slopes above the task point. Since this plan does not reward the worker in direct proportion to output, it too is not well received by labor today.

Rowan plan

In 1898, James Rowan proposed a sharing plan wherein the incentive was determined by the ratio of the time saved to the standard time.[1] The base rate was guaranteed, and the premium earning curve began at 62½ percent of standard. Since it is impossible to save all the standard time, it would be impossible for any operator to earn 200 percent of his base wage. The fundamental purpose of Rowan's plan was to protect the employer from "runaway rates" that might be established from past performance records, and still provide sufficient incentive to the operator for high continuous effort. Although this system accomplished what was intended, the fact that large gains on the part of the operator were virtually impossible discouraged high production. The fact that the worker

---

[1] "A Premium System of Remunerating Labor," *Proceedings, Mechanical Engineers* (British), 1901, p. 865.

was compensated on an incentive basis at an early stage of the earnings curve made the plan more attractive to workmen than the Halsey plan if tight rates prevailed and high production performance was impossible.

Operator earnings under this system can be expressed as follows:

$$E_a = R_a T + \frac{S_t R_a T}{T_a}$$

where

$$E_a = \text{Earnings}$$
$$R_a = \text{Rate per hour}$$
$$T = \text{Time spent on the work}$$
$$S_t = \text{Time saved}$$
$$T_a = \text{Allowed time}$$

For example, if an operator at a base rate of $3 per hour spent three hours on a job which had a standard of 3.5 hours, his earnings for the job would be:

$$E_a = (3.00)(3) + \frac{(0.5)(3.00)(3)}{3.5} = \$10.28$$

His hourly rate for this assignment would amount to $3.43.

Figure 25–4 illustrates operator earnings and unit labor costs under the Rowan plan. This system has several disadvantages that limit its use in this country. First, it limits earnings and consequently restricts production. Then, this plan is more complex, making it difficult for the workman to understand and causing more clerical work in calculation of wages earned.

For example, let us assume a base rate of $1 per hour and a standard of one hour per piece for a given job. The task point taken at 62.5 percent of standard would require 1.6 hours to do the job. As performance increased, the resulting pay, labor cost, and rates of production would be as shown in Figure 25–4 and accompanying table.

Emerson plan

In many respects, the wage payment plan advocated by Harrington Emerson is not unlike the Halsey system. Emerson assured the employee his base rate and established standards based on careful study of all details entering into the production. However, the incentive portion of his plan differed somewhat from others. At 66⅔ percent of a standard, he established a small incentive which increased as the performance increased until the task point was reached. Beyond this point, he established a straight-line earning curve which compensated the operator in direct proportion to his output plus 20 percent. The premium paid from

FIGURE 25–4

Operator earnings and unit cost curve under the Rowan plan

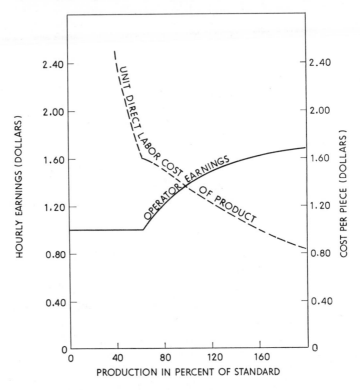

Percent of standard	Time taken, hours	Time saved, hours	Ratio of time saved to time allowed	Premium pay	Pay for job	Hourly rate
62.5	1.6	0	0	0	1.600	1.000
80	1.25	0.350	0.219	0.274	1.524	1.220
100	1.00	0.600	0.375	0.375	1.375	1.375
120	0.833	0.767	0.480	0.395	1.230	1.480
140	0.714	0.886	0.554	0.395	1.110	1.560
160	0.625	0.975	0.610	0.381	1.006	1.610
200	0.500	1.100	0.686	0.343	0.843	1.686

two thirds of task to task was empirically determined and is tabularized in Table 25–1.

Under Emerson's plan, the operator's earnings below two thirds of task may be computed from the expression:

$$E_a = R_a T$$

TABLE 25–1

Efficiency in percent	Bonus expressed as decimal proportion of base rate	Efficiency in percent	Bonus expressed as decimal proportion of base rate	Efficiency in percent	Bonus expressed as decimal proportion of base rate
67.........	0.0001	82.........	0.0433	97.........	0.1662
68.........	0.0004	83.........	0.0492	98.........	0.1770
69.........	0.0011	84.........	0.0553	99.........	0.1881
70.........	0.0022	85.........	0.0617	100.........	0.2000
71.........	0.0037	86.........	0.0684		
72.........	0.0055	87.........	0.0756		
73.........	0.0076	88.........	0.0832		
74.........	0.0102	89.........	0.0911		
75.........	0.0131	90.........	0.0991		
76.........	0.0164	91.........	0.1074		
77.........	0.0199	92.........	0.1162		
78.........	0.0238	93.........	0.1256		
79.........	0.0280	94.........	0.1352		
80.........	0.0327	95.........	0.1453		
81.........	0.0378	96.........	0.1557		

and between two thirds of task and task:

$$E_a = R_aT + F_t(R_aT)$$

and above task

$$E_a = R_aT + S_tR_a + 0.20R_aT$$

where

F_t = Factor taken from table
R_a = Rate per hour
S_t = Time hours saved
T = Time taken in hours

In adopting his plan, Emerson advocated the calculation of efficiency for a pay period of either a week or a month, thus tending to equalize the very poor and the very high daily efficiencies. For example, if during a month involving 173 working hours an operator earned 180 hours for which he was paid a base rate of $3, his earnings for the period would be:

$$E_a = (3.00)(173) + (7)(3.00) + (0.20)(3.00)(173) = \$643.80$$

Profit sharing

The Council of Profit Sharing Industries has defined profit sharing as "any procedure under which an employer pays to all employees, in addition to good rates of regular pay, special current or deferred sums based not only upon individual or group performance, but on the prosperity of the business as a whole."[2]

No one specific type of profit sharing has received general industrial acceptance. In fact, about every installation has certain "tailor-made" features which distinguish it from others. However, the majority of profit sharing systems can be placed under one of the following broad categories: (1) cash plans, (2) deferred plans, and (3) combined plans.

As the name implies, the straight cash plan involves the periodic distribution of money from the profits of the business to the employees. The payment is not included with the regular pay envelope, but is made separately, so as to identify it as an extra reward, brought about by the individual and combined efforts of the entire operating force. The amount of the cash distribution is based upon the degree of financial success of the enterprise for the bonus period. The period varies in different companies. In some installations it is as short as one month, and in others the period is one year. There is general agreement, however, that the shorter the period, the closer will be the connection between effort and financial reward to the employees. Longer periods are selected because they will reflect more truly the status of the business over that particular length of time. For example, if a period of one month is used, the employees might give excellent performance for the entire period in anticipation of a sizable bonus. However, due to conditions beyond their control, such as high inventories or slow-moving products, the profit for the period may be nothing. With no additional reward, the employees would quickly lose confidence in the plan and appreciably drop their efforts.

Another factor of importance in the selection of the period for the distribution of the profits is the amount of cash that will be shared. If the period is too short, the amount may be of such an insignificant size that the plan itself may backfire. But, if a longer period such as six months or a year is used, the amount will be adequate to accomplish the purpose of the profit sharing system.

Deferred profit sharing plans are characterized by the periodic investment of portions of the profits of the business for the employees, so that upon retirement or separation from the company, they will have a source of income at a time when their needs may be more pronounced.

The deferred type of profit sharing plan obviously does not provide the incentive stimulus to the degree that cash plans do.

However, deferred profit sharing plans do offer the advantage of being easier to install and administer. Also, this type of plan offers more security than the cash reward plan. This makes it especially appealing to the stable workman.

---

[2] Council of Profit Sharing Industries, *Profit Sharing Manual* (First National Tower, Akron, Ohio, 1949), p. 3.

Combined plans arrange that some of the profits are invested for retirement and similar benefits, and some are distributed in the form of cash rewards. This class of plans can realize the advantages of both the deferred plans and those employing the straight cash system. A representative installation might provide for sharing half the profits with the employees. Of this amount, one third may be distributed to the employees in the form of an extra bonus check, one third may be held in reserve to be given out when a less successful financial period develops, and the remaining one third may be placed with a trustee for deferred distribution.

Methods of distribution under profit sharing

There are three methods in common use for determining the amount of money to be given individual employees from the company's profits. The first and the least used is the "share and share alike" plan. Here each employee, regardless of his job class, participates in an equal amount of the profits, once he has attained the prescribed amount of company service. Proponents of this method believe that individual base rates have already taken care of the relative importance of the different workers to the company. The share and share alike plan supplies a feeling of teamwork and importance to each employee, no matter what his position in the plant may be. Just as a complex mechanism is made inoperative by removal of an insignificant pin, so an enterprise is dependent upon each and every employee for its efficient operation.

The most commonly used method of distribution under profit sharing is on the basis of the regular compensation paid to the workers. The theory is that the employee who was paid the most during the period contributed to the greatest extent to the company's profits and consequently should share in them to a greater extent. For example, a toolmaker earning $5,000 in a six-month period would receive a greater share of the company's profits than a chip-hauler who was paid $2,000 for the same period.

Another popular means of profit distribution is through the allocation of points. Points are given for each year of seniority, and each $100 of pay. Some plans also endeavor to evaluate such factors as attendance, worker's cooperation, and standards of production. The number of points accumulated by each employee for the period then determines his share of the profits. This method endeavors to take into consideration the factors that influence the company's profits and then distribute the profits on a basis that gives each employee his just share. Perhaps the principal disadvantage of the point method is the difficulty of maintenance and administration brought about through complex and detailed records.

Criteria for successful profit sharing plan

The Council for Profit Sharing Industries has summarized 10 principles which it feels is fundamental if a plan is to succeed. These are:

1. There must be a compelling desire on the part of management to install the plan in order to enhance the team spirit of the organization. If there is a union, its cooperation is essential.
2. The plan should be generous enough to forestall any feeling on the part of the employees that the lion's share of the results of extra effort will go to management and the stockholders.
3. The employees must understand that there is no benevolence involved, that they are merely receiving their fair share of the profits they have helped to create.
4. The emphasis should be placed on partnership, not on the amount of money involved. If financial return is emphasized, it will be more difficult to retain the employee's loyalty and interest in loss years.
5. The employees must be made to feel that it is their plan as well as management's and not something that is being done for them by management. The employees should be well represented on any committee set up to administer the plan.
6. Profit sharing is inconsistent with arbitrary management—it functions best in companies operating under a democratic system. This does not mean that management relinquishes its right, and in fact its obligation, to manage, but rather that management functions by leadership instead of arbitrary command.
7. Under no circumstances can profit sharing be used as an excuse for paying lower than prevailing wages.
8. Whatever its technical details, the plan must be adapted to the particular situation, and should be simple enough so that all can readily understand it.
9. The plan should be "dynamic," both as to its technical details and as to its administration. Both management and employees—and in profit-sharing companies it is often difficult to find the demarcation line—should give constant thought to ways of improving it.
10. Management should recognize the fact that profit sharing is no panacea. No policy or plan in the industrial relations field can succeed unless it is well adapted and unless it evidences the faith of management in the importance, dignity, and response of the human individual.

Attitude toward profit sharing

For the most part, union officials have not supported profit sharing. Their principal criticism is that the technique is a "hard-times, wage cutting method."[3] There can be no doubt that profit sharing, when practiced with perfect harmony between labor and management, minimizes the necessity of a union in the eyes of the employees. Therefore, union leaders can hardly be expected to uphold and propagate something that will diminish their own personal prestige, power, and income.

Where profit sharing has been practiced by a sincere, fair, and competent management team, individual workers are enthusiastic, and wholeheartedly support the plan. Attempts to unionize plants where profit sharing is flourishing, such as in the Lincoln Electric Company, have resulted in violent worker reaction against the organizers.

A successful profit sharing program depends on the profits of the company, which frequently are not under the control of the direct labor force. In periods of low profits or losses, the plan may actually weaken rather than strengthen employee morale. Also, unless the team spirit is enthusiastically supported by *all* members of supervision, the plan does not provide the incentive to continuous effort characteristic of wage incentive installations. This is a result of the length of time between performance and reward; most companies wait 12 months and use the year's end for declaring the profits of the company. In large companies, it becomes virtually impossible to instill the team idea throughout the plant, and unless this is generally done, the plan will not completely succeed.

Perhaps the greatest objection to profit sharing that the writer has observed is the taking for granted that there will be an "extra" check received at the end of the year. The employee expects to receive it, and even makes substantial purchases on a time basis in anticipation of the added remuneration. If the company has experienced a lean year and the worker gets no extra remuneration, he does not see any relation between his productivity for the past year and the fact that no bonus was received. All he feels is that he has been cheated. Thus the whole profit sharing plan fails to engender the spirit intended.

For these reasons, any employer should be very cautious before embarking on a profit sharing program. On the other hand, many companies today are experiencing high worker efficiency, decreased costs, reduction of scrap, and better worker morale as a result of profit-sharing installations. James F. Lincoln, past president and founder of the Lincoln Electric Company, who developed one of the most successful profit sharing installations, offers the following suggestions to those companies which are contemplating the installation of some type of profit sharing system:[4]

1. Determine that the system is going to be adopted and decide that whatever needs to be done to install it will be done.

---

[3] Charles E. Britton, *Incentives in Industry* (Esso Standard Oil Co., 1953), p. 30.

[4] James F. Lincoln, *Lincoln's Incentive System* (New York: McGraw-Hill Book Co.), pp. 171–72.

2. Determine what plan and products the company will make that will carry out the philosophy of "more and more for less and less."

3. Get the complete acceptance of the board of directors and all management involved in the plan, together with their assurance that they will continue to take whatever steps are necessary for a successful application of it.

4. Arrange a means whereby management can talk to the men and the men can talk back. That means full discussion by all.

5. Make sure of co-operative action on the agreed plan of operation. This will include the plan for progressively better manufacturing by all people in the organization and the proper distribution of the savings that result from it.

6. Set your sights high enough. Do not try to get just a little better efficiency with the expectation that such gain will be to the good and expect to leave the matter there.

7. Remember, this plan for industry is a fundamental change in philosophy. From it new satisfactions will flow to all involved. There is not only more money for all concerned, there is also the much more important reward—the satisfaction of doing a better job in the world. There is that greatest of all satisfactions, the becoming a more useful man.

Conclusion

Of the several incentive plans discussed in this chapter, the standard hour plan with the guarantee of the day rate is certainly the most popular today.

Incentive principles have been applied in both job shops and production shops in the manufacture of hard goods and soft goods. The incentive system has application to direct and indirect production work and has been used for purposes other than increasing production. For example, incentive principles have been used for increasing safety, improving the quality of the product, reducing waste, and stimulating regularity of employees' attendance.

Soundly administered incentive systems possess important advantages, both for workers and management. The chief benefit to employees is that these plans make it possible for them to increase their total wages, not at some indefinite time in the future, but immediately—in their next pay checks. Management obtains a greater output and, assuming that some profit is being made on each unit produced, therefore, a greater volume of profits. Normally, profits increase, not in proportion to production, but at a higher rate, for with greater output overhead costs per unit decreases.

The higher wages that result from incentive plans improve employee morale and tend to reduce labor turnover, absenteeism, and tardiness.

Since the proper functioning of incentive systems requires the performance of many prerequisites (such as good methods, standards, scheduling, and management practices) the installation of incentives normally results in important improvements in production and supervisory methods. The activities that bring about these improvements, however, should be performed even though incentives are not introduced; the improvements, therefore, are not necessarily attributable to the employment of the incentive plans.

In general, the harder the work is to measure, the more difficult will be the installation of a successful wage incentive plan. The United States Steel Company, in its *Labor Measurement and Incentive Manual*,[5] clearly expresses the criteria for determining the advisability of applying labor measurement and incentives. The points to be used as guides for making decisions are:

1. Application should not be made unless: the work on the job is subject to reasonably accurate measurement in terms of production or units related to production suitable for accounting record, report, and verification; administration of the application is subject to audit; and administrative cost to make and maintain the application is economically justifiable in relation to the direct benefits to be realized from the application.

2. Application should be made where: work available per hour to the employee is unlimited; or the attainment of capacity operation of a significant machine or process requires the employee to perform work at a pace above normal.

3. Application may be made where performance of the available work can be increased from a lower level to an index of measured performance above 125 percent on machine or process controlled operations which do not require the performance of work at a pace above normal pace.

Well-planned and administered incentives will increase production and decrease total unit cost. Usually, it will more than compensate for the price paid in increased costs of industrial engineering, quality control, and timekeeping which may have resulted through its use.

TEXT QUESTIONS

1. Under what three general classes may the majority of wage incentive plans be classified?
2. Differentiate between individual wage payment plans and group type plans.
3. What is meant by the term "fringe benefits"?
4. What company policies are included under nonfinancial incentives?
5. What are the characteristics of piecework? Plot the unit cost curve and operator earnings curve for daywork and piecework on the same set of coordinates.
6. Why has piecework diminished in popularity since World War II?
7. How does the standard hour plan differ from piecework?
8. Why are there few installations of the Taylor differential piece rate plan today?

[5] Copyright, 1951, United States Steel Company.

9. In what way is the Merrick plan similar to the Taylor differential piece rate system?

10. Why did measured daywork become popular in the 1930's?

11. Why are there many modified Halsey and Bedaux plans in existence to-day?

12. For what reason did James Rowan design a plan that restricted operator earnings?

13. An allowed time of 0.0125 hours/piece is established for machining a small component. A setup time of 0.32 hour is established also, as the operator performs the necessary setup work on "incentive." Compute:
    a) Total time allowed to complete an order of 860 pieces.
    b) Operator efficiency, if job is completed in an eight-hour day.
    c) Efficiency of the operator if he requires 12 hours to complete the job.

14. A "one-for-one" or 100 percent time premium plan for incentive payment is in operation. The operator base rate for this class of work is $2.60. The base rate is guaranteed. Compute:
    a) Total earnings for the job at efficiency determined in problem 13(b).
    b) Hourly earnings, from above.
    c) Total earnings for job at efficiency determined in problem 13(c).
    d) Direct labor cost per piece from (a), excluding setup.
    e) Direct labor cost per piece from (c), excluding setup.

15. A forging operation is studied and a rate of 0.42 minute per piece is set. The operator works on the job for a full eight-hour day and produces 1,500 pieces.
    a) How many standard hours does the operator earn?
    b) What is his efficiency for the day?
    c) If his base rate is $2.45 per hour, compute his earnings for the day. (Use a 100 percent time premium plan.)
    d) What is the direct labor cost per piece at this efficiency?
    e) What would be the proper piece rate (rate expressed in money) for this job, assuming that the above time standard is correct?

16. A 60–40 Gain Sharing plan is in operation in a plant. The established time value on a certain job is 0.75 minute, the base rate is $2.20. What is the direct labor cost per piece when the operator efficiency is:
    a) 50 percent of standard?
    b) 80 percent of standard?
    c) 100 percent of standard?
    d) 120 percent of standard?
    e) 160 percent of standard?

17. Define "profit sharing."

18. What specific type of profit sharing plan has received general acceptance?

19. What three broad categories cover the majority of profit sharing installations?

20. Upon what does the amount of money distributed depend under the cash plan?

21. What determines the length of period between bonus payments under the cash plan? Why is it poor practice to have the period too long? What disadvantages are there to the short period?

22. What are the characteristic features of the deferred profit sharing plan?

23. Why is the "share and share alike" method of distribution not particularly common? What is the basis of advocation of this technique by its proponents?

24. What 10 principles summarized by the Council for Profit Sharing Industries are fundamental for a successful profit sharing plan?

25. Why have many unions shown an antagonistic attitude toward profit sharing?

26. What suggestions has Mr. James Lincoln offered for those embarking on an incentive installation?

27. How does job enrichment differ from job enlargement?

28. Why is it usually advisable to have a range of pay rates that are applicable to each job?

GENERAL QUESTIONS

1. A workman is employed in a plant where all the rates are set on a money basis (piece rates). He is regularly employed at a job where the guaranteed base rate is $2.20. His regular earnings are in excess of $22 per day. Due to the pressure of work, he is asked to help out on another job, classified so that it pays $2.50 per hour. He works three days on this job and earns $20 each day.

   a) How much should the operator be paid for each day's work on this new job? Why?

   b) Would it make any difference if he had worked on a new job where the base rate was $2 per hour and he had earned $18? Explain.

2. An incentive plan employing a "low-rate, high-rate" differential is in use. A certain class of work has the guaranteed "low-rate" of $3 per hour and the "high-rate" for work on standard of $3.30 per hour. A job is studied and a rate of 0.036 hours per piece is set. What is the direct labor cost per piece at the following efficiencies:

   a) 50 percent?
   b) 80 percent?
   c) 98 percent?
   d) 105 percent?
   e) 150 percent?

3. A machining job is studied by a competent time study man. Since the job has been running on the approved standard method for a short time, the operator is rated low on skill. Since it is expected that the job will be a high-activity job, one that will run for a long time with several men doing the work, the time study man is especially anxious to set the standard

right. (This is interpreted to mean that the efficiency will not exceed 135 percent on the average if the job runs for a year or more.) The rate goes out into the shop and the three machine operators (one on each shift) object strongly to the "tight rate."

a) Outline the several possible courses of action the time study man may pursue.

b) Suggest the possible results from each course of action through the several steps likely to result.

CHAPTER 26

Characteristics of a sound wage incentive system

The subject of wage incentives has always been controversial to employees, unions, and management. Industries that have assured a good living wage and then applied incentive earnings that can easily be calculated for extra or prolonged effort will find that their employees will be receptive to wage incentives. In fact, where successful installations of this nature have been made, considerable labor unrest would result of any attempt was made to do away with the plan. On the other hand, in those industries where the workman finds it necessary to work at an incentive pace to earn the necessities of life, he can hardly be expected to be enthusiastic about any form of wage incentive payment.

The majority of union officials with whom the writer has been in contact oppose incentive wage payment. The principal objection by the union is fear of reduction in personnel brought about by high effort with only a fixed amount of production of goods and services available. Another reason cited for disapproval is the effect of "pitting worker against worker." Union officials state that when one workman makes high earnings and another low, a feeling of distrust and suspicion permeates the working group, which disrupts the partnership relations among workers. Actually, this criticism of incentives is rather weak and not very realistic. Perhaps the most important reason for organized labor's lack of interest in wage incentives is covered by the union statement. "A basic though rarely mentioned reason for organized labor's traditional antagonism to wage incentives is that the more directly the worker controls the amount

627

of compensation he receives, the less need he is likely to feel for union assistance in securing higher wages, although when base rates are raised or lowered, his rates are equally affected."[1]

In the Grand Lodge constitution of the International Association of Machinists (Section 6 of Article J), the policy of this labor group toward incentives is clearly expressed in the statement that "any member guilty of advocating or encouraging any of these systems where they are not in existence is liable to expulsion." Carl Huhndorff, as director of research of this labor group, stated that the aforementioned clause had never been invoked against an individual member to the best of his knowledge; however, the Grand Lodge policy "has always opposed these (incentive) plans whenever possible as we do not feel that they work to the best interests of working men and women."

There are, of course, unions which approve of incentives. In fact, the late Philip Murray, past president of the CIO, was known to look with favor upon incentive wage payment and had expressed his belief that practically any sound system of wage payment can be made to work when a harmonious relationship prevails between labor and management.

The National Industrial Conference Board has made the following statement through its senior research specialist:

. . . wage incentive practices up to the 1939 period were used as one of the whipping boys by union organizers in shops which otherwise were free of unions. However, today the union's outlook is more favorable to wage incentive methods and related techniques of time and motion study. In fact, union officials from the local level up, advocate training in time study for shop stewards in order better to understand and explain to workers the pros and cons of wage incentive.

Most managers agree with the philosophies of incentive wage payment but realize that in view of the rapid growth of union activity, the installation within their own plants may not achieve the desired objectives.

A comparison of the relative percentage of manufacturing enterprises using incentives in the years 1948 through 1970 reveals a decline since 1948. This decline of incentive plans' installations no doubt is due in part to the attitude of some labor unions. It is interesting to note that no definite pattern of attitude on the part of international unions seems to prevail. The same international union will have some locals that favor incentives and others that are bitterly opposed to them.

Prerequisites for a sound wage incentive plan

Certainly the majority of companies that have incentive installations favor their continuance and believe that their plans are (1) increasing

---

[1] Charles E. Britton, *Incentives in Industry* (Esso Standard Oil Co., 1953), p. 55.

the rate of production; (2) lowering overall unit costs; (3) reducing supervision costs; and (4) promoting increased earnings of their employees.

However, in a recent survey of 160 companies[2] where incentive wage payment was practiced, 84 replies from managers inferred that they felt that their plans were only fair, and additional improvement could be made. Five plant managers felt that their incentive systems were poor, and that some changes must be made to warrant continuance.

Before installing a wage incentive program, management should survey its plant to be sure that the plant is ready for an incentive plan. First, a policy of methods standardization must be introduced so that valid work measurement can be accomplished. If each operator follows his own pattern of performing his work, and the sequence of elements has not been standardized, then the organization is not yet ready for wage incentive installation.

Scheduling of work must be handled so that there is always a backlog of orders for each operator and chances of his running out of work are held to a minimum. Of course, this infers that adequate inventories of material are available, and machines and tools are properly maintained. Also, established base rates should be fair, and should provide for sufficient spread between job classes to recognize the positions that demand more skill, effort, and responsibility. Preferably, base rates should have been established through a sound job evaluation program.

Lastly, fair standards of performance must be developed before wage incentive installation can take place. In no case should these rates be set by judgment or past performance records. In order to be sure that they are correct, some form of work measurement based upon the time study or work sampling procedure should be used.

Once these prerequisites have been completed and management is fully sold on incentive wage payment, the company will be in a position to design the system.

Figure 26–1 illustrates the distribution of performance under daywork and incentive as experienced by one company. It will be noted that under the nonincentive plan, the average performance of the plant was 17 percent below normal performance. It is also interesting to note that when the plan was introduced the entire force of personnel coming under the plan performed somewhere between 83 and 125 percent efficiency. It had been expected that the dispersion of the plan would be from around 70 to 165 percent.

Design for a sound wage incentive plan

To be successful, an incentive plan must be fair to both the company and the operators. The plan should give the operator the opportunity to

---

[2] National Metal Trades Association.

earn approximately 25 percent above his base rate if he is normally skilled and executes high effort continuously. Management will benefit through the added productivity by being able to prorate fixed costs over a greater number of pieces, thus reducing total cost.

FIGURE 26–1

Actual and theoretical distribution of performance under incentive and daywork as recorded by one company

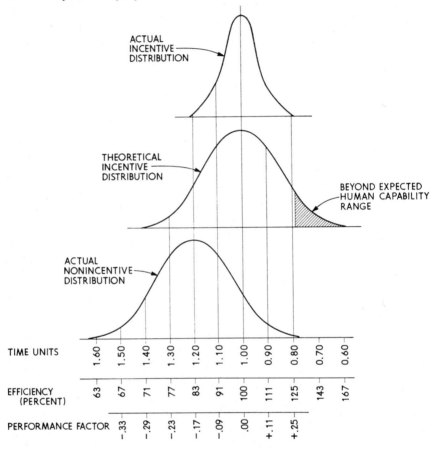

Perhaps next to fairness, the most important qualification of a good incentive plan is simplicity. In order to be successful, the plan must be completely sold to the employee, the union, and to management itself. The simpler it is, the easier it will be for all parties to understand; and with understanding the chances for approval are enhanced. Individual incentive plans are more easily understood and will work the best—if individual output can be measured.

The plan should guarantee the basic hourly rate set by job evaluation; the rate should be a good living wage comparable to the prevailing wage rate of the area for each job in question.

There should be a range of pay rates for each job and these base rates should be related to total performance. By total performance we mean giving consideration to quality, reliability, safety, attendance, as well as output. At periodic intervals, such as every six months or year, the employees rate step should be reviewed in relation to his total performance. For performance greater than standard, the operator should be compensated in direct proportion to his output, thus discouraging any restriction of production.

In order for the employee to associate his effort with compensation, the paycheck stub should clearly show both the regular and the incentive earnings. It is also advisable to indicate on a separate form, placed in the pay envelope, the efficiency of the operator for the past pay period. This is calculated as the ratio of standard hours produced during the period to the hours worked during the period.

Provision must be made in an efficient manner for unavoidable loss of time not included in the standard. Also, techniques must be established for ensuring accurate piece counts of the required quality requirements. The plan should entail control of indirect labor through measuring productivity of those involved. Indirect labor should not be given a bonus equivalent to the direct workers' unless some yardstick has been determined to justify their incentive earnings. Once the plan has been installed, management must accept the responsibility of maintaining it. Administration of the plan calls for keen judgment in making decisions, and close analysis of all grievances submitted. Management must exercise its right to change the standards when the methods and equipment are changed. Employees must be guaranteed an opportunity to express their suggestions, but the advisability of their requests must be proved before any change is made. Compromising on standards must be avoided. A liberalizing of standards already based on facts will lead to complete failure of the plan. No incentive plan will continue to operate unless it is effectively maintained by a watchful, competent management team.

Motivation for incentive effort

The methods analyst should recognize that unless operators perform at good effort, the most favorably designed work station will not result in levels of productivity synonymous with company objectives. In order to achieve high levels of productivity, in addition to good physical work center design, the conditions surrounding the work should be such so that all employees will do their best to help realize the stated objectives of the enterprise.

Some hypotheses related to motivation that the reader should be cognizant of include:

1. Work is and always has been a natural human activity. Today as always most people basically want to work and they want to achieve.
2. Almost all people want to be involved in the achievement of the goals established by their group or organization.
3. Most people will perform better if given both independence and control in their work situation.
4. Workmen expect to see a relationship between their contributions and the magnitude of resulting awards.

To introduce an effective wage incentive plan all four of the above hypotheses should be observed. It is insufficient to provide a one-for-one type incentive plan based on fair standards. When people feel equitably treated as to compensation there is no guarantee of high performance. A climate of motivation must accompany any formal incentive plan.

The reader may rightly ask, what is meant by a climate of motivation? Perhaps the first requirement in establishing the proper climate is providing a management style which emphasizes a supporting role rather than a directive role. Thus the goal should be to have all the workers feel that it is their responsibility to meet the objectives of the business and it is supervisors' responsibility to assist the workers as best they can.

Second, the goals of the enterprise should be clearly established and should be broken down into division, department, work center, and individual goals. It is important that established goals are realistic, that they emphasize not just quantity but also quality, reliability, and any other characteristic essential to the success of the business. Every workman should understand the objectives of the company and the goals related to his work. These goals should be quantified in such a manner so that every workman is cognizant of his achievement in relation to established goals.

Third, there should be regular feedback to all employees. Timely reporting should give all workers confirmation as to the results of their efforts and the impact these efforts have had on the established goals.

Fourth, every work situation should be designed so that the operator is in a position to control to a large extent the assignment he has been given. The reader will recognize that there is a considerable variation in different jobs from the standpoint of the amount of control that can be given the operator. However, experience has verified that where management has adopted the attitude of: "job enrichment is important," results are positive. Sense of responsibility is an important source of motivation as is recognition for achievement.

Reasons for incentive plan failures

An incentive plan may be classified as a failure when it costs more for its maintenance than it actually saves and thus must be discontinued. Usually, it is not possible to put a finger on just what was the immediate cause of failure for a given incentive installation. If the facts were completely known, there would be numerous reasons found for the lack of success of the plan.

In one survey, the principal causes of failure were shown to be poor employee attitude, excessive cost, product insufficiently stable resulting in high cost of standards, and allowances too liberal, thus resulting in too costly a program.

Certainly all plans should be discontinued when their cost of maintenance exceeds the benefits derived through their use. The reasons given in the aforementioned survey are, for the most part, symptoms of a sick plan, of a plan doomed for failure; they are not really causes. Actual cause of the failure of any plan is incompetence in management; a management that permits installation with poor scheduling, unsatisfactory methods, lack of standardization or loose standards, and compromising of standards has no one to blame for failure but itself.

Of course, all the requisities of a sound incentive system may be met and still the plan may be unsatisfactory because of failure to promote good industrial relations relative to the program. Employee, union, and supervision's complete cooperation must be won in order to get the team spirit which is so necessary to attain ultimate success from the incentive installation.

Bruce Payne, president of Bruce Payne & Associates, Inc., reported on 246 companies where incentive plans had either failed or developed weaknesses that necessitated revision. Three factors were enumerated as being responsible for the failures:[3]

		Percent
1.	Fundamental deficiencies in the plan	41.5
2.	Inept human relations	32.5
3.	Poor technical administration	26.0

The reasons falling under each of these divisions and their relative importance were summarized as follows:

Fundamental deficiencies		*Percent*
a)	Poor standards	11.0
b)	Low incentive coverage of direct productive work	8.6
c)	Ceiling on earnings	7.0
d)	No indirect incentives	6.8
e)	No supervisory incentives	6.1
f)	Complicated pay formula	2.0

---

[3] Britton, *op. cit.*, p. 60.

Inept human relations
- *a)* Insufficient supervisor training............................... 6.9
- *b)* No guarantee of standards............................... 5.7
- *c)* A fair day's work not required............................... 5.0
- *d)* Standards negotiated with the union............................... 4.8
- *e)* Plan not understood............................... 4.1
- *f)* Lack of top-management support............................... 3.6
- *g)* Poorly trained operators............................... 2.4

Poor technical administration
- *a)* Method changes not coordinated with standards............................... 7.8
- *b)* Faulty base rates............................... 5.1
- *c)* Poor administration, i.e., poor grievance procedure............................... 4.9
- *d)* Poor production planning............................... 3.2
- *e)* Large group on incentive............................... 2.8
- *f)* Poor quality control............................... 2.2

Administration of the wage incentive system

As has been pointed out, in order to be successful, an incentive system must be adequately maintained; it cannot maintain itself. To maintain a plan effectively, management must keep all employees aware of how the plan works and of any changes that may be introduced into the plan. One technique frequently used is to distribute to all employees an "Operating Instruction" manual outlining in detail not only company policy relative to the plan, but also all its working details with sample examples. The basis of job classifications, piece rate prices, performance rating procedure, allowances, and grievance procedure should be thoroughly explained. The technique of handling any unusual situation should be described. Finally, the objectives of the organization and the role of each employee in the fulfillment of these objectives should be presented.

In the administration of the plan, a daily check should be made of low and excessively high performances in an effort to determine their causes. Low performance not only is costly to management in view of the guaranteed hourly rate, but it will lead to employee unrest and dissatisfaction. Unduly high performance is a symptom of loose standards, or the introduction of a method change for which no standard revision has been made. In any case, a loose rate will lead to dissatisfaction on the part of employees in the immediate vicinity of the operator who is working on the job carrying the low standard. A sufficient number of such poor standards can cause the whole incentive plan to fail. Frequently, the operator who has the loose rate will restrict his daily production in fear that management will adjust the standard. This restriction of output is costly to the operator, costly to the company, and results in dissatisfaction from neighboring workmen who see a fellow employee on a soft job.

There should be a continuing effort to include in the incentive plan a greater share of the employees. When only a portion of the plant is on standard, there will be a lack of harmony among operating personnel because of significant differentials in take-home pay. The reader should be cautioned, however, that work generally should not be put on incentive unless:

1. It can readily be measured.
2. The volume of available work is sufficient so as to economically justify an incentive installation.
3. The cost of measuring the output is not excessive.

Periodic reviews of old standards should be made to assure their validity. On standards that have been proved to be satisfactory, elemental values should be recapped for standard data purposes, so that even greater utilization may be made of the time values. Thus, greater coverage of the plant relative to the use of standards can be achieved.

Fundamental in the administration of any wage incentive plan that is keyed to production is the constant adjustment of standards to change in the work. No matter how insignificant the method change may be, it is well to review the standard for possible adjustment. Several minor method improvements, in aggregate, can mount to sufficient time differential to bring about a loose rate if the standard is not changed. When revising time standards due to method changes, it is necessary to study only those elements affected by the change.

So as to keep the incentive plan healthy, the company should arrange periodic meetings with operating supervisors to discuss fundamental weaknesses of the plan, and possible improvements in the installation. At these meetings, departmental performance should be compared, and specific standards that appear unsatisfactory should be brought to light and discussed. Employees expect and should receive an equitable working climate that assures a relationship between their contributions and rewards.

Progress reports should be maintained, showing such pertinent information as departmental efficiency, overall plant efficiency, number of workers not achieving standard performance, and highest individual performance. These reports provide information that allows investigation of areas that need attention as well as those where the plan is working satisfactorily.

In the effective administration of the plan, it is essential that there be a continuing effort to minimize the nonproductive hours of direct labor. This nonproductive time for which allowance must be given to the operator represents lost time due to machine breakdowns, material shortages, tool difficulties, and long interruptions of any sort not covered in the allowances applied to the individual time standards. This time, frequently referred to as "blue ticket time" or "extra allowance time," must be carefully watched or it will destroy the purpose of the entire plan.

For example, let us assume that on a certain job a production rate of 10 pieces per hour is averaged and an hourly rate of $3 is in effect under a straight daywork operation. Thus, we would have a unit direct labor cost of $0.30. Now this shop changes over to incentive wage payment where the day rate of $3 per hour is guaranteed, and, above task, the operator is compensated in direct proportion to his output. Let us assume that the standard developed through time study is 12 pieces per hour, and that for the first five hours of the working day, a certain operator averages 14 pieces per hour. His earnings for this period would then be:

$$(\$3.00)(5)\left(\frac{14}{12}\right) = \$17.48$$

Now let us assume that for the remainder of the working day, due to a material shortage, the operator could not be productively engaged in work. He would then expect at least his base rate or:

$$(3)(\$3.00) = \$9.00$$

which would give him earnings for the day of

$$\$17.48 + \$9.00 = \$26.48$$

This would result in a unit direct labor cost of:

$$\frac{\$26.48}{70} = \$0.378$$

Under daywork, even with the low performance, the operator would have produced the 70 pieces in less than the working day. Here his earnings would have been: $8 \times \$3.00$ or $24.00 and the unit direct labor cost would have been: $24.00/70 = \$0.342$.

Under incentive effort, production performance will be considerably higher than under daywork operation, and with accompanying shorter in-process time of materials, there will need to be very careful inventory control to prevent material shortages. Likewise, a program of preventative maintenance should be introduced, so as to assure continuous operation of all machine tools. Equally important to material control is the control of all nondurable tools, so that shortages with resulting operator delays do not develop.

An effective technique often employed to control the "extra allowance time" is to key the supervisor's bonus to the amount of this nonproductive time credited to the operator. The more of this time turned in for the pay period, the less would be the supervisor's compensation. Since the foreman is in an ideal position to watch schedules and material inventories, and to maintain facilities, he can control nonproductive downtime better than anyone else in the plant.

In addition to controlling the "extra allowance" or daywork time, it is essential that exact piece counts are recorded at each work station. The piece count which determines the operator's earnings is usually done by the operator himself. To prevent the operator from falsifying his production output, controls must be established.

Where the work is small (several pieces can be held in one hand), the operator "weigh" counts his production at the end of the day or end of the production run, whichever period is shorter. This "weigh" count is verified by his immediate supervisor, who initials his production report.

On larger work, one technique that frequently is employed is to have a tray or box with built-in compartments to hold the work. The tote box will hold round numbers of the work such as 10, 20, or 50. Thus, at the end of the shift, it is a simple matter for the operator's supervisor to authenticate the production report by merely counting the number of boxes and multiplying by 10, 20, 50, or whatever number each box holds.

Conclusion

The following 15 fundamental principles are recommended as a guide for sound practice in wage incentive installation and administration:

1. *Agreement of General Principles.* Management and labor should be in real agreement on the general principles involved in the relationship between work and wages.

2. *A Foundation of Job Evaluation.* There should be a sound wage rate structure, based upon an evaluation of the skill, responsibility, and working conditions inherent in the various jobs.

3. *Individual, Group, or Plant-Wide Incentives.* It is generally conceded that standards, applied to individuals or to small integrated groups, are most effective. Such standards need to be set with the utmost care, and undoubtedly tend toward the lowest unit cost. At times, due to difficulties in recording individual production, or due to the possibilities of teamwork, group standards may be advisable. The larger the group, the less the individual response. With plant-wide incentives, some of the jealousies and transfer difficulties often inherent in group plans are eliminated, but without an unusual degree of leadership and co-operation, the incentive effect is greatly diluted.

4. *The Production-Incentive Relationship.* When production standards are properly set, and based upon well-engineered conditions, good practice has demonstrated the desirability of adopting an incentive payment in which earnings above the established standard are in direct proportion to the increased production.

5. *Simplicity.* The plan should be as simple as possible, without causing inequities. Workers should be able to understand the effect of their own efforts on their earnings.

6. *Quality Control and Improvement.* The desirable and economical degree of quality should be determined and maintained, tied in with bonus payment where advisable.

7. *Improved Methods and Procedures.* To secure the lowest costs and to prevent uneven standards and inequitable earnings, which lead to poor labor

relations, the establishment of production standards should be preceded by basic engineering improvements in design equipment, methods, scheduling, and material handling.

8. *Based on Detailed Time Studies.* Standards should be developed from detailed time studies. A permanent record of standard elemental times for each unit of an operation eliminates the occasion for many arguments. A table of basic standard times prepares the way for proper introduction of technological improvements.

9. *Based on Normal Operation under Normal Conditions.* In general, the production standard should be established by management setting up the amount of work performed per unit of time by a normal qualified operator under normal conditions.

10. *Changes in Standards.* The plan should provide for the changing of production standards whenever changes in methods, materials, equipment, or other controlling conditions are made in the operations represented by the standards. In order to avoid misunderstandings, the nature of such changes and the logic of making them should be made clear to labor or its representatives who should have the opportunity to appeal through the grievance machinery.

11. *Considerations in Changing Standards.* Except to correspond properly with changed conditions, production standards once established should not be altered unless by mutual agreement between management and labor representatives.

12. *Keep Temporary Standards at Minimum.* The practice of establishing temporary standards on new operations should be kept at a minimum. It should, in any event, be made clear to all that the standards are for a reasonably short period only.

13. *Guarantee of Hourly Rates.* Under ordinary circumstances, the employees' basic hourly rates should become guaranteed rates.

14. *Incentives for Indirect Workers.* Effective standards may be established for most indirect jobs in the same manner as for direct jobs. If the exigencies of a situation demand that some form of incentive payment be applied to indirect workers as a whole, or in groups, then the indirect man-hours should be correlated to some measurable unit, such as production or direct employee hours, so that indirect labor cost may be kept under control.

15. *Thorough Understanding of Human Relations Involved.* Finally, it should be emphasized that unless management is prepared to work on the problem with a thorough understanding of the human relations involved, it had better have no incentive plan. Whereas such a plan may be a progressively constructive force for increased production, it may also be a means of disrupting labor relations and of actually lowering production. While necessarily retaining its functions, management should take into account labor's point of view. It should impart to labor a complete understanding of the plan and patiently consider grievances, in whatever manner may be agreed upon.[4]

---

[4] From a talk by John W. Nickerson, "The Importance of Incentives," given at the Second Annual Time Study and Methods Conference, New York, N.Y.

TEXT QUESTIONS

1. What four important hypotheses related to motivation should the work measurement analyst be cognizant of?
2. Why do many union officials prefer straight daywork as a form of wage payment?
3. What are the fundamental prerequisites of a successful wage incentive plan?
4. What are the requisites of a sound wage incentive system?
5. What is extra allowance or "blue ticket" time? How may it be controlled?
6. Why is it fundamental to keep time standards up to date if a wage incentive plan is to succeed?
7. What does unduly high performance indicate?
8. What are the responsibilities of the foreman, time study department, quality control department, production department, accounting department, and industrial relations department that are essential to effective administration of a sound wage incentive system?
9. What 15 fundamental principles should be followed in order to assure a successful wage payment plan?
10. When would it be inadvisable to put an indirect labor activity on incentive?
11. How would you go about establishing a climate for worker motivation?

GENERAL QUESTIONS

1. Why do many unions object to management posting incentive earnings?
2. Should indirect labor that is not on incentive carry a higher base rate than direct labor on incentive when both jobs carry the same evaluation? Why?
3. What is the major reason that causes many union officials to disfavor any form of incentive wage payment?
4. How can the piece count be controlled within the plant?
5. How can a yardstick of performance be established in the following jobs: tool crib attendant, tool grinder, floor sweeper, chip-hauler?
6. Explain how you would enrich the position of "punch press operator."

CHAPTER 27

Training and research for methods, time study, and wage payment

From the time of the "efficiency expert" to the early World War II days, the time and motion study analyst made marked progress toward proving the necessity of analyzing work to determine the best method, to standardize on the improved method, and to establish time standards on the improved method.

Today, it is the opinion of many industrialists that World War II was won by the industrial engineer. The miracle of production was brought about primarily by the establishment of good manufacturing methods, fair time standards, and wage payment plans that provided the incentive for high and continuous effort. This area of work became increasingly important with the return to normal business conditions characterized by a competitive market.

In a survey conducted by Ralph E. Balycat on subjects found in industrial engineering curriculums and reported in the May, 1954, issue of the *Journal of Industrial Engineering*, educators ranked Motion and Time Study first in order of importance in a listing of 41 subject areas. A somewhat similar survey made 10 years later and reported in the January, 1964, issue of *Factory* magazine found industrial engineers still spend most of their time on work measurement. This information was based on the response of 250 of the larger U.S. manufacturing companies and is indicative of more than 8,700 nonclerical employees in industrial engineering. Table 27–1 presents the percent of the industrial engineer's time spent on major functions.

Today the majority of the work of the practicing industrial engineer in industry is still centered in methods, standards, and wage payments.

Independent surveys made by the author within the past year indicate that most business and industry expect that at least half of the industrial engineering effort should be directed toward work methods and measurements. It is true that the utilization of industrial engineering techniques is spreading to all areas of the modern business including marketing, finance, sales, and top management, yet the data input for almost all

TABLE 27–1

Percent of industrial engineer's time spent on major functions

		Percent
1.	Work measurement	33.4
2.	Work methods	21.1
3.	Production engineering	13.0
4.	Manufacturing analysis and control	9.9
5.	Facilities planning	8.6
6.	Wage administration	5.6
7.	Safety	2.6
8.	Production and inventory planning	2.0
9.	Quality control	1.1
10.	Other	2.7
		100.0

optimization techniques includes standard times. The importance of work measurement in such indirect areas as office activities, maintenance, shipping and receiving, sales work, inspection, and the toolroom will continue to grow.

To meet the demand, and to reap more quickly the benefits of training in this field, many industries have embarked on education programs of their own, conducted in their own plants on company time.

One might ask, "What will it cost and what are the potential savings if a methods and standards program is introduced?" The following has been the experience of the author with reference to the aforementioned question. Production under a typical daywork environment is about 80 percent of normal productivity. Thus, by establishing standards after methods have been studied, improved, and standardized under daywork operation, an improvement of 25 percent in productivity can be expected.

Of course, several items of cost need to be considered in the introduction of such a program. If the annual wages of 1 operator represents 1 unit of direct labor payroll, 100 direct labor employees will represent 100 units. Usually, one capable methods and standards analyst will be able to establish good methods and maintain reliable standards for approximately 100 employees. The cost of the methods and standards analyst can be estimated as three units of cost. In order to keep production records, make routine calculations, assist with the taking of studies, and so forth, a junior standards analyst engineering technician may be required at a salary of two units of cost. Let us estimate that inspection costs rise by two units in view of the added productivity. (This often is not the case—in fact, they frequently lessen in view of methods improvement). Secretarial help will require one unit of cost.

Thus, the total extra labor cost to introduce a methods and standards program per 100 direct labor employees is estimated at:

	Units
Methods and standards analyst	3
Junior standards analyst engineering technician	2
Secretarial assistance	1
Increased inspection	2
Total	8

The above cost estimate should be adequate for most jobbing shops with a wide variety of operations and frequent changes of products. It can be expected that costs will be considerably lower for well-standardized processes or mass-production plants.

With gross direct labor savings of 20 units and an additional administrative expense of 8 units, a good methods and work measurement program should effect a net savings of 12 units or 12 percent of a daywork direct labor payroll.

The savings in a fixed factory burden resulting from the introduction of a work measurement program may be even more significant. Since it has been estimated that a methods and work measurement program would increase productivity by 25 percent, then each dollar of fixed burden is distributed over 125 units, where formerly it was distributed over only 100 units. Thus, the fixed burden cost per unit of output is reduced to 100/125 or 80 percent of the former rate. For example, if a company's fixed burden rate is 100 percent of the direct labor cost (this is a low estimate), the reduction in burden cost is equivalent to 20 percent of the direct labor payroll.

Individual plant method training programs

Any methods training program when properly undertaken will prove to be self-supporting. In the experience of the writer, several concerns that have introduced and gone ahead with training in the area of methods have almost immediately realized substantial savings in all areas of their plants. One manufacturer of farm machinery gave a 64-hour course in methods analysis over a period of 21 weeks. In attendance were 42 foremen, assistant foremen, time study analysts, and other key operating personnel. At the termination of the course, 28 methods projects were turned in, representing methods improvement solutions that could be introduced in the plant. These ideas included machine coupling, redesign of tools and product, paper work simplification, improved layout, better means of material handling, improved dies, jigs, and fixtures, elimination of operations, adjusting of tolerances and specifications, and many other usable improvements resulting in the saving of thousands of dollars annually.

In addition to the immediate gains mentioned, the training in operation analysis and work simplification developed an analytical approach on the part of the operating personnel so that in the future they will be continually on the alert to find a "better way." They developed an appreciation of cost of manufacture, and, at the completion of the course, were more cognizant of the relationship between output and selling price.

This company, by providing the means for employee "on-the-job" training in the field of methods and related areas, has gone a long way toward assuring its place in an extremely competitive market.

Training in motion and time study

The lack of success of some time and motion study programs is in part due to a lack of understanding of the techniques by both management and the operating personnel. One of the easiest ways to assure the success of any practical innovation is to inform all affected parties as to how and why it operates. When the theories, techniques, and economic necessity of methods, work measurement, and employee motivation are understood by all parties, little difficulty will be encountered in its application. In unionized shops, it is especially important that the officers of the union at the local level understand the need and the steps involved in establishing standards of performance. Training in the areas of performance rating, application of allowances, standard data methods, and job evaluation are especially important. In the experience of the writer, the companies that have provided training in the elements of time study for union officials and stewards, as well as representatives of management, have had harmonious relationships in the field of methods, standards, and wage payment.

In addition to the informative training to acquaint the various operating and supervisory members of the plant with the philosophies and techniques of time and motion study, it is wise for industry to provide training for its personnel who plan on making this field of endeavor their life's work. Not only is it necessary to train the neophyte, but the experienced analyst should be continually checked to make certain that his conception of normal is not deviating from standard. As new developments, which are constantly being made, are recognized, the information should be circulated throughout the personnel of the methods, time study, and wage payment sections. This should be done through the medium of formalized training. Figure 27–1 illustrates a typical motion and time study lecture room and laboratory that provide a suitable place for film analysis and the establishment of synthetic standards, as well as

FIGURE 27–1

Motion and time study office and laboratory adapted for periodic training programs (Scale ¼ inch = 1 foot)

office space for the time study department which can be readily converted into a lecture room for formalized training.

It is recommended that any company that has, or plans to have, a program of work simplification or methods analysis, time study, or work measurement, and incentive wage payment, include as part of its installation a continuing training program. The devotion of a two-hour period once a week for training foremen, union stewards, direct labor, and management, will be well worth the time and money spent. The periodic verification of the rating ability of the staff of the time study department is fundamental. Figure 27–2 illustrates a group of analysts studying a horizontal milling operation. After the study has been completed, the number and length of elements will be compared, the performance factors will be considered, and the resulting standards established by the different observers will be evaluated. Frequent checks like this assure a uniformity of rating of the various time study analysts employed, and keep all members of the time study group alert and free from slovenly habits in the taking of the study.

Developing creativity

Creative work is not confined to a particular field or to a few individuals, but is carried on in varying degrees by people in many occupations:

FIGURE 27-2

Group of time study analysts studying a horizontal milling operation in order to check individual end points and performance rating factors

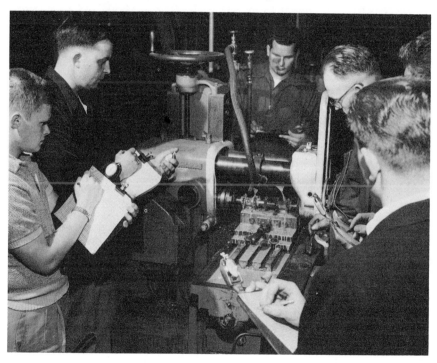

the artist sketches, the newspaper writer promotes an idea, the teacher encourages student development, the scientist experiments with a theory, the method and time study analyst develops improved methods of doing work.

Creativeness implies newness, but it is as often concerned with the improvement of old products as it is with the creation of new ones. A "how to produce something better" attitude, tempered with good judgment, is an important characteristic of the effective methods and time study analyst.

To develop creativity in the practicing methods and time study analyst is a continuing problem. Knowledge of the fundamental principles of physics, chemistry, mathematics, and engineering subjects is a good foundation for creative thinking. If the practicing analyst does not have this basic background, he should acquire it either by education programs or else through study alone. Of course, knowledge is only a basis for creative thinking and does not necessarily stimulate it.

The inherent personal characteristics of curiosity, intuition, perception, ingenuity, initiative, and persistence produce an effective creative thinker. Of these, curiosity seems to stimulate more ideas than does any other personal characteristic. One aid to development or restoration of curiosity is to train oneself to be observant. The methods and time study analyst should get in the habit of asking himself how a particular object is made, of what materials it is constructed, why it was designed of a particular size and shape, why and how it was finished as it was, and how much it cost. If he isn't able to answer these questions, he should find the answer either through analysis or by referring to source materials and consulting others. These observations lead the creative thinker to see ways in which the product or process can be improved through cost reduction, quality improvement, ease of maintenance, or improved aesthetic appeal.

One significant creative idea usually opens up fields of activities that lead to many new ideas. Frequently one idea that has application on a given product or process will have equal application on other products and similar processes.

Decision-making methods and processes

The methods and time study analyst should become trained in the various decision-making processes. Judgment alone will not always provide the best answer. The analyst is continually confronted with such questions as: "Would it be economically wise to go ahead with this process?" "Should this tool be redesigned with the probability of 0.50 that production requirements will be increased by between 500 and 1,000 pieces?" "Will it be necessary to take 5,000 work sampling observations if we are seeking an element that occurs approximately 12 percent of the time and tolerance limits are so much?" These are typical questions that must be answered, and analytical means provide a much better method than mere judgment.

To be able to handle problems similiar to these, the analyst should have a working knowledge of engineering economy, statistical analysis, and the theory of probability. More and more, the practicing method and time study analyst is realizing the necessity of a background in these fields of study so he can make the most effective decisions for his company.

Labor relations and work measurement

The importance of harmonious labor-management relations is recognized by every business owner. Sound work measurement philosophies and practice can do a great deal to promote good relations between labor and management; lack of consideration of the human element in work measurement procedures can cause sufficient turmoil to make the profitable operation of the business impossible. Management should identify and implement those conditions that will most likely result in its employees' achieving the organizational objectives.

Union objectives

To understand the relationship between work measurement and labor relations, it is important to understand the objectives of the typical labor union. Briefly, the principal objectives of the typical union are to secure for its members higher wage levels, decreased working hours per work week, increased social and fringe benefits, improved working conditions, and job security. The philosophy underlying the union movement has in the past had much to do with the opposition of organized labor to incentive systems. Unions formerly looked upon themselves primarily as fighting units and endeavored to unite workers by seeking ends common to all members. It was not to the advantage of early unions to emphasize differences in men's abilities and interests; to do this would increase rivalries and jealousies among their members and potential members. Consequently, organized labor usually sought percentage wage increases for all members of a group rather than means by which remuneration would be adjusted to the worth of individual men. The work of the methods standards and wage payment analyst came to be looked upon as means by which management sought to destroy the solidarity of workers by stressing the differences in their capabilities.

The enactment of government legislation, however, has changed the status of labor unions. Management today recognizes the union as a bargaining agent for its employees. Unions, therefore, are less fighting units than bodies concerned with the orderly negotiation of wage contracts for all their members. It is also true that many of their members will not remain content with the type of wage negotiation that concerns itself only with obtaining high minimum wages for all the group, and leaves the determination of extra rewards for the more valuable workers entirely up to management. To satisfy great numbers of their members, unions must take on the function of obtaining equitable wages (recognizing men's different skills and qualities) as well as high wages for all; in fact, unions have already done this in many instances. Methods, time standards, job evaluation, merit rating, and incentive systems are tools for assuring equitable wages and good working conditions and may soon be as important to organized labor as to management.

Labor executives, in bargaining over wage contracts, are today in an excellent position to obtain safeguards for the proper handling of the development of work methods and standards and for fair wage payment practices. They may, for example, demand that provisions be inserted in contracts: (*a*) forbidding the reduction of standard times without a method change, (*b*) requiring minimum hourly rates and payment for time lost due to no fault of the workers, (*c*) establishing grievance procedures for handling all workers' complaints arising out of the functioning of job evaluation, merit rating, and wage incentives, and (*d*) even giving labor the right to participate in job and worker-rating activities, the setting of standard times, and the determination of piece rates.

Many unions today train their own time study men. In most instances, however, these men are employed to check standard times and to explain them to workers, but do not take part in their initial establishment. However, the training the union men receive usually treats the concepts, philosophies, and techniques of methods, work measurement, and wage payment from a different point of view than that of management's time study man. For example, in a recent collective bargaining report published by the AFL–CIO for the training of union stewards in motion and time study, the following introduces the subject of time study:

Time study, which is widely used for determining work loads and wage incentive standards, is an imprecise tool and lends itself to easy abuse. Unions confronted with it must be consistently on guard against the use of arbitrary, unreasonable and unrealistic time study results.

Of the whole field of so-called "scientific management," time study is the area in which most of labor's distrust and suspicions are centered. Ever since its introduction in the 1880's most unions have opposed the use of stopwatch time study.

Labor's distrust stems from its practical experiences with time study. Problems arise both because of the inherent shortcomings of the time study process itself as well as the application of the technique in industry.

Time study is usually represented to unions as "scientific." But time study produces results which are simply judgments. They are not, and cannot be, scientific or accurate: at best they represent approximations, and at worse they are no better than wild guesses.

Time study is supposed to be a method of determining the time which should be allowed for a worker to perform a defined job according to a specific method and under prescribed conditions.

Time studies are usually made by timing workers with a stopwatch while they are doing a certain job. This time is then adjusted for such factors as delays, fatigue, personal needs and incentive factors. The result is frequently called a standard. The job or time standard may be in terms of units per hour, standard hours per 100 units or time per unit. If an incentive plan exists, the standard may also be expressed in monetary terms, such as 1 cent per piece produced.

Since most time studies are taken of an individual worker or a small group of workers, disagreements over time studies are usually expressed as grievances on specific job standards at the local union level.

While international unions can and do provide expert assistance and information to their locals, the investigation and processing of time study disputes remain primarily a local union problem.

Based on their own experiences, local union have devised approaches to time study which fall into four general categories:

1. Some locals prevent the use of time study altogether.
2. Some locals allow management to use any method of setting job standards it desires, but the locals reserve the right to bargain on the results.
3. Some locals participate directly with management in making time studies and in setting standards.
4. A majority of locals allow management to make time studies but insist on bargaining on both the methods used and their applications.

Unions faced with time study must be certain that they have complete information on how it is used by their company. In order to provide essential protection to members, this information must not be limited in any respect. It must include not only the results of time study, that is, the individual job standards, but also the plan in use by the company and the exact procedures followed.

That this information is essential to collective bargaining is apparent. Without it, a union would be unable to sensibly process grievances or discuss pertinent contract clauses.

The union's legal right to such information has been definitely established by decisions of arbitrators and the National Labor Relations Board.

In spite of this, some unions are still finding it difficult to secure all the necessary data. Some managements still claim that such information is confidential. When union pressure forces compliance, some managements attempt to restrict the information they will provide or the means of providing it.

To insure immediate availability of time study data, without question or limitation, most unions insist on a contract clause such as:

The company shall furnish to the union a copy of the time study plan presently being used. It shall make available for inspection by the union any and all records pertaining to time study and the setting of production standards including original time study observation sheets. Upon request by any shop steward or union officer, the company will furnish copies of any of the above information including copies of time studies.

Some companies, by contract, have been required to furnish the union with photostatic copies of the time study observation sheet each time a study is made.

Accuracy of Time Studies

We do not bargain standards!! is a frequent assertion by management when faced with union time study grievances.

Management claims that time studies produce facts and, of course, facts are not subject to bargaining or compromise.

If time study did result in facts, then this management position might be sound and the union might be able to bargain only on whether or not time study should be used in the plant.

But such is not the case with time study. At best, standards developed from time study are only approximations. They involve the use of considerable judgment by the time study man at every step of the time study procedure.

The actual recording of the time involves the least judgment of all, but even here a 10 percent error is expected and recognized by time study experts.

Among some of the variable factors which will significantly affect a time study result are:

1. The selection of the worker to be studied.
2. The conditions under which the work is performed during the time study.
3. The manner in which the operation is broken down into parts or elements.
4. The method of reading the stopwatch.
5. The duration of the time study.
6. The rating of the worker's performance.
7. The amount of allowances for personal needs, fatigue and delays.
8. The method of applying the allowances.
9. The method of computing the job standard from the timing data.

Inaccuracies of "Rating" Process

After a time study man has completed the stopwatch timing, he has obtained a figure which represents the time, on the average, that it took the particular worker he observed to perform the job.

This time could be used to set a standard only if the worker who has been time studied could be considered a qualified, average worker, working at a normal pace exhibiting a normal amount of skill.

If the worker observed does not meet these specifications, then the observed time must be adjusted to make it conform to the normal time. This adjusting procedure most frequently is called "rating," but is sometimes called "leveling" or "normalizing."

Rating has been defined as the process whereby the time study man compared the actual performance which he observed in a concept or idea of what normal work performance would be on the job being studied. This concept of "normal" must by its nature be carried around in the time study man's head.

During the rating process, the time study man must make two distinctly personal judgments. First, he must formulate in his mind the concept of what a normal performance should be on the job being studied and second, he must numerically compare the observed performance with his mentally conceived normal performance.

The very nature of rating opens it to abuse. By manipulating this rating factor, it is easy for the time study man to end up with practically any result he chooses.

In fact, as many unionists know, the rating factor is often used to enable the time study man to end up with a standard determined before the time study is taken. In other words, time study is often used to "prove" to the workers that a workload or standard set by the company is fair.

Time Study Men "Adjust" Findings

For example, a company may decide, without measurement of any kind, that a certain item should be produced at the rate of 60 pieces an hour or one piece per minute. Its time study man then studies the job and finds that the average time it took the operator to make one piece was 1¼ minutes. This means that only 48 pieces would be produced in an hour. Obviously, this falls far short of management's set goal of 60 pieces per hour.

So the time study man simply decides that the operator was working below "normal" during the time study and that a "normal" operator would have worked faster. The time study man then adjusts his findings; he cuts the 1¼ minutes that it took the "slow" operator by 20 percent—to come up with the standard that the company wanted of 1 piece per minute or 60 pieces per hour.

It is practically impossible for a union to prove this kind of deliberate deceit since the "normal" operator is only a figment of the time study man's imagination.

So it is easy to see that unscrupulous time study men can readily manipulate time studies.

But the situation unfortunately is not much better even when management and its time study men are trying to be completely honest and objective.

Test of Time Study Men's Estimates

Most time study men claim that they can judge worker pace within 5 percent; some have even claimed that with experience this could be reduced to an average error of 2 percent. But these claims of precision have been proved false by many studies by university researchers and management groups to determine the ability of time study men to rate workers' performance.

These studies show that time study men will, in more than half their ratings, misjudge by more than 10 percent variations in work pace. Such errors of as much as 40 percent are not at all uncommon among qualified and experienced time study men.

Specifically, the Society for the Advancement of Management, the largest national organization of industrial engineers and supervisors, recently conducted one of the most extensive rating studies ever undertaken.

The study used films of workers performing a variety of industrial operations. Time study men rated different paces of these operations. (From the calibration of the film, it was possible to get an accurate measurement of variations in pace.)

Trade unionists were not surprised at the published results of the SAM study. They showed, for example, that for 599 time study men:

1. The average error in estimating variations in work pace was 10.57 percent.
2. 59 percent of the time study men had average errors larger than 10 percent; 41 percent averaged less than 10 percent error and less than 12 percent had errors averaging below 5 percent.

One man's errors averaged as high as 22 percent. These, of course, are average errors. Some individual ratings were lower and some were higher than the averages. The SAM did not publish the range of errors, but similar studies have shown errors higher than 40 percent.

Burden on Grievance Procedure

Time study has become a major issue in union-management relations. Unions have found that grievance problems are greatly increased in plants where time study exists. Not only are there more grievances, but a greater amount of time must be spent in investigating and processing time study grievances.

One local union recently reported that in the first five months of this year, it had carried 254 grievances to the fourth step of the grievance procedure. (That's when the grievance committee meets with the plant superintendent.) Of these 254 grievances, 221 or 87 percent were time study cases.

Local Union Representatives Can Handle Time Study Problems

Some unionists have felt that time study grievances could not be handled in the same manner as other grievances. Some have felt that time study grievances could not be handled by local union representatives but that "outside" experts were needed.

While local unions may seek help in special cases, the majority of time study grievances not only should, but can be successfully handled by shop stewards. See the listing starting below under "Union Handling of Time Study Grievances," for points to be considered in handling disputes over production standards.

The most important factor to remember is that no time study is accurate. Union judgment is on a par with management's. The worker on the job is as accurate a judge as anyone of the propriety of any job standards.

Because management does not like to bargain on standards and because there is so little that is factual about time study, a large proportion of time study grievances are taken to arbitration.

Unfortunately, while many arbitrators may not be biased in favor of the company or union, they all too often accept time study as being scientific and mathematically precise. They do not recognize the shortcomings of time study and therefore are more likely to accept its results.

Despite their difficulties and shortcomings, local unions can do a good job of protecting workers against unfair management time studies. To do an effective job, however, locals need informed and alert officers and stewards. Above all union representatives should not be "snowed under" by the so-called scientific procedures and arguments of management time study men.

In locals where trouble with time study persists, the international union should be requested to give advice and assistance. Various international unions have staff members with specialized experience in handling time study difficulties.

Union Handling of Time Study Grievances

Time study grievances should be handled the same as any other grievances. The most important factor is that of getting facts.

While some knowledge of time study is helpful, it is not necessary for the shop steward or other union representative to be a time study man in order to process a time study grievance.

The union representative should:

1. Secure a copy of the company's record of the operation in dispute.
2. Make certain that the records of job conditions and job description are complete. If either is incomplete, it will be impossible to reproduce the job as it was when the time study was made, and therefore the company's time study cannot be checked. This alone is grounds for rejecting the study.
3. If the time study sheet does contain sufficient information as to how and under what conditions the job was being performed when the time study was made, then it is necessary to determine whether the job is still being performed in exactly the same way now.

    Check to see if there has been any change in machines, materials, tools, equipment, tolerances, job layout, etc. Any change should be checked to see if it affects the ability of the operator to produce at the same rate as that achieved during the time study.
4. Usually the total operation or job cycle is broken down for timing purposes into parts which are called elements. Check the elemental breakdown of the job on the time study sheet. See that the beginning and ending point of each element is clearly defined. If it is not, any attempt to measure elements and give them a time value was pure guesswork.
5. Check the descriptions of each element to see if they describe what the operator is presently required to do. Any change invalidates the original study.
6. Make sure that everything the operator is required to do as part of the job has been recorded and timed on the time study sheet. Watch for tasks which are not part of every cycle.

    Such things as getting stock, adjusting machines, changing tools, reading blueprints, and waiting for materials are examples of items most frequently missed.
7. Check for strike-outs. A time study finding is based on a number of different timings of the same job. The time study man may discard some of his timings as abnormal.

    If the time study man has discarded any of his recorded times, he must record his reasons for doing so. This enables the union intelligently to determine if the strike-out is valid. The fact that a particular time is larger or smaller than other times for the same element is not sufficient reason for discarding it.
8. Determine if the time study was long enough to accurately reflect all

of the variations and conditions which the operator can be expected to face during the job. Was it a proper sample of the whole job? If not, the time study should be rejected, as its results are meaningless.

9. See that only a simple average, and not the median, mode or other arithmetic device was used in calculating the elemental times. The average is the only proper method for time study purposes.

10. Check the rating factor on the time study sheet. Try to find out if the time study man recorded his rating factor before leaving the job or after he computed the observed times. Ask the operator who was time studied if he feels the rating factor is a proper one.

    Watch the worker who was timed work at the pace he considers proper and then at the pace required to produce the company's workload. The judgment of the worker and steward are as valid as that of the time study man.

11. Make sure that allowances for personal time, fatigue and delays have been provided in proper amounts.

12. And finally check all the arithmetic for errors.

A final note:

Most union representatives have found it unwise to take additional time studies themselves as a check, except as a last resort. It is more effective to show the errors in management's study than to try to prove a new union time study is a proper one.

A time study taken by a union is still only the result of judgment. Even when proper methods are used, they tend merely to reduce the inconsistencies of time study, not eliminate them.[1]

Company training of union time study representatives has been quite successful, in many instances, as a means to promote a more cooperative atmosphere in installing and maintaining methods, standards, and wage payment system. This procedure provides for the joint training of company and union personnel. Having received this training, union representatives are much more qualified to evaluate the fairness and accuracy of the technique and to discuss any technical points relative to a specific case.

Employee reactions

In addition to having an understanding of the unions' objectives and attitudes toward the methods, standards, and wage payment approach, it is important that the practitioner have a vivid understanding of the psychological and sociological reactions of the operator.

There are three points that should always be recognized. These are (1) most people do not respond favorably to change; (2) job security is uppermost in most men's minds; and (3) people are influenced by the group to which they belong.

[1] Collective Bargaining Report prepared by Department of Research, AFL-CIO *American Federationist,* November 1965.

One may ask, "Why is it that most people, regardless of their positions, have an inherent resistance to changing anything associated with their work patterns or work centers?"

The answer stems from several psychological factors. First, change indicates dissatisfaction with the present situation; there is a natural tendency to defend the present way since it is associated intimately with the individual. No one likes others to be dissatisfied with one's work; if change is even suggested, there is immediate reaction to expound on why the proposed change will not work.

Then, too, people tend to be creatures of habit. Once a habit is acquired, it not only is difficult to give up, but there is resentment if someone endeavors to alter the habit. If one gets in the habit of eating at a certain place, he is reluctant to change to another restaurant even though the food may be better and less expensive.

It is only natural that people as a whole desire security. The desire to feel secure in one's position is just as basic as the feeling for self-preservation. In fact, security and self-preservation are related. Most workmen prefer job security over high wages when choosing a place to work.

To the workman, all work relating to methods and standards will result in either a change or an effort to increase productivity. The immediate and understandable reaction is to believe that if production goes up, the demand will be filled in a shorter period; and without demand, there will be fewer jobs.

The solution to the problem of job security lies principally in the sincerity of the management leadership. When methods improvement results in job displacement, management has the responsibility to make an honest effort to relocate those who have been displaced. This may include provision for retraining. Some companies have gone so far as to guarantee that no one will lose his employment as a result of methods improvement. Since the labor turnover rate is usually greater than the improvement rate, the natural attrition through resignation and retirement can usually absorb any displacement of people as a result of improvement.

The sociological impact of "behaving as the group wants him to behave" also has an influence on change. Frequently the worker, as a union member, feels that he is expected to resist any change that has been instituted by management; accordingly, he is reluctant to cooperate with any contemplated changes resulting from methods and standards work. Another factor is the resistance toward anybody who is not part of one's own group. Just as any parent would take offense to a neighbor suggesting that his son part his hair on the other side, so does a member of a group take offense when a member of another group suggests changes. A company represents a "group" which has several groups within its major boundaries. These individual groups respond to basic sociological laws. Change proposed by someone outside one's own group is often received with open hostility. The workman associates himself with a different group than that of the practitioner of methods and standards and so will tend to resist any effort the analyst makes that might interfere with the usual performance within his group.

The human approach

The method of approach and behavior of the practitioners of methods engineering and work measurement is the real key to good management-labor relations and the success of the whole production system. Too many of the men practicing in this field of work today fail to have an adequate appreciation of the importance of the human approach. When doing methods work, the analyst should take time to talk to the operator and get his ideas and reactions. The work progresses so much more smoothly and effectively if the operator becomes a "part of the team." However, this he can not do and will not do unless he is asked to "join the team." The operator is closer to the individual operations than anyone else and usually has more specific knowledge relative to operation details than anyone else. It is important that his knowledge be realized, respected and utilized. Operator suggestions should be gratefully received; if they are practical and worthwhile they should be introduced as soon as possible. If they cannot be used at the present, a complete explanation should be given as to why they cannot be used.

The analyst should take time to explain all facets of the methods-standards work being undertaken, and point out how this work improves the competitive situation of the company. It can be brought out that both the security of a business and the job security of its employees depend on the business' earning a profit.

As the work progresses, the analyst should keep the operator informed on the probable results of the analysis; he should take time to answer questions related to any personal problems the operator may have in relation to his work or contemplated changes in the work.

The analyst at all times should think of himself as being in the place of the workman and then use the approach he would like to be used toward himself if he were the operator. Friendliness, courtesy, cheerfulness, respect, tempered with firmness are the human characteristics that must be practiced if one is going to be successful in this work. In short the "golden rule" must be applied.

To summarize the "how" of the human approach it would be well to consider Dale Carnegie's advice on handling people, making people like you, influencing the thinking of people, and ways of changing people. Mr. Carnegie summarizes as follows:

A. Fundamental techniques in handling people.
   1. Instead of condemning (criticizing) people, try to understand them.

2. Remember that all people *need* to feel important, therefore, try to figure out the other man's good points. Forget flattery; give honest, sincere appreciation.

3. Remember that all people are interested in *their* own needs; therefore, talk about what *he* wants and show him how to get it.

B. Six ways to make people like you.
   1. Become genuinely interested in other people.
   2. Smile.
   3. Remember that a man's name is to him the sweetest and most important sound in the English language.
   4. Be a good listener. Encourage others to talk about themselves.
   5. Talk in terms of the other man's interest.
   6. Make the other person feel important—and do it sincerely.

C. Twelve ways to win people to your way of thinking.
   1. The only way to get the best of an argument is to avoid it.
   2. Show respect for the other man's opinions. Never tell a man he is wrong.
   3. If you are wrong, admit it quickly and emphatically.
   4. Begin in a friendly way.
   5. Get the other person saying yes, immediately.
   6. Let the other man feel that the idea is his.
   7. Let the other man do a great deal of the talking.
   8. Try honestly to see things from the other person's point of view.
   9. Be sympathetic with the other person's ideas and desires.
   10. Appeal to the nobler motives.
   11. Dramatize your ideas.
   12. Throw down a challenge.

D. Nine ways to change people without giving offense or arousing resentment.
   1. Begin with praise and honest appreciation.
   2. Call attention to people's mistakes indirectly.
   3. Talk about your own mistakes before criticizing the other person.
   4. Ask questions instead of giving direct orders.
   5. Let the other man save his face.
   6. Praise the slightest improvement and praise every improvement. Be hearty in your approbation and lavish in your praise.
   7. Give the other person a fine reputation to live up to.
   8. Use encouragement. Make the fault seem easy to correct.
   9. Make the other person happy about doing the thing you suggest.

Research in methods, time study, and wage payment

The reader of this text should have recognized that many of the techniques presented are not based on a scientific method but are based on judgment, experience, and iterative methods. This is not because of choice on the part of the industrial engineer associated with methods, time study, and wage payment, but because the technology does not exist today to provide a scientific method for many aspects of this work. The techniques described in this text have been proven in countless instances; they can and do perform acceptable solutions, and have contributed significantly to the economy of the country. However, there is no doubt that many of the aforementioned techniques can be improved. In particular, the following areas are in need of more research so that objective, quantitative methods can be employed, thus assuring that judgment, bias, and favoritism cannot influence solutions to problems in such areas:

Methods
1. Man and machine relationships where arrival and service times are not characteristic of typical distributions.
2. Production and assembly line balancing.
3. Human capabilities—mental and physical. The effect of age, sex, physical structure, intelligence, and manual dexterity on worker performance.
4. Human behavior patterns. The effect of education, home life, social groups, and such on worker output.
5. Environmental factors. The effect of working conditions—such as noise, temperament, humidity—on worker output.

Time Study
1. Allowances:
   a) Fatigue. The influence of environmental factors and different work situations.
2. Appropriate time to take the time study.
3. Learning curves. Their shape for different work situations.
4. Performance rating. Development of an objective method that gives consistent, reliable results.
5. Fundamental motion data:
   a) The additivity of fundamental data.
   b) Time required for combined motions.
   c) More data on body motions.

Wage Payment
1. Job evaluation. More objective means of determining job worth.
2. Nonfinancial incentives.
   a) Human wants, reasons for motivation, and so on.

Methods

Although simulation techniques, such as "Monte Carlo," provide a solution to man and machine systems studies where the systems are too unique in light of existing mathematical models, the solution may not be optimum. Past records are used as a basis for probability distributions, and this procedure alone can introduce data where the reliability may be questioned. The assignment of a random number to a block of time can be questioned also. The size of the block of time and the point within the block of time where the event (work stoppage, delivery, and so forth) occurs is a point of concern.

The classical assembly line balancing problem does not provide usable solutions in most real life situations. Some of our most advanced industries still sort decks of cards, each card representing a standard for an operation, until a satisfactory balance has been determined by manual means. The General Electric Company, in its publication "Assembly Line Balancing," states: "There is no question but what a capable methods and time standards technician can improve on any computer-generated assignment by a few percentage points. Our goal should be to give him a very good base, much better on the average than he could do manually, from which he can make intelligent and effective improvements." This statement speaks for itself as to the need for more analytical work in this area.

The standardization of the established method advocated by practitioners of Methods, Standards, and Wage Payment is certainly not in agreement with many psychologists. The question arises as to what extent the operations of the man-machine system can be divided, and the job resynthesized and standardized for use by every individual.

The motivation of the worker as affected by the sociological system of the community and the plant may influence a constant cause system.

Much research needs to be done in job placement, where job requirements are matched with the inherent capabilities of employees. We all know of excellent milers who would come in last in a respectable hundred-yard dash. We also know first-class baseball players who would be most awkward on the basketball court. Many industrial assignments bear no information as to what human capabilities are suited for the work.

Time study

With the current technology available today it is not feasible to develop a practical, deterministic, mathematical structure of the work measurement problem. The complexity of the mathematical relationships, involving variables as yet unmeasured, is so great that mathematics has not yet developed the power to treat a phenomenon as complex as work measurement.

In William Gomberg's text *A Trade Union's Analysis of Time Study*, four sources of variation that influence the output of the operator are mentioned: mechanical, physiological, psychological, and sociological. It is Mr. Gomberg's contention that these sources of variation result in a variable chance cause system which cannot be stabilized sufficiently to be measured over an extended period. Since present-day work measurement is a sampling approach in which the time for a unit of work is assumed to be a random variable, it may be that the effect of all sources of variation results in a variable chance cause system which cannot be stabilized sufficiently to be measured accurately over an extended period.

For example, such mechanical effects as temperature, light, heat, humidity, and noise are suspected of affecting the fatigue accumulation of the worker, but little is known of the effect of fatigue on the constant chance cause system. Fatigue, a primary source of physiological variation, has been a stumbling block, as no satisfactory method of measurement has yet been found. Much experimentation in an effort to relate fatigue to physical output has not been completely successful. Some researchers[2] have tried to relate fatigue with Kefosteriod excretion, with some degree of success. Some manufacturing concerns (Du Pont and Eli Lilly) are endeavoring to correlate fatigue of different jobs through the measurement of energy consumed. This is done by measuring the heartbeat and correlating the heart rate with the oxygen consumption. Studies have indicated that the average man should expend no more than 2,500 calories during an eight-hour working day.

In practice, a fatigue allowance is often set by collective bargaining for the development of plantwide standards. This practice can result in realistic allowances in only a portion of the developed standards, in that fatigue undoubtedly varies with the type of operation and the conditions surrounding it. Surely, a different fatigue allowance for different classes of work should be applied.

Selecting the appropriate time to take a time study is a realistic problem. Mr. Ambruzzi[3] recommends that a criterion of "local and grand stability" be satisfied before an operation is ready for measurement. He suggests using the Shewhart control chart technique for this purpose. The local stability criterion covers continuous observations taken over a few hours during a day, while the grand stability criterion includes small samples of observations taken over an extended time interval considered to be under homogenous conditions. In using Ambruzzi's criterion, consideration should be given to the use of the learning curve. This curve is generally conceded to be exponential in form and, consequently, the stability criterion would be most appropriate to apply after the knee of the curve has been reached.

Assuming the validity of the statistical formulation, the analyst should be sure to recognize that an unknown mean performance time for productive work is to be estimated by work measurement. In general, measurement systems have three major components: a sensing mechanism,

----

[2] Hoagling and Pincas.

[3] Author of *Work Measurement* (New York: Columbia University Press, 1952).

a translation mechanism, and a read-out system. Each of these sources is capable of contributing bias error (positive or negative) and a variable error to the meaurements, resulting in the total error for the system.

Probably the most fertile field for additional research in the area of work measurement lies in performance rating. All performance rating systems endeavor to establish a "within company" concept of a "normal" rate of work. Arbitrary times for bench mark jobs, rated motion-picture films of representative jobs, the concept of normal embodied in predetermined time systems, and experienced time study technicians' concept of normal may be the basis for adopting the concept of normal for a company. Research needs to be undertaken to develop an objective means of rating that eliminates or minimizes the need of judgment on the part of the analyst. Perhaps the synthetic rating method using the monogram as suggested by the author can point the way toward more valid performance rating. In this connection, research needs to be accomplished to determine the variability in performance of successive elements within an operation.

The development of fundamental motion data, certainly, represents one of the most significant contributions of industrial engineering. M.T.M., Work-Factor, BMT and other systems provide the means to establish realistic standards in a short period of time by semitechnical personnel after a relatively short (three to six months) training period. However, much research needs to be done in this area.

The fact that fundamental motion data is not additive on certain motion patterns has been established in several research papers. Thus, more studies need to be made on combined motion patterns and data established for these patterns.

Existing fundamental motion data on body motions is inadequate. For example, data needs to be established for body motions (walking and other) under load and when performed at different angles of inclination.

Job evaluation

In the establishment of equitable base rates, more research needs to be done. Job evaluation removes some of the bias and favoritism that was characteristic of many wage payment programs prior to the inception of job evaluation techniques. However, even with job evaluation, job descriptions can be manipulated so that more or less points are assigned and, consequently, the base rate is affected. There is still a real need to develop a completely fair method for determining base rates.

There is much need of research in the whole area of nonfinancial incentives. What do most people really want out of life after a satisfactory wage has been earned? How can these objectives be incorporated as part of every job? What barriers are inadvertently introduced in every job through poor supervision, poor communications, and poor leadership?

Summary

The work of the motion and time study analyst influences to a large extent the labor relations within the enterprise. It is important that the analyst understands the objectives of the union that represents his plant. It is also important that the analyst knows the nature of the training that officers in his company's local are receiving. With this information he will be better able to understand the attitudes and problems of the man on the bench.

At all times the analyst must be cognizant of the necessity of using the human approach. He must always ask for and develop standards and methods that are fair to both the company and the operator.

The analyst must recognize that much of the work relating to methods, standards, and wage payment is not based on science but on judgment and experience. Consequently, he should continually be alert for the output of research taking place in the field as it is published so that he will be able to introduce quantitative techniques to supplement or supplant those that can result in inequity. He should take an active part in professional societies that are continually exploring the field in order to develop more objective techniques.

TEXT QUESTIONS

1. Outline the objectives of the typical labor union.
2. Why have unions in the past sought flat "across-the-board" wage increases for its members?
3. Explain why the union training program refers to time study as an "imprecise tool and lends itself to easy abuse."
4. What are the four approaches to time study suggested by the typical union?
5. What three points related to the psychological and sociological reactions of the operator should be recognized by the analyst?
6. What do we mean by "the human approach"?
7. What 12 ways can you get people to agree with your ideas?
8. Is methods training when conducted within a plant self-supporting?
9. Why is plantwide training in the areas of methods and time study a healthy management step?
10. Why should training in time study be looked upon as a continuing project?

11. Why is American industry more receptive to the time study analyst today than prior to World War II?
12. What order of importance does diversified industry place upon time study in the development of an industrial engineering curriculum?
13. What intangible benefits can be achieved through a methods training program on the foremen level?
14. Why should the experienced analyst be continually checked on his ability to performance rate?
15. How can a person develop creative ability?
16. What are some of the areas where research needs to be done in methods? In standards? In job evaluation?
17. What is meant by "local and grand stability"?

GENERAL QUESTIONS

1. Who should handle the training in methods, time study, and wage payment when conducted within a plant?
2. Is it advisable to provide training in the area of methods, time study, and wage payment down to the operator level? Why?
3. To what opportunities within an industry can the experienced analyst in methods and time study expect to be promoted?
4. What is the relation between work measurement and operations research?
5. Will "automation" diminish the need for the method and time study analyst?
6. What government legislation has changed the status of labor unions?
7. Why do unions often train their own time study men?
8. Would a young engineer find the work in the time study division of the CIO a challenging opportunity? Why?

Glossary of terms used in methods, time study, and wage payment

Abnormal time. Elemental time values taken during the course of a time study that are either considerably higher or lower than the mean of the majority of observations—synonym for "wild values."

Activity sampling. (See Work sampling.)

Actual time. The average elemental time actually taken by the operator during a time study.

Address. A designation indicating where a specific piece of information can be found in the memory storage.

Aerobic efficiency. The efficiency of the body during moderate work where the oxygen intake is adequate.

Allowance. An amount of time added to the normal time to provide for personal delays, unavoidable delays, and fatigue.

Allowed time. The time utilized by the normal operator to perform an operation while working at a standard rate of performance with due allowance for personal and unavoidable delays and fatigue.

Anerobic efficiency. The efficiency (ratio of work done in calories to net energy used in calories) of the body during heavy work.

Arithmetic unit. That part of the computer processing section that does the adding, subtracting, multiplying, dividing, and computing.

Assemble. The act of bringing two mating parts together.

Assignable cause. A source of variation in a process or operation which can be isolated.

Automation. Increased mechanization to produce goods and services.

Average cycle time. The sum of all average elemental times divided by the number of cycle observations.

Average elemental time. The mean elemental time taken by the operator to perform the task during a time study.

Average hourly earnings. The mean dollar and cent monies paid to an operator on an hourly basis. It is determined by dividing the hours worked per period into the total wages paid for the period.

Avoidable delay. A cessation of productive work entirely due to the operator and not occurring in the regular work cycle.

Balanced motion pattern. A sequence of motion patterns made simultaneously by both the right and left hand in directions which facilitate rhythm and coordination.

Balancing delay. The cessation of productive work by one body member as a result of orienting another body member in the process of useful work.

Base time. The time required to perform a task by a normal operator working at a standard pace with no allowance for personal delays, unavoidable delays, or fatigue.

Base wage rate. The hourly money rate paid for a given work assignment performed at a standard pace by a normal operator.

Bedaux plan. A constant sharing wage incentive plan with a high task and with the provision that the bonus for incentive effort be distributed between the employee and management.

Bench mark. A standard that is identified with characteristics in sufficient detail so that other classifications can be compared as being above, below, or comparable to the identified standard.

Binary digits. The numbers 1 and 0 (on and off) as used internally by computers.

Binomial distribution. A discrete probability distribution with mean $= np$ and variance $= np\,(1-p)$ having a probability function $= C_{n,k}\;p^{k}\,(1-p)^{n-k}$.

Bonus earnings. Those monies paid in addition to the regular wage or salary.

Breakpoint. A readily distinguishable point in the work cycle that is selected as the boundary between the completion of one element and the beginning of another element.

Change direction. A basic division of accomplishment characterized by a slight hesitation when the hand alters its directional course while reaching or moving.

Chronocyclegraph. Photographic record of body motion that may be used to determine both speed and direction of body motion patterns.

Chronograph. A time-recording device that operates by marking a tape driven at a constant speed. Time is determined by measuring the , distance between successive markings on the tape.

Coding. A system of symbols and rules that sequence the operation of the computer.

Constant element. An element that does not vary significantly in the time required to perform it when changes in the process or dimensional changes in the product occur.

Continuous timing method. A method of studying an operation in which the stopwatch is kept running continuously during the course of the study and is not snapped back at elemental termination.

Controlled time. Elapsed elemental time depending entirely on the facility or process.

Coverage. The number of jobs or the number of personnel whose jobs have been assigned a standard during the reporting period.

Curve. A graphic representation of the relation between two factors, one of which is usually time.

Cycle. A series of elements that occur in regular order and make possible an operation. These elements repeat themselves as the operation is repeated.

Cyclegraph. A photographic record of body motion.

Daywork. Any work for which the operator is compensated on the basis of time rather than output.

Decimal hour stopwatch. A stop watch used for work measurement, the dial of which is graduated in 0.0001 of an hour.

Decimal minute stopwatch. A stop watch used for work measurement, the dial of which is graduated in 0.01 of a minute.

Delays. Any cessation in the work routine that does not occur in the typical work cycle.

Differential piecework. Compensation of labor in which the money rate per piece is based on the total pieces produced during the period (usually one day).

Direct labor. Labor performed on each piece that advances the piece toward its ultimate specifications.

Disassemble. The basic division of accomplishment that takes place when two mating parts are separated.

Downtime. A period of time that is represented by operation cessation due to machine or tool breakdown, lack of material, etc.

Drop delivery. The disposal of a part by dropping it on a conveyor or gravity chute, thus minimizing move and position therbligs.

Earned hours. The standard hours credited to a workman or work force as a result of the completion of a job or group of jobs.

Efficiency. The ratio of actual output to standard output.

Effort. The will to perform productive work either mental or manual.

Effort time. That portion of the cycle time depending on the skill and effort of the operator.

Elapsed time. The actual time that has transpired during the course of a study or an operation.

Element. A division of work that can be measured with stopwatch equipment and that has readily identified terminal points.

Ergonomics. The analysis of a work situation in order to optimize the physiological cost of performing an operation.

Exponential distribution. A continuous probability distribution with mean $= \dfrac{1}{a}$ and variance $\dfrac{1}{a^2}$ having a density function $= ae^{-ax}$.

External time. The time required to perform elements of work when the machine or process is not in operation.

Fair day's work. The amount of work that is performed by an operator or group of operators that is fair to both the company and the operator, considering wages paid. It is the "amount of work that can be produced by a qualified employee when working at a normal pace and effectively utilizing his time where work is not restricted by process limitations."

Fatigue. A lessening in the capacity for the will to work.

Fatigue allowance. An amount of time added to the normal time to compensate for fatigue.

Feed. The speed at which the cutting tool is moved into the work, as in drilling and turning, or the rate that the work is moved past the cutting tool.

Film analysis. The frame by frame observation and study of a film of an operation or process with the objective of improvement.

First piece time. The time allowed to produce the first piece of an order. This time has been adjusted to allow for the operators' unfamiliarity with the method and to accommodate for minor delays resulting from the newness of the work. It does not include time for setting up the work station.

Fixture. A tool that is usually clamped to the work station and holds the material that is being worked upon.

Flow diagram. Pictorial presentation of the layout of a process showing location of all activities appearing on the flow process chart and the paths of travel of the work.

Flow process chart. Graphic representation of all operations, transportations, inspections, delays, and storages occurring during a process or procedure. The chart includes information considered desirable for analysis, such as time required and distance moved.

Foreign element. An interruption in the regular work cycle.

Frame. The space occupied by a single picture on a moving-picture film.

Frame counter. A device that automatically tabulates the number of frames that have passed the lens of the projector.

Frequency function. The complete listing of the values of a random variable together with their probabilities of occurrence.

Fringe benefits. That portion of tangible compensation given by the employer to employees not paid in the form of wages, salaries, or bonuses, such as insurance, retirement funds, and other employee services. These exclude benefits paid for by employees by pay deductions, such as their participating portions of insurance premiums and retirement funds.

Gain sharing. Any method of wage payment in which the worker participates in all or a portion of the added earnings resulting from his production above standard.

Gantt chart. A series of graphs consisting of horizontal lines or bars in positions and lengths that show schedules or quotas and progress plotted on a common time scale.

Get. The act of picking up and gaining control of an object. It will consist of the therbligs reach and grasp, and move; also sometimes includes search and select.

Grasp. The elemental hand motion of closing the fingers around a part in an operation.

Gravity feed. Conveying materials either to the work station or away from the work station by using the force of gravity.

Hand time. That part of the work cycle that is controlled by manual elements exclusive of power or mechanized pacing elements.

Human factors. Those axioms and postulates that affect operator performance that concern themselves with man's physical, mental, and emotional constraints.

Idle time. Time during which the workman is not working.

Incentive. Reward, financial or other, that compensates the workman for high and/or continued performance above standard.

Incentive pace. A performance that is above normal or standard.

Indirect labor. Labor that does not directly enter into transforming the material used in making the product, but that is necessary to support the manufacture of the product.

Input storage. Temporary storage of a group of facts by computing machine until time that this group of facts should be processed.

Instruction. A coded program step that tells the computer what to do for a single operation in a program.

Interference time. Idle machine time due to insufficient operator time to service one or more machines that need servicing, because of operator engagement on other assigned work.

Internal work. Work that is performed by the operator during the operation of the machine or equipment.

Jig. A tool that may or may not be clamped to the work station and is used to both hold the work and guide the tool.

Job analysis. A procedure for making a careful appraisal of each job and then recording the details of the work so it can be equitably evaluated.

Job evaluation. A procedure for determining the relative worth of various work assignments.

Learning curve. A graphic presentation of the progress in production effectiveness as time passes.

Leveling. A term used synonymously with performance rating. It is the assignment of a percentage to the operator's average observed time to adjust his time to the observer's conception of normal.

Loose rate. An established allowed time permitting the normal operator to achieve standard performance with poorer than average effort.

Machine attention time. That time during the work cycle in which the operator must devote his attention to the machine or process.

Machine cycle time. The time required for the machine in process to complete one cycle.

Machine downtime. That time when the machine or process is inoperative because of some breakdown or because of material shortage.

Machine idle time. That time when the machine or process is inoperative.

Man-hour. The standard amount of work performed by one man in one hour.

Man-machine process chart. Process chart showing the exact relationship in time between the working cycle of the operator and the operating cycle of his machine or machines.

Manufacturing progress function. The progress in production effectiveness with the passing of time.

Marsto-chron. A time study instrument that records elapsed time on a tape driven by a synchronous motor. Elapsed time is determined by measuring the distance on the tape between parallel markings recorded at element terminal points.

Maximum performance. That performance which will result in the highest obtainable production.

Maximum working area. That area that is readily reached by the operator when the arms are fully extended, while situated at his normal working position.

Mean of x. The expected value of x.

Measured daywork. Work for which performance standards have been established but where operator is compensated on an hourly basis with no provision for incentive earnings. (First choice.)

An incentive system in which hourly rates are periodically adjusted on the basis of operator performance during the previous period. (Second choice.)

Memomotion study. The division of a work assignment into elements by analyzing motion pictures taken at speeds of 50, 60, or 100 frames per minute, and then improving the operation.

Memory storage. That section of the computer that files or holds facts.

Merit rating. A method of evaluating an employee's worth to a company in terms of such factors as quantity of work, quality of work, dependability, and general contribution to the company.

Merrick differential piece rate. An incentive wage payment plan having three different piece rates established on the basis of operator performance.

Method. A term used to signify the technique employed for performing an operation.

Methods study. Analysis of an operation to increase the production per unit of time and consequently reduce the unit cost.

Microchronometer. A specially designed clock devised by Frank B. Gilbreth that is capable of measuring elapsed time in "winks" (0.0005 minute).

Micromotion study. The division of a work assignment into therbligs by analyzing motion pictures frame by frame and then improving the operation by eliminating unnecessary movements and simplifying the necessary movements.

Minimum time. The least amount of time taken by the operator to perform a given element during a time study.

Modal time. The elapsed elemental time value that occurs most frequently during a time study. Occasionally used in preference to the average elemental time.

Motion study. The analysis and study of the motions constituting an operation to improve the motion pattern by eliminating ineffective motions and shortening the effective motions.

Move. The term to signify a hand movement with a load.

M.T.M. A procedure analyzing any manual operation or method into the basic motions required to perform it, and assigning to each motion a predetermined time standard determined by the nature of the motion and the conditions under which it is made.

Normal distribution. A continuous probability distribution with mean $= m$ and variance $= \sigma^2$ having a density function $=$

$$\frac{1}{\sigma\sqrt{2\pi}} \exp\left[\frac{-(x-m)^2}{2\sigma^2}\right]$$

Normal operator. An operator who can achieve the established standard of performance when following the prescribed method and working at an average pace.

Normal performance. The performance expected from the average trained operator when he is following the prescribed method and working at an average pace.

Normal time. The time required for the standard operator to perform the operation when working at a standard pace without delay for personal reasons or unavoidable circumstances.

Normal working area. That space at the work area which can be reached by either the left hand or the right hand when both elbows are pivoted on the edge of the work station.

Observation. The gathering and recording of time to perform an element, or one watch reading.

Observation board. A convenient board used to support the stopwatch and hold the observation form during a time study.

Observation form. A form designed to accommodate the elements of a given time study with space for recording their duration.

Observer. The analyst taking a time study of a given operation.

Occupational physiology. Scientific study of the worker and his environment.

Occurrence. An incident or event happening during a time study.

Operation. The intentional changing of a part toward its ultimate desired shape, size, form, and characteristics.

Operation analysis. Investigative process dealing with an operation in factory or office work. Usually the process leading to operation standardization, including motion and time study.

Operation card. A form outlining the sequence of operations, the time allowed, and the special tools required in manufacturing a part.

Operator process chart. Graphic representation of an operation showing all operations, inspections, time allowances, and materials used in a manufacturing process.

Operator process chart. Graphic presentation of all movements and delays made by both right and left hands, and the relationship between the relative basic divisions of accomplishment as performed by the hands.

Output. The total production of a machine, process, or workman for a specified unit of time.

Output (applied to computer). Computer results, such as answers to mathematical problems.

Output devices. Converting results of problem solved on computer into desired form such as punched paper tape, magnetic tape, punched and printed cards.

Overall study. Recording cycle time as a verification of a developed time study standard.

Performance. The ratio of the actual production produced by an operator to the standard production.

Performance rating. The assignment

of a percentage to the operator's average observed time, based on the actual performance of the operator compared to the observer's conception of normal.

Personal allowance. A percentage added to the normal time to accommodate the personal needs of the operator.

Piece rate. A standard of performance expressed in terms of money per unit of production.

Plan. A basic division of accomplishment involving the mental process of determining the next action.

Point. A unit of output identified as the production of one standard man in one minute. Used as a basis for establishing standards under the Bedaux system.

Point system. A method of job evaluation in which the relative worth of different jobs is determined by totaling the number of points assigned to the various factors applicable to the different jobs.

Poisson distribution. A discrete probability distribution with mean $= \lambda$ and a variance $= \lambda$ having a probability function $= \dfrac{\lambda^k e^{-\lambda}}{k!}$

Position. An element of work consisting of locating an object so it will be properly oriented in a specific location.

Pre-position. An element of work which consists of positioning an object in a predetermined place so it may be grasped in the position in which it is to be held when needed.

Process. A series of operations that advances the product toward its ultimate size, shape, and specifications.

Process chart. A graphic representation of a manufacturing process.

Productive time. Any time spent advancing the progress of a piece of production toward its ultimate specification.

Profit sharing. Any procedure by which an employer pays to all employees, in addition to good rates of regular pay, special current or deferred sums, based not only upon individual or group performance but also on the prosperity of the business as a whole.

Program. Set of instructions providing the information for the computer to handle a complete program.

Qualified operator. An employee who has had sufficient training and education and has demonstrated an adequate level of skill and effort so that he can be expected to perform at an acceptable level with respect to both quantity and quality.

Queueing theory. (See Waiting line theory.)

Random variable. A chance number resulting from a trial from among the set of numbers x_1, x_2, and so on.

Rate. A standard expressed in dollars and cents.

Rate setting. The act of establishing money rates or time values on any operation.

Ratio-delay study. Making a study using the work sampling procedure where a large number of observations are taken at random intervals.

Selected time. An elemental time value that is chosen as being representative of expected performance of the operator being studied.

Setup. The preparation of a work station or work center to accomplish an operation or series of operation.

Skill. Proficiency at following a prescribed method.

Synthetic basic motion times. A collection of time standards assigned to fundamental motions and groups of motions.

Temporary standard. A standard established to apply for a limited number of pieces or limited period of time so as to account for the newness of the work or some unusual job condition.

Transmission. Facility of transmission of nerve impulses across the motor end plate in the muscle fiber.

Unavoidable delay. An interruption in the continuity of an operation beyond the control of an operator.

Use. An objective therblig occurring when either or both hands have control of an object during that part of the cycle when productive work is being performed.

Variable element. An element the time of which is affected by one or more characteristics such as size, shape, hardness, or tolerance, so that as these conditions change, the time required to perform the element changes.

Variance of x. A measure of expected dispersion of values of x about its mean.

Wage incentive. Providing a financial inducement for effort above normal.

Wage rate. The money rate expressed in dollars and cents paid to the employee per hour.

Waiting line theory. Mathematical analysis of laws governing arrivals, service times, and the order in which arriving units are taken into service.

Waiting time. That time when the operator is unable to do useful work because of the nature of the process or because of immediate lack of material.

Wild value. Elemental time values taken during a time study that are either considerably higher or lower than the mean of the majority of observations. Synonym for "abnormal time."

Wink. One division on the microchronometer equal to $\frac{1}{2,000}$ (0.0005) minute.

Wink counter. A timing device either mechanically or electrically driven that records elapsed time in winks.

Work-factor. Index of additional time required over and above the basic time as established by the Work-Factor system of synthetic basic motion times.

Work physiology. The specification of the physiological and psychological factors characteristic of a work environment.

Work sampling. Method of analyzing work by taking a large number of observations at random intervals, to establish standards and improve methods.

Work station. That area where the workman performs the elements of work in a specific operation.

Collection of helpful formulas

(1) *Quadratic*

$$Ax^2 + Bx + C = 0$$

$$x = \frac{-B \pm \sqrt{B^2 - 4AC}}{2A}$$

(2) *Logarithms*

$$\log ab = \log a + \log b$$
$$\log \frac{a}{b} = \log a - \log b$$
$$\log a^n = n \log a$$
$$\log \sqrt[n]{a} = \frac{1}{n} \log a$$
$$\log 1 = 0$$
$$\log_a a = 1$$

(3) *Binomial theorem*

$$(a + b)^n = a^n + na^{n-1}b + \frac{n(n - 1)}{2} a^{n-2}b^2 + \frac{n(n - 1)(n - 2)}{3} a^{n-3}b^3 + \cdots$$

(4) *Circle*

$$\text{Circumference} = 2\pi r$$
$$\text{Area} = \pi r^2$$

(5) *Prism*

$$\text{Volume} = Ba$$

(6) *Pyramid*

$$\text{Volume} = \tfrac{1}{3}Ba$$

674

(7) *Right circular cylinder*

$$\text{Volume} = \pi r^2 a$$
$$\text{Lateral surface} = 2\pi r a$$
$$\text{Total surface} = 2\pi r(r + a)$$

(8) *Right circular cone*

$$\text{Volume} = \tfrac{1}{3}\pi r^2 a$$
$$\text{Lateral surface} = \pi r s$$
$$\text{Total surface} = \pi r(r + s)$$

(9) *Sphere*

$$\text{Volume} = \tfrac{4}{3}\pi r^3$$
$$\text{Surface} = 4\pi r^2$$

(10) *Frustrum of a right circular cone*

$$\text{Volume} = \tfrac{1}{3}\pi a(R^2 + r^2 + Rr)$$
$$\text{Lateral surface} = \pi s(R + r)$$

(11) *Measurement of angles*

$$1 \text{ degree} = \frac{\pi}{180} = .0174 \text{ radians}$$
$$1 \text{ radian} = 57.29 \text{ degrees}$$

(12) *Trigonometrical functions*

Right triangles:

The sine of the angle A is the quotient of the opposite side divided by the hypotenuse. $\text{Sin } A = \dfrac{a}{c}$.

The tangent of the angle A is the quotient of the opposite side divided by the adjacent side. $\text{Tan } A = \dfrac{a}{b}$.

The secant of the angle A is the quotient of the hypotenuse divided by the adjacent side. $\text{Sec } A = \dfrac{c}{b}$.

The cosine, cotangent, and cosecant of an angle are respectively the sine, tangent, and secant of the complement of that angle.

Law of sines

$$\frac{a}{\sin A} = \frac{b}{\sin B} = \frac{c}{\sin C}$$

Law of cosines

$$a^2 = b^2 + c^2 - 2bc \cos A$$

(13) *Equation of straight lines*

Slope—intercept form

$$y = mx + b$$

intercept form

$$\frac{x}{a} + \frac{y}{b} = 1$$

Special tables

TABLE A3–1

Natural sines and tangents

Angle	Sin	Tan	Cot	Cos	
0	0.0000	0.0000	∞	1.0000	**90**
1	0.0175	0.0175	57.2900	0.9998	**89**
2	0.0349	0.0349	28.6363	0.9994	**88**
3	0.0523	0.0524	19.0811	0.9986	**87**
4	0.0698	0.0699	14.3007	0.9976	**86**
5	0.0872	0.0875	11.4301	0.9962	**85**
6	0.1045	0.1051	9.5144	0.9945	**84**
7	0.1219	0.1228	8.1443	0.9925	**83**
8	0.1392	0.1405	7.1154	0.9903	**82**
9	0.1564	0.1584	6.3138	0.9877	**81**
10	0.1736	0.1763	5.6713	0.9848	**80**
11	0.1908	0.1944	5.1446	0.9816	**79**
12	0.2079	0.2126	4.7046	0.9781	**78**
13	0.2250	0.2309	4.3315	0.9744	**77**
14	0.2419	0.2493	4.0108	0.9703	**76**
15	0.2588	0.2679	3.7321	0.9659	**75**
16	0.2756	0.2867	3.4874	0.9613	**74**
17	0.2924	0.3057	3.2709	0.9563	**73**
18	0.3090	0.3249	3.0777	0.9511	**72**
19	0.3256	0.3443	2.9042	0.9455	**71**
20	0.3420	0.3640	2.7475	0.9397	**70**
21	0.3584	0.3839	2.6051	0.9336	**69**
22	0.3746	0.4040	2.4751	0.9272	**68**
23	0.3907	0.4245	2.3559	0.9205	**67**
24	0.4067	0.4452	2.2460	0.9135	**66**
25	0.4226	0.4663	2.1445	0.9063	**65**
26	0.4384	0.4877	2.0503	0.8988	**64**
27	0.4540	0.5095	1.9626	0.8910	**63**
28	0.4695	0.5317	1.8807	0.8829	**62**
29	0.4848	0.5543	1.8040	0.8746	**61**
30	0.5000	0.5774	1.7321	0.8660	**60**
31	0.5150	0.6009	1.6643	0.8572	**59**
32	0.5299	0.6249	1.6003	0.8480	**58**
33	0.5446	0.6494	1.5399	0.8387	**57**
34	0.5592	0.6745	1.4826	0.8290	**56**
35	0.5736	0.7002	1.4281	0.8192	**55**
36	0.5878	0.7265	1.3764	0.8090	**54**
37	0.6018	0.7536	1.3270	0.7986	**53**
38	0.6157	0.7813	1.2799	0.7880	**52**
39	0.6293	0.8098	1.2349	0.7771	**51**
40	0.6428	0.8391	1.1918	0.7660	**50**
41	0.6561	0.8693	1.1504	0.7547	**49**
42	0.6691	0.9004	1.1106	0.7431	**48**
43	0.6820	0.9325	1.0724	0.7314	**47**
44	0.6947	0.9657	1.0355	0.7193	**46**
45	0.7071	1.0000	1.0000	0.7071	**45**
	Cos	Cot	Tan	Sin	Angle

TABLE A3–2

Areas of the normal curve

z	Area	z	Area
−3.0	.0013	0.1	.5398
−2.9	.0019	0.2	.5793
−2.8	.0026	0.3	.6179
−2.7	.0035	0.4	.6554
−2.6	.0047	0.5	.6915
−2.5	.0062	0.6	.7257
−2.4	.0082	0.7	.7580
−2.3	.0107	0.8	.7881
−2.2	.0139	0.9	.8159
−2.1	.0179	1.0	.8413
−2.0	.0228	1.1	.8643
−1.9	.0287	1.2	.8849
−1.8	.0359	1.3	.9032
−1.7	.0446	1.4	.9192
−1.6	.0548	1.5	.9332
−1.5	.0668	1.6	.9452
−1.4	.0808	1.7	.9554
−1.3	.0968	1.8	.9641
−1.2	.1151	1.9	.9713
−1.1	.1357	2.0	.9772
−1.0	.1587	2.1	.9821
−0.9	.1841	2.2	.9861
−0.8	.2119	2.3	.9893
−0.7	.2420	2.4	.9918
−0.6	.2741	2.5	.9938
−0.5	.3085	2.6	.9953
−0.4	.3446	2.7	.9965
−0.3	.3821	2.8	.9974
−0.2	.4207	2.9	.9981
−0.1	.4602	3.0	.9987
0.0	.5000		

Above table tabularizes $P(z)$ where

$$P(z) = \int_{-\infty}^{z} \frac{1}{\sqrt{2\pi}} e^{-\frac{z^2}{2}} \, dz$$

$$\text{and } z = \frac{x - u}{\sigma}$$

TABLE A3–3

Percentage points of the *t* distribution* (probabilities refer to the sum of the two tail areas. For a single tail divide the probability by 2)

Probability (*P*).

n	·9	·8	·7	·6	·5	·4	·3	·2	·1	·05	·02	·01	·001
1	·158	·325	·510	·727	1·000	1·376	1·963	3·078	6·314	12·706	31·821	63·657	636·619
2	·142	·289	·445	·617	·816	1·061	1·386	1·886	2·920	4·303	6·965	9·925	31·598
3	·137	·277	·424	·584	·765	·978	1·250	1·638	2·353	3·182	4·541	5·841	12·941
4	·134	·271	·414	·569	·741	·941	1·190	1·533	2·132	2·776	3·747	4·604	8·610
5	·132	·267	·408	·559	·727	·920	1·156	1·476	2·015	2·571	3·365	4·032	6·859
6	·131	·265	·404	·553	·718	·906	1·134	1·440	1·943	2·447	3·143	3·707	5·959
7	·130	·263	·402	·549	·711	·896	1·119	1·415	1·895	2·365	2·998	3·499	5·405
8	·130	·262	·399	·546	·706	·889	1·108	1·397	1·860	2·306	2·896	3·355	5·041
9	·129	·261	·398	·543	·703	·883	1·100	1·383	1·833	2·262	2·821	3·250	4·781
10	·129	·260	·397	·542	·700	·879	1·093	1·372	1·812	2·228	2·764	3·169	4·587
11	·129	·260	·396	·540	·697	·876	1·088	1·363	1·796	2·201	2·718	3·106	4·437
12	·128	·259	·395	·539	·695	·873	1·083	1·356	1·782	2·179	2·681	3·055	4·318
13	·128	·259	·394	·538	·694	·870	1·079	1·350	1·771	2·160	2·650	3·012	4·221
14	·128	·258	·393	·537	·692	·868	1·076	1·345	1·761	2·145	2·624	2·977	4·140
15	·128	·258	·393	·536	·691	·866	1·074	1·341	1·753	2·131	2·602	2·947	4·073
16	·128	·258	·392	·535	·690	·865	1·071	1·337	1·746	2·120	2·583	2·921	4·015
17	·128	·257	·392	·534	·689	·863	1·069	1·333	1·740	2·110	2·567	2·898	3·965
18	·127	·257	·392	·534	·688	·862	1·067	1·330	1·734	2·101	2·552	2·878	3·922
19	·127	·257	·391	·533	·688	·861	1·066	1·328	1·729	2·093	2·539	2·861	3·883
20	·127	·257	·391	·533	·687	·860	1·064	1·325	1·725	2·086	2·528	2·845	3·850
21	·127	·257	·391	·532	·686	·859	1·063	1·323	1·721	2·080	2·518	2·831	3·819
22	·127	·256	·390	·532	·686	·858	1·061	1·321	1·717	2·074	2·508	2·819	3·792
23	·127	·256	·390	·532	·685	·858	1·060	1·319	1·714	2·069	2·500	2·807	3·767
24	·127	·256	·390	·531	·685	·857	1·059	1·318	1·711	2·064	2·492	2·797	3·745
25	·127	·256	·390	·531	·684	·856	1·058	1·316	1·708	2·060	2·485	2·787	3·725
26	·127	·256	·390	·531	·684	·856	1·058	1·315	1·706	2·056	2·479	2·779	3·707
27	·127	·256	·389	·531	·684	·855	1·057	1·314	1·703	2·052	2·473	2·771	3·690
28	·127	·256	·389	·530	·683	·855	1·056	1·313	1·701	2·048	2·467	2·763	3·674
29	·127	·256	·389	·530	·683	·854	1·055	1·311	1·699	2·045	2·462	2·756	3·659
30	·127	·256	·389	·530	·683	·854	1·055	1·310	1·697	2·042	2·457	2·750	3·646
40	·126	·255	·388	·529	·681	·851	1·050	1·303	1·684	2·021	2·423	2·704	3·551
60	·126	·254	·387	·527	·679	·848	1·046	1·296	1·671	2·000	2·390	2·660	3·460
120	·126	·254	·386	·526	·677	·845	1·041	1·289	1·658	1·980	2·358	2·617	3·373
∞	·126	·253	·385	·524	·674	·842	1·036	1·282	1·645	1·960	2·326	2·576	3·291

* Reprinted from Table III of R. A. Fisher and F. Yates, *Statistical Tables for Biological, Agricultural and Medical Research* published by Oliver & Boyd, Ltd., Edinburgh, by permission of the authors and publishers.

TABLE A3–4

Random numbers III*

22 17 68 65 84	68 95 23 92 35	87 02 22 57 51	61 09 43 95 06	58 24 82 03 47
19 36 27 59 46	13 79 93 37 55	39 77 32 77 09	85 52 05 30 62	47 83 51 62 74
16 77 23 02 77	09 61 87 25 21	28 06 24 25 93	16 71 13 59 78	23 05 47 47 25
78 43 76 71 61	20 44 90 32 64	97 67 63 99 61	46 38 03 93 22	69 81 21 99 21
03 28 28 26 08	73 37 32 04 05	69 30 16 09 05	88 69 58 28 99	35 07 44 75 47
93 22 53 64 39	07 10 63 76 35	87 03 04 79 88	08 13 13 85 51	55 34 57 72 69
78 76 58 54 74	92 38 70 96 92	52 06 79 79 45	82 63 18 27 44	69 66 92 19 09
23 68 35 26 00	99 53 93 61 28	52 70 05 48 34	56 65 05 61 86	90 92 10 70 80
15 39 25 70 99	93 86 52 77 65	15 33 59 05 28	22 87 26 07 47	86 96 98 29 06
58 71 96 30 24	18 46 23 34 27	85 13 99 24 44	49 18 09 79 49	74 16 32 23 02
57 35 27 33 72	24 53 63 94 09	41 10 76 47 91	44 04 95 49 66	39 60 04 59 81
48 50 86 54 48	22 06 34 72 52	82 21 15 65 20	33 29 94 71 11	15 91 29 12 03
61 96 48 95 03	07 16 39 33 66	98 56 10 56 79	77 21 30 27 12	90 49 22 23 62
36 93 89 41 26	29 70 83 63 51	99 74 20 52 36	87 09 41 15 09	98 60 16 03 03
18 87 00 42 31	57 90 12 02 07	23 47 37 17 31	54 08 01 88 63	39 41 88 92 10
88 56 53 27 59	33 35 72 67 47	77 34 55 45 70	08 18 27 38 90	16 95 86 70 75
09 72 95 84 29	49 41 31 06 70	42 38 06 45 18	64 84 73 31 65	52 53 37 97 15
12 96 88 17 31	65 19 69 02 83	60 75 86 90 68	24 64 19 35 51	56 61 87 39 12
85 94 57 24 16	92 09 84 38 76	22 00 27 69 85	29 81 94 78 70	21 94 47 90 12
38 64 43 59 98	98 77 87 68 07	91 51 67 62 44	40 98 05 93 78	23 32 65 41 18
53 44 09 42 72	00 41 86 79 79	68 47 22 00 20	35 55 31 51 51	00 83 63 22 55
40 76 66 26 84	57 99 99 90 37	36 63 32 08 58	37 40 13 68 97	87 64 81 07 83
02 17 79 18 05	12 59 52 57 02	22 07 90 47 03	28 14 11 30 79	20 69 22 40 98
95 17 82 06 53	31 51 10 96 46	92 06 88 07 77	56 11 50 81 69	40 23 72 51 39
35 76 22 42 92	96 11 83 44 80	34 68 35 48 77	33 42 40 90 60	73 96 53 97 86
26 29 13 56 41	85 47 04 66 08	34 72 57 59 13	82 43 80 46 15	38 26 61 70 04
77 80 20 75 82	72 82 32 99 90	63 95 73 76 63	89 73 44 99 05	48 67 26 43 18
46 40 66 44 52	91 36 74 43 53	30 82 13 54 00	78 45 63 98 35	55 03 36 67 68
37 56 08 18 09	77 53 84 46 47	31 91 18 95 58	24 16 74 11 53	44 10 13 85 57
61 65 61 68 66	37 27 47 39 19	84 83 70 07 48	53 21 40 06 71	95 06 79 88 54
93 43 69 64 07	34 18 04 52 35	56 27 09 24 86	61 85 53 83 45	19 90 70 99 00
21 96 60 12 99	11 20 99 45 18	48 13 93 55 34	18 37 79 49 90	65 97 38 20 46
95 20 47 97 97	27 37 83 28 71	00 06 41 41 74	45 89 09 39 84	51 67 11 52 49
97 86 21 78 73	10 65 81 92 59	58 76 17 14 97	04 76 62 16 17	17 95 70 45 80
69 92 06 34 13	59 71 74 17 32	27 55 10 24 19	23 71 82 13 74	63 52 52 01 41
04 31 17 21 56	33 73 99 19 87	26 72 39 27 67	53 77 57 68 93	60 61 97 22 61
61 06 98 03 91	87 14 77 43 96	43 00 65 98 50	45 60 33 01 07	98 99 46 50 47
85 93 85 86 88	72 87 08 62 40	16 06 10 89 20	23 21 34 74 97	76 38 03 29 63
21 74 32 47 45	73 96 07 94 52	09 65 90 77 47	25 76 16 19 33	53 05 70 53 30
15 69 53 82 80	79 96 23 53 10	65 39 07 16 29	45 33 02 43 70	02 87 40 41 45
02 89 08 04 49	20 21 14 68 86	87 63 93 95 17	11 29 01 95 80	35 14 97 35 33
87 18 15 89 79	85 43 01 72 73	08 61 74 51 69	89 74 39 82 15	94 51 33 41 67
98 83 71 94 22	59 97 50 99 52	08 52 85 08 40	87 80 61 65 31	91 51 80 32 44
10 08 58 21 66	72 68 49 29 31	89 85 84 46 06	59 73 19 85 23	65 09 29 75 63
47 90 56 10 08	88 02 84 27 83	42 29 72 23 19	66 56 45 65 79	20 71 53 20 25
22 85 61 68 90	49 64 92 85 44	16 40 12 89 88	50 14 49 81 06	01 82 77 45 12
67 80 43 79 33	12 83 11 41 16	25 58 19 68 70	77 02 54 00 52	53 43 37 15 26
27 62 50 96 72	79 44 61 40 15	14 53 40 65 39	27 31 58 50 28	11 39 03 34 25
33 78 80 87 15	38 30 06 38 21	14 47 47 07 26	54 96 87 53 32	40 36 40 96 76
13 13 92 66 99	47 24 49 57 74	32 25 43 62 17	10 97 11 69 84	99 63 22 32 98

* Reprinted with permission from Random Numbers III of Table XXXIII of R. A. Fisher and F. Yates, *Statistical Tables for Biological, Agricultural and Medical Research* (Edinburgh: Oliver & Boyd, Ltd.).

TABLE A3–4 (Continued)

Random numbers IV*

```
10 27 53 96 23    71 50 54 36 23    54 31 04 82 98    04 14 12 15 09    26 78 25 47 47
28 41 50 61 88    64 85 27 20 18    83 36 36 05 56    39 71 65 09 62    94 76 62 11 89
34 21 42 57 02    59 19 18 97 48    80 30 03 30 98    05 24 67 70 07    84 97 50 87 46
61 81 77 23 23    82 82 11 54 08    53 28 70 58 96    44 07 39 55 43    42 34 43 39 28
61 15 18 13 54    16 86 20 26 88    90 74 80 55 09    14 53 90 51 17    52 01 63 01 59

91 76 21 64 64    44 91 13 32 97    75 31 62 66 54    84 80 32 75 77    56 08 25 70 29
00 97 79 08 06    37 30 28 59 85    53 56 68 53 40    01 74 39 59 73    30 19 99 85 48
36 46 18 34 94    75 20 80 27 77    78 91 69 16 00    08 43 18 73 68    67 69 61 34 25
88 98 99 60 50    65 95 79 42 94    93 62 40 89 96    43 56 47 71 66    46 76 29 67 02
04 37 59 87 21    05 02 03 24 17    47 97 81 56 51    92 34 86 01 82    55 51 33 12 91

63 62 06 34 41    94 21 78 55 09    72 76 45 16 94    29 95 81 83 83    79 88 01 97 30
78 47 23 53 90    34 41 92 45 71    09 23 70 70 07    12 38 92 79 43    14 85 11 47 23
87 68 62 15 43    53 14 36 59 25    54 47 33 70 15    59 24 48 40 35    50 03 42 99 36
47 60 92 10 77    88 59 53 11 52    66 25 69 07 04    48 68 64 71 06    61 65 70 22 12
56 88 87 59 41    65 28 04 67 53    95 79 88 37 31    50 41 06 94 76    81 83 17 16 33

02 57 45 86 67    73 43 07 34 48    44 26 87 93 29    77 09 61 67 84    06 69 44 77 75
31 54 14 13 17    48 62 11 90 60    68 12 93 64 28    46 24 79 16 76    14 60 25 51 01
28 50 16 43 36    28 97 85 58 99    67 22 52 76 23    24 70 36 54 54    59 28 61 71 96
63 29 62 66 50    02 63 45 52 38    67 63 47 54 75    83 24 78 43 20    92 63 13 47 48
45 65 58 26 51    76 96 59 38 72    86 57 45 71 46    44 67 76 14 55    44 88 01 62 12

39 65 36 63 70    77 45 85 50 51    74 13 39 35 22    30 53 36 02 95    49 34 88 73 61
73 71 98 16 04    29 18 94 51 23    76 51 94 84 86    79 93 96 38 63    08 58 25 58 94
72 20 56 20 11    72 65 71 08 86    79 57 95 13 91    97 48 72 66 48    09 71 17 24 89
75 17 26 99 76    89 37 20 70 01    77 31 61 95 46    26 97 05 73 51    53 33 18 72 87
37 48 60 82 29    81 30 15 39 14    48 38 75 93 29    06 87 37 78 48    45 56 00 84 47

68 08 02 80 72    83 71 46 30 49    89 17 95 88 29    02 39 56 03 46    97 74 06 56 17
14 23 98 61 67    70 52 85 01 50    01 84 02 78 43    10 62 98 19 41    18 83 99 47 99
49 08 96 21 44    25 27 99 41 28    07 41 08 34 66    19 42 74 39 91    41 96 53 78 72
78 37 06 08 43    63 61 62 42 29    39 68 95 10 96    09 24 23 00 62    56 12 80 73 16
37 21 34 17 68    68 96 83 23 56    32 84 60 15 31    44 73 67 34 77    91 15 79 74 58

14 29 09 34 04    87 83 07 55 07    76 58 30 83 64    87 29 25 58 84    86 50 60 00 25
58 43 28 06 36    49 52 83 51 14    47 56 91 29 34    05 87 31 06 95    12 45 57 09 09
10 43 67 29 70    80 62 80 03 42    10 80 21 38 84    90 56 35 03 09    43 12 74 49 14
44 38 88 39 54    86 97 37 44 22    00 95 01 31 76    17 16 29 56 63    38 78 94 49 81
90 69 59 19 51    85 39 52 85 13    07 28 37 07 61    11 16 36 27 03    78 86 72 04 95

41 47 10 25 62    97 05 31 03 61    20 26 36 31 62    68 69 86 95 44    84 95 48 46 45
91 94 14 63 19    75 89 11 47 11    31 56 34 19 09    79 57 92 36 59    14 93 87 81 40
80 06 54 18 66    09 18 94 06 19    98 40 07 17 81    22 45 44 84 11    24 62 20 42 31
67 72 77 63 48    84 08 31 55 58    24 33 45 77 58    80 45 67 93 82    75 70 16 08 24
59 40 24 13 27    79 26 88 86 30    01 31 60 10 39    53 58 47 70 93    85 81 56 39 38

05 90 35 89 95    01 61 16 96 94    50 78 13 69 36    37 68 53 37 31    71 26 35 03 71
44 43 80 69 98    46 68 05 14 82    90 78 50 05 62    77 79 13 57 44    59 60 10 39 66
61 81 31 96 82    00 57 25 60 59    46 72 60 18 77    55 66 12 62 11    08 99 55 64 57
42 88 07 10 05    24 98 65 63 21    47 21 61 88 32    27 80 30 21 60    10 92 35 36 12
77 94 30 05 39    28 10 99 00 27    12 73 73 99 12    49 99 57 94 82    96 88 57 17 91

78 83 19 76 16    94 11 68 84 26    23 54 20 86 85    23 86 66 99 07    36 37 34 92 09
87 76 59 61 81    43 63 64 61 61    65 76 36 95 90    18 48 27 45 68    27 23 65 30 72
91 43 05 96 47    55 78 99 95 24    37 55 85 78 78    01 48 41 19 10    35 19 54 07 73
84 97 77 72 73    09 62 06 65 72    87 12 49 03 60    41 15 20 76 27    50 47 02 29 16
87 41 60 76 83    44 88 96 07 80    83 05 83 38 96    73 70 66 81 90    30 56 10 48 59
```

* Reprinted with permission from Random Numbers IV of Table XXXIII of R. A. Fisher and F. Yates, *Statistical Tables for Biological, Agricultural and Medical Research* (Edinburgh: Oliver & Boyd, Ltd.).

TABLE A3–5

Useful Information

To find the circumference of a circle, multiply the diameter by 3.1416.

To find the diameter of a circle, multiply the circumference by .31831.

To find the area of a circle, multiply the square of the diameter by .7854.

The radius of a circle $\times$ 6.283185 = the circumference.

The square of the circumference of a circle $\times$ .07958 = the area.

Half the circumference of a circle $\times$ half its diameter = the area.

The circumference of a circle $\times$ .159155 = the radius.

The square root of the area of a circle $\times$ .56419 = the radius.

The square root of the area of a circle $\times$ 1.12838 = the diameter.

To find the diameter of a circle equal in area to a given square, multiply a side of the square by 1.12838.

To find the side of a square equal in area to a given circle, multiply the diameter by .8862.

To find the side of a square inscribed in a circle, multiply the diameter by .7071.

To find the side of a hexagon inscribed in a circle, multiply the diameter of the circle by .500.

To find the diameter of a circle inscribed in a hexagon, multiply a side of the hexagon by 1.7321.

To find the side of an equilateral triangle inscribed in a circle, multiply the diameter of the circle by .866.

To find the diameter of a circle inscribed in an equilateral triangle, multiply a side of the triangle by .57735.

To find the area of the surface of a ball (sphere), multiply the square of the diameter by 3.1416.

To find the volume of a ball (sphere), multiply the cube of the diameter by .5236.

Doubling the diameter of a pipe increases its capacity four times.

To find the pressure in pounds per square inch at the base of a column of water, multiply the height of the column in feet by .433.

A gallon of water (U. S. Standard) weighs 8.336 pounds and contains 231 cubic inches. A cubic foot of water contains $7\frac{1}{2}$ gallons, 1728 cubic inches, and weighs 62.425 pounds at a temperature of about 39° F.

These weights change slightly above and below this temperature.

TABLE A3–6

Decimal and Millimeter Equivalents of Fractional Parts of an Inch

Inches	Inches	mm	Inches	Inches	mm
1-32	1-64	.01563	.397		33-64	.51563	13.097
		.03125	.794	**17-32**		.53125	13.494
	3-64	.04688	1.191		35-64	.54688	13.890
1-16		.0625	1.587	**9-16**		.5625	14.287
3-32	5-64	.07813	1.984		37-64	.57813	14.684
		.09375	2.381	**19-32**		.59375	15.081
	7-64	.10938	2.778		39-64	.60938	15.478
1-8		.125	3.175	**5-8**		.625	15.875
5-32	9-64	.14063	3.572		41-64	.64063	16.272
		.15625	3.969	**21-32**		.65625	16.669
	11-64	.17188	4.366		43-64	.67188	17.065
3-16		.1875	4.762	**11-16**		.6875	17.462
7-32	13-64	.20313	5.159		45-64	.70313	17.859
		.21875	5.556	**23-32**		.71875	18.256
	15-64	.23438	5.953		47-64	.73438	18.653
1-4		.25	6.350	**3-4**		.75	19.050
9-32	17-64	.26563	6.747		49-64	.76563	19.447
		.28125	7.144	**25-32**		.78125	19.844
	19-64	.29688	7.541		51-64	.79688	20.240
5-16		.3125	7.937	**13-16**		.8125	20.637
11-32	21-64	.32813	8.334		53-64	.82813	21.034
		.34375	8.731	**27-32**		.84375	21.431
	23-64	.35938	9.128		55-64	.85938	21.828
3-8		.375	9.525	**7-8**		.875	22.225
13-32	25-64	.39063	9.922		57-64	.89063	22.622
		.40625	10.319	**29-32**		.90625	23.019
	27-64	.42188	10.716		59-64	.92188	23.415
7-16		.4375	11.113	**15-16**		.9375	23.812
15-32	29-64	.45313	11.509		61-64	.95313	24.209
		.46875	11.906	**31-32**		.96875	24.606
	31-64	.48438	12.303		63-64	.98438	25.003
1-2		.5	12.700	**1**		1.00000	25.400

HOURLY PRODUCTION TABLE

Showing 60% to 80% Efficiency

Sec per Piece	Gross Prod. Per Hr	60%	65%	70%	75%	80%
1/2	7200	4320	4680	5040	5400	5760
5/8	5760	3456	3744	4032	4320	4608
3/4	4800	2880	3120	3360	3600	3840
7/8	4114	2468	2674	2880	3086	3291
1	3600	2160	2340	2520	2700	2880
1 1/4	2880	1728	1872	2016	2160	2304
1 1/2	2400	1440	1560	1680	1800	1920
1 3/4	2057	1234	1337	1440	1543	1646
2	1800	1080	1170	1260	1350	1440
2 1/4	1600	960	1040	1120	1200	1280
2 1/2	1440	864	936	1008	1080	1152
2 3/4	1309	785	851	916	982	1047
3	1200	720	780	840	900	960
3 1/4	1107	664	720	775	830	886
3 1/2	1028	617	668	720	771	822
3 3/4	960	576	624	672	720	768
4	900	540	585	630	675	720
4 1/4	847	508	551	593	635	678
4 1/2	800	480	520	560	600	640

Sec per Piece	Gross Prod. Per Hr	60%	65%	70%	75%	80%
12 1/2	288	173	187	202	216	230
13	276	166	179	193	207	221
13 1/2	267	160	174	187	200	214
14	257	154	167	180	193	206
14 1/2	248	149	161	174	186	198
15	240	144	156	168	180	192
15 1/2	232	139	151	162	174	186
16	225	135	146	158	169	180
16 1/2	218	131	142	153	164	174
17	212	127	138	148	159	170
17 1/2	206	124	134	144	155	165
18	200	120	130	140	150	160
18 1/2	195	117	127	137	146	156
19	189	113	123	132	142	151
19 1/2	185	111	120	130	139	148
20	180	108	117	126	135	144
21	171	103	111	120	128	137
22	164	98	107	115	123	131
23	156	94	101	109	117	125

Sec per Piece	Gross Prod. Per Hr	60%	65%	70%	75%	80%
50	72	43	47	50	54	58
52	69	41	45	48	52	55
54	67	40	44	47	50	54
56	64	38	42	45	48	51
58	62	37	40	43	47	50
60	60	36	39	42	45	48
62	58	35	38	41	44	46
64	56	34	36	39	42	45
66	54	32	35	38	41	43
68	53	32	34	37	40	42
70	51	31	33	36	38	41
72	50	30	33	35	38	40
74	49	29	32	34	37	39
76	47	28	31	33	35	38
78	46	28	30	32	35	37
80	45	27	29	32	34	36
82	44	26	29	31	33	35
84	43	26	28	30	32	34
86	42	25	27	29	32	34

	757	454	492	530	568	606	24		150	90	98	105	113	120		41	25	27	29	31	33
4 3/4	757	454	492	530	568	606	24		150	90	98	105	113	120	88	41	25	27	29	31	33
5	720	432	468	504	540	576	25		144	86	94	101	108	115	90	40	24	26	28	30	32
5 1/4	686	412	446	480	515	549	26		138	83	90	97	104	110	92	39	23	25	27	29	31
5 1/2	654	392	425	458	491	523	27		133	80	86	93	100	106	94	38	22	25	27	29	30
5 3/4	626	376	407	438	470	501	28		128	77	83	90	96	102	96	37	22	24	26	28	30
6	600	360	390	420	450	480	29		124	74	81	87	93	99	98	37	22	24	26	28	30
6 1/4	576	346	374	403	432	461	30		120	72	78	84	90	96	100	36	20	23	25	27	29
6 1/2	553	332	359	387	415	442	31		116	70	75	81	87	93	105	34	20	22	24	26	27
6 3/4	533	320	346	373	400	426	32		112	67	73	78	84	90	110	33	19	21	23	25	26
7	514	308	334	360	386	411	33		109	65	71	76	82	87	115	31	18	20	22	23	25
7 1/4	497	298	323	348	373	398	34		106	64	69	74	80	85	120	30	17	20	21	23	24
7 1/2	480	288	312	336	360	384	35		103	62	67	72	77	82	125	29	17	19	20	22	23
7 3/4	465	279	302	326	349	372	36		100	60	65	70	75	80	130	28	16	18	20	21	22
8	450	270	293	315	338	360	37		97	58	63	68	73	78	135	27	16	18	19	20	21
8 1/4	436	262	283	305	327	349	38		95	57	62	67	71	76	140	26	15	17	18	20	20
8 1/2	423	254	275	296	317	338	39		92	55	60	64	69	74	145	25	14	16	18	19	19
8 3/4	411	247	267	288	308	329	40		90	54	59	63	68	72	150	24	14	16	17	18	18
9	400	240	260	280	300	320	41		88	53	57	62	66	70	155	23	13	15	16	17	18
9 1/4	389	233	253	272	292	311	42		86	52	56	60	65	69	160	22	13	14	15	17	18
9 1/2	379	227	246	265	284	303	43		84	50	55	59	65	67	165	22	13	14	15	17	17
9 3/4	369	221	240	258	277	295	44		82	49	53	57	62	66	170	21	12	14	15	16	17
10	360	216	234	252	270	288	45		80	48	52	56	60	64	175	21	12	13	15	16	16
10 1/2	342	205	222	239	257	274	46		78	47	51	55	59	62	180	20	12	13	14	15	16
11	327	196	213	229	245	262	47		77	46	50	54	58	62	185	20	12	13	14	15	15
11 1/2	313	188	203	219	235	250	48		75	45	49	53	56	60	190	19	11	12	13	14	15
12	300	180	195	210	225	240	49		73	44	47	51	55	58	195	18	11	12	13	14	14

SOURCE: National Twist Drill & Tool Co.

TABLE A3–8

SPEED AND FEED CALCULATIONS

FOR MILLING CUTTERS AND OTHER ROTATING TOOLS

TO FIND	HAVING	FORMULA
Surface (or Periphery) Speed in Feet per Minute = S.F.M.	Diameter of Tool in Inches = D and Revolutions per Minute = R.P.M.	$S.F.M. = \dfrac{D \times 3.1416 \times R.P.M.}{12}$
Revolutions per Minute = R.P.M.	Surface Speed In Feet per Minute = S.F.M. and Diameter of Tool in Inches = D	$R.P.M. = \dfrac{S.F.M. \times 12}{D \times 3.1416}$
Feed per Revolution in Inches = F.R.	Feed in Inches per Minute = F.M. and Revolutions per Minute = R.P.M.	$F.R. = \dfrac{F.M.}{R.P.M.}$
Feed in Inches per Minute = F.M.	Feed per Revolution in Inches = F.R. and Revolutions per Minute = R.P.M.	$F.M. = F.R. \times R.P.M.$
Number of Cutting Teeth per Minute = T.M.	Number of Teeth in Tool = T and Revolutions per Minute = R.P.M.	$T.M. = T \times R.P.M.$
Feed per Tooth = F.T.	Number of Teeth in Tool = T and Feed per Revolution in Inches = F.R.	$F.T. = \dfrac{F.R.}{T}$
Feed per Tooth = F.T.	Number of Teeth in Tool = T Feed in Inches per Minute = F.M. and Speed in Revolutions per Minute = R.P.M.	$F.T. = \dfrac{F.M.}{T \times R.P.M.}$

SOURCE: National Twist Drill & Tool Co.

TABLE A3–9

TABLE OF CUTTING SPEEDS

FOR FRACTIONAL SIZES

Ft. per Min.	30	40	50	60	70	80	90	100	110	120	130	140	150
Diam. In.						Revolutions per Minute							
1/16	1833	2445	3056	3667	4278	4889	....	....	....	....	....	....	....
1/8	917	1222	1528	1833	2139	2445	2750	3056	3361	3667	3973	4278	4584
3/16	611	815	1019	1222	1426	1630	1833	2037	2241	2445	2648	2852	3056
1/4	458	611	764	917	1070	1222	1375	1528	1681	1833	1986	2139	2292
5/16	367	489	611	733	856	978	1100	1222	1345	1467	1589	1711	1833
3/8	306	407	509	611	713	815	917	1019	1120	1222	1324	1426	1528
7/16	262	349	437	524	611	698	786	873	960	1048	1135	1222	1310
1/2	229	306	382	458	535	611	688	764	840	917	993	1070	1146
5/8	183	244	306	367	428	489	550	611	672	733	794	856	917
3/4	153	204	255	306	357	407	458	509	560	611	662	713	764
7/8	131	175	218	262	306	349	393	437	480	524	568	611	655
1	115	153	191	229	267	306	344	382	420	458	497	535	573
1 1/8	102	136	170	204	238	272	306	340	373	407	441	475	509
1 1/4	91.7	122	153	183	214	244	275	306	336	367	397	428	458
1 3/8	83.3	111	139	167	194	222	250	278	306	333	361	389	417
1 1/2	76.4	102	127	153	178	204	229	255	280	306	331	357	382
1 5/8	70.5	94.0	118	141	165	188	212	235	259	282	306	329	353
1 3/4	65.5	87.3	109	131	153	175	196	218	240	262	284	306	327
1 7/8	61.1	81.5	102	122	143	163	183	204	224	244	265	285	306
2	57.3	76.4	95.5	115	134	153	172	191	210	229	248	267	287
2 1/4	50.9	67.9	84.9	102	119	136	153	170	187	204	221	238	255
2 1/2	45.8	61.1	76.4	91.7	107	122	138	153	168	183	199	214	229
2 3/4	41.7	55.6	69.5	83.3	97.2	111	125	139	153	167	181	194	208
3	38.2	50.9	63.7	76.4	89.1	102	115	127	140	153	166	178	191
3 1/4	35.3	47.0	58.8	70.5	82.3	94.0	106	118	129	141	153	165	176
3 1/2	32.7	43.7	54.6	65.5	76.4	87.3	98.2	109	120	131	142	153	164
3 3/4	30.6	40.7	50.9	61.1	71.3	81.5	91.7	102	112	122	132	143	153
4	28.7	38.2	47.7	57.3	66.8	76.4	85.9	95.5	105	115	124	134	143
4 1/2	25.5	34.0	42.4	50.9	59.4	67.9	76.4	84.9	93.4	102	110	119	127
5	22.9	30.6	38.2	45.8	53.5	61.1	68.8	76.4	84.0	91.7	99.3	107	115
5 1/2	20.8	27.8	34.7	41.7	48.6	55.6	62.5	69.5	76.4	83.3	90.3	97.2	104
6	19.1	25.5	31.8	38.2	44.6	50.9	57.3	63.7	70.0	76.4	82.8	89.1	95.5
6 1/2	17.6	23.5	29.4	35.3	41.1	47.0	52.9	58.8	64.6	70.5	76.4	82.3	88.2
7	16.4	21.8	27.3	32.7	38.2	43.7	49.1	54.6	60.0	65.5	70.9	76.4	81.9
7 1/2	15.3	20.4	25.5	30.6	35.7	40.7	45.8	50.9	56.0	61.1	66.2	71.3	76.4
8	14.3	19.1	23.9	28.7	33.4	38.2	43.0	47.7	52.5	57.3	62.1	66.8	71.6
8 1/2	13.5	18.0	22.5	27.0	31.5	36.0	40.4	44.9	49.4	53.9	58.4	62.9	67.4
9	12.7	17.0	21.2	25.5	29.7	34.0	38.2	42.4	46.7	50.9	55.2	59.4	63.6
9 1/2	12.1	16.1	20.1	24.1	28.2	32.2	36.2	40.2	44.2	48.3	52.3	56.3	60.3
10	11.5	15.3	19.1	22.9	26.7	30.6	34.4	38.2	42.0	45.8	49.7	53.5	57.3
11	10.4	13.9	17.4	20:8	24.3	27.8	31.3	34.7	38.2	41.7	45.1	48.6	52.1
12	9.5	12.7	15.9	19.1	22.3	25.5	28.6	31.8	35.0	38.2	41.4	44.6	47.8
Ft. per Min.	30	40	50	60	70	80	90	100	110	120	130	140	150

Source: National Twist Drill & Tool Co.

TABLE A3–10

Comparative Weights of Steel and Brass Bars

Steel—Weights cover hot worked steel about .50% carbon. One cubic inch weighs .2833 lbs. High speed steel 10% heavier.
Brass—One cubic inch weighs .3074 lbs.
Actual weight of stock may be expected to vary somewhat from these figures because of variations in manufacturing processes.

Size, Inches	Weight of Bar One Foot Long, Lbs.					
	Steel			Brass		
	○	□	⬡	○	□	⬡
1/16	.0104	.013	.0115	.0113	.0144	.0125
1/8	.042	.05	.046	.045	.058	.050
3/16	.09	.12	.10	.102	.130	.112
1/4	.17	.21	.19	.18	.23	.20
5/16	.26	.33	.29	.28	.36	.31
3/8	.38	.48	.42	.41	.52	.45
7/16	.51	.65	.56	.55	.71	.61
1/2	.67	.85	.74	.72	.92	.80
9/16	.85	1.08	.94	.92	1.17	1.01
5/8	1.04	1.33	1.15	1.13	1.44	1.25
11/16	1.27	1.61	1.40	1.37	1.74	1.51
3/4	1.50	1.92	1.66	1.63	2.07	1.80
13/16	1.76	2.24	1.94	1.91	2.43	2.11
7/8	2.04	2.60	2.25	2.22	2.82	2.45
15/16	2.35	2.99	2.59	2.55	3.24	2.81
1	2.67	3.40	2.94	2.90	3.69	3.19
1 1/16	3.01	3.84	3.32	3.27	4.16	3.61
1 1/8	3.38	4.30	3.73	3.67	4.67	4.04
1 3/16	3.77	4.80	4.16	4.08	5.20	4.51
1 1/4	4.17	5.31	4.60	4.53	5.76	4.99
1 5/16	4.60	5.86	5.07	4.99	6.35	5.50
1 3/8	5.04	6.43	5.56	5.48	6.97	6.04
1 7/16	5.52	7.03	6.08	5.99	7.62	6.60
1 1/2	6.01	7.65	6.63	6.52	8.30	7.19
1 9/16	6.52	8.30	7.19	7.07	9.01	7.80
1 5/8	7.05	8.98	7.77	7.65	9.74	8.44
1 11/16	7.60	9.68	8.38	8.25	10.51	9.10
1 3/4	8.18	10.41	9.02	8.87	11.30	9.78
1 13/16	8.77	11.17	9.67	9.52	12.12	10.49
1 7/8	9.39	11.95	10.35	10.19	12.97	11.24
1 15/16	10.02	12.76	11.05	10.88	13.85	12.00
2	10.68	13.60	11.78	11.59	14.76	12.78
2 1/16	11.36	14.46	12.53	12.33	15.69	13.60
2 1/8	12.06	15.35	13.30	13.08	16.66	14.42
2 3/16	12.78	16.27	14.09	13.87	17.65	15.29
2 1/4	13.52	17.22	14.91	14.67	18.68	16.17
2 5/16	14.28	18.19	15.75	15.50	19.73	17.09
2 3/8	15.06	19.18	16.62	16.34	20.81	18.02

SOURCE: Brown & Sharpe Manufacturing Co.

TABLE A3–11

S. A. E. Standard Specifications for Steels

S. A. E. STEEL NUMBERING SYSTEM

A numerical index system is used to identify compositions of S. A. E. steels, which makes it possible to use numerals that are partially descriptive of the composition of materials covered by such numbers. The first digit indicates the type to which the steel belongs. The second digit, in the case of the simple alloy steels, generally indicates the approximate percentage of the predominant alloying element and the last two or three digits indicate the average carbon content in points, or hundredths of 1 per cent. Thus, 2340 indicates a nickel steel of approximately 3 per cent nickel (3.25 to 3.75) and 0.40 per cent carbon (0.35 to 0.45).

In some instances, it is necessary to use the second and third digits of the number to identify the approximate alloy composition of a steel. An instance of such departure is the steel numbers selected for several of the High Speed Steels and corrosion and heat resisting alloys. Thus, 71360 indicates a Tungsten Steel of about 13 per cent Tungsten (12 to 15) and 0.60 per cent carbon (0.50 to 0.70).

The basic numerals for the various types of S. A. E. steel are listed below:

Type of Steel	*Numerals (and Digits)*
Carbon Steels	1xxx
Plain Carbon	10xx
Free Cutting, (Screw Stock)	11xx
Free Cutting, Manganese	X13xx
High Manganese	T13xx
Nickel Steels	2xxx
0.50 Per Cent Nickel	20xx
1.50 Per Cent Nickel	21xx
3.50 Per Cent Nickel	23xx
5.00 Per Cent Nickel	25xx
Nickel Chromium Steels	3xxx
1.25 Per Cent Nickel, 0.60 Per Cent Chromium	31xx
1.75 Per Cent Nickel, 1.00 Per Cent Chromium	32xx
3.50 Per Cent Nickel, 1.50 Per Cent Chromium	33xx
3.00 Per Cent Nickel, 0.80 Per Cent Chromium	34xx
Corrosion and Heat Resisting Steels	30xxx
Molybdenum Steels	4xxx
Chromium	41xx
Chromium Nickel	43xx
Nickel	46xx and 48xx
Chromium Steels	5xxx
Low Chromium	51xx
Medium Chromium	52xxx
Corrosion and Heat Resisting	51xxx
Chromium Vanadium Steels	6xxx
Tungsten Steels	7xxx and 7xxxx
Silicon Manganese Steels	9xxx

SOURCE: Brown & Sharpe Manufacturing Co.

HORSEPOWER REQUIREMENTS

FOR TURNING

When metal is cut in a lathe there is a downward pressure on the tool. This pressure, called chip pressure, depends on the material cut, shape and sharpness of the tool, and the size and shape of the chip.

For average conditions, a simple formula which will give sufficiently accurate results for power estimating purposes is as follows:

$P = CA$, where

A = cross sectional area of the chip in square inches, which is the product of depth of cut and feed per revolution of the work.

C = a constant depending on material being cut.

P = chip pressure on the tool in pounds.

Values of C

MATERIAL CUT	CONSTANT C
Low alloy steel	270,000
High alloy steel	350,000
High carbon steel	340,000
Medium carbon steel	300,000
Mild Steel	270,000
Cast iron—soft	132,000
Wrought iron	198,000
Malleable iron	170,000
Brass and bronze	110,000

Horsepower may be figured by using the following formula:

$H. P. = \dfrac{P \times S}{33,000}$ where

Example 2: Assuming that SAE 4140 is heat treated so that its strength is 100,000 pounds per square inch, the horsepower necessary to cut it, when other conditions remain the same as in Example 1, is:

$$H. P. = 3.25 \times 100,000 \times \dfrac{3.14 \times 4}{12} \times 200 = 7.8 \text{ as before.}$$
$$\overline{33,000}$$

Multiplying the result by 1.25, we get 10 horsepower.

FOR MILLING

Generally accepted approximate values of power for steel cutting is one horsepower per $\frac{3}{4}$ cubic inches of material removed per minute, although 1 cubic inch can be used for rapid estimating purposes. The horsepower is figured using the following formula:

$H. P. = KdfNnw$, in which

d = depth of cut taken in inches

f = feed per tooth in inches

$H. P.$ = horsepower necessary to cut

K = a constant depending on material cut

n = number of teeth in the cutter

N = number of revolutions per minute the cutter makes

w = the width of cut in inches

For estimating the horsepower, approximate values of constant K are given below:

MATERIAL CUT	CONSTANT K
Bakelite	0.2
Brass	0.4
Cast Iron, soft	0.5
Cast Iron, medium hard	0.7
Cast Iron, hard	1.0
Steel: 120 Brinell	1.2
150 Brinell	1.4

H. P. = the horsepower necessary to revolve the work against the cutting pressure.

P = pressure on the tool in pounds.

S = cutting speed in feet per minute, and is equal to $\dfrac{3.14 \times D}{12}$

in which D is the diameter of the work.

Example 1: Determine the horsepower necessary to take a cut ¼ inch deep, with feed of ⅟₆₄ inch per revolution, on SAE 4140 steel bar 4 inches in diameter turning 200 times per minute.

Solution: Using C = 325,000

$$P = 325{,}000 \times \tfrac{1}{4} \times \tfrac{1}{64} = 1220 \text{ pounds}$$

$$\text{The H. P.} = 1220 \times \frac{3.14 \times 4}{12} \times \frac{200}{33{,}000} = 7.8$$

This should be multiplied by 1.25 to allow for the efficiency of the machine, thus:

H. P. = 7.8 x 1.25 = 9.7 or 10.

When the tensile strength of the material cut is known, the following formula may be used for computing the horsepower necessary to cut the material:

$$\text{H. P.} = \frac{3.25\ ATS}{33{,}000} \text{ where}$$

A = the cross section area of the chip in square inches, and is equal to the product of depth of cut and feed per revolution.

H. P. = the horsepower necessary to cut the metal.

S = the cutting speed in f.p.m.

T = the ultimate strength of the material cut.

Source: *Vascoloy-Ramet Corp.*

175 Brinell	1.5
250 Brinell	1.7
300 Brinell	1.9
400 Brinell	-2.0
500 Brinell	2.3
600 Brinell	2.5

It is to be noted that for a given material cut, fixed width of cut, and fixed number of teeth, the horsepower will vary with the depth of cut, the feed per tooth and the r.p.m.

Example: Assuming a width of cut 2 inches, the depth ⅛ inch, the feed 0.004" per tooth, what horsepower will be required to mill with a 3-inch 6-tooth cutter running at 600 r.p.m. and cutting steel 250 Brinell hardness.

Solution: $K = 1.7$ from Table; $d = \frac{1}{8}''$ or $0.125''$; $f = 0.004''$; $n = 6$; $N = 600$, and $w = 2''$.

Substituting these values in the formula, we get:

$$\text{H. P.} = 1.7 \times 0.125 \times 0.004 \times 6 \times 600 \times 2 = 6.14$$

If the machine was powered with a 5 horsepower motor, we could reduce the r.p.m. and come within the capacity of the machine, using formula: $N = \dfrac{\text{H. P.}}{Kdfnw}$ in which the symbols have the same meaning as before.

Substituting the known values in this formula, we get:

$$N = \frac{5}{1.7 \times 0.125 \times 0.004 \times 6 \times 2} = 490 \text{ (approx.)}$$

The speed of the machine should not be allowed to drop more than 50 per cent from that recommended on page 25, since this would impair the performance of the cutter. 490 r.p.m. for a 3-inch cutter will give us a cutting speed

$$S = \frac{3.14 \times 3 \times 490}{12} = 385 \text{ f.p.m. (approx.)}$$

TABLE A3–13

+00000000 01	+00000000 01	+40000000 51	+10000000 51	+78539750 50	+31415900 51	+00000000 00	0001 000
+00000000 40	+00000003 14	+15000000 51	+42500000 50	+00000000 01	+00000000 00	+00000000 00	0002 000
+40000000 51	+10000000 51	+00000000 01	+13166432 51	+00000000 00	+00000000 00	+00000000 00	0003 015
+00000000 01	+00000000 02	+40000000 51	+12500000 51	+12271836 51	+49087344 51	+00000000 00	0004 000
+00000000 32	+00000004 90	+12500000 51	+42500000 50	+00000000 01	+00000000 00	+00000000 00	0005 000
+40000000 51	+12500000 51	+00000000 01	+12186924 51	+00000000 00	+00000000 00	+00000000 00	0006 015
+00000000 01	+00000000 03	+40000000 51	+15000000 51	+17671444 51	+70685776 51	+00000000 00	0007 000
+00000000 26	+00000000 06	+12500000 51	+47500000 50	+00000000 01	+00000000 00	+00000000 00	0008 000
+40000000 51	+15000000 51	+00000000 01	+12920935 51	+00000000 00	+00000000 00	+00000000 00	0009 015
+00000000 01	+00000000 04	+40000000 51	+17500000 51	+24052798 51	+96211192 51	+00000000 00	0010 000
+00000000 22	+00000009 62	+10000000 51	+50000000 50	+00000000 01	+00000000 00	+00000000 00	0011 000
+40000000 51	+17500000 51	+00000000 01	+12122121 51	+00000000 00	+00000000 00	+00000000 00	0012 015
+00000000 01	+00000000 05	+40000000 51	+20000000 51	+31415900 51	+12566360 52	+00000000 00	0013 000
+00000000 20	+00000012 56	+10000000 51	+55000000 50	+00000000 00	+00000000 00	+00000000 00	0014 000
+40000000 51	+20000000 51	+00000000 01	+12793782 51	+00000000 00	+00000000 00	+00000000 00	0015 015
+00000000 02	+00000000 01	+41250000 51	+10000000 51	+78539750 50	+32397647 51	+00000000 00	0016 000
+00000000 41	+00000003 23	+15000000 51	+42500000 50	+00000000 01	+00000000 00	+00000000 00	0017 000
+41250000 51	+10000000 51	+00000000 01	+13193287 51	+00000000 00	+00000000 00	+00000000 00	0018 015
+00000000 02	+00000000 02	+41250000 51	+12500000 51	+12271836 51	+50621324 51	+00000000 00	0019 000
+00000000 33	+00000005 06	+12500000 51	+47500000 50	+00000000 01	+00000000 00	+00000000 00	0020 000
+41250000 51	+12500000 51	+00000000 01	+12839626 51	+00000000 00	+00000000 00	+00000000 00	0021 015
+00000000 02	+00000000 03	+41250000 51	+15000000 51	+17671444 51	+72894707 51	+00000000 00	0022 000
+00000000 27	+00000007 28	+12500000 51	+47500000 50	+00000000 01	+00000000 00	+00000000 00	0023 000
+41250000 51	+15000000 51	+00000000 01	+12950110 51	+00000000 00	+00000000 00	+00000000 00	0024 015
+00000000 02	+00000000 04	+41250000 51	+17500000 51	+24052798 51	+99217792 51	+00000000 00	0025 000
+00000000 23	+00000009 92	+10000000 51	+50000000 50	+00000000 01	+00000000 00	+00000000 00	0026 000

23AUG

This is a FOR TRANSIT coding of the oil sand mix core problem specifying a single clamp for lengths 9 inches or less and two clamps for longer lengths. The following definitions are listed:

CLO: initial length
DL: increment length
NL: number of lengths to be used in calculation
CDO: initial diameter
DD: increment diameter
ND: number of diameters to be used in calculation

$Y = f\dfrac{L}{D}$ was stored in tables as whole numbers and handled as subroutine function ADJYF which was separately programmed for "table lookup."

CT was stored in tables as whole numbers and handled as subroutine function CORTF which was separately programmed for "table lookup."

TABLE A3–13 (Continued)

0000001500+	6164718866+	9595916572+	ADJYF	551EK
0000001500+	6376798366+	9595926572+	CORTF	552EK
0000001500+	8278798366+	9190916572+	SQRTF	101EK

```
         C          CYLINDRICAL OIL-SAND CORES
         C          FORMULA M-11-NO.15 - NIEBEL
         C          AUGUST 24, 19
         C
         1          READ, CLO, DL, NL
         2          READ, CDO, DD, ND
         3          PI = 3.14159
         4          DO 15 I=1,NL
         5          DO 15 J=1,ND
         6          CL = CLO + (I-1) * DL
         7          CD = CDO + (J-1) * DD
         8          A = PI * CD**2 / 4.0
         9          V = A * CL
        10          LD = (CL / CD) * 10.0
        11          KV = V * 100.0
        12          Y = ADJYF(LD) / 100.0
        13          CT = CORTF(KV) / 1000.0
                    PUNCH, I,J,CL,CD,A,V,LD,KV,
                   1 Y,CT
        14          AT = 0.173*V + 0.021*CL
                   1 + 0.0157*A
                   2 + SQRTF(0.0067 + 16.0E=6*V**2)
                   3 + Y*CT + 0.327
        15          PUNCH, CL, CD, AT
        16          STOP
        17          END
08/21/
```

TABLE A3–14

Tables of waiting time and machine availability for selected servicing constants*†
(values expressed as percentages of total time where $T_1 + T_2 + T_3$ 100%)

k = 0.01

n	(a) T_3	T_1	(b) T_3	T_1
1	0.0	99.0	0.0	99.0
10	0.1	99.0	0.1	98.9
20	0.1	98.9	0.2	98.8
30	0.2	98.8	0.4	98.6
40			0.6	98.4
50			0.9	98.1
60			1.3	97.8
70			1.8	97.2
80			2.7	96.3
85			3.4	95.7
90			4.2	94.9
95			5.2	93.8
100			6.7	92.4
105			8.5	90.6
110			10.7	88.4
115			13.4	85.8
120			16.3	82.9
121			16.9	82.3
122			17.5	81.7
123			18.1	81.1
124			18.8	80.4
125			19.4	79.8
126			20.0	79.2
127			20.6	78.6
128			21.2	78.1
129			21.8	77.5
130			22.4	76.9
131			22.9	76.3
132			23.5	75.7
133			24.1	75.2
134			24.6	74.6
135			25.2	74.1
136			25.7	73.5
137			26.3	73.0
138			26.8	72.5
139			27.3	71.9
140			27.9	71.4
141			28.4	70.9
142			28.9	70.4
143			29.4	69.9
144			29.9	69.4

k = 0.02

n	(a) T_3	T_1	(b) T_3	T_1
1	0.0	98.0	0.0	98.0
5	0.1	98.0	0.2	97.9
10	0.2	97.8	0.4	97.6
15	0.4	97.7	0.7	97.4
20	0.6	97.5	1.1	97.0
25	0.8	97.2	1.6	96.5
30	1.2	96.9	2.2	95.9
35			3.1	95.0
40			4.3	93.8
45			6.1	92.0
50			8.7	89.5

k = 0.02 (cont.)

n	(a) T_3	T_1	(b) T_3	T_1
51			9.3	88.9
52			10.0	88.3
53			10.7	87.6
54			11.5	86.8
55			12.3	86.0
56			13.1	85.2
57			14.0	84.3
58			14.9	83.4
59			15.9	82.5
60			16.8	81.5
61			17.9	80.5
62			18.9	79.5
63			19.9	78.5
64			21.0	77.5
65			22.0	76.4
66			23.1	75.4
67			24.2	74.4
68			25.2	73.3
69			26.2	72.3
70			27.2	71.3
71			28.2	70.4
72			29.2	69.4

k = 0.03

n	(a) T_3	T_1	(b) T_3	T_1
1	0.0	97.1	0.0	97.1
5	0.2	96.9	0.4	96.7
10	0.5	96.6	1.0	96.2
15	1.0	96.2	1.8	95.4
20	1.6	95.5	3.0	94.2
25	2.8	94.4	4.7	92.5
26	3.1	94.1	5.2	92.1
27	3.4	93.7	5.7	91.6
28	3.8	93.4	6.2	91.1
29	4.3	92.9	6.8	90.5
30	4.8	92.4	7.4	89.9
31			8.1	89.2
32			8.9	88.5
33			9.7	87.7
34			10.6	86.8
35			11.6	85.9
36			12.6	84.9
37			13.7	83.8
38			14.9	82.6
39			16.1	81.4
40			17.4	80.2
41			18.8	78.9
42			20.1	77.5
43			21.6	76.2
44			23.0	74.8
45			24.4	73.4
46			25.9	72.0
47			27.3	70.6
48			28.7	69.2

k = 0.04

n	(a) T_3	T_1	(b) T_3	T_1
1	0.0	96.2	0.0	96.2
2	0.1	96.1	0.2	96.0
3	0.2	96.0	0.3	95.9
4	0.2	95.9	0.5	95.7
5	0.3	95.8	0.7	95.5
6	0.5	95.7	0.9	95.3
7	0.6	95.6	1.1	95.1
8	0.7	95.5	1.3	94.9
9	0.8	95.4	1.5	94.7
10	1.0	95.2	1.8	94.4
11	1.1	95.1	2.1	94.1
12	1.3	94.9	2.4	93.8
13	1.5	94.7	2.8	93.5
14	1.8	94.5	3.2	93.1
15	2.0	94.2	3.6	92.7
16	2.3	94.0	4.0	92.3
17	2.6	93.6	4.5	91.8
18	3.0	93.3	5.1	91.3
19	3.4	92.9	5.7	90.7
20	3.9	92.4	6.4	90.0
21	4.5	91.8	7.1	89.3
22	5.2	91.2	8.0	88.5
23	6.0	90.4	8.9	87.6
24	6.8	89.6	9.9	86.7
25	7.9	88.6	11.0	85.6
26	9.0	87.5	12.2	84.5
27	10.4	86.2	13.4	83.2
28	11.9	84.7	14.8	81.9
29	13.6	83.0	16.3	80.5
30	15.5	81.3	17.9	79.0
31			19.6	77.4
32			21.3	75.7
33			23.0	74.0
34			24.8	72.3
35			26.6	70.6
36			28.4	68.9
37			30.1	67.2

k = 0.05

n	(a) T_3	T_1	(b) T_3	T_1
1	0.0	95.2	0.0	95.2
2	0.1	95.1	0.2	95.0
3	0.2	95.0	0.5	94.8
4	0.4	94.9	0.7	94.5
5	0.5	94.7	1.0	94.3
6	0.7	94.6	1.4	94.0
7	0.9	94.4	1.7	93.6
8	1.1	94.2	2.1	93.3
9	1.4	93.9	2.5	92.9
10	1.6	93.7	3.0	92.4
11	2.0	93.4	3.5	91.9
12	2.3	93.0	4.1	91.4
13	2.7	92.6	4.7	90.8
14	3.2	92.2	5.4	90.1
15	3.8	91.7	6.2	89.3

k = 0.05 (cont.)

n	(a) T_3	T_1	(b) T_3	T_1
16	4.4	91.0	7.1	88.5
17	5.2	90.3	8.1	87.6
18	6.1	89.5	9.1	86.5
19	7.1	88.5	10.4	85.4
20	8.4	87.3	11.7	84.1
21	9.8	85.9	13.1	82.7
22	11.5	84.3	14.7	81.2
23	13.4	82.5	16.5	79.6
24	15.5	80.5	18.3	77.8
25	17.8	78.2	20.2	76.0
26	20.3	75.9	22.2	74.1
27	22.8	73.6	24.3	72.1
28	25.3	71.2	26.4	70.1
29	27.9	68.8	28.5	68.1

k = 0.06

n	(a) T_3	T_1	(b) T_3	T_1
1	0.0	94.3	0.0	94.3
2	0.2	94.2	0.3	94.0
3	0.4	94.0	0.7	93.7
4	0.6	93.8	1.1	93.3
5	0.8	93.6	1.5	92.9
6	1.1	93.3	2.0	92.5
7	1.4	93.1	2.5	92.0
8	1.7	92.7	3.1	91.4
9	2.1	92.4	3.7	90.8
10	2.6	91.9	4.5	90.1
11	3.1	91.4	5.3	89.4
12	3.8	90.8	6.2	88.5
13	4.5	90.1	7.3	87.5
14	5.4	89.2	8.4	86.4
15	6.5	88.2	9.7	85.2
16	7.8	87.0	11.2	83.8
17	9.3	85.6	12.8	82.3
18	11.1	83.9	14.6	80.6
19	13.2	81.9	16.5	78.8
20	15.6	79.7	18.6	76.8
21			20.8	74.7
22			23.1	72.5
23			25.5	70.3
24			27.9	68.0
25			30.3	65.8

k = 0.07

n	(a) T_3	T_1	(b) T_3	T_1
1	0.0	93.5	0.0	93.5
2	0.2	93.2	0.4	93.1
3	0.5	93.0	0.9	92.6
4	0.8	92.7	1.4	92.1
5	1.1	92.4	2.0	91.6
6	1.5	92.1	2.7	91.0
7	1.9	91.7	3.4	90.3
8	2.4	91.2	4.3	89.5
9	3.1	90.6	5.2	88.6
10	3.8	89.9	6.3	87.6

* All tables assume random calls for service. Column (a) is for constant servicing time and column (b) for an exponential distribution of servicing times. It is hoped that the missing values in column (a) can be secured by approximation in the near future.

† Where no entry appears in column the figures were not available.

TABLE A3-14 (Continued)

n	(a) T_3	T_1	(b) T_3	T_1
	$k = 0.07$ (cont.)			
11	4.7	89.1	7.5	86.4
12	5.7	88.1	8.9	85.1
13	7.0	86.9	10.4	83.7
14	8.6	85.4	12.2	82.1
15	10.4	83.7	14.1	80.3
16	12.6	81.6	16.2	78.3
17	15.2	79.3	18.5	76.2
18	18.1	76.6	21.0	73.9
19	21.1	73.7	23.5	71.5
20	24.4	70.7	26.2	69.0
21			28.9	66.5
	$k = 0.08$			
1	0.0	92.6	0.0	92.6
2	0.3	92.3	0.5	92.1
3	0.6	92.0	1.2	91.5
4	1.0	91.2	1.9	90.9
5	1.4	91.2	2.7	90.1
6	2.0	90.8	3.5	89.3
7	2.6	90.2	4.5	88.4
8	3.4	89.5	5.7	87.3
9	4.3	88.6	7.0	86.1
10	5.4	87.6	8.5	84.8
11	6.7	86.4	10.1	83.2
12	8.4	84.8	12.0	81.4

n	(a) T_2	T_1	(b) T_3	T_1
	$k = 0.08$ (cont.)			
13	10.4	83.0	14.2	79.5
14	12.8	80.8	16.5	77.3
15	15.6	78.2	19.0	75.0
16	18.8	75.2	21.8	72.4
17	22.2	72.0	24.6	69.8
18	25.7	68.8	27.6	67.1
19	28.2	66.5	30.5	64.4
	$k = 0.09$			
1	0.0	91.5	0.0	91.7
2	0.4	91.4	0.7	91.1
3	0.8	91.0	1.4	90.4
4	1.3	90.6	2.3	89.6
5	1.9	90.0	3.3	88.7
6	2.6	89.4	4.5	87.7
7	3.4	88.6	5.8	86.5
8	4.5	87.6	7.3	85.1
9	5.7	86.5	9.0	83.5
10	7.3	85.0	10.9	81.7
11	9.3	83.2	13.1	79.7
12	11.7	81.0	15.6	77.5
13	14.5	78.4	18.3	75.0
14	17.8	75.4	21.2	72.3
15	21.5	72.0	24.2	69.5
16	25.3	68.5	27.4	66.6
17	29.2	65.0	30.6	63.7

n	(a) T_2	T_1	(b) T_2	T_1
	$k = 0.10$			
1	0.0	90.9	0.0	90.9
2	0.4	90.5	0.8	90.2
3	1.0	90.0	1.8	89.3
4	1.6	89.5	2.8	88.3
5	2.3	88.8	4.1	87.2
6	2.2	88.0	5.5	85.9
7	4.4	86.9	7.1	84.4
8	5.8	85.7	9.0	82.7
9	7.5	84.1	11.2	80.8
10	9.7	82.1	13.6	78.5
11	12.4	79.8	16.3	76.1
12	15.6	76.8	19.3	73.4
13	19.2	73.4	22.5	70.4
14	23.3	69.8	25.9	67.4
15	27.4	66.0	29.4	64.2
16	31.5	62.0		
	$k = 0.15$			
1	0.0	87.0	0.0	87.0
2	0.9	86.2	1.7	85.5
3	2.1	85.1	3.6	83.8
4	3.9	83.8	6.0	81.8
5	5.5	82.2	8.7	79.4
6	8.0	80.0	11.8	76.7
7	11.2	72.2	15.4	73.5
8	15.2	73.7	19.5	70.0
9	20.1	69.5	23.8	66.2
10	25.5	64.8	28.4	62.3
11	31.0	60.0		

n	(a) T_2	T_1	(b) T_2	T_1
	$k = 0.20$			
1	0.0	83.3	0.0	83.3
2	1.5	82.0	2.7	81.1
3	3.6	80.4	5.9	78.4
4	6.3	78.1	9.8	75.2
5	10.0	75.0	14.2	71.5
6	14.7	71.1	19.2	67.4
7	20.6	66.2	24.6	62.8
8	27.3	60.6	30.3	58.1
9	32.6	56.1		
	$k = 0.30$			
1	0.0	76.9	0.0	76.9
2	3.0	74.6	5.1	73.0
3	7.4	71.3	11.1	68.4
4	13.3	66.7	18.0	63.1
5	21.1	60.7	25.4	57.4
6	29.9	53.9	33.0	51.6
	$k = 0.40$			
1	0.0	71.4	0.0	71.4
2	4.8	68.0	7.5	66.0
3	11.8	63.0	16.3	59.8
4	21.2	56.3	25.6	53.1
5	31.9	48.6	34.9	46.5

Index

A

A. C. Spark Plug Division of General Motors, 313
Abnormal time, 320, 665
Accuracy, importance of
  formula work, 464–65
  time study work, 331–32
Actual time, 665
Address, 497, 665
Adjustment factor in developing formula, 476–77
Administration of wage incentive system, 634–38
Aerobic efficiency, 108, 665
Alignment charts, for
  control limits for work sampling studies, 525
  determining number of observations, 316, 522
  facing and turning time, 404
  leveling, 284, 346
Allowances
  application, 356–59, 373
  avoidable delay, 370
  clean work station, 371–72
  computation of, 356–75
  definition, 370
  extra, 370–71
  fatigue, 357, 359–66
  International Labour Office values, 365
  machine interference, 366–70
  necessity for, 356–57
  oil machine, 372

Allowances—*Cont.*
  personal, 357, 359
  power feed, 372–73
  purpose of, 356
  table for, 357
  unavoidable delay, 357, 366
  values, 374
  work sampling for determining, 533
Allowed time, 377, 665
American Institute of Industrial Engineers, 16
American Management Association, 15–16
American Material Handling Society, 109
American Society of Mechanical Engineers
  plant layout model standards, 126
  plant layout template standards, 124–26
  process chart standards, 28
  Saratoga meeting, 10
Analysis
  design, 55–135
  film, 211–48
  material, 69–80, 293–94
  material handling, 109–19
  method, 40, 293–94
  motion, 181–201
  operation, 40–109
  plant layout, 119–31
  process of manufacture, 82–88
  setup and tools, 88–97

Analysis—*Cont.*
  tolerances and specifications, 64–69
  working conditions, 97–109
Analyst, responsibilities to time study, 271–73
Analytical ability required of time study analyst, 272
Anerobic efficiency, 108, 665
Approach to the operator, 293
Areas of the normal curve, 678
Arithmetic unit, 497–99, 665
Assemble
  definition, 177
  example, 177
  symbol, 171
Attention time, 370
Audit of time standards, 384
Automatic control, 67
Automation, 543–45, 586–604
Auto-starter, 134–35
Average elemental time, 317, 666
Average hourly earnings, 608, 666
Average method of selecting time, 317–18
Average performance, 269–70, 318, 326–28
Avoidable delay
  allowance for, 370
  definition, 179, 666
  example, 179
  symbol, 171

B

Babbage, Charles, 9
Balance fatigue, 182
Balancing delay, 165, 666
Balancing working force, 156–64
Barnes, R. M., 180
Barth, Carl G., 13
Base time, 666
Base wage rate, 608, 666
Basic divisions of accomplishment
  assemble, 177
  avoidable delay, 179
  disassemble, 178
  grasp, 173–74
  hold, 175
  inspect, 177
  move, 175
  plan, 179
  position, 176
  preposition, 176–77
  reach, 174
  release, 176
  rest to overcome fatigue, 179
  search, 173
  select, 173
  unavoidable delay, 178
  use, 178

Basic Motion Timestudy, 443–48
Basic motion times, 417–55
Bausch & Lomb Co., 98
Bedaux point plan, 614, 666
Bench-mark elements, 326, 343, 345, 666
Binary bits, 500, 666
Binomial theorem, 154, 512, 666, 674
Black and white film, 220
Blanking dies, 96
Blue ticket time, 635–36
Board, observation, 281, 284
Body dimensions, 191–92
Bonus earnings, 605–6
Boredom, effect of, 104–7
Brandeis, Louis, 11
Break-even chart, 89, 200
Breaking operation into elements, 297–99
Budgetary control, 581
Buffing wheels, 103

C

Calculating the time study, 319–20
Camera, motion-picture, 216–17, 283–84
Camera, random activity analysis, 245–46
Capital investment, recovery of, 251–54
Carbide tooling
  dies, 96
  drills, 95–96
  fly cutters, 95
Card dealing, rating, 326
Carroll, Phil, 388
Cash flow, 252–54
Castings, good and poor design, 57–58
Chair for operator, 190–93
Change direction, 666
Change, resistance to, 40–41
Charts
  alignment, 284, 316, 346, 404, 522, 525
  break-even, 89, 200
  control, 523–29
  crossover, 89, 200
  flow process, 28–35
  gang, 149–52
  lost time analysis, 358
  man and machine process, 141–49
  operation, 20–28
  operator, 164–68
  simo, 235, 238
Check, over-all time, 319
Checking formula, 484
Chi-square, 514
Chronocycle graphic studies, 248, 666
Chronograph, 248, 666
CIO, 14, 628
Circle circumference and area, 674
Clamps, quick-acting, 96

Classification of motions, 181
Classification method of job evaluation, 260–61
Clean work station allowance, 371–72
Cleanliness, promotion of, 102
Coining, 53
Collecting data for standard data, 389
Color, use of, 194
Colored film, 220
Combination cuts, 195–97
Combination motions, 435, 443–44, 447, 459
Comparative weight of steel and brass bars, 688
Comparison of various methods, 574
Compensation of labor, 605–23
Computation
of allowances, 356–75
of standard, 319–21
Computer, digital, 496–508, 586–604
Conditions
improvement of, 97–109, 190–95
recording of, 295–96
table of values for rating, 336
working, 97–109, 190–95
Conference of Scientific Management, 15
Consistency in performance rating, 332
Consistency table of values for rating, 337
Constant elements, 389, 666
Continuous method of observation, 306–7, 667
Control charts, 523–29
Control unit, computer, 499
Controlled time, 667
Controlling cost of labor, 580–81
Conversion factor, 377
Cooke, Morris L., 14, 15
Core formula, 488–97
Corollaries to laws of motion economy, 211–13
Cosines, law of, 675
Cost
factory, 257–59
relation to
tolerances, 65
volume, 40–41
Council of Profit Sharing Industries, 618
Creativity, developing, 645–46
Crew-balance, 243–45
Cross-over chart, 89, 200
Curved motions, 183
Curves
definitions, 469, 667
ellipse, 470–71
hyperbola, 469–70
normal, 328, 352, 518
parabola, 471

Curves—*Cont.*
plotting, 403–7
straight line, 405–7
Customer service, improved with standards, 583–84
Cutting speeds
drilling, 392
milling, 399
turning, 396–97
Cutting times, 392
Cycle graphic studies, 248, 667
Cycle time allowances, 357
Cycle(s)
definition, 667
number to observe for stop watch study, 310–16
number to observe for work sampling, 520–21
Cylindrical grind, 67

D

Data
collecting for formulas, 466–67
standard, 387–413
Data processing and the establishment of standards, 586–88
Daywork, 611, 667
Decibel levels, 101
Decimal equivalents, 683
Decimal hour watch, 278–82, 667
Decimal minute watch, 278–82, 667
Decision-making methods, 646–47
Delay allowances
avoidable, 370
fatigue, 359–66
machine interference, 366–70
personal, 357, 359
unavoidable, 357, 366
Delays, 667
Design, ways of improving, 55–64
Design considerations
assemblies, 56
castings, 56–58
fabricated parts, 56
forgings, 56–58
formed parts, 56
machined parts, 56
molded parts, 56
punchings, 56
screw machine parts, 56
tools and equipment, 182
treatments and finishes, 56
welded parts, 56
Determination of labor standards, 258
Developing creativity, 645–46
Differential piecework, 667
Difficulties encountered in time study, 308–10

Digital computer
  description of, 496–500
  flow charts, 504–6
  language of, 503
  as logic processors, 500–502
  programming, 503, 506–8
  uses of, 496, 504, 586–604
Dimensional Motion Times, 449
Dimensions, human, 191–92
Direct financial plans, 605–6
Direct labor, 667
Disassemble
  definition, 178, 667
  example, 178
  symbol, 171
Dividing operation into elements, 297–99
Doffing yarn operation, 207–8
Drill
  calculation of drill lead, 393
  deep hole drilling, 95–96
  drill feeds, 392, 686
  drill press standard data, 411
  drill speeds, 392
Drop delivery, 188, 667
Dust removal, 102–3

E

Each piece time, 378
Earning curve, 609–10, 613, 616
Eastern rate case, 11
Eastman Kodak Co., 217
Editor, splicer, and reviewer, 224
Education of time study man, 272; *see also* Training
Effective utilization, 270
Efficient layout of available space, 574–75
Effort
  classifications, 336
  definition, 335, 667
  impact on job evaluation, 263
  rating, 335–36
Effort time allowances, 357
Elapsed times
  abnormal, 320
  average, 317
  definition, 667
  summary of, 321–22
Elements
  analyzing for formula construction, 468
  breaking job into, 297–99
  definition, 297, 667
  duration, 297–98
  foreign, 309–10
  missed by observer, 308
  missed by operator, 308
  number to study, 310–17
  performed out of order, 308–9

Elements—*Cont.*
  recording time consumed by, 307–8
  wild, 310, 320
Ellipse, 470–71
Emerson, Harrington, 13
Emerson wage payment plan, 615–17
Employee reactions to time study, 654–56
Engstrom, Harold, 418
Equipment
  micromotion, 216–19
  time study, 278–91
Errors in time values, 321
Estimating labor standards, 268
Exhaust pipe diameters, 103
Expense work standards, 563–65
Exponential distribution, 667
Exponential form, 473–74
Exposure meter, 221
Expression
  final standard, 378–79
  formula, 484
External time, 667
Extra allowance, 370–71

F

Factor, leveling, 325–44
Factor comparison method of job evaluation, 260
Factory cost, determination of, 257–58
Fair day's work, 269–70, 667–68
Fatigue
  allowances, 365
  balance, 182
  definition, 360, 668
  factors affecting, 360
  measuring, 361–64
  reduction, 361–64
  rest to overcome, 172, 179
  temperature impact, 98–100
Feed, 392, 396–97, 399, 686
Feet, work done by, 186
Film
  analysis equipment, 216–17
  black and white, 220
  color, 220
  costs of, 220
  size of, 216
  storage of, 225–27
Finger motions, 184–85
Finger and wrist motions, 185
Finger, wrist, and lower arm motions, 185
Finger, wrist, lower arm, and upper arm motions, 185
Finger, wrist, lower arm, upper arm, and body motions, 185–86
First-aid, 104
First piece time, 668

Fixed locations for tools at workplace, 188
Fixture and jig design, 90–91
Flood lights, 222
Floor plan, 128–30
Flow chart for computer programming, 504–6
Flow diagram, 36–37, 668
Flow process chart
  construction of, 30–31
  definition, 28, 668
  examples, 34–35
  symbols, 28
  uses of, 31–36
Fogs, classification and disposal of, 102–3
Follow-up of method, 572–73
Footlambert recommendations, 98
Foot-operated mechanisms, 186, 203, 205
Forearm motions, 181, 185
Foreign elements, 309–10, 668
Foreman, responsibilities to time study, 273–74
Forgings, good and poor design details, 57–58
Forming standard times, 403–5, 475–77
Forms
  lost time analysis, 358
  process chart
    flow, 34–35
    gang, 149–50
    man and machine, 142–47
    operation, 21–24
  simo chart, 235, 238
  time study, 285–88
  work sampling, 523–24
Formula
  accuracy check, 484
  advantages, 464
  analysis, 468–69
  application, 463
  characteristics of, 464–65, 469–82
  computation of expression, 484
  construction, 463–96
  definition, 463
  developing synthesis, 483
  elements, 466–67, 487
  example of making cores, 488–97
  factor X solution, 474–77
  master table of detail time studies, 466–67
  number, 485
  procedure, 487
  report, 485
Frame, 211
Frame counter, 224, 668
Frame-by-frame analysis, 233–35
Fringe benefits, 357, 668
Frustrum of right circular cone, volume and lateral surface, 675

Fumes, disposal of, 102–3
Functional layout, 121–23
Fundamental motions, 172

G

Gain sharing, 668
Gang process chart
  construction of, 149–50
  definition of, 149
  uses of, 151–52
Gantt, Henry Laurence, 13–14
Gantt chart, 668
Gantt memorial medal, 16
Gases, disposal of, 102–3
General Electric Company, 55–56, 159, 310, 353
Get, 437, 439–41, 668
Gilbreth, Lillian M., and Frank B., 12–13, 172
Gomberg, William, 659
Good housekeeping, promotion of, 102
Grade description plan of job evaluation, 260
Grasp
  definition, 173, 668
  examples, 174
  symbol, 171
  types, 174
Gravity bins, 188
Gravity chutes, 188
Group incentive plans, 605–6
Guards, 103

H

Halsey incentive plan, 612–14
Hand motions, 184–85
Hand tools, 182, 187
Hand wheels, design of, 197–98
Handling materials, 109–19
Heat fatigue, 100
Height of chair at work station, 192–93
Hold
  definition, 175
  examples, 175
  symbol, 171
Holmes, W. G., 417
Horizontal plane of work area, 188–90
Horsepower requirements, 401–3, 690–91
Hourly production table, 684–85
Housekeeping, good, 102
Human approach, 17, 656–57
Human body dimensions, 191–92
Hyperbolic relationship, 469–70

I

Illumination, proper, 98–99, 193
Incentive wages, 605–23
Incentives, plant-wide, 15
Independent variable, 403

Indirect financial plans, 606
Indirect labor standards
  advantages, 546, 568
  computer program for, 597–604
  established by work sampling, 535–40
  maintenance standards, 566–69
  material handling standards, 566
  office work, 563–65
  supervisory standards, 565–66
  toolroom standards, 547
  universal, 567–68
Individual differences in performance,
  327
Individual incentive plans, 605–17
Industrial engineering, 640–41
Industrial Management Society, 17
Information on time study form, 295–96
Input storage, 497
Inspect
  definition, 177
  example, 177
  symbol, 171
Inspection
  lot-by-lot, 66
  spot, 65
  statistical, 66
Installation of new method, 254–55
Instruction, computer, 499, 669
Instruction sheet, 239
Interference time, 366–70, 669
International Association of Machinists,
  628

J

Jig and fixture design, 90–91
Job analysis, 258–59, 669
Job description, 259
Job evaluation
  classification method, 260–61
  definition, 7
  factor comparison method, 260
  grade description plan, 260
  point system, 261–65
  ranking method, 261–62
  research in, 661–62
Job rating, 264
Judgment in performance rating, 325,
  348–50

K

Knee motions, 185–86, 435, 443, 444–45
Knurling formula, 505

L

Labor
  cost of, 257–59
  measurement of, 268–69
Labor relations and work measurement,
  647

Laboratory, motion study, 213–14
Lathe, turret controls, 195–97
Lathe work
  determination of cutting times, 395–98
  feeds, 396–97
  setup standard data, 380–82
  speeds, 396–97
Law of cosines, 675
Law of sines, 675
Law of motion economy, 182–98, 211–13
Layout, plant, 123–27
Layout work station, 182–98
Learning curve, 328–31, 669
Least squares method, 406–7, 477–81
Left- and right-hand chart, 20–28
Lens, motion-picture camera, 217–18
Leveling
  characteristic of sound system, 331–33
  concept of normal, 326–27
  definition, 325–26
  effects of, 327–28
  necessity for, 325
  objective rating, 343–44
  rating at the work station, 332–33
  rating elements versus over-all study,
    333–34
  speed rating, 342–43
  synthetic rating, 340–42
  training for, 348–54
  uses, 327–28
  Westinghouse system, 334–40
Levers, 197
Light meter, 221
Lighting
  amount required, 98–99
  improvement of, 97–98
Lincoln, James F., 621–22
Line balancing, 156–64
Logarithm formulas, 331, 674
Logarithmic paper, 329
Logic processors, 499–501
Loose rate, 612, 634, 669
Lost time analysis chart, 358
Lowry, Stewart M., 165, 334

M

Machine attention time, 370, 669
Machine coupling, 142
Machine cycle time, 669
Machine down time, 669
Machine interference, 366–70
Machine time allowances, 357, 366–73
Machine time recording, 282
Machine utilization, 87–88
Machine wrapping, 85
Maintenance of standards, 383–85
Maintenance standards, 566–69
Man and machine process chart
  construction of, 142–47

Man and machine process chart—*Cont.*
  definition, 141, 669
  uses of, 147–49
Man and machine relationships, 152–64
Management problems facilitated through standards, 583
Manufacturing progress function, 328–31, 670
Marsto-chron, 670
Master standard data, 450–54
Master table of time studies, 466–67
Material
  analysis of prior to taking time study, 292–95
  costs, 70–71
  easier to process, 73
  economical use of, 73–77
  improvement possibilities, 70–79
  less expensive, 69–70
  salvage, 77
  supplies, 77–79
  tool, 77–79
Material handling
  definition, 109
  equipment, 111–14
  pallets, 115–17
  principles, 118–19
  standards, 548
Maximum and normal working area, 188–90
Maynard, H. B., 165, 334
Measured daywork, 611, 670
Mechanical advantage, designing for, 197–98
Mechanizing manual work, 87
Memomotion study
  applications, 243
  definition, 243, 670
  equipment, 245–48
  uses of, 243
Memory unit, 497–99
Merrick, Dwight V., multiple piece rate plan, 14, 611
Method of least squares, 406–7
Methods engineering
  definition, 3
  research in, 657–62
  scope of, 3
  systematic procedure, 5
Methods improvement
  indirect and expense work, 545–46
  using micromotion study, 211–48
  using operation analysis, 40–139
Methods and standards automation, 588
Methods-Time Measurement, 431–43
Metronome, 290–91
Microchronometer, 224, 670
Micromotion study
  analysis, 211–48

Micromotion study—*Cont.*
  camera, 216–17
  checklist, 237
  cost, 211
  definition, 211, 670
  equipment, 216–19
  film, 220
  flood lights, 222–23
  laws of, 211–13
  light meter, 221
  microchronometer, 224
  optical screen, 224–25
  preparing for, 213–15
  projection equipment, 223–24
  splicer, 224
  training aid, 215
  tripod, 222
  viewer, 224
Midvale Steel Company, 9
Military Establishment Appropriation Act, 11–12
Millimeter equivalents, 683
Milling machine work
  calculation of cutter lead, 400
  calculation of cutting time, 398–401
  feeds, 399, 686
  speeds, 399, 686
Modal time, 670
Models, plant layout, 125–26
Momentum, employment of, 183
Monotony, 192–93
Monte Carlo simulation, 555–63
Morrow, R. L., 340
Motion analysis in planning, 198–201
Motion classifications, 181, 184–86
Motion economy
  corollaries, 211–13
  hand as holding device, 133–34
  laws, 182–98, 211–13
  principles of, 131–34, 180–82
  workplace layout, 133–34, 182–98
Motion picture
  analyzing, 233–36
  equipment
    camera, 216, 283–84
    cost, 216
    floodlights, 222
    light meter, 221
    microchronometer, 224
    optical screen, 224–25
    projector, 223–24
    splicer and viewer, 224
    tripod, 222
  film
    analysis, 233–36
    size, 216
    taking, 230–33
Motion study
  applied to planning, 198–201

Motion study—*Cont.*
  classes of motion, 181
  definition, 9, 171
  development of, 9–18, 171
  fundamental motions, 172–79
  history of, 12–13
  laws of motion economy, 182–98, 211–13
  micromotion technique, 211–48
  principles of motion economy, 180–82
  visual technique, 131–34, 171
Motion-Time Analysis, 448–49
Motion and time study office, 644
Motions
  ankle, 185
  body, 185
  finger, 184–85
  forearm, 185
  knee, 185–86
  leg, 185–86
  shoulder, 185
  symmetrical, 182–83
  wrist, 185
Motivation for incentive effort, 631–32
Move
  definition, 175
  examples, 175
  symbol for, 171
Moving pictures, 230–32
  analyzing, 233–37
  preparing for, 213–15
  taking of, 230–33
M.T.M.—General Purpose Data, 436–37
M.T.M.-2, 438–43
Multiple cuts, 195–97
Multiple regression, 481–83
Mundel, M. E., 343
Murray, Philip, 14, 628

N

National Electrical Manufacturers Association, 262–63
National Metal Trades Association, 266
Natural trigonometric functions, 677
Nip point guards, 103
Noise, 101
Nomograms
  control limits, 525
  cutting time, 404
  number of observations to study, 316
  random observations, 522
  synthetic leveling, 284
Nonfinancial incentives, 607
Nonsymmetrical motions, 183
Normal curve, 328, 352, 518
Normal distribution, 328, 670
Normal pace, 269–70, 326
Normal time, 325–26
Normal working area, 188–90

Number of observations to be studied
  General Electric method, 310
  nomogram for, 316
  statistical determination, 311–13
  Westinghouse method, 311
Numbers, random, 680–81

O

Objective rating, 343–44
Observation board, 281, 284
Observation number
  to be studied for time study, 310–16
  for work sampling, 520–21
Observation sheet, 285–88
Observer's position, 296–97
Occupational physiology, 671
Office space for motion and time study, 644
Office work
  establishing standards, 563–65
  improvement of, 137
Oil machine allowance, 372
Operation analysis
  approach, 41–42
  definition, 40, 671
  procedure, 42–48
  program, 6
  scope, 40–41
Operation card, 379
Operation process chart
  construction of, 21–24
  definition, 20, 671
  symbols, 21
  uses of, 24–28
Operator
  approach to, 293
  choosing for micromotion study work, 214
  choosing for time study work, 292–93, 344
  performance, 318–19
  responsibility to time study, 275–76
Operator process chart
  construction of, 165–67
  definition, 164–65, 671
  uses of, 167–68
Opportunities for methods and time study personnel, 1–3
Optical screen, 224–25
Oral presentation of methods, 254
Orderliness, 102
Organization chart, 4
Organizations engaged in promotion of motion and time study
  American Institute of Industrial Engineers, 16
  American Management Association, 15–16

Organizations engaged in promotion of motion and time study—*Cont.*
Conference of Scientific Management, 15
Society for the Advancement of Management, 16
Society of Industrial Engineers, 15
Society to Promote the Science of Management, 15
Overall rating, 321

P

Pace, normal concepts of, 342–43
Packing Ivory bars, 74–75
Parabola, 471
Partial setups, 382–83
Past records for determination of standards, 268–69
Payment, wage plans, 627–38
Performance rating
alignment chart to assist, 284, 346
analysis of, 344–48
characteristic of sound system, 331–33
concept of normal, 326–27
definition, 325–26
effects of, 327–28
necessity for, 325
objective rating, 343–44
rating elements versus overall study, 333–34
rating at the work station, 332–33
speed rating, 342–43
synthetic rating, 340–42
training for, 348–54
uses and effects, 327–28
Westinghouse system, 334–40
Perronet, 9
Personal allowances, 357, 359, 672
Personal protective equipment, 104
Personnel work improved through time study, 583
Physiology, utilizing work, 104–9
Piecework, 607–8
Pipe exhaust diameters, 103
Pipe vise jaws analysis, 201–6
Plan
definition, 179, 672
example, 179
symbol, 171
Planning, 92–93
Plant capacity, determined by time study, 575
Plant layout
making the floor plan, 128–29
making the layout, 123–24
models, 125–26
process arrangements, 121–23
product arrangements, 121–23
templates, 124–25

Plant layout—*Cont.*
three-dimensional layouts, 126–27
types, 121–23
Plant location, 129–30
Plant method training, 642–43
Plant-wide incentives, 15
Plotting curves, 403–7
Point system of job evaluation, 261–65
Polynomial equation, 480
Position
definition, 176
examples of, 176
symbols, 171
Power feed machine time allowance, 372–73
Power function, 471–72
Power tools, use of, 198
Power transmission guards, 103
Precedence matrix, 162
Pre-position, 176–77, 672
Prerequisites of sound wage incentive system, 628–29
Presgrave, Ralph, 443
Primary approaches to operation analysis, 48, 134–36
Principles of motion economy, 180–82
Prism volume, 674
Process of manufacture, 82–88
Process charts
definition, 19
floor, 28–36
gang, 149–52
man and machine, 141–49
operation, 20–28
operator, 164–68
symbols, 21, 28
types, 19–20
Process layout, 121–23
Procter and Gamble Co., 137–39
Product function, 1–2
Product layout, 121–23
Production control, 92–93
Production department activities, 1–4
Production operation card, 379
Production table, 684–85
Profit sharing
cash plans, 618
combined plans, 619
criteria for success, 620
deferred plans, 618
definition, 672
method of distribution of profits, 619
Projection equipment, 223–24
Projection welding, 60
Projector, 223–24
Punch press standard data, 405, 409
Purchasing new equipment facilitated by time study, 576

Purpose of operation, 48–55
Pyramid volume, 674

Q

Quadratic formula, 674
Qualifications time study man, 271–73
Qualified employee, 275–76, 346, 672
Quality control, 64–68
Quantitative techniques for man and machine relationship, 152–64
Questioning attitude, 26–28
Questions, check list for operation analysis, 79–80, 90–92
Queuing theory, 369–70, 549–55
Quick-acting clamps, 96
Quotations by computer technology, 592–97

R

Random activity analysis camera, 245–46
Random elapsed time describer, 289–90
Random numbers, 680–81
Random servicing, 152
Ranking method of job evaluation, 261–62
Rating performance
   characteristic of sound system, 331–33
   concept of normal, 326–27
   definition, 325–26
   effects of, 327–28
   necessity for, 318–19, 325
   objective rating, 343–44
   rating elements versus overall study, 333–34
   rating at the work station, 332–33
   speed rating, 342–43
   synthetic rating, 340–42
   training for, 348–54
   uses, 327–28
   Westinghouse system, 334–40
Ratio-delay, 511–40, 672
Reach
   definition and examples, 174
   symbol, 171
Readings, watch
   continuous, 306–7
   snapback, 302–6
Reciprocal function, 469
Recording significant information on time study, 295–96
Reflectance, 98
Reflectors, 222
Regression line equations, 407, 477–83
Release
   definition, 176
   examples, 176
   symbol, 171
Report of proposed method, 251–54
Report formula, 485

Research in methods, time study, and wage payment, 657–62
Resistance to change, 40–41
Resistance welding
   methods, 83–84
   projection welding, 83–84
   spot welding, 83–84
Responsibility to time study
   foreman, 273–74
   observer, 271–73
   operator, 275–76
   union, 274–75
Rest to overcome fatigue
   definition, 179
   example, 179
   symbol, 171
Rewinder, splicer, and editor combination, 224
Rhythm in work, 194–95
Right circular cone
   lateral surface, 675
   total surface, 675
   volume, 675
Right circular cylinder
   lateral surface, 675
   total surface, 675
   volume, 675
Right- and left-hand analysis, 20–28, 198–205
Right triangle computations, 400
Rolling sheet metal, formula, 475–77
Roosevelt, Franklin D., 14
Rowan incentive plan, 614–15

S

S. A. E. standard specifications for steels, 689
Safety
   disposal of dusts and gases, 102–3
   first-aid, 104
   guards, provision for, 103
   personal protective equipment, 104
Salvage materials, 77
Screwdriver power, 198
Search
   definition, 173
   examples, 173
   symbol, 172
Segur, A. B., 418
Select
   definition, 173
   examples, 173
   symbol, 172
Selection
   of factors for job evaluation, 262–65
   of operator for micromotion study, 214
   of operator for time study, 292–93, 344
Semilogarithmic paper, 472–73

Setup
definitions, 380–81, 672–73
improving possibilities, 88–97
partial, 382–83
standards, 380–82
and tools, 88–97
Shop management, 10
Shutter in motion-picture camera, 218–220
Simo chart, 235, 238
Simultaneous equations for developing standard data, 391
Simultaneous motions, 182–83
Sines, law of, 675
Skill
definition, 334, 673
impact on job evaluation, 263
table for rating, 335
Slide rule, 288
Slope equation for, 330–31, 405–7, 472
Snapback method of recording observations, 302–6
Society for the Advancement of Management, 16
Society of Industrial Engineers, 15
Society to Promote the Science of Management, 15
Sound, control of, 100–102
Specifications and tolerances, 64–69
Speed indicator, 288–89
Speed rating, 342–43
Speeds and feeds
drilling, 392, 686–87
milling, 399, 686–87
turning, 396–97
Sphere surface and volume, 675
Splicer, film, 224
Spot welding, 83–84
Standard costs through time study, 581
Standard data
calculation of cutting times, 392
definition, 387
development of, 388–92
drill press work, 393–94, 411
indirect labor, 566–67
lathe work, 395–98
milling machine work, 398–401
plotting curves, 403–7
press work, 405, 409
simultaneous equations for developing, 391
turret lathe, 410
using, 407–13
welding, 408
Standard hour plan, 608–9
Standard time
expressing, 378–79
maintenance, 383–85

Standards
expense, 563–65
indirect, 546–47
maintenance of, 383–85
setup, 380–82
supervisory, 565–66
temporary, 379–80
universal indirect, 567–69
Stegemerten, G. J., 165, 334
Stocker, Harry E., 118
Stop watch
decimal hour, 278–82
decimal minute (0.01), 278–82
decimal minute (0.001), 278–82
Storage of films, 225–27
Straight-line equations, 405–7
Straight-line layouts, 121–23
Straight-line motions, 183
Straight piecework, 607–8
Stroboscopic photography, 208
Student's "t" distribution, 312, 679
Supervisory bonus, 581
Supervisory standards, 565–66
Supplies, full use of, 77
Symbols
flow chart, 28
flow process chart, 28
operation process chart, 21
plant layout templates, 124–25
therbligs, 172
Symmetrical motions, 182–83
Synchronous servicing, 152
Synthesis of time study formula, 483
Synthetic basic motion times
application of, 454–55
Basic Motion Time Study, 443–48
definition of, 418
development of, 455–58
Dimensional Motion Times, 449
history of, 417–19
Master Standard Data, 450–54
Methods Time Measurement, 431–43
Motion Time Analysis, 448–49
necessity of, 419
Work-Factor, 419–31
Synthetic rating, 340–42

T

Taylor, Frederick W., 9–11, 387
Taylor differential piece rate plan, 609–10
Taylor Society, 15
Temperature, control of, 98–100, 193–94
Templates for plant layouts, 124–25
Temporary standards, 379–80, 673
Therbligs
delay, 172, 180
effective, 172, 180
ineffective, 172, 180

Therbligs—*Cont.*
  summary, 179–80
  symbols, 172
Three-dimensional pictures, 213–14
Time lapse photography, 243–48
Time recording machines, 282
Time study
  allowances, 293, 319
  analysis of materials and methods, 293–94
  approach to operator, 293
  board, 281, 284
  calculation of, 319–20
  definition, 6
  development of, 9–18
  difficulties encountered, 308–10
  dividing operation into elements, 297–99
  elements of, 292–322
  equipment, 278–91
  foreman's responsibility, 273–74
  forms, 285–88
    information on, 295–96
  leveling, 325–54
  number of cycles to study, 310–13
  observer's position, 296–97
  observer's responsibility, 271–73
  procedure, 292–322
  rating performance, 318–19
  recording significant information, 295–96
  recording times, 307–8
  requirements of, 268–76
  research in, 657–62
  responsibilities
    of analyst, 271–73
    of foreman, 273–74
    of operator, 275–76
    of union, 274–75
  scope of, 3
  selection of operator, 292–93, 344
  snapback, 302–6
  taking of, 299–302
  training equipment, 289–91
  uses of, 574–83
  watch, 278–82
Tippett, L. H. C., 511
Tolerances and specifications, 64–69
Tooling
  carbide, 95–96
  design of, 93–94
  efficient, 94–96
Tools, full use of, 77
Tools and setup, 88–97
Training
  equipment for work measurement, 289–91
  for methods, standards, and wage payment, 640–62

Training—*Cont.*
  with motion-picture films, 215
  for performance rating, 348–54
  time study, 346–54
  work sampling, 517–19
Transport empty, 172
Transport loaded, 172
Triangulation for determining milling cutter lead, 400
Trigonometrical functions, 675
Tripod, 222
Turret lathe instruction sheet, 239
Turret lathe standard data, 410

U

Unavoidable delay
  allowance for, 366
  definition, 178, 673
  example, 178–79
  symbol, 171
Union objectives, 647–54
Union responsibilities to time study, 274–75
United States Steel Co., 371
Universal indirect standards, 567–68
Use
  definition, 178, 673
  example, 178
  symbol, 171
Uses of time standards
  basis for
    balancing work force with available work, 576–77
    budgetary control, 581
    purchasing new equipment, 576
    supervisory bonus, 581
    wage incentive plans, 574, 605–23
  comparing various methods, 574
  determination of labor costs, 580–81
  determining plant capacity, 575
  improving plant layout, 574–75
  improving production control, 578–80
  personnel standards are raised, 583
  problems of management are simplified, 583
  quality standards are enforced, 581–83
  service to customer is bettered, 583–84
  standard cost methods, 581
Using standard data, 407–13

V

Variable elements, 389, 673
Ventilation, adequate, 100, 193–94
Viewer, 224
Visual motion study, 131–34
Visual requirements at work station, 98–99, 193

W

Wage incentive plan
  administration of, 7, 634–37
  characteristics, 627–38
  design for, 629–31
  prerequisites, 628–29
  principles, 627–28
  reasons for failures, 633–34
Wage payment, 7, 627–38
Wage payment system
  administration of systems, 634–37
  Bedaux point system, 614
  characteristic of sound system, 627–38
  direct financial plans, 605–6
  Emerson plan, 615–17
  Halsey plan, 612–14
  indirect financial plans, 606
  measured daywork, 611–12
  Merrick multiple piece rate, 611
  nonfinancial, 607
  piecework, 607–8
  prerequisites of sound wage incentive
    system, 628–29
  profit sharing, 617–22
  Rowan plan, 614–15
  scope of, 7
  standard hour, 608–9
  Taylor differential piece rate, 609–10
Waiting line theory, 369–70, 673
Waiting time for selected servicing con-
    stants, 694
Walsh-Healy Act, 100–101
War Labor Board, 14–15
Warner and Swasey turret lathe standard
    data, 410
Watch; *see* Stop watch
Watertown Arsenal, 11
Weight influence on time, 420–21, 427,
    433, 439, 444
Welding
  formula for, 473–74
  methods of resistance, 83–84
  spot, 83–84
  standard data, 408
Westinghouse Electric Corporation
  formula report, 485

Westinghouse Electric Corp.—*Cont.*
  number of cycles to observe in taking
    the time study, 311
  operation analysis program, 48
  primary approaches to operation analy-
    sis, 6, 48
  rating system, 334–40
Wild elements, 310, 320, 673
Wink, 234, 673
Work center
  arrangement of, 131–34
  conditions, 97–109
  development of, 5
Work-Factor
  detailed, 420–29
  ready, 431
  simplified, 429–30
Work measurement system, 268–320
Work physiology, 104–9, 673
Work sampling
  advantages of, 512
  application of, 533–40
  definition, 511
  determining allowances, 533
  determining indirect labor standards,
    535–40
  determining machine utilization, 533–
    35
  frequency of observations, 521–23
  observations needed, 520–21
  planning the study, 519–20
  recording data, 302–7
  selling, 517–19
  theory of, 512–13
  use of control charts, 523–29
  use of random activity analysis camera,
    243, 529–32
Work simplification, 3
Work station, 131–34, 182–98
Worker, approach to, for time study, 293
Working area
  maximum, 188–89
  normal, 188–89
Working conditions, 97–109, 360
Workplace layout, 131–34, 182–98
Wrist motion, 185

*This book has been set in 10 and 9 point Cale-
donia, leaded 2 points. Chapter numbers are
in 10 and 24 point Helvetica and chapter titles
are in 24 point Helvetica. The size of the type
page is 27 by 45 picas.*